VISUAL OPTICS

(VOLUME I)

VISUAL OPTICS

Volume I
OPTICS OF VISION

BY

H. H. EMSLEY, B Sc.

LATE HEAD OF APPLIED OPTICS DEPARTMENT, NORTHAMPTON POLYTECHNIC, LONDON

FIFTH EDITION

Butterworth Scientific
London Boston Sydney Wellington Durban Toronto

Originally published by The Hatton Press Ltd., which is now part of IPC Business Press Ltd. It is now reprinted by Butterworths in association with IPC Business Press Ltd., and the journal *The Optician.*

Fifth Edition 1953
Reprinted 1957
Reprinted 1962
Reprinted 1969
Reprinted 1971
Reprinted 1972
Reprinted 1973
Reprinted 1976
Reprinted 1977
Reprinted 1979
Reprinted 1982

ISBN: 0 407 93415 4

Printed in Great Britain by
Billing & Sons Ltd, Guildford and London

PREFACE

The kind reception accorded to my text on Visual Optics in various countries has encouraged me, in preparing this fifth edition, to accede to requests that I should extend the text by the addition of chapters devoted to the physiology of vision. In consequence of this extension the book is now subdivided into two volumes.

Volume I, being substantially the same as previous editions except for the transference to the second volume of the chapters on Binocular Vision and its Anomalies, thus deals with what may be called the optics of vision. Volume II, containing the transferred chapters and the new matter, is concerned with the physiology of vision.

The book is intended as a class book for students who are already familiar with the elements of ocular anatomy and physiology, optics and spectacle lenses. It has been found satisfactory for teaching purposes to commence the study of Chapters I and XVII simultaneously and then to proceed through the two volumes in parallel. Matter appearing in small (8 point) type may be omitted on a first reading.

The opportunity has been taken to carry out a systematic revision. Visual optics is concerned with events arising from the interaction of radiation and living organisms in the retina and nervous system and from the contemporaneous interplay of consciousness. Investigation into these events calls for the employment of the analytical methods of physics in association with the broader biological methods necessary when considering sensation and perception. Because of the difficulties involved in this association the progress of visual optics has been retarded. There has, however, been considerable research into the physiology of vision during the last twenty-five years, not only on account of the need to broaden the foundations on which rest the techniques of eye examination, particularly in relation to binocular vision, but also because of the need of physicists and illuminating engineers to know more about vision. The whole subject is consequently in a state of flux and some controversy. Controversial matters would be out of place in a class book of this kind, but the main trends of recent work have been incorporated in the simple outline here presented.

I have abstained from giving details of instruments; these are best obtained in the laboratory and from the manufacturers' literature. The exercises marked (S.M.C.) and (B.O.A.) have been taken from the examination papers of the Worshipful Company of Spectacle Makers and the British Optical Association respectively.

During the original writing of the book I received much help from discussions with my former colleagues at the Northampton Polytechnic, London. I am indebted to them and particularly to Mr. J. Adamson, M.Sc., who collaborated with me in the preparation of Chapters XII to XVI. It is a pleasure also to accord my thanks to Dr. W. D. Wright and Mr. E. F. Fincham for helpful criticism of many parts of my manuscript of Chapters XVII to XXIII. Naturally the great works of Helmholtz and Donders have provided inspiration and I am conscious of help received from the Report on the *Discussion on Vision* and other publications by the Physical Society and from the writings of my friend, Mr. W. Swaine.

In tracing the biographical details to be found here and there in the text and in the Appendix I was kindly assisted by the late Dr. M. von Rohr, Mr. Chas. Goulden and Professor A. K. Noyons of Utrecht; to whom and to those firms who have provided blocks and illustrations I tender my thanks.

H. H. EMSLEY.

EVESHAM,

January, 1952.

CONTENTS OF VOLUME 1

VISUAL OPTICS

VOLUME I

CHAPTER I

INTRODUCTION. OPTICS AND VISION

1.1. Optics and Applied Optics.

OPTICS, a sub-science which springs from the basic sciences of physics and biology, deals with the means and processes whereby we see things. It is concerned with the study of vision ; with the means that enable us to widen our vision ; and with the three agencies that are essential for vision, namely radiation (including light), the visual mechanism of our nervous system and the mind.

The universe consists of atoms of matter and of energy. Energy may be manifest in several forms ; and it may travel from one body to another, in which case it is radiant energy or radiation. All objects and materials at temperatures above absolute zero (–273° C.) continually radiate energy from one to another, the energy travelling through space in the form of waves. The energy transmitted by a "wireless" transmitting station provides an example the general nature of which is familiar to everyone. Whereas this radiation has a wavelength of the order of tens or hundreds of metres, the radiation emitted by other sources may include wavelengths measured in thousandths or millionths of a millimetre, or even less. The range of wavelengths of the energy radiated and the rate at which it is emitted depend upon the nature of the source. This may be a natural source such as the sun or a star or a glow-worm or an artificial one like a candle or electric lamp. Whatever the source and whatever the wavelength, the radiation always travels through empty space at the same enormous speed of 186,000 miles per second or just under 300 million metres per second—one of the constants of nature. When it reaches some solid, liquid or gaseous body, various effects may arise depending upon the characteristics (wavelength, intensity, etc.) of the radiation and upon the nature of the body. Some of the radiation may pass through the body (e.g. glass, water, air) ; in all cases *its velocity is reduced.*

Suppose there is an electric lamp suspended in a dark room and connected to the mains through a resistance. Before the current is switched on, the lamp filament and everything in the room are in thermal equilibrium. The radiation emitted by them all is of too long a wavelength, i.e. too low a frequency, to produce any noticeable effect on the senses of any person who may be present. If the current is switched on and kept low by means of the resistance, the extra energy delivered to the filament will increase the frequency of oscillation of many of its constituent atoms. Its temperature will rise and it will radiate more energy, this extra energy having a shorter wavelength than before. A person receiving this energy on nerve endings in his skin will experience a SENSATION of heat. If the current is increased, atoms of the filament are thrown into more rapid oscillation; extra radiation is emitted of still higher frequency so that now some of the wavelengths may be short enough to produce certain photo-chemical actions in the retina at the back of the person's eye. As a result nervous impulses are transmitted to the visual areas of his brain which are stimulated and a sensation of LIGHT is aroused; the person "sees" the filament. At first the sensation will be a reddish one, due to the relatively long wavelengths, and it will change through yellow to nearly white as the temperature of the filament rises and higher frequency radiation is added to the original radiation.

A blind person would not see the filament; although the same radiation is entering his eye there is no sensation, no light. Light, then, is a sensation, a subjective phenomenon arising in the brain of a seeing individual. It is evoked by an objective physical agency in the form of radiation of a certain range of wavelengths, namely from about 390 to 750 millionths of a millimetre, comprising what is called the visible spectrum. Both the radiation and a functioning visual mechanism are necessary for vision.

Nevertheless, it has long been the custom to ascribe the term light not only to the sensation but also to the radiation giving rise to it; hence the definition

> LIGHT *is radiant energy capable of stimulating the eye and causing a visual sensation.*

Light entering the eye may be specifically referred to as the visual stimulus. The term light is often used to include ultra-violet and infra-red radiations lying outside the limits of the above definition—see the "optical range" in Fig. 17.1.

Any event in which light plays a part occurs at some stage in the following sequence:

1. During the process of emission of light from the source.
2. During its propagation from the source through space and optical media such as air, water, glass (lenses, etc.), crystals, etc.
3. When it is absorbed by various substances and is transformed into other forms of energy.
4. When it eventually reaches the retina of a functioning eye and sets up photo-physiological actions which finally result in "seeing".

The whole subject of optics might therefore be conveniently divided into these four main parts, each of which would contain many subdivisions, as broadly indicated below:

1. The Emission of Radiation.

   Radiation; atomic structure; quantum theory; origin of spectra; light sources.

2. The Propagation of Light.

   Geometrical optics; wave theory; interference, diffraction, polarisation; dispersion; transparent media and crystals; magneto-and electro-optics; optical instruments; aberration theory; photometry.

3. The Absorption and Transformation of Radiation.

   Thermal, electrical, chemical and biological effects; fluorescence etc.; absorptive media and metals; spectroscopy.

4. Vision—Ophthalmic Optics.

   Visual optics; visual physiology; retinal processes; the senses of light, colour and form; binocular vision; the anomalies of vision; perception.

The word optics dates from the sixteenth century and referred at first to the study of sight. Gradually, as a wider knowledge of light and radiation has been acquired, the word has come to refer also, and indeed mainly, to the study of light. Consequently, Part 4 of the above classification now requires a qualifying adjective to relate it specifically to the eye ; hence such descriptions as *Ophthalmic Optics* (Gr. *ophthalmus* = eye) or *Physiological Optics*.

When the study of optics is confined to elucidating the nature and behaviour of light or the visual mechanism, without regard to the numerous technological applications, it is frequently called *Pure Optics*. Wide as the scope of this subject has become, the field of enquiry is enormously extended in *Applied Optics*, which term may be used to describe the countless ways in which light and radiation are applied to serve human needs. The selection of branches of Applied Optics given below is by no means exhaustive ; it contains no reference to cosmic optics (astronomy) for example ; it will doubtless be considerably extended as further applications are discovered. In these subdivisions of applied optics contact is made with other branches of science or with various arts and technologies—physics, chemistry, psychology, engineering, etc.—and numerous highly specialised technologies emerge.

SOME BRANCHES OF APPLIED OPTICS

Radiometry : spectro-radiometry ; optical pyrometry.
Photometry : illuminating engineering.
Optical Instruments : theory, design, testing.
Optical Instruments : manufacture ; applications ; optical workshop methods.
Optical Engineering : optical measuring appliances.
Refractometry — Colorimetry
Interferometry — Polarimetry
Crystallography : stereo-chemistry.
Photo-elasticity. — Electronics ; light-sensitive cells.
Photography. — Cinematography.
Spectroscopy. — Radiology.
Ophthalmology. — Ophthalmics.
Optical properties of metals and thin films.
Chemical aspects of light.

1.2. Vision. Ophthalmic Optics.

Amongst the biological effects of light under (3) above, that occurring when it reaches the retina at the back of the eye (see Figs. 1.3 and 1.4) is the most important, for out of it arises the whole process of seeing. There are three main essentials for vision: light to stimulate the nerve endings (rods and cones in the retina) of the visual mechanism; a visual mechanism to transform this light energy into nervous energy and transmit the latter to the brain which co-ordinates the impulses received and initiates the appropriate responses; and lastly, a consciousness or mind to interpret the visual pattern and control the responses.

In order that a person shall see something that exists in the world external to him, the thing seen must send energy in the form of light into one at least of his eyes. This light is refracted into an image which is formed on his retina and constitutes the physical stimulus. Assuming that the eye and visual mechanism are being maintained in a functioning condition, certain photo-chemical actions are then set up in the percipient rod and cone layer of the retina and a series of electrical impulses is despatched along a number of visual nerve fibres, through various cells and relay-stations, to a localised area of the brain; this roughly completes the second, physiological, stage of the visual process. There then arises in the brain, in a manner about which we know very little, an awareness of the stimulus which we call a sensation. A sensation is a change in consciousness.

This sensation may be faint or intense depending upon the brightness of the object; it will be of a certain colour depending upon the wavelength constitution of the light; and it will have a certain duration in time.

Trains of impulses reach the brain from both eyes, not only from those retinal areas that were stimulated by light from the one object, but from all the other objects and intermediate spaces in the field of view. The brain is simultaneously receiving messages from the other senses such as hearing, smell and touch and from the organs and muscles in all parts of the body. All this information is brought together and co-ordinated in certain association areas of the brain which is thereby enabled to take note of the whole external state of affairs and of the position and balance of the body in relation to it; and so to initiate such responses as will enable the individual to act in a suitable manner.

Much of this may happen below the level of consciousness, in the mid-regions of the brain; but even so, the activities are usually directed towards the preservation and well-being of the individual, enabling the various organs to "adapt" themselves to the ever-changing character of their environment. According to circumstances, a certain external object engages the interest of the individual; it enters the realm of consciousness and is "perceived". This *percept* is evidently a complex integration of the original visual sensation together with all the other information received by the brain. The brain of an adult has stored up information (memory) of previous experiences of a similar kind and is thereby enabled to recognise the object and give it a name. The percept will depend upon the extent of the person's previous experience, upon his present physiological condition, and upon the interest he is taking in the particular object. The percept is far more comprehensive and complex than a simple sensation; it is the summation of many things of different *kinds*.

During a visual act these various components of it occur continuously and re-act on one another, but for the purposes of study they may be subdivided into:

(a) a *physical process* involving the external physical agency, light, and the optical system of the eye and ending with the formation of a physical image, the RETINAL IMAGE, on the rod-cone layer of the retina, just as in any other optical instrument. This image constitutes the physical STIMULUS.

(b) a *physiological process* comprising the physico-physiological exchanges that occur in the retina; the transmission of the resulting afferent nervous impulses to the brain where a visual SENSATION is aroused, which has magnitude (luminosity), quality (colour) and duration; the co-ordination of sensations from the two eyes and from other sources (senses and organs) in preparation for an appropriate response.

(c) a *psychological process* which arises when the co-ordination above mentioned occurs at the conscious level; it then becomes perception in the mind and the synthesised sensations become a PERCEPT.

We see that the fourth branch into which we have divided the subject of optics, concerned with vision, has special characteristics. It deals with the interaction between a physical agency, light, and living organisms in the retina and nervous system. An organism is a going concern with a purpose of its own; its survival and reproduction are matters of extreme importance. And running parallel with these physiological actions, consciousness is involved. The final percept formed somewhere in the inner consciousness of the individual, in what some call his *mind*, is a complex integration of physical, physiological and psychological components. What is the nature of the connection between consciousness and these parallel physico-physiological phenomena? *Is* there a mind? Has it a separate existence, and a controlling influence; or is it itself merely the integration of sensation, perception and memories?

Experimental investigation in the domain of vision (as in other senses) is difficult. The analytical methods of physical science, in which the subject of enquiry can be resolved into successive elementary concepts such as atoms and electrons, cannot be applied, or at least can be applied only in a modified organic form. Numerous physical, physiological and psychological factors are involved in even the simplest visual act. These must be adequately controlled if reliable and comparative results are to be obtained in experiments. It is extremely difficult for the observer to rid himself of the psychological elements of experience and memory in the final perceptual picture formed in his mind (we will use the term) and to extricate the simple sensation from it. We always think of and "see" snow as white whatever may be the intensity and "colour" of the light reflected from it. A piece of white chalk in dim illumination may be reflecting the same quantity and quality (colour) of light into our eyes as a piece of coal in brighter surroundings, so that the stimulus and consequently the immediate sensation are identical in the two cases. Yet we continue to associate whiteness with the chalk and blackness with the coal. These are simple examples illustrating the entanglement of psychological factors in any visual act or experiment.

Visual science has suffered much from the confusion of all these factors and from the lack of adequate controls in many of the experimental investigations; in consequence, its progress has been much less impressive than that of physical science and its literature contains many statements that are unreliable or misleading.

It will be understood how difficult it is, in experiments linking stimulus and sensation, to define a "normal observer" and to know whether such a one is operating.

Not only may an observer classified as normal be temporarily below par physiologically; but he may, perhaps for a reason beyond his control, be incapable of the normal interest in and attention to the work in hand, or of eliminating some psychological factor which is vitiating the results.

1.3. Ophthalmics.

When the study of the visual process in the visually normal individual is expanded to include the detection, measurement and treatment of the functional anomalies that afflict some individuals, and with the instruments and appliances used in such work, we have a branch of applied optics which we may describe as Ophthalmics and which might be broadly subdivided as below:

I. The Stimulus. Optics of Vision—

1. Radiation, Light, Colour.
2. Optical System of Eye. Optical Correction.
3. Ophthalmic Instruments.

II. The Visual Mechanism. Physiology of Vision—

4. Binocular Vision.
5. Stimulus and Sensation: Development of Sensation; Discrimination of Sensation; Senses of Light, Form and Colour.
6. Physico-physiological Processes.
7. Theories of Vision. Perception.

III. Ophthalmic Methods and Clinical Practice.

IV. Ophthalmic Lenses and Mountings

V. Social Ophthalmics.

In preparation for the study of these sections of Ophthalmics the student is presumed to be familiar with the elementary principles of optics and with the anatomy and physiology of the eye and visual mechanism. It may, however, be of assistance, particularly to the non-specialising reader, to give a brief outline of the visual mechanism and process in this chapter. This is desirable also for another reason. The phenomena of vision are all so closely interdependent that the different sections of the subject do not follow one another in logical order, as in mathematics and mechanics; it is necessary to obtain a general idea of the whole subject before proceeding to more intensive study of any one section of it.

1.4. The Brain and Some Laws of Sensation.

Afferent nervous impulses from the eyes and other organs of special sense (ears, touch endings, etc.) pour continuously into the central nervous system where the information

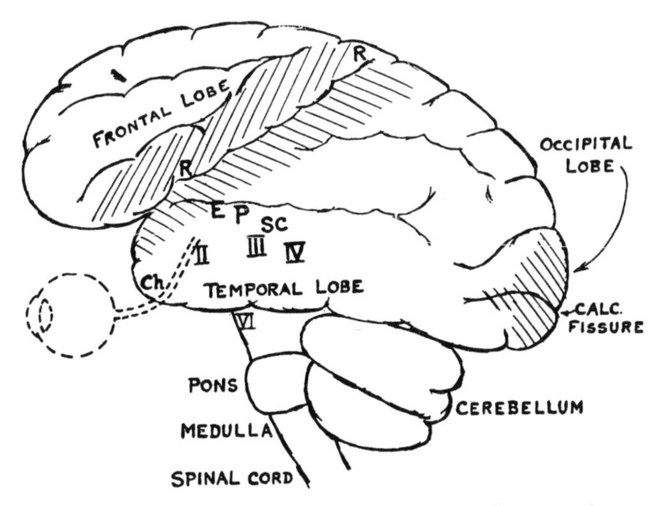

FIG. 1.1—LATERAL VIEW OF LEFT HEMISPHERE. SHADED AREAS ARE SENSORY AND MOTOR.

Ch. Chiasma.
E. Lateral Geniculate.
S.C. Superior Colliculus.
P. Pulvinar.
II. Optic Tract.
III, IV, VI. Oculo-motor Nerve Nuclei.

concerning the individual's environment is co-ordinated and from which efferent impulses are transmitted to the muscles and glands throughout the body. The most important part of the central nervous system in man is the brain or cerebrum which is divided into two lateral halves, the right and left hemispheres, separated by a deep longitudinal fissure. Each hemisphere is divided into numerous convolutions or lobes, of which the occipital lobe is concerned with vision.

By means of a complex system of nerve fibre bundles, the thousands of millions of nerve cells in the different lobes of the cortex of the same hemisphere of the brain are inter-connected so that their activities may be associated; the two hemispheres are connected with one another; and thirdly, the cerebrum is connected with the midbrain and lower brain levels such as the pons, the medulla, the cerebellum, and with the spinal cord. Broadly, it is supposed that the portions of the hemisphere posterior to the fissure of Rolando RR, shown shaded in Fig. 1.1, are the *sensory areas*, concerned with the reception of afferent impulses from the various sense organs; those from the eyes being received by the right and left occipital lobes. The shaded portion of the frontal lobe, the *motor area*, is responsible for initiating efferent impulses to produce voluntary movements of the limbs and organs after the information received from one sense, vision for example, has been brought into association with that derived from the other senses and with the stored-up knowledge accumulated from heredity and past experience; which processes of association are supposed to be carried out in the *association areas*, which are left unshaded in the diagram.

Of the twelve cranial nerves, which have their nuclei of origin in the mid-brain and brain stem, the optic nerve II and the third, fourth and sixth—*the oculo-motor nerves*—are indicated in Fig. 1.1.

The sensory nerve endings subserving the various senses are specially adapted to transform some kind of external stimulus into nerve impulses. The skin is provided with touch endings which are capable of dealing with stimuli in the form of pressure, heat, etc. The taste endings of the tongue respond to chemical stimuli which are transformed, when the resulting nerve impulses reach the appropriate sensory region of the cortex, into the sensation of taste. The important senses of hearing and vision are provided with elaborate end organs, the ear and the eye, specially formed to deal with stimuli in the form of sound waves and light waves respectively. In all the senses the nerve impulses or currents travel along the nerve fibres at a speed ranging from about 30 to 120 metres per second, in man. No sensation is aroused in consciousness until the impulses reach the appropriate central lobe. The absence of light, or of the eye, or of the nervous connections, or of the brain, each results in blindness.

The particular kind of stimulus for which a given nerve ending is specially adapted is called the ADEQUATE STIMULUS for that ending. Thus the adequate stimulus for vision is the short wave range of electro-magnetic radiation which we call light, lying between $\lambda = 390$ mμ and $\lambda = 750$ mμ approximately. A sensation of light may be aroused by mechanical or electrical stimulation of the retina or optic nerve, and a "flash of light" will result from a blow on the eye; but these are *inadequate* stimuli for vision. Much more energy has to be expended to cause a sensation when the stimulus is "inadequate" than when it is the adequate stimulus.

(A) MÜLLER'S LAW* of specific nerve energies (1826).

The nerve impulses conducted along the nerve fibres attached to the nerve endings are similar in all nerves, whatever endings they serve. The sensation that will be aroused depends upon the particular area of the brain to which the impulses are conducted. Thus stimulation of the retina or optic nerve by any means produces the sensation of "light"; on the other hand, whereas radiant energy incident on the retina produces the sensation of light, falling on the skin it produces the sensation of heat. To sum up: *each sensory nerve gives rise to its own particular sensation, however it is stimulated.*

(B) WEBER'S LAW or the psycho-physical law (1834).

It is common experience that, in any of the special senses (touch, hearing, vision, etc.), a sensation is not aroused until the stimulus has reached a certain minimum value which is called the *threshold value* or liminal value of the stimulus. As the stimulus is gradually increased the sensation also increases but the two do not vary in direct proportion; the sensation is not doubled when the stimulus is doubled. Such close correspondence would not be expected since the energy of the physical stimulus and the state of consciousness are entirely different things.

The amount by which a stimulus must be increased in order that a change of sensation shall be appreciated is called the *differential threshold value* of the stimulus. It is found to be a general principle in all the senses that, over a considerable range of stimulus intensity *the increase of stimulus which produces a just perceptible increase of sensation bears a constant* RATIO *to the whole stimulus.*

* Johannes MÜLLER. See Appendix for brief historical notes.

This is WEBER'S law and is of considerable importance.

Applying the law to the sense of vision: if two adjacent portions of a screen are equally bright with an intensity of 100 units and it is found necessary to increase the intensity of one portion to 101 units before the eye can appreciate the difference; then, if the starting brightness be made 200 units, the difference between the two portions of the screen must be 2 units to be appreciated. The *ratio* which the increase bears to the whole stimulus is in both the assumed cases 1 : 100. This fraction is sometimes called the FECHNER fraction.*

The fact that the law is true only under certain conditions and within certain limits† does not detract from its importance as a factor of seeing. It is in consequence of it that the general appearance of objects round about us does not materially alter as the level of illumination fluctuates, except of course when the illumination falls to very low values.

We shall see later that we cannot measure sensations; but that is of less importance in the ordinary business of living than the ability to distinguish slight differences in sensation.

(C). THE ALL-OR-NONE PRINCIPLE.

When a stimulus has reached an intensity sufficient to originate impulses along a nerve fibre, any increase in stimulus produces no further change in the individual impulses. It causes, however, an increase in the frequency with which successive impulses follow each other along the fibre and it affects a larger number of fibres in the bundle. According to this view a slight pain involves few fibres and a low frequency of impulses; a severe pain a large number of fibres and a high frequency. In a given fibre variations of stimulus intensity can be transmitted only by variations of the frequency of the impulses.

(D). SENSATION, CO-ORDINATION, PERCEPTION.

All organs of the body that are supplied with afferent nerves continuously send information of their condition to the nervous system. They exert a controlling influence along the efferent nerves without consciousness being involved. Such actions are *reflex actions*, the control being

---

* G. T. FECHNER (1858) attempted to state WEBER'S law in more precise terms; WEBER'S law is sometimes called the WEBER-FECHNER law.

† §21.4.

exercised by the lower, sub-cortical regions of the central nervous system. Adopting the terminology of PAVLOV, these reflex activities can be subdivided into *unconditioned* reflexes and *conditioned* reflexes. The former are inherited by the individual and are often said to be instinctive; they are characteristic of the species to which the individual belongs. Built up on these are the conditioned reflexes which the individual acquires himself out of his own experiences; throughout life they are extended and modified.

According to circumstances the stimuli from the organs may enter the realms of consciousness and arouse vague sensations in the brain, of well-being or discomfort, for example; or consciousness may be aroused in a quite definite manner, giving rise to acute sensations. When consciousness is aroused, the central nervous regions—sensory and associations areas—and the mind are involved. What may be called internal sensations acquaint us with the changes in our own body and our personality and are generally diffuse; the sensations of hunger, pain, fatigue, etc. are generally of this type.

External sensations, which provide us with news of the outer world, via the organs of special sense, are more exact or "specific" in character, and are subject to finer gradations of intensity and quality. Depending upon the extent to which the attention and interest of the individual are aroused, these are elaborated by the mind into a perpetual pattern or *percept*, which is a much more comprehensive entity than a simple sensation.

A *sensation* is the simplest state of consciousness, by which we appreciate any alteration, e.g. light, colour, a sound, a taste, etc., without associating it with any internal or external causes. The new-born infant experiences mainly internal sensations such as hunger, etc. Its visual, auditory, tactile and other sensations are appreciated only as changes in its own being and are not related externally to their causes, of which the infant knows nothing. But by degrees, by seeing, feeling and moving about, it learns to associate and relate one sense with another and to realise that the cause of two impressions, say visual and tactile when it handles an object, is something external to itself. Further experience enables the child to associate its visual and other sense impressions with words used to describe the objects or phenomena by which they are produced. Such experience is stored in the mind as memories. As these accumulate, the individual is enabled to compare present with past perceptions, to identify objects and to reason about them.

Simple sensations are scarcely possible to the adult since they are immediately converted into a unitary percept and related or " projected " to the external cause, knowledge of which has been acquired from previous experiences.

A given stimulus arouses different percepts in different individuals according to their several cortical states, inherited and acquired. It arouses different percepts in the same individual at different times, according to the experience he has acquired up to that moment and depending upon the degree of attention that the mind is able or willing to devote to that particular stimulus. A stimulus that results in a very definite percept on one occasion may be partially or completely ignored—inhibited or suppressed—on another occasion if it suits the individual to do so. For example: in a company of people, when several conversations are proceeding around us, we pay attention only to the one individual and suppress all other sounds; again, the trained microscopist suppresses that which is seen by the eye not applied to the microscope.

In the processes of co-ordination and response, we see that the central nervous system acts at two levels; a conscious level, involving perception, and a subconscious level. The higher and more complicated activities of life, especially those involving thought and judgment, are executed at the conscious level; but the subconscious activities are vitally necessary for the proper functioning and adaptation of the body. The threshold of consciousness dividing these two realms of activity does not apparently remain at a fixed and constant level. Functions which on one occasion are performed by the conscious mind may on other occasions be " taken over " by the subconscious mind, leaving the conscious mind free to concentrate on some higher problem. Many daily actions concerned in eating, dressing, shaving, motor-driving, etc., are performed subconsciously by the experienced adult, but they had to be executed consciously in the less experienced early days of the individual. And the conscious mind of the adult may sometimes be required to intervene if some occurrence or accident interferes with the usual rhythmical sequence of the action.

(E). The Localisation or Projection of Sensation.

We see that although sensations exist only in the brain, they do not *seem* to be there, but are projected outwards to the nerve endings—and even beyond these in the case of hearing and vision. A man whose leg has been amputated may still feel pain " in the feet and toes." The actual stimulation is due to an abnormal condition at the point of amputation, but the pain is referred or projected to the place, namely the toes, where the affected nerve fibres ordinarily terminate. In a similar way, visual sensations are projected into space. Although images of external objects are formed on the retina, we see nothing *in the eye*, but attribute them to the external field of view. That which is seen is a sign or token of the object that produces it.

What we call the field of view is the external projection into space of mental images in the brain. These correspond to the actual external physical objects in normal vision with a properly functioning visual apparatus ; but they may not so correspond in the case of a defective visual apparatus, or even with a normal apparatus which has been, purposely or accidentally, placed in unusual or incorrect adjustment. Our eyes sometimes deceive us.

If the retina is stimulated in some way, not normally by the light from external objects, but by pressure on the globe (*phosphenes*) or by specks or imperfections (e.g. *muscæ volitantes*) floating about in the transparency of the vitreous humour, we " see " the effect not in the eye, but beyond in the field of view.

1.5. Sketch of the Visual Apparatus.

The main features of the visual apparatus are represented in plan in purely diagrammatic form in Fig. 1.2 ; a horizontal section of the right eye in somewhat more detail in Fig. 1.3. The visual apparatus consists essentially of a certain area of the brain which extends forwards in the form of two bundles of nerve fibres each of which passes from the occipital lobe through the central visual tract, lateral geniculate body, optic tract, chiasma and optic nerve, to spread out over a hemi-spherical surface called the retina, R. Each retina is held in position and protected by a nearly spherical eyeball which also supports an optical system, consisting of the cornea and crystalline lens, capable of refracting light into images on the retina.

The optical system is provided with a circular aperture or pupil (in the iris) which dilates and contracts by involuntary reflex action as the quantity of light impinging on the retina decreases or increases, and with other causes.

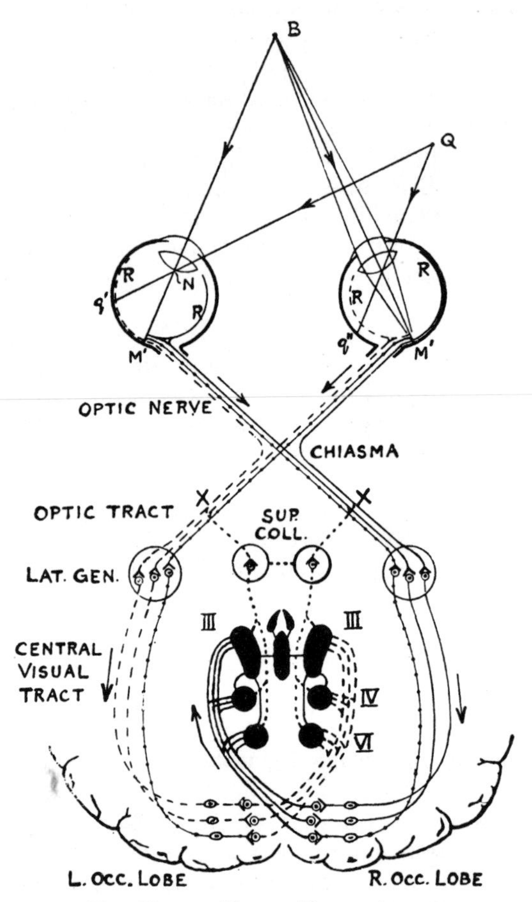

Fig. 1.2—The Visual Nerve Paths (diagrammatic).

There is provided an arrangement, the ciliary muscle, whereby the focal power of the crystalline lens can be varied so as to focus, successively, objects at varying distances accurately on the retina, which remains at a fixed distance behind the lens system. The eyeballs are set in the head in such a way that they are both directed forwards and by means of a system of muscles attached externally to them can be rotated as a pair in practically all directions round about he mean forward direction. In consequence of this arrangement the two eyes can be brought to bear upon common objects in all parts of a wide extent of the exterior field of view, an essential basis for the complete binocular vision enjoyed by man.

Each optic nerve comprises about a million separate nerve fibres. After entry to the eyeball these spread out over the internal surface of the retina and are connected, through a system of nerve-cell relays, to the sensitive visual receptors called RODS and CONES (about 120 million rods, 6·5 million cones) the tips of which point outwards from the centre

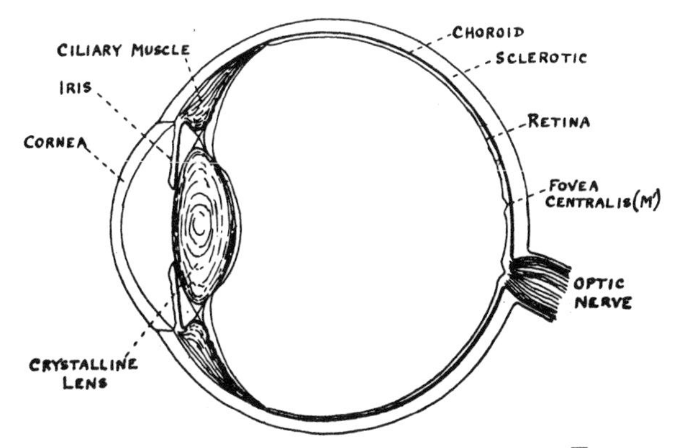

Fig. 1.3—HORIZONTAL SECTION OF RIGHT EYE.

of the eyeball and make contact with the black pigment epithelium which surrounds the retina (Fig. 1.4). The various layers of the retina are transparent and the incident light passes through them all on its way to the rods and cones where the conversion of light energy to nervous energy takes place. The rods and cones are distributed over the retina in a significant manner. Over a small central area M' which we may call the *rod-free area*, of diameter 0·4 to 0·5 mm., there are cones only. Within this is a small pit called the FOVEA CENTRALIS (somewhat elliptical with long axis horizontal) of mean diameter 0·2 mm. The diameters of the cones increase progressively from $2 \cdot 0\mu$, or even less than this at the very centre, to $3 \cdot 5\mu$ or so ($1\mu = 0 \cdot 001$ mm.). The average cone diameter in the central fovea nay be taken as 2μ and over the rod-free area as 3μ. Ve shall usually take a mean diameter of

$2 \cdot 5\mu$ when carrying out ordinary calculations. The cones vary in length but are 0·08 mm. long on the average within the fovea. They are packed so that the average population is about 150,000 per square millimetre, the number in the central fovea being therefore about 6000. The whole of this rod-free area is included within a region called the macular area or yellow spot of about 1·5 mm. diameter which contains a yellow " pigment " the density of which varies between individuals and tends to increase with age in any individual.

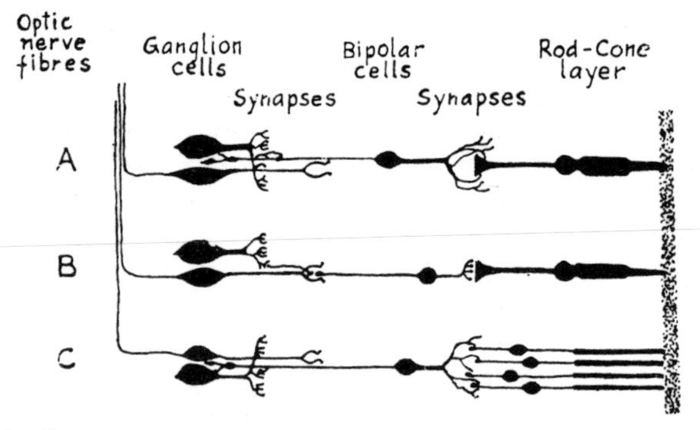

FIG. 1.4—CONNECTIONS BETWEEN RODS (C) AND CONES (A AND B) THROUGH NEURONES IN RETINA, TO NERVE FIBRES (AFTER POLYAK).

As we move outwards from the fovea to the peripheral regions of the retina, R, the cones become somewhat thicker and shorter and more widely spaced. Rods begin to make their appearance and increase in number until far out on the retina we find the rods twenty or thirty times more numerous than the cones. The rod population is densest at 15° to 20° out from the fovea; the foveal cones are provided with an equal number of nerve fibres, or at least the number of fibres is comparable with the number of cones; further out, several cones correspond to one nerve fibre and a hundred or more rods may share one nerve path. In these peripheral regions there is a system of interconnection between the receptors within the retina itself, so that although the number of nerve fibres leaving the retina on their way along the optic nerve to the brain, is much smaller than the number of receptors, yet one rod may be connected to several ganglia, and consequently many rods are linked up with one another.

Thus the fovea is much more strongly represented in the cortex than other regions of the retina. There is evidence (POLYAK) that the cones in the centre of the fovea are connected to their nerve fibres by a more direct route (B, Fig. 1.4) than cones situated outside the central foveal area (A, Fig. 1.4). C shows a typical rod connection.

Over the slightly oval area where the optic nerve enters the globe and where the nerve fibres bend round to commence their paths over the retinal surface, there are no nerve endings. This is the only region where the retina, in health, is insensitive to light. It is called the BLIND SPOT.

The "backing layer" of pigment epithelium absorbs light which would otherwise be reflected about in the eye. A substance known as VISUAL PURPLE has been found* within or on the surface of the rods and it is possible that an allied substance exists in or around the cones. It is believed that these substances are decomposed or bleached under the action of light, the products of the decomposition starting a train of impulses which travel back through the layers of the retina, along the fibres to the optic nerve and thence to the brain. In darkness the visual purple is regenerated. It has been found that the curve which represents the extents to which visual purple absorbs the various wavelengths from 390 to 750mμ is very similar to the curve (the so-called scotopic luminosity curve) which expresses the sensitivity of the eye, at low illuminations, to the same wavelengths.†

The optic nerves do not pass from the two retinæ to the central brain connections independently of one another, but are brought together in a significant way in the CHIASMA (Fig. 1.2). The nerve fibres are here segregated so that those from the right-hand halves of the two retinæ, that is from the temporal half of the right retina and the nasal half of the left retina, enter the right optic tract, which conveys them to the right side of the brain. Fibres from the left hand halves of the retinæ (the left temporal and right nasal) pass similarly to the left hemisphere of the brain. Thus fibres from the nasal halves of both retinæ cross over in the chiasma to the contra-lateral optic tract. It is generally held, though not conclusively established, that the fovea has special representation in that fibres from both halves of both foveæ enter both optic tracts.

---

* First by H. MÜLLER (1851).

† §§ 1.11 and 20.9.

The fibres in each optic tract are apparently divisible into four groups of which we need to consider only the so-called *visual fibres* passing back to the lateral or external geniculate body, and the *pupillo-motor fibres* which branch off as indicated at X and proceed to the superior colliculus in the roof of the mid-brain. Excitation of the endings of these pupillary fibres in the retina gives rise to a reflex action, through the superior colliculus and third (oculo-motor) nerve, resulting in innervation of the muscles controlling the size of the pupil. We are more concerned with the visual fibres, comprising the great bulk of the total, most of which* are relayed in the lateral geniculate body and leave the latter as a new set of fibres in the central visual tract which

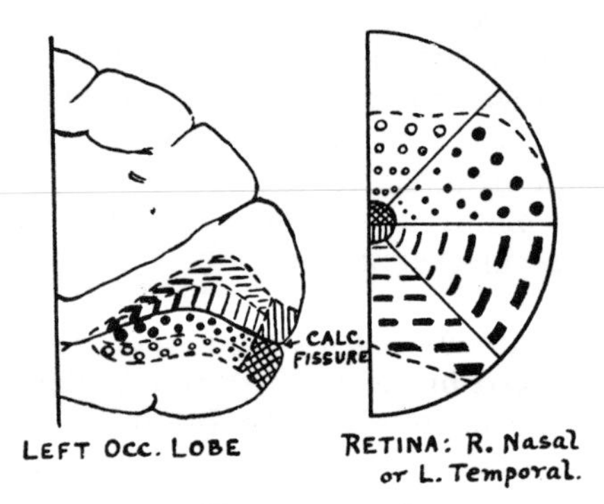

FIG. 1.5—PROJECTION OF RETINA ON OCCIPITAL CORTEX (GORDON HOLMES).

The markings in the retinal portion of the diagram represent the projected visual field.

presently spread out (the optic radiation) to make contact with the right or left occipital lobe of the cortex.

The visual fibres from the macular and peripheral regions of the retina occupy definite positions in the bundle forming the optic tract and this localisation of the fibres is apparently preserved through the lateral geniculate and central tract to the cortex. Thus it has been established that the foveæ are represented in the posterior tips of the occipital lobes and that retinal points further and further from the fovea are associated with cortical regions removed more and more inwards ; it is also believed that the upper half of the projected field is represented by the lower portion of the

* Some of these fibres pass to the pulvinar and thence, without relaying to the cortex.

occipital lobe, below the calcarine fissure, and the lower field by the areas of the lobe above this fissure. This scheme of retino-cerebral connections is illustrated diagrammatically in Fig. 1.5 due to Gordon HOLMES, who bases it upon his investigations into war wounds. The right half of the diagram represents the nasal half of the right eye or the temporal half of the left eye, the fibres from both of which are conducted to the left occipital lobe, indicated in the left half of the diagram.

Fig. 1.2 also indicates diagrammatically the nuclei of the third, fourth and sixth cranial nerves, or oculo-motor nerves, to which fibres pass from the occipital lobes and from the superior colliculus. These nerve nuclei are responsible for discharging efferent impulses to the intrinsic and extrinsic eye muscles.* The network of connections between the various portions of the higher and lower levels of the brain, already mentioned, thus embraces the oculo-motor nerve nuclei in its ramifications.

It follows from the arrangement described that corresponding areas of the two retinæ are associated with a common region of the *same* lobe of the visual cortex. Thus if the eyes are directed upon an object B (Fig. 1.2) which is therefore imaged on the two foveæ M′, the retinal images q′ and q″ of some object Q situated in the right visual field are formed on the left halves of both retinæ. The impulses resulting from the stimulation of the two areas q′ and q″ are conducted to the left occipital lobe. We shall see that this is of great importance in binocular vision, in enabling us to appreciate the stereoscopic relief of external space and also in that it provides a common path from the two eyes to the oculo-motor nerves, an essential basis for the co-ordinated movements of the eyes.

1.6. The Physical Process.

From each bright point in the visual field the eye admits a pencil of light, of a width determined by the diameter of the pupil, and travelling at 300×10^6 metres per second. Each pencil is brought to a focus by the eye's optical system, the position of the focus in relation to the retina depending upon the distance of the object and upon the state of focus or "accommodation" of the optical system at the moment. The retina is thus covered with innumerable

---

* See §12.16 and Fig. 12.15.

images, some in focus and some (blur circles) out of focus, each corresponding to a definite object point in the field. To each is conveyed radiant energy of an intensity, represented by the amplitude of the vibrations of the radiation, depending upon the brightness and distance of the conjugate object point ; and of a composition or spectral quality, represented by the frequency or wavelength of the

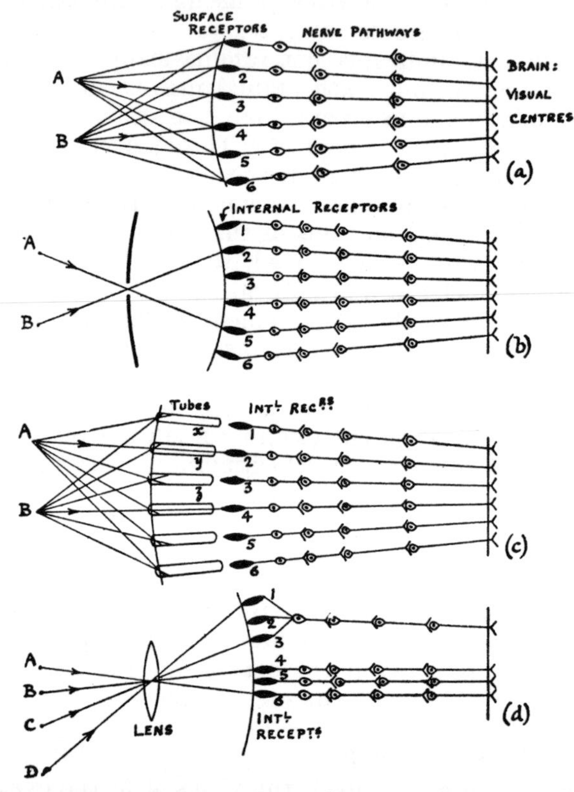

Fig. 1.6—Reception of Light Stimuli ; Provision for Differentiation of Space.

vibrations, corresponding to the " colour " of the object. The retinal images are not coloured ; they merely vary in vibration frequency, the attribute of colour being the resulting sensation in the brain.

The external field is of three dimensions, height, width and depth. The inverted picture spread over the hemispherical retina is of two dimensions only. The lateral position of an object such as Q, Fig. 1.2, is accounted for by the opposite displacement of its blurred images from the foveæ M′; and its depth in the field, relative to the point B upon which the eyes are directed, is registered by the difference between these displacements M′ q′ and M′ q″ on the two retinæ. It is important to realise that all the external information available to the observer from which he must form his mental appreciation of the light and shade, colour, size, form and texture of the objects and their spatial arrangements in the field, is contained in this distribution of sharp and blurred images over the retinæ of his two eyes.

In order that we shall be able to discriminate separate objects in the field, and their detail, it is necessary that their RETINAL IMAGES shall stimulate separate receptors and that each receptor, or at least a small group of adjacent receptors, shall have an independent nerve path to the brain. And if we are to distinguish *fine* detail, the receptors must be very small, numerous and close together. We have seen that the receptors and their nerve fibres fulfil these requirements, especially at the fovea centralis. Now we see the necessity for the optical system—to form punctate images. It will be shown later* that these images which, in consequence of the wave nature of light, are diffraction patterns of finite dimensions, are nevertheless sufficiently small to correspond with the retinal pattern of receptors.

This dual provision, retinal and optical, for the recognition of the spatial arrangement and detail of objects in our environment may be better appreciated by reference to Fig. 1.6. The receptors and nerve paths are shown diagrammatically only; the circles and arrow heads are supposed to represent nerve cells and relays (synapses) respectively. If the visual receptors were located, as in (a), at the surface of the body, as they are in primitive animals like the earthworm, light from the source A would stimulate *all* the receptors; nerve currents would travel along all the nerve paths and a general sensation of light would result. No information would be supplied to the brain as to the location of the point A except that it was on that side of the body, nor would it be possible to differentiate A from a second source B. The two sources would merely produce a stronger general stimulus.

---

* §2.7.

Methods of separating the stimuli from the two sources are indicated in (b), (c) and (d); in each case the receptors are below the surface. The pinhole eye shown in (b) ensures that separate impulses are transmitted, corresponding to A and B, along nerves 5 and 2. Certain molluscs, such as the pearly nautilus, possess eyes of this kind. Case (c) illustrates the principle of the compound eye found in certain insects (e.g. the fly and dragon-fly) and other invertebrates. The tubes x, y, z are blackened or pigmented on the inside. Source A can stimulate receptor No. 2 only, and B No. 4 only.

In all vertebrates this separation of the stimuli from different sources is accomplished by means of a lens system, as in (d). Separate images of A and B are formed respectively on receptors 6 and 4, between which is shown an unstimulated (or less stimulated) receptor; and A will be differentiated mentally from B. On the other hand C will not be differentiated from D, although they are even more widely separated than A and B, since the receptors 1 and 3 in a peripheral region of the retina are shown connected to a common nerve path.

1.7. The Physiological Process.

The above describes the arrangements provided to enable us to discriminate the separate existence of object points and so appreciate the detail, shape and size of objects. This faculty is called the *form sense* and the capability of the eye in this sphere is often described as its VISUAL ACUITY. This sense is most acute at the fovea, where the receptors are closely packed and consist entirely of cones. It will be necessary to discuss it in more detail later.

It has been assumed that the stimuli on the individual receptors are transformed in some way into energy capable of being propagated along the nerve paths. It is not yet known *how* this transformation takes place, although hypotheses have been made, based upon theoretically and experimentally acquired knowledge, as to certain changes that occur in the retina when it is stimulated by light. There are movements of the pigment from the epithelium along the filiform processes lying amongst the rods and cones; an important chemical change is the bleaching, and subsequent regeneration, of the visual purple; a difference of potential existing between the receptors and the nerve fibre layer of the retina is disturbed. The final effect of such reactions is the starting off of a series of electrical pulses which pass inwards through the three neurones: the rod or cone, the bipolar cell and the ganglion and so along the nerve fibres, the frequency with which these pulses follow one another depending upon the *intensity* of the stimulus.

The capability of the visual apparatus to detect light as such and to appreciate differences in light intensity in adjacent parts of the field is known as the LIGHT SENSE.

In SCOTOPIC VISION (i.e. night or twilight vision or, generally, vision at low illuminations) the peripheral portions of the retina are the more sensitive; the fovea is the least sensitive part of the retina and is indeed night blind in comparison. This accounts for the better vision of faint stars when viewed eccentrically rather than directly.

Our discrimination of form (visual acuity) is also considerably reduced in low illumination; but form acuity is not needed under these conditions of darkness so much as the capability to distinguish objects and movements in the field generally. At ordinary and higher illuminations—PHOTOPIC VISION—conditions are reversed, the fovea being by far the most sensitive region.

Since the fovea is populated by cones only, whereas further out in the retina the rods predominate, the above is evidence in favour of the view that the cones are responsible for functioning in ordinary and high illumination, and the rods in low illumination; which is the central idea of what is called the *duplicity theory* concerning vision. There is much supporting evidence that the retina contains this duplex mechanism.

We have seen how the retinal image provides the basis for the form sense by virtue of its configuration; and for the light sense by reason of the variations of light intensity over it. Our appreciation of colour, or our COLOUR SENSE, must depend in some way upon the only remaining variable, the *wavelength* or *frequency* of the radiation.

Experiment shows that in ordinary illuminations the colour sense is very much more acute at the fovea than elsewhere; our appreciation of colour decreases in extra-foveal vision. The cones, then, appear to be the receptors concerned in colour vision. The question arises as to how the nerve impulses carry information concerning the wavelength composition of the light on the retina to the brain, in response to which a sensation of colour is aroused.

From the experimental fact of colour mixture, that every light gives rise to a sensation which can be accurately matched by the sensation produced by a suitable mixture of only three lights, we seem to be driven to the conclusion either (a) that there are three types of cones, as suggested by Thomas YOUNG; or (b) that some kind of triple mechanism exists in the cones themselves or in their connections to the visual centres, which results in a varying or "modulating" of the nerve current according to the vibration frequency of the stimulating light. In the absence of more precise data concerning the inter-connections between the nuclear and/or other layers of the retina and the physico-physiological exchanges occurring in the stimulated retina, and even concerning the nature of light itself, the problem remains unsolved.

Even if we accept as an accomplished fact the transformation of the radiant retinal image into nerve impulses capable of transmitting the required information as to intensity and wave length of the stimulation and its topographical situation, the physiological process is not yet ended. The impulses from the retinal image have to be conducted along the optic nerve (nerve II) and tracts to the visual centres of the brain.

From the rod and cone receptors the impulses travel radially inwards. In peripheral retinal regions there is at once a condensation of the retinal image since the impulses from several rods and cones converge on to a single bipolar cell and then through ganglion cells to the one nerve fibre. The hundred million stimuli have been reduced to impulses in only a million fibres. The details of the foveal image, however, are preserved more intact since here there are as many, or nearly as many, fibres as receptors. The impulses travel over the retinal surface as a NEURAL IMAGE, which shrinks rapidly towards the exit of the optic nerve, beyond which it assumes an elongated form on its way to the chiasma. Here a re-grouping of the fibres takes place as already explained, in consequence of which each optic tract behind the chiasma carries a binocular representation of the opposite half of the visual field. Through the optic tract, lateral geniculate body and central tract the neural image is conveyed and, as it were, handed over to the right or left occipital lobe, as the case may be. It is not until this station is reached that consciousness, or sensation, is aroused.

CO-ORDINATION—PERCEPTION

1.8. The Psychological Process.

The physical light images on the retinæ have thus been transformed into neural or cortical images. Up to the stage at which these arrive at the brain, the process from the retina has been entirely physiological. The reception of these images by the cells in the brain is followed by the process of co-ordination or perception as explained in §§ 1.2 and 1.4.

We have already seen that two impressions of any given portion of the field arrive at a given lobe of the cortex, one from each retina; and the process of co-ordination or perception includes the blending or fusing of these two impressions into a single binocular percept and the interpretation of this percept.

In many animals and birds the eyes are situated at the sides of the head and are directed, therefore, upon independent portions of the external field. Any object is seen by only one eye, and such creatures, although possessing two eyes, obtain an extensive *monocular* view only (Fig. 2.4); they are therefore in a favourable position to detect movements of their enemies and their prey over a wide area, an arrangement essential to their survival.

Our eyes, and those of the primates generally, differ from those of the birds and lower animals in several important respects. In the first place, both our eyes are directed forwards, the fields of the two eyes overlapping over a considerable region in front—the common or BINOCULAR FIELD—within which every object* is seen by *both* eyes. Secondly, the nerve connection from retina to cortex, including the characteristic *semi*-decussation of the fibres in the chiasma, provides that each object point is represented binocularly in the cortex. Again, the system of eye muscles and their central connections is such that the eyes move together as a pair in a co-ordinated manner. Finally we possess at the centre of each retina the tiny region, the fovea, which is pre-eminent over all other regions of the retina; in the first place, because of its richness in cones, represented by an equivalent number of fibres, the discrimination of detail is vastly superior at the fovea than elsewhere over the retinal surface; and secondly, it is probably more comprehensively represented in the

* Except those imaged on one or other of the blind spots.

cortex than is any other retinal area and the impulses from it are consequently more intense.

Granted that the eyes can be rotated to bring the foveæ to bear upon a selected object in the binocular field, this unique arrangement provides the basis for the superposition or "fusing" and synthesis of two aspects of the field, within which the chosen object—the POINT OF FIXATION—stands out with special emphasis and distinctness. This enables concentrated and thoughtful attention to be given to this one object, and has been mainly responsible for the development of the higher faculties found in man.

1.9. Response. Ocular Adjustment and Binocular Vision.

Following on the reception of the visual stimuli by the occipital lobes, and of other stimuli by their appropriate sensory lobes of the cortex, a certain external state of affairs engages the attention of the individual. Depending upon the nature of these external conditions, it becomes necessary to turn the eyes to some new region of space, and to move certain limbs or perhaps the whole body, to meet the conditions. Efferent impulses are discharged from the appropriate "centres" of the frontal lobes and these, travelling outwards through the lower levels of the brain, stimulate the required nerve nuclei, which in their turn discharge innervations to the muscles it is required to bring into action. Such actions as these, which are consciously directed by the cortex (the frontal lobes) are *voluntary* movements. Many such operations are carried out without the intervention of consciousness, and are called *involuntary* or *reflex* movements. Thus the dilation and contraction of the pupil, already referred to, is a reflex action; the path followed by the nervous impulses does not include the cortex, and consciousness is not involved.

Confining our attention to the eyes: when a certain object has engaged the attention, the eyes (and perhaps the head) move under the action of their external muscles in such a way as to bring the images of this object upon the two foveæ. The ciliary muscles immediately contract to focus these images sharply, and the pupils dilate or contract according to the distance of the object and the brightness of it and its surroundings. If, at one moment, the eyes are directed as in Fig. 1.2, the object B is seen by DIRECT VISION; it is seen distinctly since its images are focused on the foveæ M′, and singly since these images can be fused in the cortex. An object such as Q is seen by INDIRECT VISION. It is seen indistinctly; partly because its images q′ and q″ are blurred images and partly because they are formed on areas of the retinæ where vision is less sharp than at the fovea; and it will probably be seen "double" since the image q′ in the left eye is formed on a part of the left retina that does not closely *correspond* with the part stimulated by q″ in the right eye. If now the observer wishes to examine the object Q, the oculo-motor nerves III, IV and VI are stimulated and the resulting efferent impulses to the eye muscles cause the eyes to move round and converge upon Q, the eyes accommodating and the pupils contracting to sharpen the images. The final meticulous adjustment of the eyes is carried out under the compelling desire for FUSION of the two uniocular images into a single perceptual image in the cortex. If, due to any cause, the retinal images do not fall on the two foveæ, the resulting afferent impulses transmitted to the cortex do not "correspond" there; the object is seen double, or a condition of binocular DIPLOPIA exists. The brain will make great efforts, if necessary, to overcome this confusing condition and obtain single vision.

In normal cases no difficulty is experienced in directing both foveæ on the desired object and so obtaining BINOCULAR FIXATION; we then obtain BINOCULAR SINGLE VISION of that object if the retinal images are sufficiently alike to be fused. The two retinal images of other objects in the field are also brought into association, their perceptual images appearing nearer or more distant than the central object of fixation, and higher or lower or to the right or left of it, according to the relative distinctness of their retinal images and the relative directions and distances of these from the foveæ. In this way we obtain the sense of depth or relief of the visual field; that is, STEREOSCOPIC VISION.

The realisation of these conditions depends upon a wonderful mechanism of co-ordination in the visual apparatus. Through the processes of evolution, vision has become the dominant sense in man, ousting the sense of smell. It has become very highly specialised; some of its functions (e.g. monocular fixation) are present at birth, others (binocular fixation and depth perception) have to be learned during childhood, from education and experience. A complicated mechanism is more easily deranged than a simple one and, in general, those faculties the most recently acquired or learned are the more easily upset and the more susceptible to modification or development by training.

FURTHER EFFECTS OF STIMULATION

Certain consequences with important effects on vision arise from the following facts: firstly, that the physiological response to a physical stimulus falling on the retina takes a finite time to materialise, and a state of retinal activity persists for a while; secondly, that the response is not due only to the individual stimulus, but depends upon the effects of preceding stimuli and also upon the condition of surrounding parts of the retina and of the retina of the other eye—these are called INDUCTION effects.

1.10. Time Relations. Persistence of Vision.

There is a certain latent period between the moment a single stimulus reaches the retina and the resulting sensation. This period depends upon the nature of the stimulus and upon the condition of the particular retinal area stimulated, but is of the order of 0.1 second. The sensation that then appears is the *primary image.* When this fades away, there appear so-called *after-images* which vary in their appearance and behaviour according to the conditions. These after-images may be seen by anyone after gazing fixedly for a time at some bright object such as a window and then turning the eyes to the ground or to a wall, or even merely shutting the eyes.

If the retina is subjected to a succession of stimuli at equal intervals, a sensation of flicker arises when the stimuli follow one another at a certain speed. If the speed be increased sufficiently, a sensation of continuous uniform brightness is experienced, the resultant impression being, within certain limits of intensity, the mean of the periodic impressions (TALBOT-PLATEAU law, 1834). The speed of the successive stimuli just necessary to produce complete fusion of the separate sensations into a continuous uniform sensation is the *critical frequency of flicker* and depends, among other things, upon the intensity of the stimuli. It was found by FERRY and PORTER that, within certain limits, the critical frequency is a logarithmic function of the intensity.

There are many everyday examples of this fusion of intermittent stimuli, such as the invisibility of the spokes of a rapidly revolving wheel and the effects produced on the screen in a moving picture theatre. The number of stimulations per second to obtain a continuous sensation varies from about 10 in low illuminations to 30 or more at higher intensities.

On the other hand, although stimuli must not be repeated too rapidly if they are to be perceived as separate, yet in reading the eyes travel over the printed matter at a rate resulting in forty or more letters being seen and interpreted in one second. The fovea thus recovers from one impression sufficiently to be appreciably stimulated by a succeeding impression with remarkable speed and precision, even allowing for the feats of interpretation executed by the brain as the result of long and continuous experience.

1.11. Induction

The response of a given area of the retina to stimulation depends upon the state induced in that area by previous stimulation. The effects due to this time element in events are included under the term TEMPORAL INDUCTION.

If the eye is suddenly exposed to bright light after being kept in the dark, clear vision is at first impossible; after a certain time, however, the eye becomes LIGHT ADAPTED and vision normal. Conversely, very little can be seen on suddenly entering a dark room from bright surroundings until the eye has gained increased sensitiveness from the process described as DARK ADAPTATION. Vision in these two states of the eye is called photopic (light adapted) and scotopic (dark adapted). We have already seen that evidence indicates that photopic vision is due to the cones and scotopic vision to the rods.

The state of adaption of the eye considerably affects its performance. Its sensitivity in the detection of faint sources will increase 100,000 fold after half an hour in a dark room, especially in peripheral parts of the retina. The colour sense also is profoundly affected. The ordinary prismatic spectrum, extending from red through yellow and green to blue, becomes a monochromatic grey in low illuminations, the brightest part of this scotopic spectrum being situated, not in the part corresponding to greenish-yellow ($\lambda = 555$ mμ) which is brightest at ordinary illuminations, but nearer to the blue end at $\lambda = 510$ mμ. The well-known PURKINJE phenomenon is dependent on this. As the illumination is diminished, colours near the red end of the spectrum lose their brightness more rapidly than colours of shorter wavelength, blue becoming brighter than red until finally all colour disappears, the spectrum appearing grey and brightest round about the position $\lambda = 510$ mμ.

If the eye is directed steadily to a bright object for some time and then shifted to a white surface, a black spot appears in its place. If the original object were coloured, the after-image appears of the complementary colour. After stimulation of a certain kind the retina exhibits a sensitivity to stimulation of an opposite kind, a phenomenon called SUCCESSIVE CONTRAST.

Spatial Induction.

If, as previously remarked, the retinal receptors are not independent of one another, but there is some kind of inter-connection between the intermediate synaptic layers of the retina, we should expect stimulation of one area of the retina to affect the sensitiveness of other areas. That such is the case is established by the familiar phenomena of SIMULTANEOUS CONTRAST. A piece of grey paper placed partly on a white background and partly on a black background appears much darker on the white than on the black. Place a grey strip of paper on a larger piece of blue and cover the whole with white tissue paper ; the strip appears decidedly yellow. If the background is of red paper, a bluish-green colour is induced in the strip. The induced colour is approximately complementary to the adjacent stimulating colour. There are many experimental methods of exhibiting these effects.

The performance of the eye in discriminating fine detail, and in using instruments such as field glasses, is affected similarly by the conditions of illumination of the surrounding field.

ANOMALIES OF THE VISUAL APPARATUS

1.12. Broad Classification.

The visual apparatus may suffer from many abnormalities and defects of function. Some of these require medical and/or surgical as distinct from optical attention : others can be treated or corrected by purely optical means or by suitable forms of ocular exercises. Many require both medical and optical attention.

We may classify the anomalies broadly as follows:

1. *Diseases or Abnormalities* that exhibit manifest objective signs, external or internal, of their presence.
2. *Diseases or Abnormalities* presenting no obvious objective sign. These may be sub-divided under two heads according as:

   (A) the primary cause is situated in some part of the visual apparatus; or

   (B) the primary cause lies outside the visual apparatus, the condition therein being a secondary one.
3. *Functional Anomalies*, divisible into those that are:

   (A) not correctable by optical devices or ocular exercises;

   (B) correctable, or partially correctable, by optical devices and/or ocular exercises.

Passing over the first category, the remaining conditions will give rise to some abnormal subjective symptom and/or will present some objective sign which, although not obvious, will yet be detectable if appropriate methods of examination be employed. The subjective symptom may vary from severe pain or discomfort to one of such a character that the subject himself is unaware of it until special tests make it evident to him. Examples of the former are the pain caused by such a condition as glaucoma and the severe headaches, etc., sometimes resulting from a condition of vertical oculo-motor imbalance (hyperphoria); the latter type is represented by certain forms of defective colour vision. Similarly, the objective sign may be evident on preliminary inspection or it may be one that is discovered only after careful examination; to use the example of glaucoma again, although it is a serious complaint and at certain stages of its development it occasions severe pain, yet in its incipient stage it gives rise to no subjective symptom and its only objective sign is a change in the appearance of the fundus near the optic disc, a sign easily missed in an ordinary routine examination.

Diseases or abnormalities in the second category of the above classification are clearly likely to interfere with the physical or physiological or psychological stages of the visual process. Mention of them falls within the scope of a book of this kind in so far as they occasion subjective visual symptoms and, alternatively, as they may be detected by optical or opto-mechanical methods and appliances. Under heading 2(A) may be mentioned such conditions as the following:

Abnormal conditions in the eye itself: if in the anterior regions they may be revealed with a hand magnifier under focal illumination; if in the media, iris or lens, a plane or long focus concave mirror (retinoscope) may be of service, or a hand ophthalmoscope; or perhaps a slit-lamp and corneal microscope may be required. Affections of the retina, besides affecting the visual acuity, may give rise to markings and abnormal colorations over the fundus or in the retinal blood vessels, objective signs observable with an ophthalmoscope; or, further, they may result in blind or defective regions within the visual field (scotomata) which can be detected with the aid of such instruments as perimeters, campimeters and scotometers.

Abnormal conditions in the post-retinal visual tracts: if, for example, the right optic tract were damaged or severed at any point between the chiasma and occipital lobe (Fig. 1.2), the whole of the left side of the visual field would be wiped out, a condition called *hemianopia* (homonymous). If the chiasma were affected as, for example, by disease of the pituitary body, which lies just below it, in such a way that the fibres passing from the nasal halves of the retinæ were destroyed, the temporal half of the field of each eye would be lost—*bitemporal hemianopia.*

There are many pathological conditions originating outside the visual apparatus—class 2(B)—which produce some abnormal sign or functional defect in the eyes. Thus abnormal appearances of the retina, revealed by the ophthalmoscope, may be due to diabetes or other condition; pupils that do not respond in the normal way to light, or to atropine although they contract during accommodation (Argyll Robertson pupil), reveal optic atrophy due to certain spinal lesions.

We are to be concerned, however, almost exclusively with functional anomalies.

1.13. Functional Anomalies.

In the absence of abnormalities of the kind mentioned above, the visual apparatus may still not function efficiently. The functional defect may be evident to the subject, or it may not; it may be of little or no detriment to him in his everyday work and he may be unaware of it, although it would probably prevent him from carrying out special duties or ordinary work under special conditions. On the other hand he may be well aware of the anomaly either because his sight is in some way manifestly below normal or because his efforts to overcome the derangement produce a condition of eyestrain and ocular discomfort (*asthenopia*).

Some of these defects of function—class 3(A)—cannot be corrected or relieved. They include such conditions as the various grades of congenital defective colour vision, which are the result of an inherited absence or arrested development of some part of the visual mechanism concerned in colour vision. Although the subject may be unaware of his disability and competent to do his ordinary work, he may be a source of danger in occupations (engine driving, navigation, etc.) where the discrimination of colour is of importance. Hence it is necessary that the condition be diagnosed with as much certainty as possible.

Conditions of this kind may be acquired, as by the excessive use of alcohol or tobacco, in which case they may be cured or alleviated by removal of the cause.

The second category of these functional anomalies—class 3(B)—includes those that are amenable to correction or relief by optical means (spectacles) or to alleviation by appropriate ocular exercises. They cannot all be treated by these means; as we have seen, defects of function may be caused by lesions of one kind and another of class 2 and some of these require medical attention; e.g. paralytic squint, progressive myopia and certain anomalies of accommodation. But in the great majority of the functional anomalies of the class we are now considering, the treatment is wholly or mainly optical. They may be subdivided into:

1. ANOMALIES OF REFRACTION.
2. ANOMALIES OF BINOCULAR VISION.

The first step in the visual process requires that a sharp image of the object of attention shall be formed on the foveal cones. This feat may fail of accomplishment either because the image is not sharp, or because it does not fall on the fovea, or both; circumstances caused respectively by inaccuracies in the eye's optical system or in the length of the globe. An eye in this condition is said to be AMETROPIC or to possess an ERROR OF REFRACTION. As we shall see, there are many varieties of these anomalies of refraction.

To obtain comfortable binocular and stereoscopic vision, the process of fusion of the right and left uniocular impressions must be efficiently executed in the brain and the eyes must be capable of extremely delicately co-ordinated movements. Many conditions, to be enumerated later, may arise to interfere with these important processes and so introduce a want of balance, if not a manifest squint, in the oculo-motor system, or a faulty perception of space. These are ANOMALIES OF BINOCULAR VISION.

The attainment of perfection in the refractive, accommodative and binocular functioning of the eyes would entail a mathematical precision in the formation and interrelation of all the parts of the visual apparatus such as is never realised in living beings. There is no more reason to expect perfection or uniformity in the visual mechanism than in other bodily proportions and functions. The visual apparatus, however, is highly specialised and great demands are put upon it under modern conditions, so that " eyestrain " in some form or other is common.

A careful examination will reveal some functional error or other in every individual, but no treatment is called for unless the error is accompanied by symptoms. In the case of medium and high errors the vision will be definitely impaired and frequently no other symptom is complained of. If the error be small, there may be no subjective signs of defective vision since it is possible for the subject to rectify the error to a greater or lesser extent by muscular effort, of the ciliary or extrinsic muscles. The result of the continual effort, however, may impose a strain (EYESTRAIN) which sets up muscular and nervous fatigue and reflex symptoms which are classifiable under the general term ASTHENOPIA. The symptoms may vary over a wide range: temporary blurring of vision and drowsiness when reading or doing other forms of close work, especially in artificial illumination and poor ventilation; pain in the eyes or orbits and various unhealthy conditions of the lids and conjunctiva; headaches in nearly all possible forms; and more serious conditions.

EXERCISES. CHAPTER I.

1. Describe Weber's law concerning stimulus and sensation and the extension of it proposed by Fechner. What quality of vision is expressed by the Fechner fraction and what do you think is the importance of it in everyday life ?

2. Give a clear diagram showing the paths of the so-called visual fibres from the right and left retinæ to the right and left occipital lobes of the cortex ; and from the latter to the oculo-motor nerve nuclei. In view of this anatomical arrangement explain the meaning of " corresponding " areas of the two retinæ.

3. What are the fundamental requirements for an animal to possess the sense of vision ? How do the sense organs of such an animal differ from those of an animal which possesses only the light sense ?

4. Give a general account of the distribution of the rods and cones over the human retinal surface ; and give figures for the dimensions of the fovea centralis and of the cones lying within it.

5. What provision, optical and retinal, is made in the human eye to enable the detail and position in space of objects to be discriminated ? Show how the eyes of the pearly nautilus and of insects are adapted to possess this same faculty of form sense.

6. On what characteristics of the stimulating light do the intensity and colour of the sensation respectively depend ? Why did Thomas Young postulate the existence of three kinds of receptors in the retina ?

7. Explain generally the meaning of the terms : light sense, form sense, colour sense, scotopic vision, photopic vision ; retinal image, neural image.

8. Explain the arrangements in the visual apparatus of man whereby he obtains binocular vision as distinct from the monocular vision obtained by other two-eyed creatures, such as birds.

9. Give a general account of the manner in which the eyes after the reception of the visual impulses in the cortex, are moved into position to obtain binocular single vision of the desired object. Include a brief explanation of the terms : direct vision, indirect vision, fusion, diplopia and binocular fixation.

10. Write a short account and give a classification of the anomalies of the visual apparatus. Assuming the following conditions to be possible, what would you expect to be the consequence of them ?

(*a*) total absence of cones in the retina ;
(*b*) total absence of rods in the retina ;
(*c*) absence of the crystalline lens of one eye.

11. What do you understand by the term " scotomata " ? Explain with the aid of diagrams the position and nature of scotomata caused by partial or complete destruction on the right-hand side of the head of (*a*) the optic nerve, (*b*) the optic tract, (*c*) the visual cortex (B.O.A.).

OPTICAL SYSTEM OF THE EYE

CHAPTER II

THE RETINAL IMAGE. VISUAL ACUITY

2.1. Introductory.

FOR the present we will assume a visual apparatus that is physiologically and psychologically sound: in which, therefore, the processes set up by stimulation of the retina and the subsequent summation and interpretation by the brain are carried out in a normal manner. The final perceptual image may then be considered as a true mental

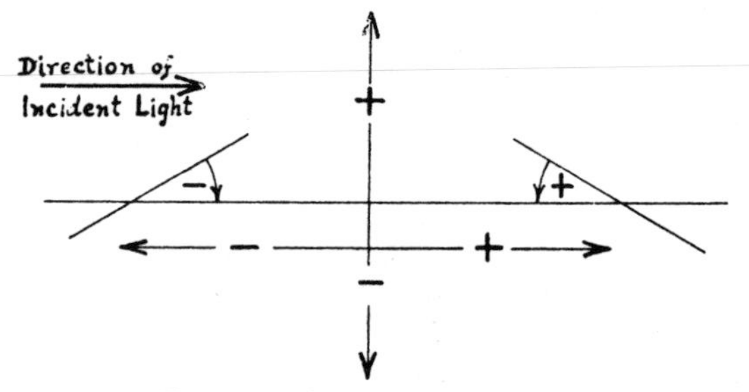

FIG. 2.1—SIGN CONVENTION.

counterpart of the objects in the external field according as they are accurately portrayed in the retinal images. In the present chapter we will consider the formation and optical characteristics of the retinal image.

NOTE ON NOMENCLATURE AND SIGN CONVENTION.

It will be convenient to collect together the main fundamental relationships concerning image formation by optical systems, with which the student is already familiar.

In conformity with the custom adopted by practical workers in optics, especially in ophthalmic optics, we shall call a converging lens or system positive and a diverging lens or system negative. The posterior or second focal length f', measured from the system to the second (image space) focal point is positive. The direction of the incident light, which we shall take generally as proceeding from left to right, is positive. Distances measured from the system, or other reference point, are positive to the right and upwards: negative to the left and downwards. For angles, counter-clockwise rotation is positive: see Fig. 2.1.

Let n, n'	= refractive indices of object and image spaces.
l, l'	= distances of object and image from system—metres.
h, h'	= sizes of object and image—metres.
x, x'	= distances of object and image from first and second focal points respectively—metres.
f, f'	= focal lengths in object and image spaces—metres.
$L = \frac{n}{l}$	= reduced vergence of light in object space—dioptres.
$L' = \frac{n'}{l'}$	= reduced vergence of light in image space—dioptres.
$F = \frac{n'}{f'} = -\frac{n}{f}$	= equivalent or "true" power of system—dioptres.

Within the paraxial region the relative positions of object and image (conjugate foci) with respect to an optical system of equivalent power F are given by the simple but important expression

$$\boldsymbol{L' = L + F} \tag{2·1}$$

which may be written

$$\frac{n'}{l'} = \frac{n}{l} + F \tag{2·1a}$$

For a system in air ($n = n' = 1$) the expression becomes

$$\frac{1}{l'} = \frac{1}{l} + F \tag{2·1b}$$

The magnification, or ratio of image size to object size, is given by

$$\boldsymbol{m = \frac{h'}{h} = \frac{L}{L'} = \frac{l'}{l} \times \frac{n}{n'}} \tag{2·2}$$

which for a system in air becomes

$$m = \frac{h'}{h} = \frac{L}{L'} = \frac{l'}{l} \tag{2·2a}$$

In the case of a distant object subtending an angle w at the optical system, the image size h' is given by

$$\left.\begin{aligned} h' &= f \tan w \\ &= fw = -\frac{nw}{F} \text{ for small angles} \end{aligned}\right\} \quad 2·3$$

It is often convenient to express the magnification of an object at a finite distance in terms of x and x', namely

$$m = -\frac{f}{x} = -\frac{x'}{f'} \tag{2·4}$$

from which $x x' = f f'$ (Newton's equation) (2·4a)

The equivalent power of a system, F, can be determined when the "constants" of the system are known. In the simple case of a spherical refracting surface the constants are the refractive indices n and n' of the object and image spaces respectively and the radius of curvature, r, of the surface; and

$$F = \frac{n' - n}{r} \tag{2·5}$$

from which $f = -\dfrac{nr}{n'-n}$ and $f' = \dfrac{n'r}{n'-n}$

and $$f' + f = r$$

If the system be a thin lens of refractive index n and situated in air, the powers of its individual surfaces are

$$F_1 = \frac{n-1}{r_1} \text{ and } F_2 = \frac{1-n}{r_2}$$

and its total power $F = F_1 + F_2$

If the lens be of finite thickness t, then its true or equivalent power is given by

$$F = F_1 + F_2 - \frac{t}{n} F_1F_2 = -\frac{g}{n} F_1F_2$$

where g is distance from second focal point of first surface to first focal point of second surface ; and its back and front *vertex* powers by

$$\text{(back)} \quad F'_v = \frac{F_1}{1 - \frac{t}{n} F_1} + F_2 = \frac{F}{1 - \frac{t}{n} F_1}$$

$$\text{(front)} \quad F_v = \frac{F_2}{1 - \frac{t}{n} F_2} + F_1 = \frac{F}{1 - \frac{t}{n} F_2}$$

These expressions for equivalent and vertex powers apply to any two systems of powers F_1 and F_2 separated by a distance t in a refractive index n.

If e = distance of first principal point from first surface (or system)
e' = distance of second principal point from second surface (or system)

$$e = \frac{t}{n} \frac{F_2}{F}; \quad e' = -\frac{t}{n} \frac{F_1}{F}$$

2.2. The Simple or Reduced Eye.

The optical system of the human eye has two components, the cornea and the crystalline lens, separated by the aqueous humour and followed by the vitreous humour. In the average eye the power of the cornea is about 43 dioptres ; the power of the crystalline lens is about half this amount when it is relaxed or unaccommodated, but can be increased by the process of accommodation when necessary to view near objects. It is the unaccommodated eye we are dealing with here. Although, as will be seen later, the normal eye is optically complex, its optical system can be closely represented, for ordinary calculation purposes, by a single spherical surface of power F_e = 60 D. separating air outside from a medium of refractive index $\frac{4}{3}$ (the same as for water) inside the eye. This is called the simple or REDUCED EYE ; its single refracting surface occupies a position $1\frac{2}{3}$ mm. back from the anterior surface of the cornea of the actual eye, as will be proved later.

The radius of curvature and focal lengths of this single surface are therefore:

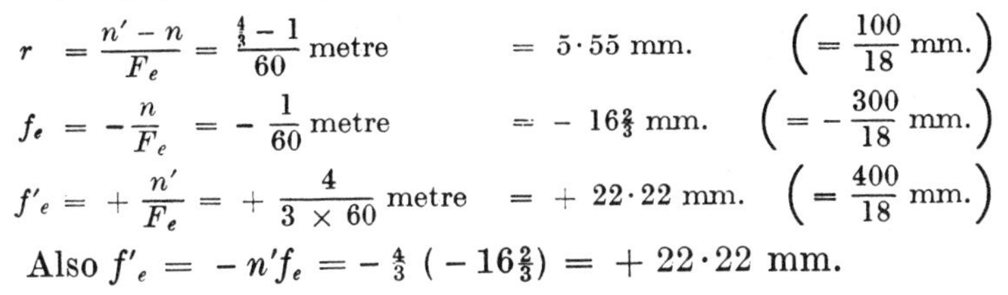

$$r = \frac{n' - n}{F_e} = \frac{\frac{4}{3} - 1}{60} \text{ metre} = 5 \cdot 55 \text{ mm.} \quad \left(= \frac{100}{18} \text{ mm.} \right)$$

$$f_e = -\frac{n}{F_e} = -\frac{1}{60} \text{ metre} = -16\tfrac{2}{3} \text{ mm.} \quad \left(= -\frac{300}{18} \text{ mm.} \right)$$

$$f'_e = +\frac{n'}{F_e} = +\frac{4}{3 \times 60} \text{ metre} = +22 \cdot 22 \text{ mm.} \quad \left(= \frac{400}{18} \text{ mm.} \right)$$

Also $f'_e = -n'f_e = -\frac{4}{3}(-16\frac{2}{3}) = +22 \cdot 22$ mm.

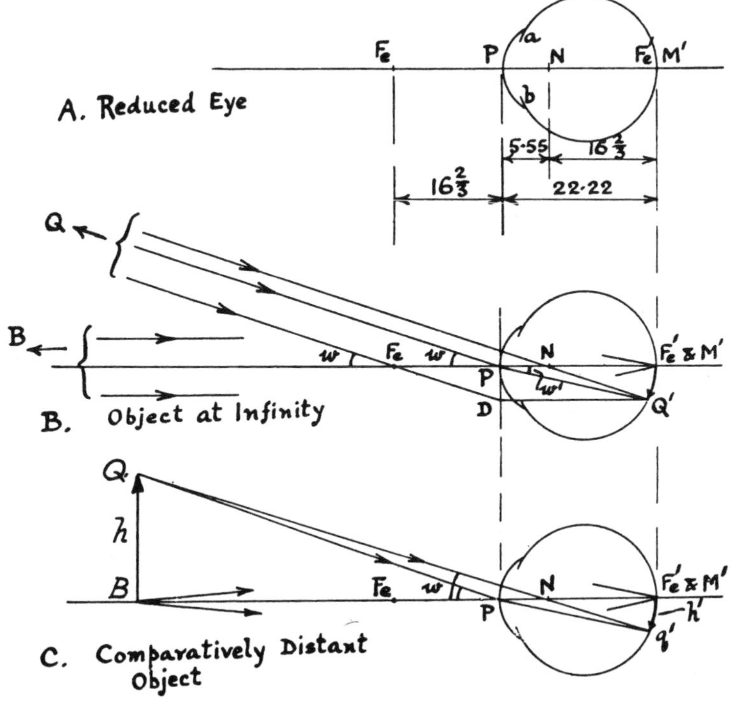

FIG. 2.2—THE SIMPLE OR REDUCED EYE.
Visual Angle w. Angle $M'PQ' = w'$

It is represented in Fig. 2.2A. The surface is at P; its centre of curvature or NODAL POINT is at N, where PN = 5·55 mm.; F_e and F'_e are its first and second focal points; $PF_e = f_e = -16\frac{2}{3}$ mm.; NF'_e also $= -f_e = 16\frac{2}{3}$ mm.; $PF'_e = f'_e = PN + NF'_e = 5 \cdot 55 + 16\frac{2}{3} = 22 \cdot 22$ mm. The line $F_ePNF'_e$ is the optical axis.

The length of the eye is independent of the power of its optical system; the retina may lie within or without the point F'_e. If the retina pass through the point F'_e, as it does in Fig. 2.2, then distant objects are imaged sharply on it and are seen distinctly. An eye in this ideal state of focus is said to be EMMETROPIC. Although it is the simplification of the optical system to a single surface that is implied in the term reduced eye, it is usual to assume the latter to be emmetropic.

2.3. Visual Angle and Retinal Image.

Fig. 2.2B shows a pencil of parallel rays incident on the reduced eye from a distant extra-axial object point Q and making an angle w with the optical axis. After refraction by the surface at P all the rays intersect in the image point Q′ lying in the second focal plane which is also the plane of the retina. The ray directed towards the point N is normal to the surface and consequently proceeds to Q′ without deviation. The ray passing through the eye's anterior focal point F_e traverses the eye in a direction DQ′ parallel to the axis. The ray incident at P proceeds after refraction along the direction PQ′ making an angle w' with the axis. It obeys the law of refraction, as do all rays, and we have

$$\sin w = n' \sin w' \ (n = 1, \text{ for air})$$

When the angles are small, as they are in practically all the problems we have to deal with, this becomes

$$w' = \frac{w}{n'} = \tfrac{3}{4} w$$

The retinal image of the distant axial object point B is similarly formed, at F'_e or M′, by a pencil of parallel rays proceeding parallel to the axis. The retinal image of an object of finite size BQ is inverted, but the mental act of projecting it into space results in a perceptual image in which Q, the projection of Q′, lies above B, the projection of M′*.

Strictly, the image is sharply focused on the retina only when the object is at infinity, but so long as the object does not approach nearer than, say 6 metres, which is the usual testing distance in clinical routine and is considered as "distant," we may assume the sharp image to be on the retina. Fig. 2.2C shows an object BQ of size h at a distance l

* §§1.4 and 2.5.

from the reduced eye. It matters little, in the circumstances, whether we reckon the distance l from the surface P or from N since these points are so close together.

The angle w included between the pencils from the extremities B and Q of an object is defined as the VISUAL ANGLE subtended by the object, or the *apparent size* of the object. In Fig. 2.2C either the angle QNB or the angle QPB can be taken to represent the visual angle. Thus in the case of an object at a finite distance

$$\text{visual angle, } w = -\frac{h}{l}; \quad \text{or } \tan w = -\frac{h}{l}$$

When, in the case of a very distant object, w is given; or, in the case of a nearer object, h and l are given, then the size of the sharp image formed on the retina can be calculated as for any optical system, as indicated by expressions (2.3), (2.2) and (2.4) of §2.1.

We shall sometimes be called upon to deal with retinal images that are not in focus on the retina, in which case these expressions will not give its size. All cases, however, are covered by the following mode of calculation: calling the size of the retinal image h', which is M′Q′ in case B and M′q′ in case C, Fig. 2.2, we have for very distant or nearer objects, as is evident from the diagrams

$$\begin{aligned} h' &= -w' \times (\text{length of eye, PM}') \\ &= -\frac{w}{n'} \times (\text{length of eye, PM}') \end{aligned} \tag{2.6}$$

The angle w is expressed in radians. The minus sign indicates that with a positive angle w, as in Fig. 2.2, the image is negative, i.e. inverted.

Example. A ship is 150 feet long and distant 2 miles. Find the visual angle it subtends and the size of the retinal image formed in the normal eye.

Ans. $w = -\frac{h}{l} = \frac{150}{2 \times 1760 \times 3}$ radian

(or $\frac{150 \times 100}{2 \times 1760 \times 3} = 1{\cdot}42$ centrads, ∇, or prism dioptres, $\triangle$)

$h' = -\frac{w}{n'} \times \text{PM}' = -\frac{3}{4} \times \frac{150}{2 \times 1760 \times 3} \times 22{\cdot}22\,\text{mm.} = -0{\cdot}237\,\text{mm}$

The object is very distant and the sharp focused image is forme on the retina; hence the same result is obtained, as the student shoul verify for himself, by using expressions (2·2) and (2·4).

Note.—It is useful to remember that

$$1 \text{ radian} = \frac{180}{\pi} \text{ or } 57 \cdot 3 \text{ degrees} = 3440 \text{ minutes} = 206{,}000 \text{ seconds},$$

very nearly ; also that 1 minute of angle corresponds to 5μ on the retina.

In practically all calculation work concerning the eye we shall use this reduced eye of a single refracting surface.

2.4. The Fundus and Field of Vision.

Two significant regions of the fundus or background of the eye are : the MACULA LUTEA or yellow spot within which is the small pit called the FOVEA CENTRALIS and the larger rod-free area already mentioned*; and the OPTIC DISC or blind spot where the optic nerve enters the eye and which contains no percipient elements. The *average* dimensions

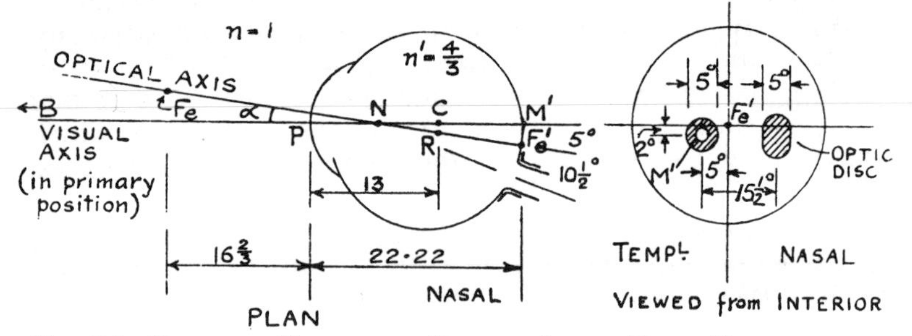

FIG. 2.3—FUNDUS ; VISUAL AND OPTICAL AXES. RIGHT EYE LOOKING STRAIGHT AHEAD ALONG PRIMARY LINE (DIAGRAMMATIC).

and relative positions of these are indicated diagrammatically in Fig. 2.3, which depicts a sectional plan of the right eye and a frontal view of the fundus as seen from the interior of the eye or by direct ophthalmoscopy.

The macula lutea is roughly a circle of diameter 1·5 mm. (5°) : around its centre M′ is the fovea centralis of diameter 0·2 mm. (40′). The blind spot is a vertically oval area about 1·5 mm. (5°) by 2 mm. (7°) ; its centre is about 4·5 mm. ($15\frac{1}{2}°$) to the nasal side of and 0·5 mm. ($1\frac{1}{2}°$) above the fovea.†

It is to be understood that these are average dimensions : there are appreciable variations between individuals, the macula for example varying from 1 to 3 mm. in diameter.

* § 1.5.

† It may come as a surprise to the student to realise that the blind spot is large enough to prevent our seeing ten or eleven full moons placed side by side ; and yet its existence is ordinarily unnoticed.

The line joining the point of fixation B to the centre of the fovea M′, and which coincides with the chief ray of the pencil of light from B through N to M′, is the VISUAL AXIS or *fixation line.* In the simple reduced eye we assume for simplicity that this coincides with the optical axis. In the actual eye the several (corneal and crystalline lens) surfaces are not exactly centred upon any common line ; but by means to be discussed later we can find a line which takes a mean course through their several centres of curvature. This is the OPTICAL AXIS of the eye. Contrary to what might be expected, it is usually inclined quite definitely to the visual axis, cutting the retina in a point referred to as the posterior pole (and which in the emmetropic eye is the second focal point) which is on the average 1·5 mm. (5°) to the nasal side of and rather more than 0·5 mm. ($1\frac{1}{2}$°) above the point M′. The non-coincidence of the visual and optical axes is probably an accompaniment of the gradual evolutionary movement of the eyes round towards the forward-looking position. We shall assume that the actual eye consists of spherical surfaces centred on one common line, the optical axis.

The angle between the optical and visual axes is then called the ANGLE ALPHA (α)* of average value 5°. Depending upon the relative positions of M′ and the posterior pole, it may in individual eyes have larger or smaller values than this ; it may even be negative in high myopia, M′ falling to the nasal side of the posterior pole. It tends to be less than the average in myopia and greater in hypermetropia.

When the eyes observe a distant object lying straight ahead in the median plane,† the two visual axes are parallel, each occupying its PRIMARY POSITION coincident with the *primary line.* The *optical* axes are then divergent, usually. An external observer judges the position of the eye largely by the apparent direction of an imaginary line perpendicular to and central with the iris, the circumference of which corresponds to the base of the cornea ; this line falls approximately on the above defined optical axis. Hence the eyes appear somewhat divergent, especially for large values of alpha, and may simulate a divergent squint or may mask an existing convergent squint.‡ The angle alpha is thus of some clinical importance.

---

* §10.3. † §§5.1 and 12.8. ‡ §14.5.

The rotations of the eye are executed around the CENTRE OF ROTATION, R, which can without much error be taken as a fixed point on the optical axis. As the eye rotates, the successive positions of the visual axis pass very closely through a common point C lying on the primary line, adjacent to R. This point, which may be called the CENTRE OF PROJECTION of the eye, is about 13 mm. back from the reduced surface at P—that is $14\frac{2}{3}$ mm. back from the cornea ; see §10·7.

With the eye stationary, the projection outwards into space, through the nodal point, of all active points of the retina constitutes the VISUAL FIELD. Practically the whole

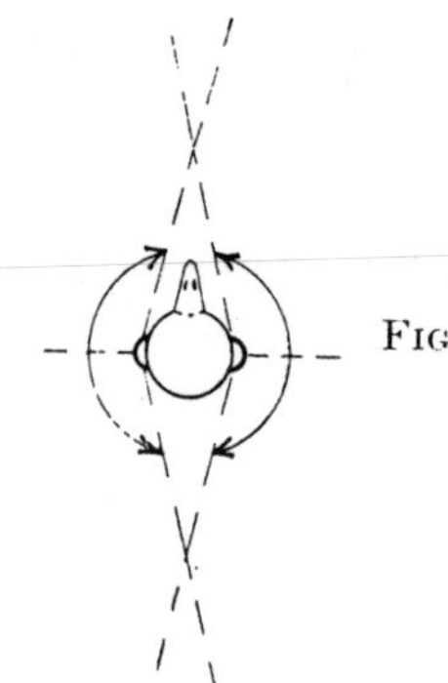

FIG. 2·4—VISUAL FIELD OF A BIRD.

of the retina (except the blind spot) is capable of initiating visual sensations, but the effective or "relative" visual field is restricted by the prominence of the nose, brows and cheek to the average figures : 70° up, 75° down, 60° nasally and 95° temporally—in ordinary illumination. It is only objects sufficiently large and bright to produce a certain stimulus intensity that can be seen in the extreme peripheral portions of this field ; the field is reduced considerably for small objects. Thus a small white disc subtending 5 minutes can be seen over a field of only 40 degrees or so ; and the extent of the field varies also according to the colour of the object.

The extensive *uniocular* field of birds and many animals and the binocular field of man with his forward-looking eyes have already been mentioned—Fig. 2.4.

The existence of the blind spot is easily made evident by a simple experiment, due to MARIOTTE (1668). Make a small black spot such as D, Fig. 2.5, on a sheet of paper ;

move the point of a pencil from the spot slowly to the left, observing the pencil with the right eye only, the left eye being occluded. Keeping the right eye fixed on the moving pencil point, the black spot will presently disappear when the pencil has reached a position B. D is then within the projection of the blind spot. Measurement of the separation of the pencil and black spot and of the distance of the eye from the paper will roughly confirm the value of 15½° separating M′ and the blind spot. This is the basis of

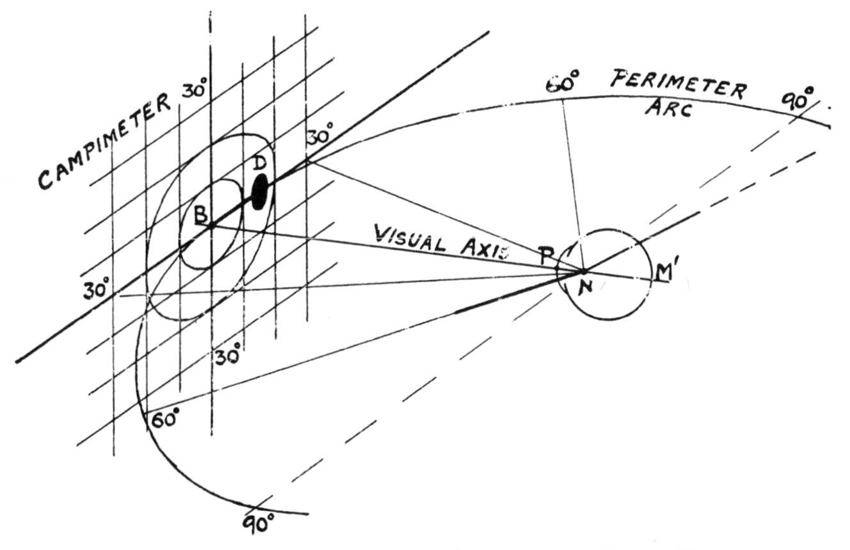

FIG. 2.5—FIELD OF VISION (HORIZONTAL)—RIGHT EYE.

clinical methods for mapping out the visual field. The eye maintaining fixation for the point B, Fig. 2.5, a light or a white (or coloured) disc is moved about over a black surface which is flat in a *campimeter* and spherical and concentric with the retina in a *perimeter*.

The test object is moved outwards from the fixation point, or inwards towards it, in a systematic manner, various meridians being explored in turn, and the positions (if any) where the object disappears from the subject's view are noted or automatically recorded by the instrument. In this manner the extent of the field is plotted under the given conditions of illumination and any pathological defects in it (scotomata) are located. The perimeter enables the whole field to be investigated: the campimeter is restricted to the central portions, but since the flat screen can be large and at an appreciable distance (and the tangent increases more rapidly than the angle), the scale and hence the accuracy of plotting are increased.

In most optical problems the separation of the fovea M′ and the posterior pole is of no significance; since matters are simplified thereby, we shall use the 60 D. reduced eye of §2.2 in all work except in special cases.

2.5. The Sense of Position. Monocular Perception of Direction and Size.

In total darkness or when looking into a completely homogeneous field, the eyes are continually in motion since there is no one definite object to fix either the individual's attention or his gaze. This lack of fixation is a contributory cause of miners' nystagmus, for instance. If, using one eye only, we gaze into such a field and a small object such as a star appears somewhere within it, we immediately become aware of the direction of the object. We know whether it is directly ahead or to one side or the other; we have located its direction relative to the position of the head and body. This is so because of impulses transmitted to the brain from the muscles of the body generally, the neck and the labyrinth and from the extraocular muscles—the so-called *proprioceptive* impulses. Information is thereby registered in the cortex as to the position of the body on the ground, of the head relative to the body and of the eyes relative to the head. Moreover, in the presence of several objects in the field, we are able to judge of their positions relative to one another because we are able to discriminate the excitation of one retinal receptor from excitation of its neighbours; each receptor, or at least each small retinal area, having in effect its counterpart in the occipital lobes (§1·5).

We are born with this localising property of sensation, which is termed LOCAL SIGN. It applies not only to the retina, but to the other organs of special sense also. We are able, for example, to discriminate between two pin pricks on various parts of the body, providing the points stimulated are sufficiently far apart. If the retina were not sub-divided in this way, we should be able to appreciate that light existed somewhere in space (the light sense) but we should have no power of discriminating one part of the field from another (the form sense).

As we have seen, the pre-eminent part of the retina is the fovea; the object point fixed is seen far more distinctly than the surrounding field. The peripheral portions of the field are necessary, however, to enable us to appreciate the relative direction in the field of the object fixed. A person with good central (foveal) vision and no peripheral vision has to be led about, whereas a person with a central scotoma and normal peripheral vision is able to get about unaided. Peripheral vision is therefore an important factor in our appreciation of direction and space; and being sensitive to movement, particularly in low illumination, is extremely serviceable in calling our attention to possibly important happenings outside the small area of our main attention.

The disposition of all peripheral receptors, or of their projections in the visual field, is referred to the fovea, or its projection, as the point of reference. An image formed on the fovea is projected out along the visual axis and we may consider space and the retinal surface as divided into four quadrants by two planes, one vertical and one horizontal,* intersecting in this axis. In monocular vision an image formed on a peripheral receptor within one of these quadrants is projected out along a line joining the receptor to the nodal point and *all such lines of direction are mentally related to the visual axis passing through the fovea.* The rotation of the eye into the direction necessary to place the fovea on the image of the object to be fixed may be carried out reflexly or consciously, by means of innervations transmitted from the occipital or frontal lobes respectively.

With one eye we can thus form a reliable judgment of direction, better probably than with two eyes.

Judgment of the angular separation of two object points or of the angular subtense of an extended linear object depends upon the existence of two stimulated areas on the retina, or a line of stimulation of a certain length. This angular separation is appropriately represented by the angle between the direction lines of these stimulated areas, i.e. the angle they subtend at the nodal point, or the *visual angle.* For accuracy in this judgment, if the objects are separated by an appreciable amount, the eye rotates to fix one extremity after the other. G. T. STEVENS† maintains that our estimations of direction and angular size are made on the basis of the amount of muscular effort or

---

* §12.4. † *The Motor Apparatus of the Eyes* (1906).

innervation required to rotate the eye, or which would be required to rotate it if the movement were to be carried out.

Our estimate of the actual *linear* dimensions of an object is based upon this angular size, registered by the extent of the retinal image, coupled with the estimated distance of the object from the eye. An eye looking into a homogeneous field would appreciate the visual angle subtended by an object 1 cm. in diameter at 50 cm. distance, but no judgment could be made of the actual linear extent of 1 cm. if there were no knowledge of the 50 cm. distance. In the absence of anything upon which to base an estimate of the distance, the object might as well be 10 cm. in diameter at 500 cm., or 100 cm. in diameter at 5,000 cm. (If the object were *very* near, then the effort of accommodation required to fix it would provide some information as to its distance.) Conversely, we are assisted in our estimates of the distances of objects by a knowledge of their sizes. Knowing the average size of, say, a man, the extent of his image on the retina gives us his angular subtense, from which two pieces of information we estimate his distance.

This association between the perception of size and of distance is well illustrated in the behaviour of after-images. If an after-image be induced and then the eye turned upon a screen, the image appears smaller as the screen is approached to the eye and larger as the screen recedes, although the area of retina stimulated remains unaltered.

The size of the retinal image, then, is of importance in supplying information as to the angular subtense of the corresponding object. We shall see later that if, for some reason, we make an inaccurate estimation of the distance of the object, it will appear too large or too small.

A *continuous* movement of a small object in the field in relation to a fixed reference object can be detected when the angular velocity of the moving object is as low as 1 to 2 minutes of arc per second. Regular to and fro movements of the order of 10 seconds of arc can be appreciated.

2.6. Monocular Perception of Depth.

We shall see in Chapter XII that binocular vision is much superior to monocular vision in estimating the relative distances of objects and in appreciating their solid form, or relief. Nevertheless there are certain factors which assist to this end even in monocular vision.

1. *The apparent size*: as already explained, experience teaches us the sizes of familiar objects and this information, coupled with the size of the retinal image of such objects, enables an estimate of their distances to be formed.

2. *Overlapping of objects*: an object that is partially concealed by another is obviously further away.

3. *Mathematical perspective*: parallel lines, as they recede into the distance, appear to intersect on the horizon. The fore-shortening of objects brought about in this way assists us in our perception of depth.

4. *Aerial perspective*: the outlines of distant objects tend to become softened and their colour to approximate to a dim blueness due to the intervening depth of atmosphere, and experience teaches us to interpret such appearances in terms of distance. When the atmosphere is unusually clear as in mountainous districts, distances are underestimated.

5. *Light and shade*: a sphere is distinguished from a flat surface because of the manner in which light is reflected from it; and in drawing, the appropriate shading supplies what would otherwise be a mere circle with the characteristic appearance of a solid sphere. Of still greater effect are the shadows cast by objects situated in different planes.

Artists make use of the above phenomena to produce the illusion of relief in their drawings and paintings.

6. *Parallax*: if two objects at different distances are observed and the head is moved laterally, the further object appears to move in the same direction as the head and the nearer object in the opposite direction. The rates and directions of such parallactic movements assist in our appreciation of relative distances.

With two eyes the object is seen from two points of view at the same time; in monocular vision it can be seen from two points of view in quick succession by moving the head.

7. *Accommodation*: the amount of accommodation required to see objects distinctly varies with their distance and is consequently a contributory factor in assessing their relative distances. It is a factor that is effective, however, only for quite near objects and even then only to a small extent.

It will be observed that, with the exception of accommodation, all these aids to monocular perception of depth and solidity are psychological in character and depend upon the acquirement of experience. A person who has been one-eyed for a considerable period will be quite adept at judging relative distances. In the aggregate these monocular factors can produce, under favourable conditions, a truthful impression of relief ; but the impression is far from spontaneous and is not accurate. If conditions are arranged so that these factors are not allowed to operate, as when viewing a single unfamiliar object in an otherwise homogeneous or dark field, then no estimate of distance can be made with one eye only. Merely the *direction* of the object can be judged.

FORM SENSE. VISUAL ACUITY.

2.7. Resolving Power of the Eye.

The inner end or base of a foveal cone subtends at the nodal point an angle of about $0 \cdot 0025 \div 16\frac{2}{3} \times 206{,}000 = 30$ seconds. Projected outwards into space it thus covers one inch at 185 yards or nearly one millimetre at the usual clinical testing distance of 6 metres.

The image of a bright point object formed by a perfect optical system of circular aperture is not just a point as is assumed in geometrical optics but, in consequence of the wave nature of light, consists of a central bright circular disc surrounded by alternate dark and bright rings of decreasing intensity (AIRY, 1834). The size of this diffraction pattern decreases and approximates more and more to a point as the aperture of the system increases ; this is one reason why large diameter telescopes are used in astronomical work. Fig. 2.6 illustrates the images of two point objects formed on the mosaic of foveal cones by an eye the optical system of which is assumed free from imperfections. Only the first bright ring round each central disc is shown ; moreover, the cones are indicated as lying in regular rows, a regularity not attained in the actual eye.

For the present we will consider just one of the images. The sizes of the central Airy disc and surrounding rings can be calculated from the well known AIRY-RAYLEIGH relation.* For a circular pupil of radius y and for light

* Refer to FINCHAM'S *Optics*.

of wavelength λ in air the radius of the first dark ring subtends at the nodal point an angle θ_N given by

$$\theta_N = 0 \cdot 61 \frac{\lambda}{y}$$

which expression provides also the theoretical limit of resolution of the eye.

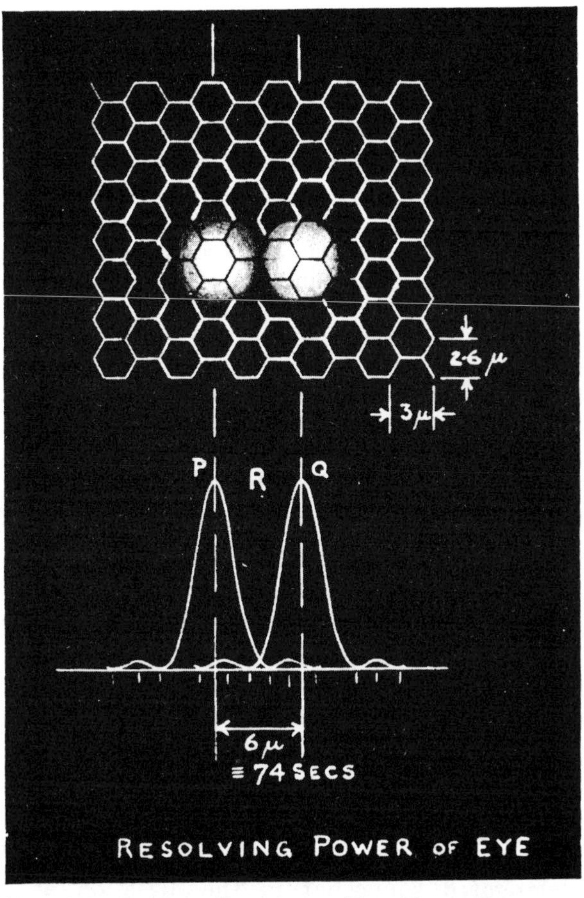

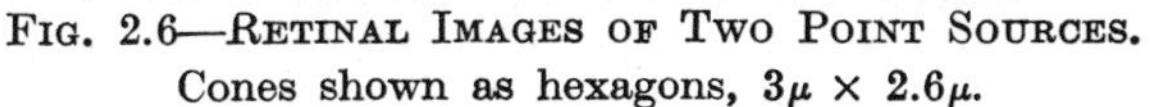

FIG. 2.6—RETINAL IMAGES OF TWO POINT SOURCES. Cones shown as hexagons, $3\mu \times 2.6\mu$.

For light of $\lambda = 555$ mμ (yellow-green) and a 3 mm. diameter pupil this gives a value $\theta_N = 47$ seconds, corresponding to a linear size h' on the retina of $0 \cdot 0038$ mm.

The intensity of illumination in the image is represented by the curve below, from which it will be seen that the maximum intensity at the centre of the disc is very much greater (about 57 times) than that in the first surrounding bright ring; and that most of the light (about 84 per cent.) forming the image falls within the central disc. The diameter of the disc up to the middle of the first dark ring, where the intensity has dropped to zero, is 94 seconds or 0·0076 mm., or about 3 foveal cones.

Thus even in an optically perfect eye the central disc of the image of a single point source strays over several cones. This disc is surrounded by a ring of light covering many more cones, in which the intensity may exceed the threshold value of the retina when the source being viewed is of ordinary intensity. Further, there is always a spreading or irradiation of light over the surface of the retina whenever an isolated area of it is illuminated, the extent of which is less in the dark races of mankind.

In the presence of this comparatively wide distribution of illumination over the fovea, it is remarkable that the individual "sees" the object sharply as a point. The central cone is, of course, stimulated to a much greater extent than its neighbours, the brain summing up the whole effect in such a manner that the difference is accentuated in the cortex (spatial induction) and the final *perceptual* image is very approximately a point. It is in this sense that in geometrical optics we refer, justifiably, to the images of point objects as point images.

In the actual eye the distribution of light over the retina is affected by various imperfections or aberrations in the optical system* and the theoretical Airy disc above described is modified to some extent. Generally the patch of light on the retina is larger and the light spread over it in an irregular manner.

If two adjacent cones are more or less equally stimulated and to a greater extent than the surrounding region, the brain will interpret the stimulation as from one luminous object elongated somewhat in the direction of the line joining the two cones, although the light may have arrived from two separate small sources very close together. The question arises as to how near two point sources may approach one another and still be appreciated as separate

* Chapter XI.

sources. It was stated long ago by Robert HOOKE that a very good eye can distinguish two point objects, such as two stars, as separate when they subtend an angle of one minute. In normal eyes the figure varies from 60 to 120 seconds according to the acuteness of the visual apparatus and the conditions as to the brightness of the sources and their surroundings.

The images shown in Fig. 2.6 are separated by 74 seconds of arc, corresponding to a linear separation of two cones on the retina. This is sufficient separation for the objects to be discriminated as separate points or " resolved " by a fairly acute eye. Since the sources are independent of one another (incoherent) the total intensity at any place on the retina may be found by summing the ordinates of the separate intensity curves shown in the lower part of the diagram. In the case illustrated the intensity at R midway between the two images is about one tenth of either maximum. In the actual eye the proportion will be higher on account of the disturbing effect of aberrations. If the objects were to approach closer together, the intensity at R would increase and the drop in intensity from the peaks at P and Q, to the point R would be too small to be appreciated, although there may still be a distance greater than the diameter of a cone between the peaks. The two sources would then appear as an oval patch—they would not be resolved. In order that two luminous points shall be separately discriminated, or resolved, the two peaks of the composite retinal image must fall on two points with at least a cone width between them and the intensity on this intermediate cone must be less than at the peaks by an amount that can be appreciated by the visual apparatus.

In maintaining fixation, the head and eye are in continuous motion round about the mean fixation position, the light pattern of the image thus travelling over different groups of cones in rapid succession; a scanning process. The final perception is the result of an averaging process in the cortex but, even so, is dependent in the first place upon the existence at successive moments of a less stimulated cone between others more strongly stimulated. The eye's resolving power is thus determined by the diameters of the foveal cones, by the light difference acuity, and by the performance of the optical system, a limit to which is set by the wave nature of light itself. It is remarkable how closely these factors are adjusted to one another.

Poor resolving power in an eye may be due to imperfections in its optical system resulting in a wide and/or irregular distribution of light in the retinal image, or to defective light difference acuity in or behind the retina, e.g. *amblyopia.*

If the two luminous sources differ in colour, there will be a variation across the retinal image of wavelength as well as light intensity, thus accentuating the difference between the two peaks and the intermediate region. The resolving power should be higher in these circumstances.

As an extension of the resolving power of the eye for isolated point sources is its ability to resolve the details of a grating—GRATING ACUITY. The pattern formed on the retina will consist of parallel streaks of a certain intensity corresponding to the bright bars of the grating, separated by streaks of lower intensity, the transition from the one intensity to the other being gradual and of the form represented by a curve of the type illustrated in Fig. 2.6. The grating will be resolved when the difference in intensity between the streaks is sufficient to be appreciated. For this to occur the bright bars must not be too close together ; experiment shows that the grating element (bright bar plus dark bar) must subtend at the eye an angle approaching 2 minutes, with eyes of good acuity.

The fact that the performance of actual eyes approaches so closely (60 seconds for a good eye) to the limit (47 seconds for a 3 mm. pupil) set by the nature of light shows that the many imperfections of the optical system are not usually of serious moment and we may investigate the principles of our subject of visual optics in relation to an eye in which the laws of geometrical optics apply ; we may assume the image of a point object to be a point. But we must be prepared to take into consideration the optical imperfections of the eye, or to examine its performance in relation to the physical nature of light, whenever circumstances arise in which these aspects assume a dominating influence.

2.8. Contour Acuity.

In recognising the outlines or contours of objects and detecting discontinuities in such, the eye is capable of an extraordinary precision. Whereas the discrimination of separated points or lines is possible when their separation is of the order of 60 to 120 seconds, a break, ab, Fig. 2.7, in a line can be detected and the lines set into coincidence when ab subtends at the eye an angle as small as 10 seconds. This so-called VERNIER ACUITY is even as high as 2 to 4 seconds with good observers such as those accustomed to the use of instruments like rangefinders.

Many attempts have been made to explain this high acuity. Experiment shows that the accuracy of such

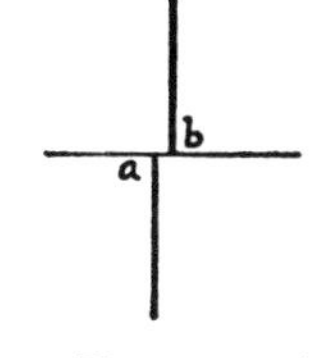

FIG. 2.7—VERNIER ACUITY—COINCIDENCE SETTING.

observations increases if the time allowed for the observation exceeds 0.10 second and is greater for long lines than for short ones; which suggests that a movement of the image over the foveal cones is required and that large numbers of the latter are concerned. The following is a possible explanation*: large numbers of the irregularly disposed cones in the neighbourhood of the edge of the image of one line are stimulated to different extents as they lie

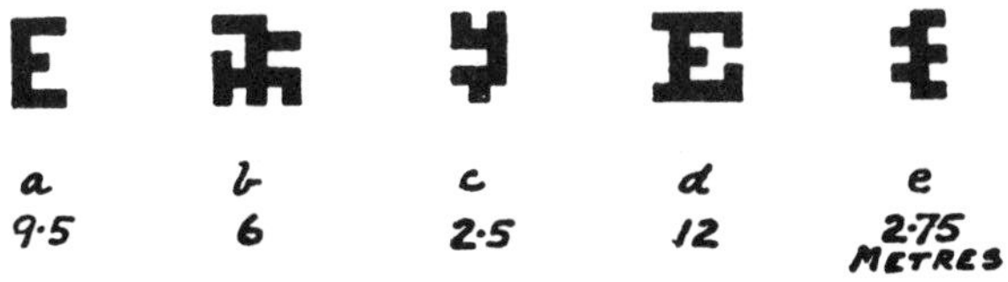

a	b	c	d	e
9·5	6	2·5	12	2·75 METRES

FIG. 2.8—RESOLUTION OF LETTERS AND PATTERNS (CONTOUR ACUITY).

in the region where the intensity falls gradually from the maximum to zero. The corresponding nerve impulses are integrated in the cortex and a mean position for the edge of the line assigned therein. The accuracy with which a displacement of this mean position can be detected is therefore not limited by the dimensions of a single cone.

In the task of recognising more complicated contours such as geometrical patterns and printed letters and numerals—LETTER ACUITY—the psychological stage of the

* ANDERSON and WEYMOUTH (1923).

visual act, involving the integrating and interpreting of the stimuli, becomes relatively more prominent; and it assumes an increasingly important role in the case of patterns that are familiar to the observer. In such cases the previous experience of the observer may enable him to recognise the object even though the retinal image is faulty or not in focus. Letters and numerals are consequently more easily discriminated than unfamiliar patterns possessing the same sized detail. The characters illustrated in Fig. 2.8, constructed of such a size that their limbs and spaces each subtend one minute at 10 metres, were recognised by two or three young observers of good acuity at the average distances stated in the diagram. The familiar letter is seen to be recognised much more easily than the unfamiliar patterns.

2.9. Out-of-Focus Effects.

In §2.7 we discussed the vision of a point source by an eye free from optical defects, the point image being *in focus* on the fovea. If for some reason the focus of the homocentric refracted pencil does not fall on the retina, the latter receives from a point source a circular patch of light often called a BLUR CIRCLE. This may happen because the

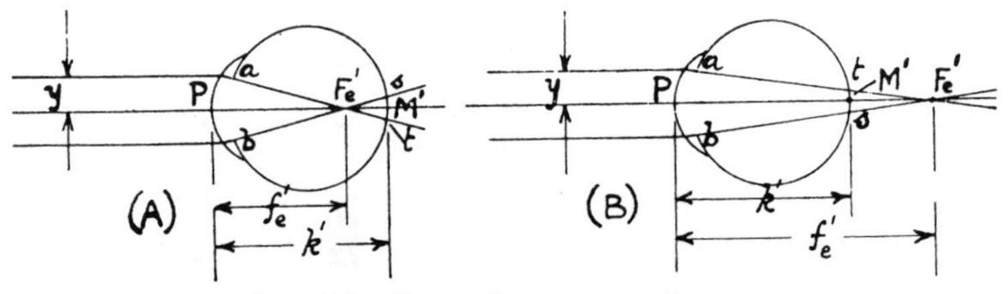

FIG. 2.9—BLUR CIRCLES ON RETINA.

eye is ametropic* or may be produced by blurring or "fogging" the eye with positive spheres, in which case the focus will lie within the retina as in Fig. 2.9A. Whether the focal length of the optical system is less than the globe length PM′ of the eye or exceeds it, as in Fig. 2.9B, the diameter of the blur circle st depends upon the pupil diameter $2y$ and upon the out-of-focus distance F'_eM', and can be easily calculated.

The blur circle increases as the pupil expands, whereas the Airy disc at the focus decreases (§2.7). If we take an

* Chapter III.

eye with the standard optical system $F_e = 60$ D and $f'_e = 22 \cdot 22$ mm. but in which the axial length is say 22·60 mm.* instead of the 22·22 mm. of the emmetropic eye, then for a 3 mm. diameter pupil

$$\text{diameter of blur circle} = \frac{3 \times \cdot 38}{22 \cdot 22} = 0 \cdot 051 \text{ mm.}$$

This diameter subtends an angle of 10 minutes at the nodal point and includes about 17 cones ; the blur circle has about $6\frac{3}{4}$ times the diameter and 45 times the area of the Airy disc and covers something like 250 cones. The distribution of light intensity across the blur will be of the form indicated in Fig. 2.10 and the eye would see a circular patch fading gradually into the surrounding darkness. As the focus is removed further from the retina the patch increases in size and becomes fainter, until ultimately it is indistinguishable.

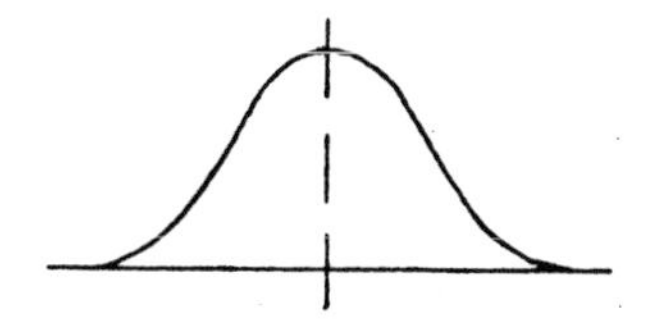

FIG. 2.10—TO ILLUSTRATE DISTRIBUTION OF LIGHT INTENSITY ACROSS BLUR CIRCLE.

Characters such as the letters on the test chart consisting of several black strokes in different directions will remain distinguishable until the blurring has reached a certain degree, which degree will be greater the wider is the separation of the strokes in the letter. The letter B will become confused more quickly than the letter L of the same overall dimensions. It will be understood, too, that a stroke or other character observed under a gradually increasing amount of blur will lose its identity more quickly if the *contrast* between it and its surroundings is not marked. A black stroke on a grey background, or a yellow one on a red background, will disappear sooner than a black stroke on a clean white background.

In the actual eye the optical imperfections of its optical system will be operative and will complicate the effects just described.†

* This figure has been chosen as it is the length of an eye suffering from a refractive error (myopia) of 1 dioptre. (Chap. III.)

† Chapter XI.

2.10. Visual Acuity.

In everyday life the eye is called upon to distinguish the details and forms of a great variety of objects. This faculty we call the form sense and the capability or acuteness of the eye in performing it we speak of generally as its visual acuity. We see that the faculty is a composite one including

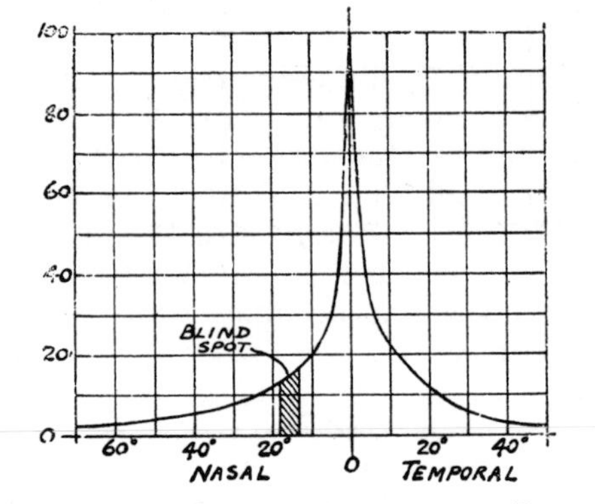

FIG. 2.11—VARIATION OF ACUITY OVER RETINA.

the resolving of point sources and "gratings" and the distinguishing of the outlines of familiar and unfamiliar objects. The ability of the visual apparatus to appreciate this variety of form and detail is founded, we have seen, on its possession of an optical system to form sharp images and a multitude of tiny receptors with localised representation in the cortex; and on its capability to appreciate light differences and colour differences.

The cones rather than the rods are responsible for form vision and visual acuity is consequently very much higher at the fovea than elsewhere over the retina. The variation of acuity over the retina is represented in Fig. 2.11, which is due to WERTHEIM (1894). It falls rapidly from the centre of the fovea; only 5 degrees out from the centre it has already dropped to one third of its central value.

Visual acuity depends to a marked extent upon the illumination of the test object and its surroundings. Although faint sources and movements can be perceived in comparative darkness (scotopic vision) especially in the extra foveal regions, we cannot recognise *details* in poor illumination. Attempts to do so, to read or carry on fine work, in inadequate or badly distributed illumination, lead to eyestrain and its attendant evils.

The manner in which visual acuity is affected by the illumination of the test object and of the surrounding field is illustrated in Fig. 2.12, which is the result of a careful investigation by LYTHGOE (1932). When only the test

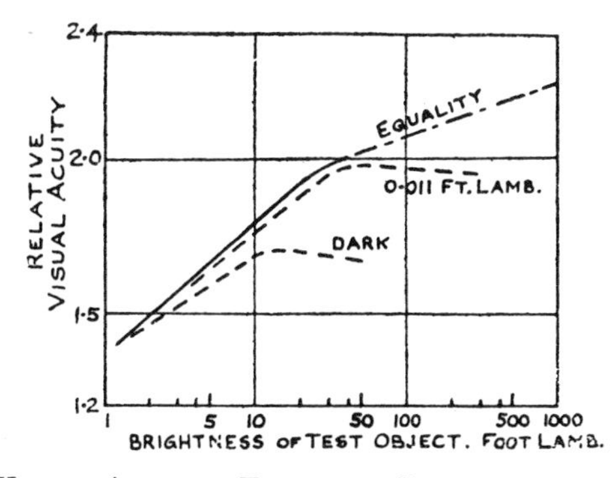

FIG. 2.12—VISUAL ACUITY. EFFECT OF BRIGHTNESS OF TEST OBJECT AND OF SURROUND. BRIGHTNESS OF SURROUND MARKED AGAINST CURVE. (LYTHGOE, 1932.)

object itself is illuminated, the surroundings being kept completely dark, the acuity rises to a maximum value of about 1·7 when the brightness of the test object reaches 10 foot-lamberts or so,* and decreases if the test object is made brighter. When the surroundings have a brightness of 0·011 ft. lamb., the visual acuity rises steadily to a maximum value of nearly 2 as the brightness of the test object is raised to 50 ft. lamb. The best results are obtained when the surrounding field has the same brightness as the test object; a surrounding field brighter than the test object reduces the acuity again. These effects arise partly by reason of the variation of pupil size that they produce but mainly because of the influence that one region of the retina can have on the performance of another region; a subject which is discussed under "spatial induction" in Chapter XX.

It has been shown that, keeping the retinal illumination constant by adjusting the brightness of the field, the acuity remains substantially constant as the pupil diameter changes from 2 to 6 mm.; below 2 mm. the acuity falls in proportion to the diameter because of diffraction effects (§2.7).

---

* A foot-lambert is the brightness of a surface emitting or reflecting one lumen per square foot of area; it is equivalent to $\frac{1}{\pi} = 0.32$ candles per square foot. Refer to Volume II, Chapter XVIII.

2.11. Tests of Visual Acuity.

We test the visual acuity of an eye, for a given type of test object, by determining the smallest visual angle under which the object can be clearly distinguished. This may be done either by varying the distance from the eye of any object of given size or, keeping the distance fixed, by presenting objects of gradually decreasing size. The latter is more convenient clinically and has the advantage also that we thereby test the acuity in a fixed state of accommodation. From previous paragraphs it is evident that the acuity expressed in angular subtense varies greatly according to the type of object presented to the eye. To obtain a constant scientific measure of the acuity we should choose as object a geometrical character that is universally employable for people of all nationalities and that does not unduly

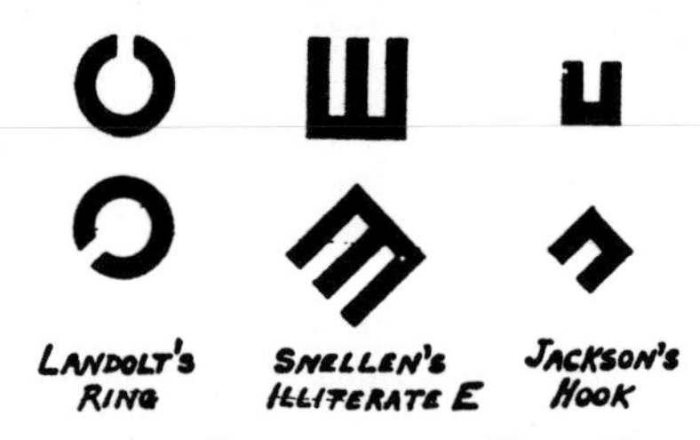

FIG. 2.13—GEOMETRICAL PATTERNS AS TEST OBJECTS FOR VISUAL ACUITY.

favour any class of people (e.g. the educated) at the expense of the others. We should therefore rule out as far as possible the psychological stage of the visual act by making the object an unfamiliar pattern which will not be clearly recognised until the physical process of forming a good image on the retina has been achieved. Even then it is to be understood that we are testing eyes on a particular type of object; and two eyes found to have equal acuity with this object may not have equal acuity under some other test.

Tests requiring the resolution of two points or dots, or of a grating, are too specific. Gratings are unreliable also because it is possible for the "streaky" nature of such and the direction of the lines to be recognised before the grating is really being resolved; moreover, the acuity of all eyes varies with the orientation of the grating.

Geometrical forms such as the broken ring of LANDOLT and others represented in Fig. 2.13 have been proposed from time to time. The LANDOLT ring is constructed so that its total diameter subtends 5 minutes, its thickness and the gap each one minute, at certain stated distances in metres. The gap is orientated in various directions in the different characters and the subject is required to recognise the gap and name its position. A chart incorporating this test object was drawn up by HESS and adopted by the Eleventh International Ophthalmological Congress in 1909.

SNELLEN proposed his so-called " illiterate E " test as being serviceable for children and subjects who are unable to read; the subject is asked merely to indicate the direction in which the prongs of the E are pointing. The AMMON and JACKSON hooks and the LANDOLT ring are useful similarly.

2.12. Clinical Testing. The Test Chart.

In clinical testing we are not concerned only with determining the optimum visual acuity, on a particular kind of test object. Our aim is rather to determine the best optical correction for the eye. In order to subject the eye to a test comparable with the varied tasks imposed upon it in everyday life we should use characters of complicated form and of varying degrees of contrast with their background. At the same time, however, the test should permit of simple questions to, and simple answers from, the subject; and his answers should be capable of rapid checking. To make the test precise the characters used should *quickly* become unrecognisable when not seen clearly.

These requirements may be met fairly satisfactorily by printed letters and numerals which are consequently widely used in clinical testing. It is to be noted that we thereby test the *letter acuity*. Following the proposals of SNELLEN who, acting on the suggestion of DONDERS, produced his first " optotypes " in 1862, the letters are constructed so that their constituent parts, the limbs and the spaces between these, each subtend an angle of one minute at certain specified distances. Most of the letters adopted by SNELLEN were enclosed in a square the sides of which subtend 5 minutes at the stated distances. The test is usually carried out at a distance of 6 metres (20 feet) which is accepted as sufficiently far away for the eye to be in its relaxed, unaccommodated state; in ophthalmic practice an object at 6 metres is considered a " distant " object.

Fig. 2.14 illustrates the principle of construction of the test letters. A complete test chart contains many lines of such letters, black on a white background, of sizes such that their detail subtends one minute at distances of 60, 48, 36, 24, 18, 15, 9, (7.5), 6, 5, 4 and 3 metres.

The linear size of the limbs or spaces of the 6-metre letter is given by

$$x \text{ (mm.)} = 6000 \times 1 \text{ minute or } 6000 \tan 1'$$
$$= 6000 \times 0\cdot000292$$
$$= 1\cdot75 \text{ mm., very nearly.}$$

The whole (5′) letter is thus 8·75 mm. in height—very nearly. The size of the corresponding retinal image of the whole letter in the standard reduced eye is thus

$$h' = 16\tfrac{2}{3} \tan 5' = \tfrac{50}{3} \times \cdot 00145 = 0\cdot024 \text{ mm.}$$

or about 10 cones in linear extent.

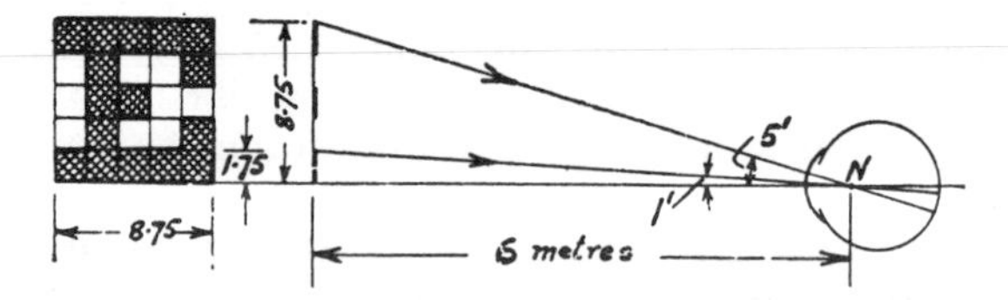

FIG. 2.14—ILLUSTRATING CONSTRUCTION OF TEST TYPES—SNELLEN.

The 60-metre letter subtends 50 minutes at the 6-metre testing distance. Its size is 87·5 mm. and its retinal image 0·24 mm.; the retinal image of this largest letter of the chart is just about contained within the central foveal area.

An eye which can just read the 6-metre letters at the 6-metre testing distance is considered conventionally as possessing unit visual acuity. The acuity is recorded in the form of a fraction the numerator of which gives the testing distance and the denominator of which gives the distance at which the letters that are just distinguished subtend 5 minutes; and at which they would be read by an eye with normal, or unit, acuity. Thus the vision of an eye with unit acuity would be recorded as 6/6.

A distinction is to be drawn between the performance of the unaided eye, which we will call the VISION (V) of the eye and the best performance of the same eye when it has been provided with its proper optical correction; this is the quantity we call the VISUAL ACUITY (V.A.). Granted a satisfactory performance by the optical system in forming the retinal image, this depends upon the "acuteness" of the retina and visual brain centres. Thus

$$\left.\begin{matrix}\text{Vision—unaided}\\ \text{or V.A.—aided}\end{matrix}\right\} = \frac{\text{Testing distance in metres}}{\text{Distance in metres at which best line subtends } 5'}$$

$$= 6/6 \text{ for normal eye}$$

$$= 6/9, 6/12 \ldots . 6/60 \quad \text{for eyes which}$$

can only read the 9, 12 . . . 60 metre letters at 6 metres.

Some eyes have acuity as high as 6/3. Inasmuch as the separation of the middle points of adjacent limbs of the letters subtends 2 minutes at the corresponding distance, the normal vision 6/6 is approximately equivalent to a resolving power for lines, or a grating acuity, of 2 minutes.

The letters on one line are not all equally legible: the letter B is one of the most difficult usually. It will frequently happen in practice, therefore, that the subject will be unable to read *all* the letters in his last line.

If the vision of an eye is subnormal to the extent that even the large 60-metre letter cannot be read at 6 metres, the chart is brought nearer to the subject until the letter is recognised and the vision recorded as, say, 4/60 or 3/60 according to the distance. If 1/60 cannot be attained, the distance is recorded at which the fingers can be counted with the light behind the subject; or next, the appreciation of the movements of the outstretched hand is asked for. Failing this, the subject faces the light and the examiner moves his hand about between the subject and the light —*shadow perception.* Finally, it is determined whether the subject can appreciate a light shone directly into his eye —*light perception.*

Special test charts with pictures of familiar objects are used for very young children—see Chapter XIV.

The test chart may be used in conjunction with a plane mirror facing the subject, the chart being hung above or to one side of his head. The sum of the distances of the chart from the mirror and of the subject from the mirror is to be 6 metres. When used in this way the letters on the chart must be reversed so that they are seen in their proper orientation in the mirror; this is a *reversed chart.* The mirror must be of good quality, and flat, otherwise the letters and characters seen in it will be distorted and fictitious results obtained.

The brightness of the chart must be adequate (above 10 ft. lamberts and preferably 25 or more if the surroundings are not quite dark) and uniform over the chart. A means of varying the illumination on the chart may sometimes be an advantage.* Visual acuity is affected by the contrast between the letters and their background. The chart should therefore be kept clean so that records taken from it shall maintain a constant value. It is possible to obtain charts which have been treated so as to render them washable. The possibility of the subject memorising the letters should be borne in mind. Double or quadruple charts, arranged like the leaves of a book or on a rotating drum, are used to counteract this. In a well-made chart the smallest letters should be as sharp and clean-cut as the larger letters. Such charts, produced by the photo-lithographic process, are procurable.

The question as to whether tests on the eyes should be conducted in darkened surroundings or in daylight will be alluded to subsequently.

Reading Types.

A set of letters was drawn up by SNELLEN for use in testing near vision at or about the ordinary reading distance of 30–40 cm. They have been superseded by reading types consisting of ordinary printed matter of various sizes. JAEGER'S reading types are the ordinary printers' founts (brilliant = J1, pearl = J2, pica = J10, etc.) each size of type being marked usually with an arbitrary number J1, J2, etc. and also with a number expressing the distance in metres at which the individual letters subtend 5 minutes and at which distances they should therefore be read by a person of normal acuity (and sufficient accommodation). The reading types drawn up by G. COWELL are carefully constructed so that the limbs are as nearly as possible one-fifth of the height of the letters, each size of type being marked as above.

In practice these types are used rather for obtaining information about the accommodation of the subject and in determining the correction he requires for near work.

2.13. Subnormal Vision. Pinhole Disc.

Vision may be below normal either because a sharp image is not formed on the retina or because the physiological and

---

* §4.5.

psychological processes at and behind the retina are defective. If the retina, through disease or other cause, is distorted or does not function properly, or if the cerebral mechanism is inefficient in interpreting the image, the light sense or form sense will be affected and the eye is said to be AMBLYOPIC. Visual acuity will then be always subnormal* even though the optical performance be good. On the other hand the vision of the eye represented in Fig. 2.9 will be poor, since each point of the object is represented by a confusing blur on the retina. An object such as a thin vertical line would be imaged on the retina as at (a) Fig. 2.15.

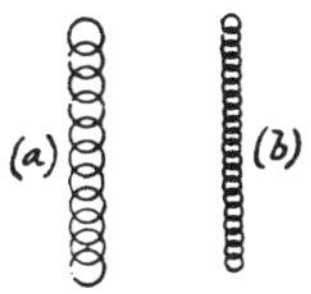

(a) (b)

FIG. 2.15—BLUR CIRCLE AND PINHOLE EFFECT.

If a disc containing a small pinhole aperture were placed before the eye, the pencil ab (Fig. 2.9) and consequently the blur circles would be considerably reduced in size. The image would be sharpened up as indicated at (b) Fig. 2.15. Vision would be improved therefore if the eye is not amblyopic but little or no improvement would occur if it were. The pinhole disc thus gives useful information at the commencement of a test in cases of subnormal vision. In cases of good vision, the focus F'_e being on or very near to the retina, the pinhole will produce no improvement; it will even tend to impair vision due to the reduction in light intensity on the retina. The pinhole should not be too small or diffraction will mar the sharpening effect; the diameter should not be less than 0·5 to 0·75 mm.

In passing, it will be observed from Fig. 2·9 that a reduction in pupil size, by means of a pinhole or contraction, decreases the rate of change of diameter of the pencil as the focus is moved relatively to the retina; i.e. depth of focus is increased.

A disc pierced by two small holes, first employed by SCHEINER, is frequently useful. Through such a disc the eye depicted in Fig. 2.16(A) or (B) would see a distant object apparently doubled. The two narrow pencils admitted to the eye form two small out-of-focus images at s and t. Projected into space through N, the projection of t is below that of s in case (A) and above in case (B). If the upper

* Unless the amblyopia has been acquired as in the case of a squinting subject, in which case it may be removed or reduced by appropriate training —see Chapter XIV.

aperture were covered, to the first eye the lower of the two apparent objects would disappear; and to the second eye the upper object would disappear. This SCHEINER DISC

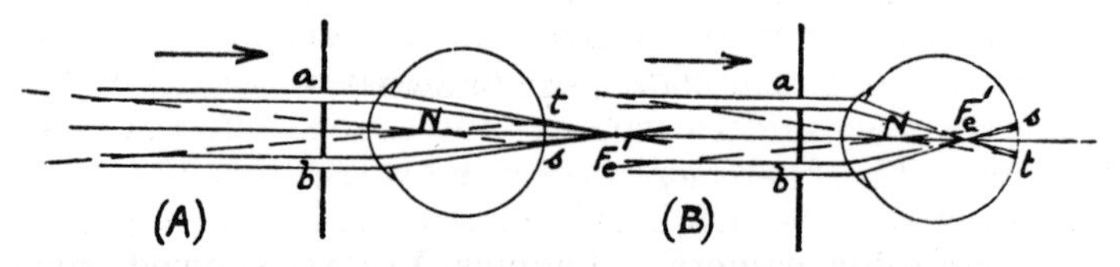

FIG. 2.16—ILLUSTRATING THE SCHEINER DISC.

will be mentioned later in connection with ametropia and accommodation. The principle is often used in ophthalmic instruments.

A third kind of aperture, useful mainly in connection with astigmatic eyes, is the STENOPAIC SLIT. It consists of a blank disc provided with an opening in the form of a slit about 0·75 mm. wide.

All these discs are of an external diameter (about 38 mm.) convenient for insertion in the ordinary trial frame.

Experiment. It will be instructive for the student at this stage to determine and record his own vision on an adequately illuminated test chart at 6 metres, each eye separately, and to note the effect of a pinhole before the eye. To obtain an idea of the vision of people with various amounts of optical error (ametropia, Ch. III) the experiment should be continued by recording the letter vision obtained after placing positive spherical lenses before the eye, starting with +0·25 D and continuing with +0·50, +0·75, +1·00, +1·50, etc. up to say +2·50 D; each eye separately without and with pinhole. Repeat with corresponding negative lenses up to −6 D or so and carefully consider the results obtained, for future reference.

2.14. Accommodation.

With a sound eye, an object can be seen distinctly when its image is sharply focused on the fovea. Objects at various distances can be seen distinctly, but not all at the same time. Hold a pen before the eye and look, with one eye, beyond it at a vertical window bar which is much further away. The pen is seen indistinctly. When the attention is directed to the pen so that it is distinct, the window bar in its turn becomes indistinct. We are conscious that in changing the focus, from the distant to the near object, or vice versa, some change has taken place in the eye.

Fig. 2.17 shows a pencil of light from a distant object point Q brought to focus by the eye's optical system on the fovea at M′. If no change occurred in the eye, an object at B would be imaged at some point B′ behind the fovea, the pencil from B would form an out-of-focus blur patch on the retina and B would appear indistinct. It is evident that for B to be seen clearly some change must take place in the eye. The conditions would be satisfied if the retina moved back to B′; this is the focusing method adopted in the photographic camera. Thomas YOUNG showed, however, by experimenting on his own eye, that the length of the globe does not change. The effect could be produced by an increase in the power of the optical system; and this could theoretically be brought about by an increase in the power of the cornea or of the crystalline lens or

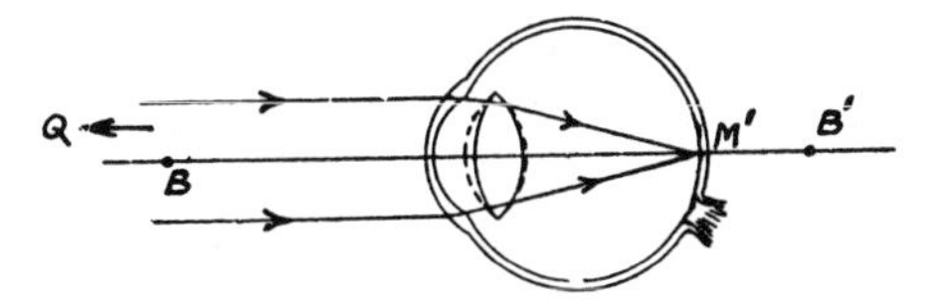

FIG. 2.17—ACCOMMODATION.

by a bodily displacement of the crystalline lens towards the cornea. It was again demonstrated by YOUNG that the power of the cornea remains unchanged when the eye changes its focus or *accommodates*. He did this by immersing his eye in water, whereby the refractive power of the cornea is practically eliminated since its refractive index (1·376) is very nearly the same as that of water. Replacing the cornea by a positive lens of appropriate power, he found that his ability to accommodate was not affected.

We are left with the crystalline lens as the agent for effecting accommodation. It is easy to show that the amount of movement of the crystalline lens that is possible in the eye (that is, the depth of the anterior chamber) is totally inadequate to account for the increase of power required to focus near objects. This leaves us with the last possibility, namely, an increase in the power of the crystalline lens itself. As the result of modern experimental work* there can be no doubt that this does actually happen: that during the process of accommodation the front surface,

* See also §10.2.

and to a smaller extent the back surface, of the crystalline lens becomes steeper, as indicated by the dotted lines in Fig. 2.17; the axial thickness increases and the equatorial diameter correspondingly decreases. The resulting increase in power enables a near object B to be focused on the retina at M′.

Many suggestions have been put forward to account for the mechanism whereby this change in form of the crystalline lens is brought about. The two most prominent hypotheses have been those of HELMHOLTZ and TSCHERNING. The soft lens substance is enclosed in a highly elastic capsule

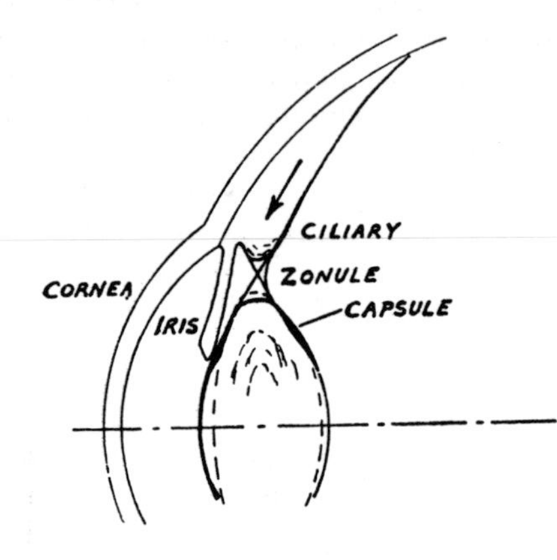

FIG. 2.18—THE LENS IN ACCOMMODATION.

which is suspended from the ciliary body by the zonule as indicated in Fig. 2.18; the zonule forms an elastic radially disposed coupling between the lens capsule and the ciliary body. The latter contains the radial and circular ciliary muscle fibres, the contraction and relaxation of which slackens and tightens the zonule. HELMHOLTZ maintained that in the unaccommodated state of the eye (distant objects under view) the zonule is in a state of outward radial tension and the lens therefore relatively flat; that when the ciliary muscle contracts during accommodation this tension is relieved and the lens (which he considered to be elastic) bulges out to its natural more curved form.

TSCHERNING (1898) rightly pointed out, however, that only the axial portion of the lens becomes more highly curved, the peripheral parts becoming flatter. He attributed this change of shape to an *increase* in the tension of the zonule during accommodation flattening out the lens except at its central portion, which assumes its steeper shape on account of the comparatively dense central nucleus of the lens. He later (1909) modified this conception and suggested that the ciliary muscle caused the vitreous humour to be pressed forward against the back of the lens which, together with the pull of the zonule, resulted in the central bulge of the lens.

Later investigations have shown that as far as the zonule is concerned, HELMHOLTZ'S view is correct and the zonule is relaxed. Evidence of this is given by the observations that during accommodation the thickness of the lens is increased and its diameter reduced. This change in diameter can be seen in eyes from which the iris is absent, and in these cases, the inner edge of the ciliary body, from which the lens is suspended, has been seen to move forward and inward. The relief of tension upon the lens in accommodation has also been proved by observations of an eye in which, following a perforation of the lens capsule, the lens substance had been absorbed leaving an empty transparent capsule. When this subject was looking at a distant object, the front and back surfaces of the capsule were parallel and close to one another. When the subject accommodated for a near object, the front of the capsule bent forward in the centre to a steep curve, while the back became lax and sagged backward irregularly.

In the Helmholtz theory it is presumed that the lens is elastic, but this has been proved to be untrue. Also it is supposed that the lens is held in a flattened condition when the eye is at rest and is only allowed to assume its natural form during accommodation. Further, this theory does not explain the central bulge in the front surface. According to FINCHAM the natural form of the lens substance is its unaccommodated form ; the central bulge and peripheral flattening during accommodation are due to the fact that the elastic capsule varies in thickness as represented, in an exaggerated form, in Fig. 2.18 ; thus the slackening of the zonule allows the capsule to mould the soft plastic lens substance into the form shown.

The fact that this characteristic form of the front surface of the lens is produced by a slackening of tension is shown by the photographs (Fig. 2.19) of the front of the lens in the eye immediately after removal from a young subject. In the first photograph the cornea and iris have been removed, leaving the lens suspended by the zonule. In the second photograph the zonule has been cut so that all tension upon the lens is relieved. The surface has changed from an approximately spherical curve with radius of 12 mm. to one having a steep central curvature, radius 5 mm., and a flatter periphery, radius 12 mm.

Accommodation is seen to depend upon the plasticity of the lens substance and upon the power of the ciliary muscle. The actual change in lens form, which results in a near object being imaged on the retina, is spoken of (after FUCHS) as the PHYSICAL ACCOMMODATION and is measured,

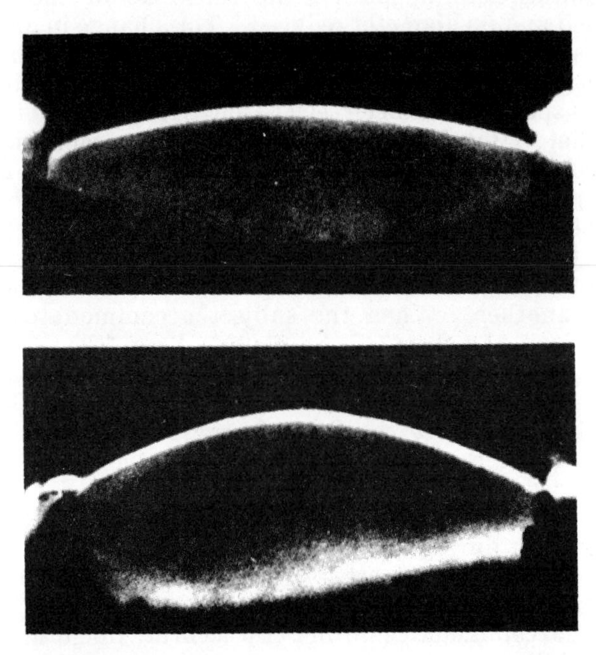

FIG. 2.19—ANTERIOR SURFACE OF CRYSTALLINE LENS.
Above—lens suspended by zonule ;
Below—zonule has been cut and tension on lens relieved (FINCHAM).

as we shall see, in dioptres. The ciliary effort necessary to produce this change in lens form is called the PHYSIOLOGICAL ACCOMMODATION, the unit of ciliary muscle contraction having been given the name *myodioptre*, which is intended to express the contractile effort of the muscle necessary to produce a change of accommodation of one dioptre.

The accommodation necessary to see a near object distinctly is normally accompanied by a movement of convergence of the two eyes to bring the visual axis of each on to the object of regard. The pupil also contracts and, if the head happens to be held forward, the lens moves bodily forward to a small extent because of the freedom given to it by the relaxed zonule. The ciliary muscle controlling accommodation, the medial recti responsible for convergence, and the sphincter pupillæ for pupil contraction, are all three innervated by the same, third cranial, nerve.

Accommodation is specially active in young people; we shall see later that the degree or "amplitude" of accommodation that can be exerted by an individual decreases as age advances.

Changes of accommodation are carried out rapidly so that most people see distant and near objects clearly in rapid succession without realising that anything of the nature of a change of power of the lens has occurred in the eye.

The above remarks have been concerned only with the mechanism whereby the process of accommodation is accomplished and not at all with the question as to how the brain decides that, in a given case, accommodation is needed. If the eye is made to look through suitably placed apertures into a "homogeneous field" such as the interior of a uniformly white-painted and illuminated spherical globe, and if a vertical black line is introduced into this field, how does the brain decide whether it is a sharply defined line on which the eye is not focusing or a blurred streak on which it is focusing? It is not easy to answer this question (see §23.2.)

2.15. The Pupil.

Under the antagonistic actions of the dilatator and sphincter muscles in the iris the pupil is in continual tremor round about a mean diameter of 2·5 to 4 mm. normally. Its extreme diameters are 1·5 and 8 mm. It is somewhat larger in myopes and in women, smaller in hyperopes, men and very old people. The two pupils are usually equal in size; inequality is called *anisocoria*, which is caused by various pathological conditions but may be physiological.

The pupil contracts and dilates reflexly under various conditions such as:

1. Reaction to light: direct and indirect (consensual).
2. The near reflex: the pupil contracts when the eyes converge and accommodate.

3. Various sensory and emotional stimulations (e.g. pain, fear).
4. Drugs: the pupil may be artificially dilated by the instillation of drugs called *mydriatics*, e.g. atropine, homatropine, etc. and contracted by drugs called *miotics* such as eserine and pilocarpine.

The direct light reflex: the pupil expands in dark surroundings and contracts when bright objects enter the field of view, the extent of these variations of diameter depending upon the changes in the illumination on the retina; and, for the same illumination, being greater when the stimulus falls on the macular area than on other retinal areas—this is of importance in ophthalmoscopy. The *rate* of variation of pupil size depends upon the relative *change* of brightness, not upon the absolute brightness. A rapid change and a slow change produce the same final diameter. The contraction under increase of brightness is much more rapid than the dilatation under decrease of brightness. If, for example, the conditions change from complete darkness to a brightness of 100 foot-lamberts, the pupil will contract, after a latent period of about $\frac{1}{3}$ second, from 8 mm. to 3 mm. or so within a period of 4 or 5 seconds. Under the reverse process, brightness to darkness, the pupil will expand from its original diameter of 2 to 3 mm. to a diameter of 6·5 mm. within 10 seconds or so but will require 10 minutes or longer to attain its maximum diameter of 8 mm.

The indirect or consensual light reflex: in all animals in which the optic nerve fibres partially decussate at the chiasma, stimulation of one retina causes not only direct contraction of the pupil of that eye but also a contraction of the other pupil. The consensual effect on the unstimulated eye is slower than the direct. When both eyes are stimulated, the effects are added and the rate of contraction increased.

The reason for these pupil reactions under light stimulus is not too clear. In closing down from 8 mm. to 2 mm. the pupil area is reduced to one sixteenth; but the eye adapts itself to brightnesses varying between 10^4 foot-lamberts or more to less than 10^{-2} foot-lambert, i.e. a ratio of a million to one; thus the eye does not appear to rely much on the pupil to shield it from bright conditions.* And as we

---

* §20.6.

have seen, pupil variation above 2 mm. has little or no effect on visual acuity.

DIRECTIONAL SENSITIVITY OF THE RETINA.

It was discovered by STILES and CRAWFORD in 1933 that the apparent brightness of a patch of light depends considerably on the angle at which the beam of light strikes the retina. Thus if a narrow pencil of light is admitted to the eye at a point distant 2 mm. temporally from the centre of the pupil it produces only 75 per cent. of the effect produced by a pencil of equal intensity which is incident centrally; and at 2 mm. nasalward the effect is reduced to 40 per cent.

This is a most important fact, for which an adequate explanation is not yet forthcoming. It cannot be ignored in formulating a theory of vision and has a practical bearing on the method of making photometric observations.

EXERCISES. CHAPTER II.

1. Taking the reduced eye as a single spherical surface of power 60 D separating air from water of refractive index $\frac{4}{3}$, show that the anterior and posterior focal lengths are $16\frac{2}{3}$ and 22·22 mm. respectively and the radius of curvature 5·55 mm. Assuming the retina passes through the second focal point (the eye emmetropic) find the size of the retinal image of an object 50 cm. long at a distance of 6 metres from the eye.

2. Find the visual angle, expressed in minutes of arc and in prism dioptres, subtended by each of the following objects and the size of the retinal image in mm. formed in the standard reduced eye in each case: (*a*) a ship 120 feet long at a distance of 3 miles; (*b*) object 2 mm. long at $33\frac{1}{3}$ cm. distance; (*c*) object 8·75 mm. high at 6 metres distance.

3. Assuming the value 3 μ for the diameter of a foveal cone, find the angle subtended at the nodal point (*a*) by one cone, (*b*) by the fovea centralis, 0·3 mm. horizontally and 0·2 mm. vertically. What extent of space, at a distance of six metres from the eye, is "covered" by the fovea ?

4. If h' represents linear dimensions in mm. on the retina of the standard eye and θ represents their angular subtense at the nodal point in degrees, show that:

$$h' = 0{\cdot}29\ \theta \text{ and } \theta = 3{\cdot}44\ h'.$$

5. If the blind spot of the eye subtends an angle at the nodal point of 7° vertically and 5° horizontally, what extent of object will be invisible at a distance of $\frac{1}{3}$ metre from the eye ?

6. Donders long ago proposed a reduced eye in which the radius of curvature was 5 mm. and the refractive index $\frac{4}{3}$. Find the dioptric power and focal lengths of this eye and the size of the retinal image of the object of question 1.

7. Taking the reduced eye as of 60 dioptres power and the refractive index of its contents as $\frac{4}{3}$, draw the eye, four times full size; mark in their correct positions the focal points, nodal point and centre of rotation. Show the course of two rays from the upper extremity of a distant object standing on the axis and subtending a visual angle of 20 prism dioptres.

8. With the aid of two diagrams explain briefly the meaning of the following quantities and show their positions in relation to the eye: optical axis, visual axis, fixation line, angle alpha, macula, optic disc, centre of rotation.

9. Give an account of the means whereby an appreciation of the relative distances of objects in the field and their solidity can be obtained in monocular vision. What is meant by "local sign"?

10. With the aid of a diagram showing the image of a point source on the mosaic of foveal cones, explain what is meant by the resolving power of the eye for point sources. Calculate the theoretical resolving power of an eye the pupil diameter of which is 4 mm., for light of wavelength 555 mμ.

11. Upon what factors does the acuteness of vision depend? Discuss the capability of the eye of distinguishing detail in the following cases: (*a*) when viewing two close stars or distant point sources; how does this depend upon the pupil size? (*b*) when viewing a grating; (*c*) when "aligning" two vertical lines on either side of a horizontal separating line as in coincidence setting or scale reading; (*d*) when reading Snellen types. (S.M.C. Hons.)

12. What causes the natural blind spot? Where is it situated in the eye and in the field of vision? Why is it not always obvious and what tests can be performed to demonstrate its presence? (S.M.C.)

13. How is it that, although the image formed on the retina is inverted, we do not see anything upside down? In what ways do we estimate the size of objects? (B.O.A.)

14. Upon what factors does acuity depend? How are they related to the structure of the eye? How can the acuity at other parts of the retina than the fovea be demonstrated? Show in a diagram how it varies with the angular distance from the fovea. (B.O.A. Hons.)

15. Taking the reduced 60 D eye, of refractive index $\frac{4}{3}$, find the diameter of the blur circle formed on the retina corresponding to a point source (*a*) at infinity; (*b*) at 50 cm. distance, if the globe length of the eye is 25 mm. and its pupil diameter 5 mm.

16. If a -5 D thin lens be placed in contact with the refracting surface of the standard reduced eye, find the diameter of the retinal blur circle corresponding to a distant point source, the pupil diameter being 6 mm. What angle does this blur circle subtend at the eye's nodal point and how many cones are contained in its diameter? (Diameter of cones = 3 μ.)

17. Give the argument in support of the employment of printed letters in routine testing. Describe, with diagrams, other kinds of test objects that are sometimes used, and which may have advantages over printed letters in measuring and recording visual acuity.

18. Explain the basis on which Snellen constructed the letter types for use in routine testing. On this basis calculate the sizes of the letters

on the 6 m., 9 m., 36 m., and 60 m. lines on the chart. If the test is used at 6 metres, calculate the sizes of the retinal images of each of the above letters formed in the standard eye.

19. What is the visual acuity of an eye just capable of reading Snellen letters 18 mm. square seen by reflection in a plane mirror 2 metres from the subject and 3 metres from the chart ?

20. Why is the visual acuity at the fovea better than at peripheral parts of the retina ? Calculate the size of, and draw carefully, a letter E to be just read by a person, whose vision is **6/24**, at a distance of 9 metres. If a pinhole improves vision in such a case, what do you conclude ?

21. Discuss the advantages and disadvantages of different systems of measuring acuteness of vision. Explain why different systems give different measures. (S.M.C.)

22. Upon what principles are test types constructed ? Why is it important that they should be (*a*) well illuminated, (*b*) evenly illuminated ? (B.O.A.)

23. What are the factors that determine the resolving power of the eye ? Account for the low visual acuity which exists in the dark adapted eye.

24. Explain how the vision of a subject may be subnormal although his visual acuity is good. Is the converse true ?

A person without optical correction reads Snellen letters 70 mm. square at a distance of 8 feet ; what is the record of his vision ? After correction he reads the same letters at 10 metres ; what is his visual acuity ?

25. Write a short account, aided by an appropriate diagram, of the uses of a pinhole disc in testing vision.

26. What ways of effecting the accommodation are theoretically possible ? By what experiments did Young eliminate some of these ? (B.O.A.)

27. Explain what is meant by the vernier acuity or aligning power of the eye. Give a possible explanation to account for the extraordinary accuracy of the eye in this respect in comparison with its capacity to resolve two point sources or lines situated side by side, as in a grating.

28. Discuss briefly the several subdivisions of the general property of the eye called its visual acuity. About what acuity would be recorded in a test on Snellen letters in the case of an eye the resolving power of which for point sources is found to be 80 seconds ? And what would be approximately the angular dimensions of the grating element discriminated by this eye ?

29. Calculate the diameter of the first dark ring of the Airy disc in the case of the human eye. Assume static emmetropic eye of power $+60 \cdot 0$ D, diameter of pupil 2 mm., wavelength of incident light in air 6000 Angström units. What would be the angular subtense in prism dioptres at the nodal point and how would you describe the resolving power ? (S.M.C.)

30. An observer E sees with one eye a man at a position A distant 100 metres. If the man walks away from A in a direction perpendicular to EA, the observer continuing to fix the point **A,** how far will he walk

before he disappears from view ? The blind spot is 5° in horizontal diameter and its centre is 15½° from the fovea.

31. How do you measure resolving power, grating acuity and Snellen letter acuity ? Is there any connection between these measures in the case of normal vision ? What would be the theoretical resolving power of a normal eye (+60 D) for yellow light (6000 Angström units) with pupil diameter (*a*) 6 mm., (*b*) 1·5 mm. ? (S.M.C.)

32. How can it be shown experimentally that changes in accommodation occur through changes in the shape of the crystalline lens ? What are the chief theories as to how this change is brought about ? (B.O.A.)

33. It is often said that the lens of the eye forms the image upon the retina. Criticise this statement and explain what you consider the most important function of the lens. (B.O.A.)

34. Explain the construction of the standard test chart for the estimation of acuity, showing how the elements of the letters shall fulfil the conditions. How is the fundamental dimension of the element of a letter obtained ? How can the presence of astigmatism be inferred from the patient's errors in the naming of the letters ? Give reasons for your answer. (B.O.A.)

35. Indicate the positions of the focal planes, principal planes and nodal points of the human eye. Calculate the size of the retinal image of an object 1 in. high situated 50 feet from the observer. (B.O.A.)

REFRACTION OF THE EYE

CHAPTER III

AMETROPIA—SPHERICAL

3.1. Emmetropia and Ametropia.

IN the physiologically normal eye we are considering (i.e. the eye as an optical instrument), the essential and sufficient requirement for good vision is that a sharp point image of each object point shall be formed on the fovea. To achieve this the refracting surfaces of the eye must be spherical so that the refracted convergent pencils within the eye shall be homocentric or *stigmatic* (converging to a point); and the media must be clear and transparent.

An eye in which point images are formed and in which, the eye being unaccommodated, these fall on the retina when the object is at infinity, is called an EMMETROPIC eye. In such an eye the fovea M' is conjugate to infinity, and coincides therefore with the eye's second focal point F'_e, Fig. 3.1a. The eye will see clearly a distant object or the test letters at 6 metres. The fineness of the detail it can discriminate will depend further upon its visual acuity. The globe length of the eye, measured from the reduced surface at P, is equal to the second focal length. Emmetropia (Em) may be considered as the condition of ideal focus or " refraction."

If in the unaccommodated eye a distant object point is not imaged as a point on the retina, the eye is said to be AMETROPIC (a = not or without). It is an eye *out of focus* for distant objects. This condition of ametropia (Am) may arise in two main ways.

AMETROPIA—STIGMATIC OR SPHERICAL.

The eye forms point images but the points do not fall on the retina when the object is distant. The axial length of the globe is not equal to the second focal length PF'_e; the points M' and F'_e do not coincide. Blur circles are formed on the retina and vision of distant objects is subnormal.

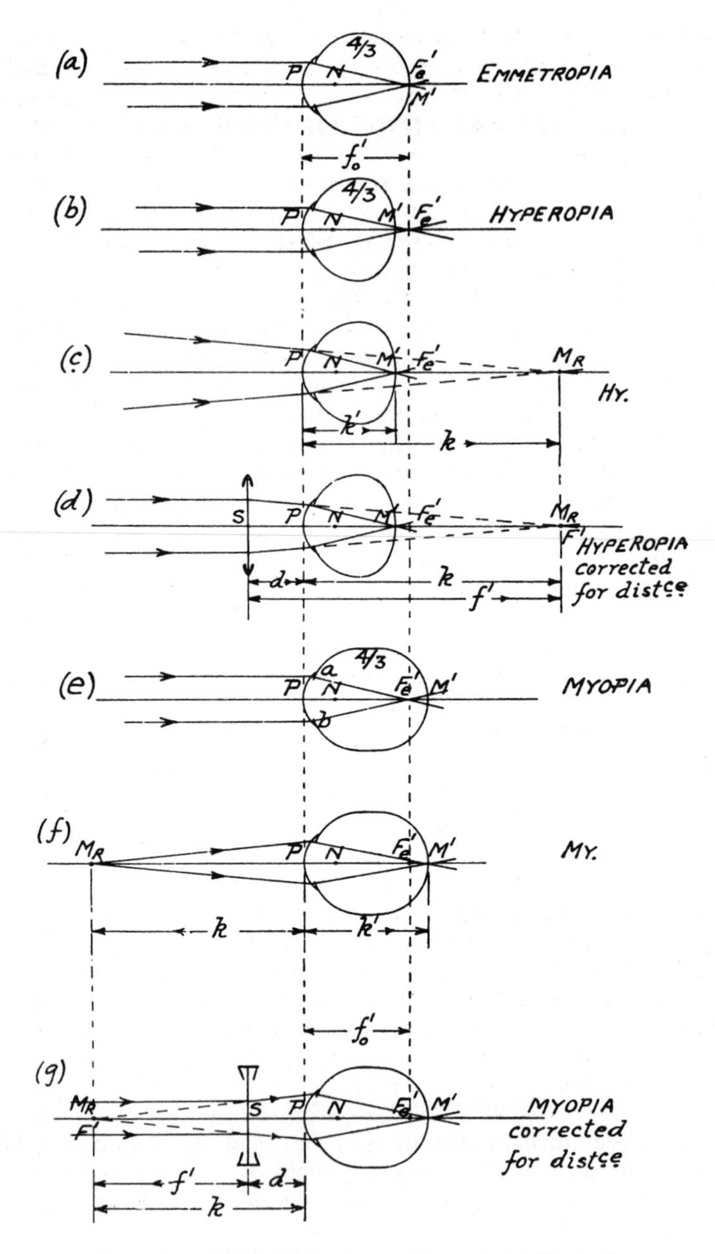

FIG. 3.1—EMMETROPIA AND AMETROPIA (AXIAL).

AMETROPIA—ASTIGMATIC.

The eye does not form point images. Due to non-sphericity or other irregularity in its surface, the refracted pencil within the eye is astigmatic. Blur ellipses or focal lines are formed on the retina and vision of distant objects is subnormal.

Spherical ametropia may again be subdivided into :

A. AXIAL AMETROPIA—in which the non-coincidence of M' and F'_e is due to error in the axial length PM';

B. REFRACTIVE AMETROPIA—in which the non-coincidence of M' and F'_e is due to error in the dioptric power of the eye's optical system ; a departure from the normal power of 60 dioptres. The power of the eye may be at fault because of :

B (i) Anomalies of the refractive indices of the cornea, humours, or crystalline lens ; probably the latter. This subdivision may be called *index ametropia* ;

B (ii) Anomalies in the curvature of the corneal or lens surfaces, these being steeper or shallower than normal—*curvature ametropia ;*

B (iii) Anomalies in the position of the lens relative to the cornea ;

B (iv) Absence of the crystalline lens—a special condition called *aphakia*, which will be considered later.*

We may summarise by tabulating these focal conditions of the eye, thus :

EMMETROPIA, the condition of ideal focus.

AMETROPIA
- SPHERICAL
  - A. AXIAL.
  - B. REFRACTIVE.
    - (i) Index.
    - (ii) Curvature.
    - (iii) Lens position.
    - (iv) Aphakia.
- ASTIGMATISM.

Since astigmatism is due to an anomaly of the refracting system, it is a condition of refractive ametropia. We will leave its consideration to the next chapter, confining ourselves at present to spherical ametropia.

---

* §3.13.

3.2. Hypermetropia and Myopia.

Whether the *reason* for the ametropia be an axial error or a refractive error, we may evidently have two main classes of ametropia according as the second focal point lies behind or in front of the retina. If the globe is short in relation to the focal length, as indicated in Fig. 3.1b the eye is said to be HYPERMETROPIC (long sight), a term sometimes abbreviated to *hyperopic ;* when the globe is relatively long as in Fig. 3.1(e), the eye is MYOPIC (short sight).* Evidently light must be incident on the hyperopic eye as a *convergent* pencil in order to be brought to a focus at M′; and as a *divergent* pencil in the case of myopia ; hence hyperopia and myopia may be considered as positive and negative departures from emmetropia, respectively. In both conditions a blur circle is formed on the retina when parallel light is incident, and so the vision of distant objects, including the vision of the test letters at 6 metres, is subnormal.

We shall still continue to represent the optical system of the eye by the reduced surface at P. The power of this surface is 60 dioptres in axial ametropia.

Considering hyperopia (H) first, there will be some point M_R behind the eye that is conjugate to the fovea M′. In (c) a pencil shown converging to M_R is refracted by the optical system to M′. This point M_R is called the FAR POINT of accommodation (or punctum remotum) of the eye. It is the point for which the eye is correctly focused when accommodation is fully relaxed. Evidently the distance F'_eM' by which the globe length falls short of the second focal length, determines the position of M_R and hence the convergence with which the light must enter the eye at P in order that it will be brought to focus at M′. Since in the emmetropic eye *parallel* light is focused at M′, this convergence measures the departure of the hyperopic eye from the ideal focus condition of emmetropia ; that is, it measures the ametropia of the eye.

The ametropia of the eye is often called its STATIC REFRACTION or its REFRACTIVE ERROR, the word " static " referring to the fact the eye is in its unaccommodated or static condition.† The word static is usually omitted, it being presumed that the eye is relaxed unless otherwise specified. It is in some respects unfortunate that the term refraction has been

* The word myopia is of Greek derivation meaning " I close the eye "—myopes tend to close the eyes to obtain a pinhole effect.

† Or practically so when testing at 6 metres.

introduced into the literature in connection with a condition adequately described by the word ametropia: it has, however, become well established and we shall continually use it.

The ametropia or refractive error of the eye, then, is given by the convergence to, or the nearness or dioptral distance of, the far point, which is expressed in dioptres; the number of dioptres being equal to the reciprocal of the far point distance, PM_R, expressed in metres. Thus if M′ is so far short of F'_e that its conjugate, M_R, the far point, is one metre behind P, then the incident pencil, to be focused at M′ after refraction, must have a convergence at P of one dioptre. We say the (static) ocular refraction or ametropia is + 1 D, or 1 D of hyperopia. If the far point be 20 cm. behind P, the ocular refraction is + 5 D; and so on.

In general, when the far point distance, measured *from* P *to* M_R is k metres, the ocular refraction reckoned at P is given in dioptres by K, where

$$K = \frac{1}{k}$$

The length of the eye, PM′ $= k'$, is the conjugate distance to k and putting $K' = \frac{n'}{k'}$ to represent the convergence of the light within the eye, we have the simple but important conjugate foci relation

$$K' = K + F_e \tag{3.1}$$

connecting the globe length, ametropia and dioptric power of the eye.

F_e is the power of the eye.

The far point of the emmetropic eye is at infinity ($k = \infty$) and its ametropia or refraction zero ($K = 0$).

To enable the unaccommodated hyperope to see distant objects distinctly, the parallel pencils from separate object points must be rendered convergent before entering the eye by such an amount that they would focus in points lying in a plane through M_R. Clearly a positive spherical lens is required for the purpose. Fig. 3.1(d) indicates such a (*thin*) lens placed at the SPECTACLE POINT, S, and a parallel pencil incident on it from the axial point of the distant object. For this pencil to be refracted towards the eye's far point, the second focal point F′ of the lens must coincide with the latter, as shown in the diagram. Under these conditions the eye is said to be "corrected for distance", the lens of focal length SM_R being the *distance correcting lens*. We will assume the correcting lenses to be thin.

In myopia (M) the globe is relatively too long. The far point, conjugate to M′, must therefore lie somewhere in front of the eye and the far point distance, $PM_R = k$, is negative. The far point in this case is real whereas in hyperopia it is virtual. In Fig. 3.1(f) a pencil *diverging* from the far point is refracted by the eye to a focus at M′. The ocular refraction or ametropia, $K = \frac{1}{k}$, is negative. To correct such an eye for distance, parallel pencils must be rendered divergent, a negative spherical lens being required. The myopic eye is shown corrected in (g) since the second focal point of the lens at S coincides with the far point.

Whether the ametropia be hyperopia or myopia, we find that *the second focal point of the distance correcting lens must coincide with the eye's far point.*

We may look upon the positive lens required to correct hyperopia either as a means of imposing the requisite convergence on the incident pencils or as a means of supplying the relative deficiency in the dioptric power of the eye's optical system. Similarly the negative lens required in myopia may be considered as imposing the requisite divergence on the incident light or as counteracting the relative excess of power in the eye.

The terms we have been using in describing these optical conditions we owe to DONDERS, who clarified the underlying conceptions of the subject and laid the foundation upon which is based the present practice in determining these conditions clinically.

It will probably have occurred to the student that the hyperope can overcome his refractive error by accommodating, since by this means he increases the power of his optical system and shifts the focal point F'_e to the fovea M′. This is indeed the case, the hyperope often being in ignorance of his refractive error since he is able to see distant objects clearly by accommodating; the strain resulting from his continuous effort may cause (accommodative) asthenopia, however. We shall return to this point later. On the other hand, distant objects are always indistinct to the uncorrected myope, accommodation making matters worse for him.

When provided with his proper correcting lens, the ametrope is artificially made emmetropic and will be able to read the 6/6 or 6/5 or 6/3 line of the test chart, according to the *acuteness* of his visual apparatus—the previously blurred letters are now imaged sharply on his retina. If, in this corrected condition, positive lenses are added, distance vision is blurred; the eye is said to be "fogged." If negative lenses are added, however, vision may for a while remain more or less unaltered, since the negative lenses may be overcome by accommodation. The experiment of §2.13 should be reconsidered in this light.

3.3. The Correcting Lens. Spectacle Refraction.

Whether the ametropia of the given eye is axial or refractive, its amount is given by the dioptral distance of the far point from the eye. It will be clear from Fig. 3.1(d) and (g) that the focal length of the required correcting lens depends upon its position with respect to the eye. If the distance *from* the lens *to* the reduced eye surface at P be denoted by d metres and the second focal length of the correcting lens by f'_1, then in both the hyperopic and myopic cases we have

$$SM_R \text{ or } SF' = SP + PF'$$

i.e.

$$f'_1 = d + k$$

and the power of the correcting lens is given in dioptres by

$$\frac{1}{f'_1} = F_1 = \frac{1}{k+d}$$

$$\text{or } F_1 = \frac{K}{1 + dK} \qquad (3\cdot 2)$$

The power of the correcting lens is frequently called the SPECTACLE REFRACTION of the eye. It differs from the *ocular* refraction K, reckoned at the refracting surface or principal point P of the eye itself, by an amount dependent upon the separation d. Wherever the lens be placed, the essential requirement for correction is that its second focal point must coincide with the eye's far point, which is k metres from P. Thus the *effective* power of the spectacle lens at the point P must be equal to the ocular refraction K.

Example. The far point of a hyperopic eye is 12·5 cm. behind the eye. Find the ocular refraction and the spectacle refraction of this eye, the correcting lens to be worn 12 mm. from the *cornea.*

Answer. Refer to Fig. 3.1(d)

$$PM_R = k = +12\cdot 5 \text{ cm.};$$

hence ocular refraction $K = \frac{1}{k} = \frac{100}{12\cdot 5} = +8\cdot 0$ D.

Since P is $1\frac{2}{3}$ mm. back from the cornea

$$SP = d = 13\tfrac{2}{3} \text{ mm.}$$

focal length of lens $= 13\frac{2}{3} + 125 = 138\frac{2}{3}$ mm.

$$\text{power of lens} = F_1 = \frac{1000}{138\frac{2}{3}} = +7\cdot21\ \text{D} = \text{Spectacle refraction}$$

or from Equation 3·2.

$$F_1 = \frac{8}{1 + \dfrac{13\frac{2}{3} \times 8}{1000}} = \frac{8}{1\cdot109} = +7\cdot21\ \text{D}.$$

If the distance d be neglected as it may be in rough-and-ready calculations and when the correcting lens is weak, we see that $F_1 = K$ or the ocular and spectacle refractions are the same. In practice the distance d is made as small as is consistent with the lens clearing the eyelashes or eyebrows and hence varies to some extent with different individuals. The average separation of lens (or back vertex of lens actually) and cornea is about 12 to 13 mm.; that is, the lens is a little within the anterior focal point of the eye. When specific information on this point is not given, we shall assume a standard value of 14 mm. from the spectacle point S to P, equivalent to $12\frac{1}{3}$ mm. from S to the *cornea*. Thus the distance from S to the centre of rotation in the standard case is 14 + 13 = 27 mm.

The aim of practical methods concerned with the determination of ametropia is to arrive at the prescription of the correcting lens; clinically, the spectacle refraction is of more importance than the ocular refraction and is usually understood when referring to the refraction of the eye.

As already mentioned, in circumstances where the separation d may be neglected, the two quantities are equal. This is practically the case with the special correcting lenses called CONTACT GLASSES which are inserted with their outer rim in contact with the sclerotic and with their central optical portion consequently almost in contact with the cornea.*

Up to the present it has not been necessary to enquire whether the ametropia is axial or refractive. The above relations are true in either case. It will be observed, however, that the ametropia illustrated in Fig. 3.1 is axial. The focal length PF'_e of the eye is constant throughout, the ametropia being due to deficiency or excess of axial length. This was done because in the vast majority of cases that have been examined, the axial length after enucleation of the eye was found to be at fault by an amount corresponding approximately to the previously ascertained ametropia. Except when specified to the contrary we shall therefore assume the refractive error to be axial. This

* See §10.12; and EMSLEY and SWAINE's *Ophthalmic Lenses*.

necessitates our assuming that the dioptric power of all such eyes has a constant value; and this value we take as 60 dioptres for the human eye. That is, we shall assume the single 60 D surface of our reduced eye of §2.2; if, then, the axial length of a given eye is 22·22 mm. it is emmetropic; it is hyperopic or myopic if the axial length is respectively less or greater than this value.

An eye can, of course, be emmetropic if its power differs from 60 D provided its axial length differs from the standard value by a corresponding amount; in which case the eye in comparison with the agreed standard eye, has both axial and refractive ametropia of equal and opposite degrees. Thus an eye of axial length 20·51 mm. and dioptric power 65 D, will be emmetropic. And we can imagine a small animal with an emmetropic eye of small dimensions.

In an eye with a given amount of ametropia, corrected for distance, the *size* of the sharp retinal image will vary according as the ametropia is axial or refractive: we will return to this question later.

In an eye corrected for distance, parallel light, after refraction by the lens and the eye, commences its journey to M′ within the eye with vergence K'; hence K' is the *back vertex power* of the lens-eye system.

In both hyperopia and myopia the spectacle refraction is algebraically less than the ocular refraction.

It will be understood from Fig. 3.1 that moving a *given* correcting lens from its correcting position to a position further from the eye, will move its focal point away from the far point, and the lens will become too positive for correction. A positive lens will now be too strong and a negative lens too weak.

3.4. Axial Ametropia and Axial Length.

By the term axial length we mean usually the axial length PM′ of the *reduced eye*; the length from the *cornea* to M′ is greater than this (by $1\frac{2}{3}$ mm. in the standard case).

For a given amount of ametropia K, equation (3.1) becomes

$$K' = K + 60 \text{ in axial ametropia}$$
$$\text{and } 60 = K + F_e \text{ in refractive ametropia.}$$

since in the latter case the axial length has the emmetropic value, the refractive error K being caused by a departure of F_e from the standard value of 60 D.

Example. An eye has axial myopia of 10 D. Calculate (*a*) the error in axial length; (*b*) the power of lens, to be worn 14 mm. from the reduced surface, to correct the eye for distance; (*c*) the diameter of the retinal blur circle corresponding to a distant object point, the pupil diameter being 4 mm.

Answer.

(*a*) We are given $K = -10$ D and $F_e = 60$ D

$$K' = K + F_e = -10 + 60 = +50 \text{ D} = \frac{n'}{k'}$$

hence $k' = \frac{n'}{50}$ metres $= \frac{4 \times 1000}{3 \times 50}$ mm. $= 26\frac{2}{3}$ mm.

and axial error $= 26 \cdot 67 - 22 \cdot 22 = 4 \cdot 45$ mm.

(*b*) Far point distance $PM_R = k = -100$ mm.

focal length of lens $= SM_R = 14 - 100 = -86$ mm.

power of lens $= \frac{1000}{-86} = -11 \cdot 63$ D

which could have been obtained directly from (3.2).

(*c*) Referring to Fig. 3.1(e),

we have $F'_eM' = 4 \cdot 45$ mm. and ab $= 4$ mm.

$$\frac{\text{diam. of blur circle}}{4} = \frac{F'_eM'}{PF'_e} = \frac{4 \cdot 45}{22 \cdot 22}$$

or diam. of blur circle $= 0 \cdot 8$ mm.

(the area of which covers about 60,000 cones).

If the above calculation be repeated for other degrees of ametropia, it will be found that for moderate degrees of axial ametropia:

axial error $= \frac{3}{8}$ *mm. per dioptre of ametropia, approximately;*

although it increases more rapidly than the ocular refraction in myopia and less rapidly in hyperopia.

3.5. Vision in Ametropia.

The relationship between the degree of ametropia, or fogging with positive lenses, and the corresponding letter vision varies amongst different individuals because of different pupil sizes and the effects of aberrations and irregularities, but the following table gives a rough guide which is of service in routine testing. In hyperopia the error will be masked by accommodation.

MYOPIA (or FOGGING) and VISION.

Myopia in D	0 to 0.25	0·50	1·00	1·50	2·00	2·50
Letter Vision	$\frac{6}{4}$ to $\frac{6}{6}$	$\frac{6}{9}$	$\frac{6}{15}$	$\frac{6}{24}$	$\frac{6}{36}$	$\frac{6}{60}$

It will be observed that the deterioration of letter vision is more rapid than the increase of ametropia.

When, with the appropriate correcting lens in position, a sharp image of distant objects has been formed on the retina of the unaccommodated eye, the subject attains his optimum vision, his visual acuity. In most cases this will be 6/6 or better; but in high degrees of myopia, even normally, the best vision attainable will be less than this on account of degenerations in the macular region caused by the stretching of the retina and choroid.

3.6. Accommodation. Amplitude and Range.

Fig. 3.2 represents a myopic eye, the far point M_R and the fovea M′ being conjugate points when the eye is relaxed. Let us suppose the myopia is 3 D, in which case the distance PM_R is $-\frac{1}{3}$ metre and the light from M_R, after refraction by the eye, has a convergence of $-3 + 60 = +57$ D, assuming the myopia to be axial. If an object (such as a fine black line on a white card) be moved from the position M_R towards the eye, it will be seen distinctly so long as the eye is capable of accommodating sufficiently to form its image on M′.

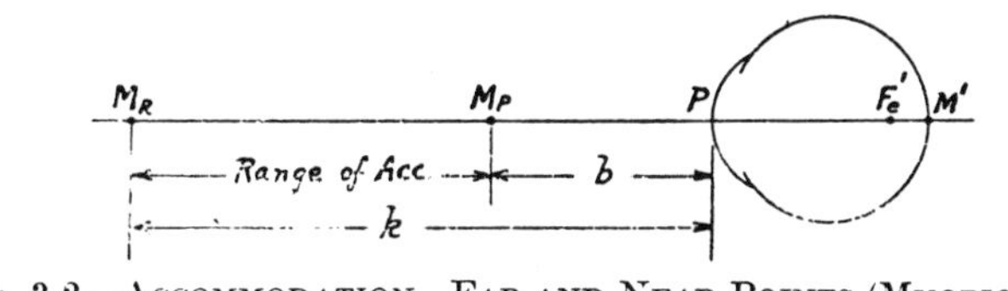

FIG. 3.2—ACCOMMODATION. FAR AND NEAR POINTS (MYOPIC EYE).

The nearest point at which distinct vision can be obtained, the accommodation being fully exerted, is called the NEAR POINT of accommodation, M_P; or the punctum proximum. We will suppose the near point in our example to be 10 cm. from P. Light from M_P reaches P with divergence -10 D. The dioptric power of the eye must have increased from 60 D to 67 D in order that the convergence within the eye shall remain at the 57 D necessary for the formation of the image on M′ $(-10 + 67 = +57$ D). The dioptral distance of the object has changed by 7 D from -3 D at the far point to -10 D at the near point, the eye having accommodated 7 D to overcome this change. This seven dioptres is the power or AMPLITUDE OF ACCOMMODATION. The linear distance *from* the far point *to* the near point is the RANGE OF ACCOMMODATION. It is $23\frac{1}{3}$ cm. in our example.

In the case of a hyperope of 3 D the far point is $\frac{1}{3}$ metre behind the eye. Light converging towards it has a convergence, after refraction by the eye, of + 3 + 60 = + 63 D on its way to M′. As the eye accommodates, light entering it with less and less convergence can be focused on M′; the first three dioptres of accommodation makes the subject virtually emmetropic. Assuming a total amplitude of 7 D, as in the above myopic eye, the remaining 4 dioptres enables the subject to see distinctly an object brought up to a position 25 cm. in front of P, which position is the near point of this eye. The conjugate foci relation is now − 4 + 67 = + 63 D. The range of accommodation in this case extends from a point $\frac{1}{3}$ metre behind the eye to infinity and from infinity up to 25 cm. in front of the eye. A real object can be seen, of course, only throughout the latter part of this total range: and this is referred to as the *range of distinct vision.*

In an emmetrope with 7 D amplitude, the far point is at infinity (0 + 60 = + 60 D); the near point is at − 7 D or 14·29 cm. before the eye (− 7 + 67 = + 60 D); the range of accommodation, which is at the same time the range of distinct vision in this case as in the myopic case, is from infinity up to 14·29 cm. before the eye.

It is important to note that in every case the convergence of the light within the eye remains unchanged as the eye accommodates. If the eye were to remain static, a + 7 D sphere, in the above cases, placed in contact with the eye would enable it to see an object distinctly at the near point. Thus the amplitude of accommodation can also be described as *the power of the lens, placed at P, which images the near point at the far point.*

It is seen that, for a given amplitude of accommodation, the myope is more favourably placed for near vision. His range of distinct vision, however, is strictly limited. The myope described above can see objects distinctly over a range of only 23 cm.

The manner in which the amplitude decreases with age will be discussed in Chapter VI.

If we represent the distance in metres from the eye (P) to the near point M_P by the symbol b, and its reciprocal in dioptres by B, the above discussion may be summed up thus:

When eye is static $K' = K + F_e$ (static) dioptres
„ „ „ accom. $K' = B + F_e$ (acc) „

$$\text{hence } K - B = F_e\,(\text{acc}) - F_e\,(\text{static}) \quad \text{dioptres}$$
$$= F_e\,(\text{acc}) - 60\ \text{D normally}$$

i.e. representing the amplitude of accommodation by A dioptres, we have

$$\boldsymbol{A} = \boldsymbol{K} - \boldsymbol{B} \text{ dioptres} \tag{3.3}$$

which is *always* positive.

It may be of service to collect in the form of a table a few simple examples of the inter-relation of refractive condition and accommodative amplitude, which the student should verify for himself. The last column, giving the probable age of the subject, will be understood after we have dealt with this question in Chapter VI.

It is to be noted that all the quantities concerned have been reckoned with reference to the eye at P. If the spectacle point were to be taken as the point of reference from which to measure the far point and near point distances, the amplitude referred to this point would be greater than A as above defined. This point will arise later (§6.1).

REFRACTIVE CONDITION, AMPLITUDE of ACCOMMODATION and AGE.

	k cm.	b cm.	K dprs.	B dprs.	A dprs.	Probable Age Years.
1. Em. can see distinctly up to 25 cm. ..	∞	−25	0	−4	4	42–45
2. Em. can see distinctly up to 10 cm. ..	∞	−10	0	−10	10	15–20
3. Hyperope of 2 D can accom. up to 25 cm.	+50	−25	+2	−4	6	35–40
4. Myope of 2 D can accom. up to 25 cm.	−50	−25	−2	−4	2	48–50
5. Far pt. 1 metre in front: near pt. at 12·5 cm.	−100	−12·5	−1	−8	7	30–35
6. Amp. of acc. 4·5 D; far pt. 25 cm. behind	+25	−200	+4	−0·5	4·5	40–43
7. Range of acc. 7·5 cm.; far pt. at −5 D ..	−20	−12·5	−5	−8	3	45–48
8. Far pt. with +4 D.S. 25 cm. in front; near pt. with same lens 10 cm. in front	∞	−16	0	−6	6	35–40

If an eye with ocular refraction K accommodates by an amount A', less than its full amplitude A, it is then in correct focus for some point M lying between its far point M_R and its near point M_P; M is conjugate to M′ in that particular state of accommodation. Representing the distance PM by c metres and its reciprocal by C dioptres, we have

$$A' = K - C$$

an expression of which equation (3·3) is a special case.

3.7. Hyperopia and Accommodation.

A hyperope with sufficient accommodation can see distant objects clearly by accommodating. The accommodative effort may be replaced by a positive lens placed before the eye. The lens thus " accepted " reveals hyperopia that has hitherto been masked by accommodation. Usually, however, the whole of the hyperopia is not shown up even by the strongest plus lens accepted, since a certain amount of contraction of the much used ciliary muscle persists. The degree of hyperopia still hidden in this way by the tone of the ciliary muscle is called LATENT HYPEROPIA (H_L). The amount revealed and measured by the strongest positive lens accepted (i.e. with which the eye's optimum visual acuity is maintained) is the MANIFEST HYPEROPIA (H_M). The sum of these is the *total* hyperopia (H) ; thus

$$H = H_M + H_L$$

The total hyperopia can be determined only when *all* the accommodation is forced to relax, as by paralysing the ciliary muscle with a cycloplegic such as atropine ; otherwise the latent H of the given subject remains an unknown quantity.

If, as in older people, the amplitude of accommodation is small, or if the hyperopia is considerable ; i.e. if the hyperopia exceeds the accommodative amplitude, the subject will be unable to correct all his error by accommodation and his distance vision will be subnormal. The degree of hyperopia still outstanding when accommodation is fully exerted is called ABSOLUTE HYPEROPIA (H_A).

Two examples will serve to illustrate.

1. A subject's vision, tested on the chart at 6 metres, is poor, say about 6/48. Vision improves on adding positive spheres and reaches its maximum value, say 6/6 (the V.A. of the eye) with +2 D sphere. At this stage the subject's total amplitude is still being exerted. The +2 D sph. measures his *absolute* H. With the addition of a further +3 D vision remains unchanged, but deteriorates with further plus power. The +3 D sph. has been substituted for an equal amount of accommodation. He may still be exerting a certain amount of accommodation, due to the tone of the ciliary muscle, which he cannot relax

further: this extra amount, if any, masking his latent H. The total positive power so far accepted, +5 D, measures the *manifest* H. It is found that, following a suitable interval after the instillation of atropine, the subject will now accept a further + 0·50 D. Now we know that his *latent* H. is +0·50 D and his total H., +5·5 D. His total amplitude is 3·5 D.

The +3 D sph. represents the amount of H. the subject ordinarily corrects by what we may call his free or *available* amplitude: it is given by the difference between the weakest and strongest plus spheres with which his maximum vision is maintained.

2. A younger subject is tested with the following results: The near point, by a method to be described later (§6.5) is found to be 25 cm. before the eye. Vision unaided is 6/5 and remains so on gradual addition of positive spheres up to +2·50 D. Atropine is instilled* and after an interval for ciliary paralysis to take place, a further +1·50 D is accepted, vision remaining at 6/5.

In this case H_M = 2·50 D; H_L = +1·50 D; H (total) = + 4 D. There is no absolute H. The total amplitude of accommodation is 8 D of which the free amplitude is 6·5 D.

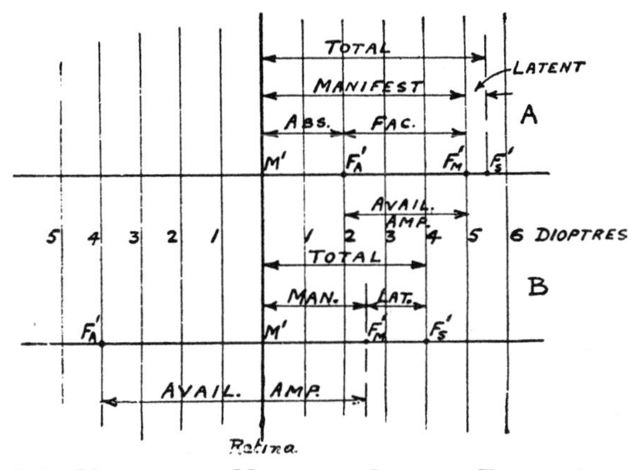

FIG. 3.3—HYPEROPIA—MANIFEST, LATENT, TOTAL, ABSOLUTE.

The relationship between these various subdivisions of hyperopia may be further clarified by referring to Fig. 3.3. The thick vertical line represents the retina; the second focal point of the eye's optical system occupies the position F'_S when all accommodation is made to relax by atropine; F'_M is the position of this focal point when all except this latent amount is relaxed: when all the accommodation is exerted the focus is at F'_A. Diagram (A) refers to the first of the above examples and (B) to the second.

* It is not to be understood that this is necessarily a routine procedure; we are merely discussing an experimental example.

If a subject be provided with a lens correcting his manifest H, it will frequently be found that on a subsequent re-test a somewhat higher positive lens will be accepted, a portion of the latent H having become manifest in the interval, during which the accommodation previously needed to see distant objects clearly has not been exerted.

In young people, with an active accommodation, the proportion of latent to the manifest H revealed by lenses is large, the proportion gradually diminishing as age advances, and the crystalline lens becomes more sclerosed, until somewhere in the period 40 to 55 years, depending upon the individual, the latent disappears and all the hyperopia is manifest. The proportionality might be expressed *roughly* by

$$\text{Total H} = \frac{H_M \times 40}{\text{Age}}$$

3.8. Determination of Ametropia or Far Point.

To determine the condition of the eyes with reference to one or other of their functions, we may adopt one of two main methods : a SUBJECTIVE method or an OBJECTIVE method. In the former the subject is invited to express an opinion as to the appearance of some kind of test object, the nature and manipulation of which depend upon the particular function—refraction, accommodation, binocular vision, etc.—being investigated. The result depends, to some extent at least, upon the subject's judgment, which in turn is compounded of the physical, physiological and psychological processes in the complete visual act. Success is dependent upon the subject's intelligent co-operation.

Objective methods, on the other hand, are carried out independently of observations by the subject. The examiner bases his opinion as to the condition and the optical correction required entirely upon observations carried out by himself. In clinical practice both subjective and objective methods are frequently used to investigate the one function, the results being checked against each other ; or the one supplementing the other.

In ordinary optical systems or instruments we can investigate their out-of-focus condition or "ametropia" by means of direct observations on the image screen, whereas in the case of the eye this is inaccessible directly and we are forced to work outside the eye, within the object space.

We will leave consideration of objective methods to later chapters and confine ourselves here to a preliminary description of certain subjective methods of estimating the refractive condition. A fuller discussion must be deferred until we have considered astigmatism. Our aim is to determine the far point and then to render the eye artificially emmetropic by means of a lens that will image distant objects at this far point (Fig. 3.1). Until the test object is placed, actually or virtually by optical means, at the far point it will appear indistinct to the myope or relaxed hypermetrope, each point of it being imaged as a blur circle on the fovea. In subjective methods it is presumed that when the test object is seen with maximum distinctness, the image lies upon the percipient rod and cone layer of the retina and the far point and ametropia are determined. When this optical condition is achieved the subject will attain his optimum visual acuity when tested on the test chart.

Thus in one type of subjective method, which may be called the VISUAL ACUITY METHOD, an adequately illuminated test chart is presented to the subject at a fixed distance, which is usually 6 metres. Vision is recorded for each eye separately. If vision be subnormal, worse than 6/6, each eye is tested through a pinhole disc. If vision is improved thereby, the cause of the poor vision is almost certainly ametropia; if there is no improvement, either the eye is amblyopic or the retinal image is of poor quality due to imperfections in the eye's optical system. In the amblyopic case no improvement is possible by optical means. Assuming a case in which the subnormal vision is due to ametropia, it is now sought to improve vision by means of spherical lenses. If a positive trial case sphere of, say, + 1 D is "accepted," that is if vision is either improved or unchanged, hypermetropia is established. In the former case, there must be at least 1 D of absolute H; in the latter case, 1 D of the accommodation previously exerted has been relieved. By adding positive spheres up to the maximum power with which the best vision attained is not deteriorated, we arrive at a measure of the manifest H. The second focal point of this last lens will be as near the subject's far point as the latent H will allow.

If vision is made worse with the first positive sphere and is improved by a negative sphere, myopia is established,* in which case the negative power is increased until vision *ceases to improve*.

* Or a condition masquerading as myopia; see §6.7.

If accommodation is active and changeable during the test it will mitigate against accuracy in arriving at this initial spherical correction. On this account the subject is made to relax his accommodation as much as possible by encouraging the hypermetrope to accept the strongest plus sphere with which his highest vision is maintained (except in cases of poor vision); and by restricting the negative sphere in myopia to the weakest with which his best vision is attained. This question of control of accommodation will arise more forcibly when dealing with astigmatism.

The vision obtained with the best sphere may still be subnormal and below the visual acuity of the subject because of astigmatism, which it is then necessary to investigate (Ch. IV). Visual acuity tends to be low in high degrees of myopia; vision may, for example, be raised to, say, 6/18 with a −10 D sphere, further addition of negative power producing no improvement, although the proper refractive condition may be 15 D or so of myopia. These high myopes are frequently benefited by telescopic spectacles which magnify the size of the retinal image.*

In the visual acuity method just described, the brightness of the test letters and their contrast with the background remain appreciable and constant and we base our test only upon the subject's ability to recognise the form and detail of the test letters. It was mentioned in §2.12 that the test characters should vary considerably in contrast as well as in form; and it has been proposed that ametropia might be measured by means of a test in which the subject is to recognise the mere presence of a simple test object in conditions of low (threshold) illumination and contrast. An important advantage claimed for this procedure is that there will be little or no inducement to the subject to accommodate during the test. Insufficient evidence is available as to whether this "sensitometric" method will be clinically successful.

3.9. The Simple Optometer.

In the method just described the test object (the test chart) is maintained at a fixed distance and successive lenses are placed before the eye until this is imaged at the far point of the subject under test, efforts being made to encourage the subject not to accommodate. Although this is the subjective method usually adopted in clinical practice, it is theoretically possible to *move* the test object along the optical axis of a lens of constant power mounted at the spectacle point until the image formed by this lens occupies the far point position of the eye, in which position it is

* *Ophthalmic Lenses*; Ch. XVII.

seen with maximum distinctness, provided the eye does not accommodate. Arrangements of this kind are called optometers; the principle of the simplest form of such an instrument is illustrated in Fig. 3.4.

Suppose we are testing a hyperope of spectacle refraction +2 D. We place the optometer lens at the spectacle point S; we will suppose its power to be +4 D. Then an object placed at B (second diagram) 50 cm. in front of the lens, will be imaged at the subject's far point, which is 50 cm. behind the spectacle point (from $L' = L + F$ we have $-2+4=+2$ D). If an object such as a clear black line on a white card is moved up from a distance, it will first

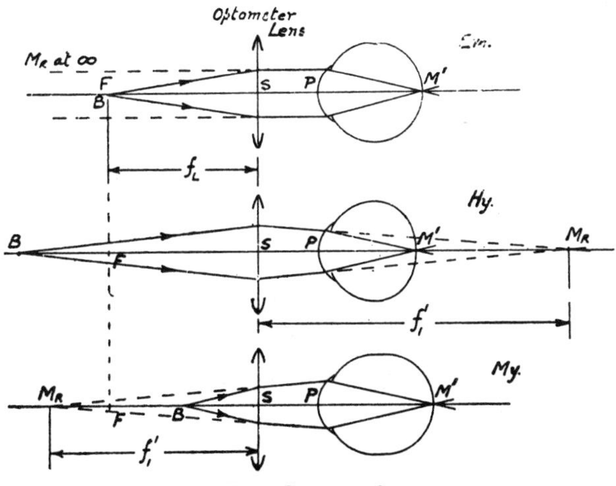

Fig. 3.4—The Simple Optometer.

be seen distinctly at this position B. We could place the + 4 D sphere in a holder at the end of a rule a metre or so in length and hold the rule stretching horizontally out from the eye with the lens at the spectacle point. A point on the rule 50 cm. from the lens could be marked + 2, or H2.

Using the same lens and arrangement in the case of an emmetrope, it would be necessary to approach the object card to a position 25 cm. from the lens, the anterior focus of the lens, before the eye could see it distinctly (first diagram); this position on the rule would be marked O or Em. For a myope of spectacle refraction 6 D the clear position of the test object would be 10 cm. from the lens

(– 10 + 4 = – 6 D) as indicated in the third diagram of Fig. 3.4.

With a rule scaled in this way—adioptric scale—we could theoretically determine the far point and hence ametropia of any eye. It is sometimes called a SIMPLE OPTOMETER or far point measure. The actual positions of its divisions depend upon the power of the lens with which it is to be used. The student should construct such optometers on strips of paper for use with, say a + 3 D optometer lens and with a + 5 D sphere. He will observe the wide separation of the hyperopia divisions with the weaker lens and the crowding of the myopia divisions with the stronger; and he should note particularly that the scale is not a uniform scale.

The point B at which the object is seen clearly 50 cm. before the + 4 D lens in H and 10 cm. from the lens in M, is sometimes referred to as the *artificial* far point with that particular lens. The + 4 D sphere has rendered the hyperope artificially myopic to the extent of 2 D spectacle myopia; it makes the 6 D myope artificially myopic 10 D. It is to be noted that with the optometer lens at the spectacle point, and reckoning distances with reference to this point, the optometer scale gives readings of *spectacle* refraction.

Such a simple method of determining ametropia is not sufficiently accurate for practical purposes since (*a*) it is well-nigh impossible to prevent the subject from accommodating, the known proximity of the test object supplying a powerful incentive to do so. The results are on this account too myopic, and they are variable. (*b*) There is an appreciable range of the object over which it is difficult to estimate the clearest position—due to depth of focus.

The principle of the optometer should nevertheless be grasped as it lies at the root of a proper understanding of many problems of visual optics.

Example. With a + 5 D sphere before the eye, the far point was found to be at a distance of one metre and the near point at 12·5 cm. Find (*a*) the static refraction and far point (*b*) the amplitude of accommodation and near point.

Answer. Since nothing is said about the separation of the lens and eye, we may neglect it and assume the lens at the eye.

(*a*) Light from artificial far point reaches lens with divergence of – 1 D and hence leaves it with – 1 + 5 = +4 D of convergence. Static refraction is thus 4 D of manifest hyperopia; and the far point is 25 cm. behind the eye.

(*b*) Light from artificial near point reaches lens with divergence of -8 D and leaves it with $-8+5=-3$ D of divergence. The eye is now overcoming -3 D (divergence) as against $+4$ D (convergence) in its static state and must have increased its power, or accommodated, by 7 D which is the required amplitude. The near point is at a distance of $\frac{100}{-3}=-33\frac{1}{3}$ cm.—in front of the eye.

(or from $A = K - B$, $A = +4-(-3) = +7$ D).

Example. With a $+4$ D sphere placed 15 mm. from the eye, the far point is at 14·0 cm. and the near point at 7·64 cm. from the lens. Find the ocular refraction and amplitude of accommodation of the eye.

Answer.

For the far point, $\frac{100}{-14\cdot 0}+4 = -3\cdot 14$ D.

Light leaves lens with divergence $-3\cdot 14$ D; i.e. from a point $\frac{100}{-3\cdot 14} = -31\cdot 85$ cm. from the lens or

$-(31\cdot 85 + 1\cdot 5) = -33\cdot 35$ cm. from the eye

∴ the ocular refraction is practically -3 D—myopia.

For the near point, $\frac{100}{-7\cdot 64}+4 = -9\cdot 09$ D.

Light leaves lens as from a point $\frac{100}{-9\cdot 09} = -11\cdot 0$ cm. from the lens, or $-(11\cdot 0 + 1\cdot 5) = -12\cdot 5$ cm. from the eye.

∴ the refraction of the eye in this accommodated or "dynamic" state is -8 D.

Amplitude $= -3-(-8) = +5$ D.

3.10. Subjective Optometers.

Many variations of the simple optometer have been suggested from time to time. None of them is as convenient or accurate as the visual acuity method with the test chart, but a few will be briefly described because of their historical interest or their value in demonstrating principles of some importance, or their application to certain objective methods.

THE SCHEINER DISC.

Referring to Fig. 2.16, an emmetrope observing through such a disc a spot of light at 6 metres, one eye being occluded, would see just one spot. A myope or hyperope (relaxed), would see two projections of the spot. Covering the upper aperture, a, would result in the lower projection disappearing in the case of a hyperope; to a myope the upper projection would disappear. Positive or negative spheres could be placed before the eye and disc until the two projections coalesce into one, the eye being then corrected. An optometer using this principle, a collimator with two slits over its objective, was suggested by STAMPFER.

YOUNG'S OPTOMETER.

This again is an application of the Scheiner principle, being an improvement on an optometer made by PORTERFIELD (1747).* With this instrument YOUNG did some

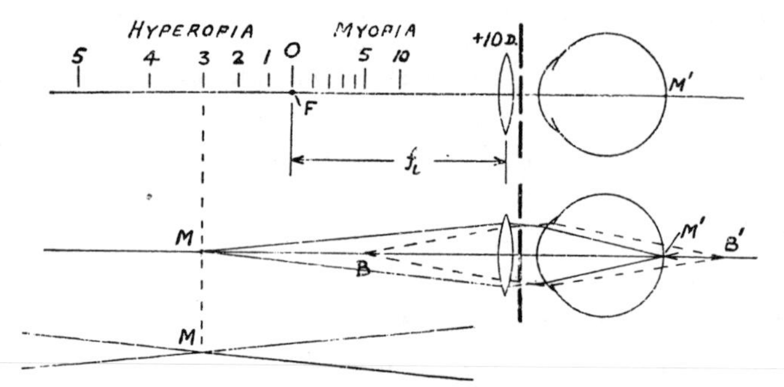

FIG. 3.5—YOUNG'S OPTOMETER.

remarkable work, discovering and measuring the astigmatism and the spherical aberration in his own eyes. It consists essentially of a short rule at the end of which is a positive lens,† as in the simple optometer, the lens being provided with a diaphragm containing two vertical slits separated by about 1·5 mm. (Fig. 3.5). Along the length of the upper surface of the rule, which is black, is a fine white line running away from the eye. An observer looking through the lens and slits along this line is artificially myopic with the + 10 D sphere and his artificial far point lies at some point M. All other points of the line, such as B, will appear doubled, the line as a whole appearing to the observer as indicated in the third diagram. A small cursor slides along the rule and can be placed at the position M where the two apparent lines cross.

TELESCOPE OPTOMETERS.

To see a distant object clearly through a telescope, an unaccommodated emmetrope slides the eyepiece in or out until its first focal point coincides with the second focal point of the objective, in which position parallel light emerges

* The original use of the term *optometer* is credited to PORTERFIELD.

† The instrument made by Ivan WERLEIN of Paris, in the Northampton Polytechnic laboratories, has a + 10 D spherical lens.

from the instrument and it is said to be in infinity adjustment. A myope would have to push the eyepiece in towards the objective and a hypermetrope would require to pull it out towards his eye, by an amount depending upon the degree of ametropia. Thus the eyepiece tube could be scaled in dioptres and the telescope used as an optometer. The same end would be served by leaving the eyepiece in a fixed position and moving the objective longitudinally instead. This would probably be more convenient to use. Simple calculation will show that the telescope must be of appreciable length in order to obtain a reasonably wide scale.

It was proposed by von GRAEFE (1863) to adopt a Galilean telescope for this purpose and by HIRSCHBERG (1877) an astronomical telescope.

CHROMATIC OPTOMETERS.

The chromatic aberration of the eye can be made evident (unless prevented by abnormal colour vision in the subject)

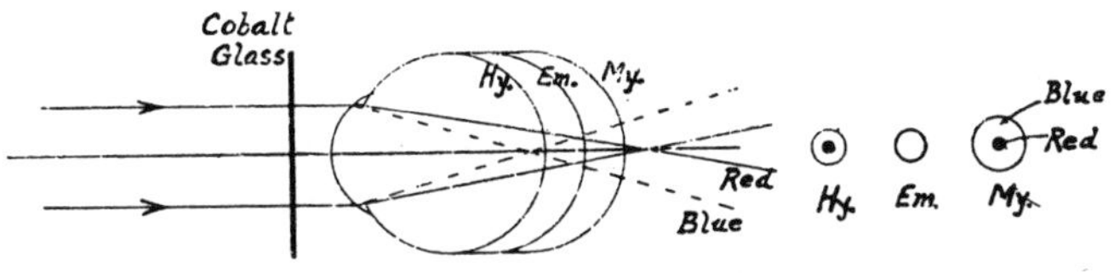

FIG. 3.6—CHROMATIC OPTOMETER—COBALT DISC.

by observing a small circular disc of white light at, say, 6 metres or so through a piece of cobalt glass, which transmits red and blue light but absorbs intermediate colours more or less completely.* As indicated in Fig. 3.6, to the myope the disc will appear to be red at the centre with a surrounding fringe of blue; the hypermetrope will see a central spot of blue with a red surround. In the emmetropic eye the red and blue blur circles on the retina will be fairly equal in area and by over-lapping will give the appearance of a purple disc, perhaps with a blue border.

The arrangement can thus be made to act as an optometer by placing before the eye appropriate positive or negative lenses to move the yellow-green focus on to the retina and so restore the hypermetropic or myopic appearance of the test light to that characteristic of emmetropia. A subjective test based on this principle, called the *duochrome test*, and capable of a much higher order or precision than

* See also §11.3.

the above crude cobalt glass arrangement, will be described subsequently (§4.10).

For reasons already stated the optometers described above are inaccurate, at least in clinical work and, moreover, further difficulties arise when the eye being tested is astigmatic. It is the application of them to subjective testing that we have considered. Their principle can be applied, however, to a class of *objective* instruments, capable of much greater accuracy, to which reference will be made later (§7.14).

3.11. The Retinal Image in Ametropia.

The term "image" usually refers to the *sharp* focused image formed by an optical system; it is conjugate to the

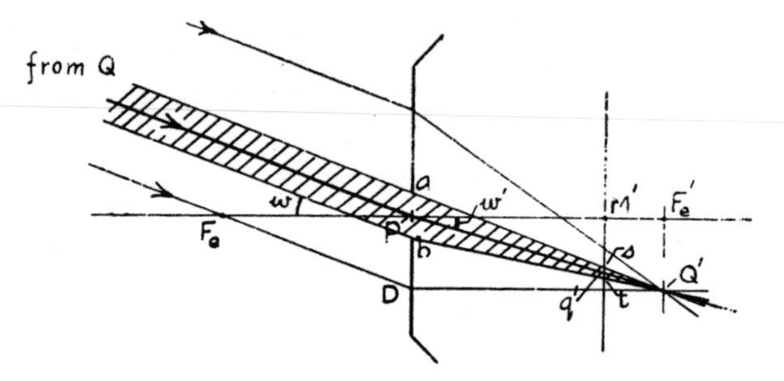

FIG. 3.7—BLUR CIRCLE st ON RETINA OF AMETROPIC EYE. PUPIL OF SYSTEM, ab, COINCIDES WITH REDUCED SURFACE AT P, AND CENTRE q′ OF BLUR CIRCLE IS DETERMINED BY RAY FROM P. WHEN EYE ACCOMMODATES, SHARP IMAGE = M′q′.

object and corresponds to it, point for point. In a relaxed ametropic eye, however, the image of a distant object formed on the retina is a *blurred* image; it does not become a sharp focused image until the proper correcting lens is applied to the eye.

In optical systems generally the properties of the blurred image of an object depend upon the size of the exit pupil of the system and its location. The particular case of the reduced eye can be studied with reference to Fig. 3.7 which represents a hyperopic eye with reduced surface at P, retina at M′ and second focal point at F'_e. Parallel rays from the upper extremity Q of a distant object subtending an angle *w* are converged to the focus Q′ in the second focal plane—the F'_e plane. The ray refracted at P makes angle w' with the axis within the eye (§2.3); the ray incident at D, through F_e, would traverse the eye as the ray DQ′ parallel to the axis, were it admitted by the pupil.

It will be shown later that the pupil of the eye *ab*, may be considered as coinciding with the reduced surface at P. Corresponding to the object point Q a blur circle st is formed on the retina; its centre q′ is determined by the ray traversing the eye from P. It will also be shown that we can assume the surface P of our reduced eye to remain substantially unchanged in position during accommodation. Thus when the eye accommodates the ray Pq′ remains unaltered since the angle w does not vary. But since the curvature of the surface increases, the rays refracted at a and b now come to a sharp focus at q' instead of Q′ and the blur circle st collapses to a point q′.

If Q is the upper extremity of a distant object BQ standing on the axis, the retinal image of BQ consists of a series of blur circles the centres of which extend from M′ to q′. If, due to high ametropia or other cause, the blurring is considerable, the total size of the blurred image does not have much significance; it is too indistinct to be usefully recognisable; but when the extent of blurring is moderate it is useful to refer to the size of the blurred image, which will be defined as the distance M′q′ between the centres of the extreme blur circles of the total image. Thus the blurred image and the sharp image obtained after accommodation both have the same size, M′q′.

AXIAL AMETROPIA.

In Fig. 3.8 (A) are represented the positions H, F'_e and M of the retinæ of eyes with axial hyperopia, emmetropia and axial myopia respectively. In the standard emmetropic eye $PF'_e = 22{\cdot}22$ mm. It is evident that the blurred image Hq′ on the hyperopic retina is smaller than the sharp image F'_e Q′ on the emmetropic retina; and that the myope's blurred image Mm is larger. In practice the hyperope will accommodate to see the distant object clearly in which case Hq′ represents a sharp image, smaller than F'_eQ'.

If an object be placed at the myope's far point, the image Mm will be sharp. The emmetrope and hyperope will accommodate and their sharp retinal images Hq′ and F'_eQ' respectively, will be smaller than the myope's.

REFRACTIVE AMETROPIA.

When the ametropia is refractive, the axial length of the globe PM′ is the same for all three eyes (Fig. 3.8 B). M′ coincides with the second focal point F'_e of the standard emmetropic eye. The dioptric power of the optical system is less than 60 D in H. and greater in M. If we do not know the extent to which the decrease in power in H. and the increase in M. is due to the cornea or to the crystalline lens, or both, or whether the ametropia is of the curvature or index type, we are unable to determine the position of the equivalent system (its equivalent, or reduced, surface and nodal point) in relation to the cornea and retina. For comparative purposes, however, we shall probably make little error in assuming the reduced surface to be still at P, its usual emmetropic position.

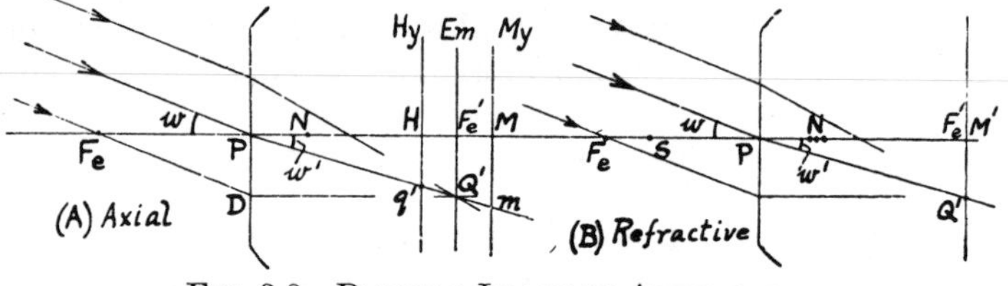

FIG. 3.8—RETINAL IMAGE IN AMETROPIA.

The power F_e of the refractively ametropic eye at rest is then given by $(60 - K)$ since the convergence K' of the light within the eye is constant and equal to 60 D, the emmetropic power; and $K' = K + F_e$. F_e is thus 80 D in 20 D of refractive myopia; 50 D in 10 D of refractive hyperopia, and so on. The radius of the reduced surface (PN) will be larger than the emmetropic value of 5·55 mm. in hyperopia and shorter in myopia.

The blurred image in myopia and the sharp image in emmetropia and hyperopia (after accommodation) are all the same size M′Q′, except that the blur circle diameter must be added in the case of myopia. An object at the myope's far point will be sharp, provided the emmetrope and hyperope have sufficient accommodation, and the same size, in all three eyes. Their dioptric power will also be identical in the three eyes when thus accommodated.

To all eyes, whether ametropic or not, a given object at a given distance is seen under the same visual angle and (apart from other possibly disturbing ocular anomalies) will be similarly judged by the three individuals—Em, H and M. Such judgment as to angular size is made on the basis of comparison with the mental appreciation of a unit of length such as the inch, yard, metre, etc., the retinal images of which in the three individuals differ from one another in the same proportions as the images of any other object.* If the seeing conditions to which a given individual has become habituated are changed, as when a previously uncorrected myope first begins to wear a correction, or when an object is viewed through prisms,† then estimations of the sizes of objects may for a while be faulty.

3.12. The Retinal Image in Corrected Ametropia.

Although the main reason for providing an ametropic eye with its distance correcting lens is to make sharp what was previously a blurred image, a secondary effect of the lens is to alter the size of the image. Whether the ametropia be axial or refractive the retinal image of the unaided eye is enlarged by the correcting lens in hyperopia and diminished in myopia, except in the ideal case when the correcting lens is in contact with the reduced surface at P. This magnifying (or minifying) effect of the spectacle lens may be of importance, especially in relation to binocular vision.

Fig. 3.9A represents the (axially) hyperopic eye of Fig. 3.7. The parallel rays from the distant object point Q make the slope angle w_o with the axis; after refraction at the P surface of the eye they would all reunite in the image Q′ in the F'_e plane. The important ray incident at P is refracted at angle w'_o $(= w_o \div n')$ with the axis and cuts the retina at q′. M′q′ is the size of the blurred image of the distant object BQ. Were the eye to accommodate this blurred image would become sharp but would not change in size.

When the positive correcting lens of power F_1 is inserted at the spectacle point S(Fig. 3.9B) the parallel rays from Q are refracted by this lens to the image point Q'_1, lying in the plane through the far point, M_R, which is also the second focal point of the correcting lens. The rays, such as GP and SE, now entering the eye are all converging to the point Q'_1. The image $M_RQ'_1$ is now the object for the eye; it is a virtual object and, as shown by the ray GPQ'_1, it subtends an angle w at the point P. Thus the effect of the correcting lens has been *to increase the angle* w_o

* Compare §2.5. † §5.4.

at which the ray is incident at P in case A (unaided eye) to angle w in case B (aided eye). In consequence, w'_o of case A is proportionately increased to w' and the blurred retinal image of case A becomes the larger sharp image M′q′ of case B.

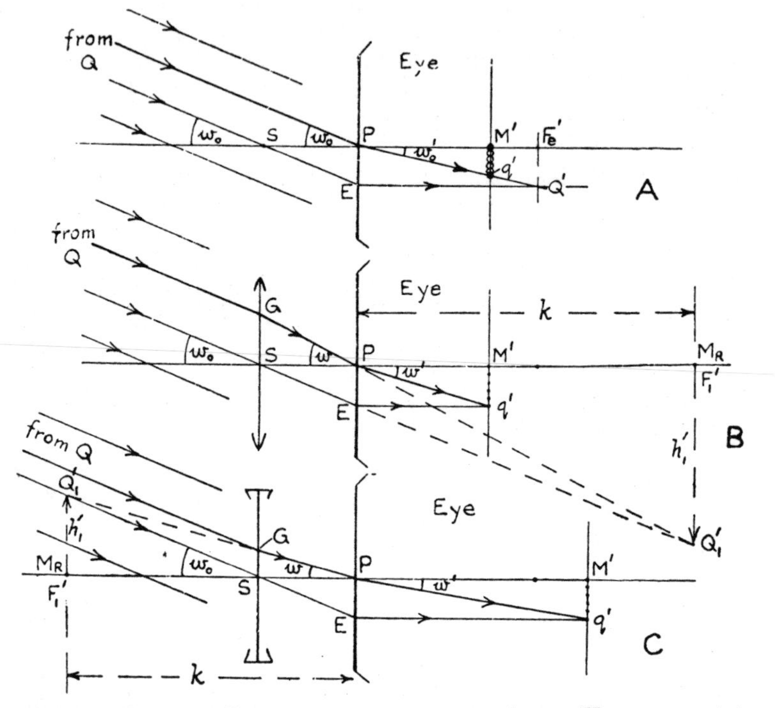

FIG. 3.9—RETINAL IMAGE IN UNCORRECTED AXIAL HYPEROPIA (A), CORRECTED AXIAL HYPEROPIA (B), AND CORRECTED AXIAL MYOPIA (C). IN (B) AND (C) ANGLE w_o IS CHANGED TO w.

The ratio of the retinal image of a distant object in the corrected ametropic eye to the blurred or sharp image formed in the *same* eye when uncorrected is called the SPECTACLE MAGNIFICATION. Fig. 3.9 shows that this is greater than unity in the hyperopic eye; and similar reasoning, in conjunction with Fig. 3.9C which depicts a corrected myopic eye, shows that it is less than unity in myopia; unless the lens is placed at P when the spectacle magnification is unity whatever the refractive error. This last condition is realised approximately in *contact lenses*, which are fitted to the sclera nearly in contact with the cornea.

Spectacle magnification (S.M.) is easily obtained from Fig. 3.9B or C

$$\text{SM} = \frac{w}{w_0} = \frac{\dfrac{\text{M}_\text{R}\text{Q}'_1}{\text{PM}_\text{R}}}{\dfrac{\text{M}_\text{R}\text{Q}'_1}{\text{SM}_\text{R}}} = \frac{\text{SM}_\text{R}}{\text{PM}_\text{R}} = \frac{K}{F_1} \tag{3·4}$$

$$\text{or S.M.} = \frac{\text{Distance of far point from spectacle point}}{\text{Distance of far point from eye}}$$

which applies to all cases, hyperopic or myopic, axial or refractive.

The ratio between the retinal image in the corrected ametropic eye and that in the standard emmetropic eye we will call the RELATIVE SPECTACLE MAGNIFICATION (R.S.M.). The value of this quantity, unlike spectacle magnification, depends upon whether the ametropia is axial or refractive. It can be deduced from Fig. 3.9 that in *axial* ametropia the R.S.M. is equal to unity in both hyperopia and myopia when the spectacle lens is placed at the anterior focal point of the eye ; is less than unity in hyperopia and greater than unity in myopia when the lens, as is usual in practice, is fitted within the focal point of the eye. The departure from unity is, however, very small except in high refractive errors such as aphakia or myopia of high degree.

In *refractive* ametropia the R.S.M. is equal to the S.M. as will be understood by remembering that the image in the uncorrected eye is the same size as the sharp retinal image obtained in the standard emmetropic eye.

Thus whether an individual's ametropia is axial or refractive, the provision of his correcting lens will increase (H) or decrease (M) the size of the retinal image obtained without the correction, but to a very small extent (practically nothing in the case of contact glasses) unless the ametropia is very high. The relation between his corrected image and that of an emmetrope does depend on the nature of the ametropia, however. It is probable that, although ametropia is mainly axial, a proportion of the defect is always refractive ; and we cannot compare the size of the retinal image in a given subject with that obtained by an emmetrope since we have no means of finding how much of the defect is axial and how much refractive. But, as stated earlier, it will be assumed axial unless stated otherwise.

This subject will be discussed further in Chapter X. It is of importance in connection with binocular vision ; which may be interfered with if there is much disparity between the retinal images in the two eyes. When the refractive conditions of the two eyes differ appreciably, a condition called *anisometropia*,* the retinal images after correction are unequal in size.

Example. (*a*) An eye has axial hyperopia correctable with a +8 D sphere placed 14 mm. in front of the reduced eye surface or principal point, P. Find the axial length of this eye and the size of the retinal image formed in it, when unaided, of an object 10 metres high at a distance of 800 metres.

(*b*) Find the size of the retinal image of the same object when the eye is corrected for distance; and also in the standard emmetropic eye.

(*c*) Give the spectacle magnification and the relative spectacle magnification.

Answer. Using first principles:—

(*a*) Far point is 125 mm. behind spectacle point or 111 mm. behind reduced surface, P. Hence ocular refraction $K = \frac{1000}{111} = +9{\cdot}01$ D.

Vergence within eye $= K' = K + F_e = 69{\cdot}01$ D

hence length of eye from P $= k' = \frac{1000}{69{\cdot}01} \times \frac{4}{3} = 19{\cdot}32$ mm.

Visual angle $= w_o = \frac{10}{800} = \frac{1}{80}$ radian; or $\tan w_o = \frac{1}{80}$

Image size $h' = M'q'$ in Fig. 3.9A.

$= w'_o \times PM' = (\frac{3}{4} \times \frac{1}{80}) \times 19{\cdot}32 = 0{\cdot}1812$ mm.

(*b*) Lens at spectacle point, S, forms an image at eye's far point, the size of which is $\frac{1}{80} \times 125$ mm.

This subtends at the eye (P) an angle $\frac{125}{80} \times \frac{1}{111}$ radian.

Retinal image $h' = \left(\frac{3}{4} \times \frac{125}{80 \times 111}\right) \times 19{\cdot}32 = 0{\cdot}204$ mm.

Image in Em. eye $= (\frac{3}{4} \times \frac{1}{80}) \times 22{\cdot}22 = 0{\cdot}2083$ mm.

(*c*) Spectacle magnification $= \dfrac{\text{Image in corrected Am. Eye}}{\text{Image in uncorrected Am. Eye}}$

$= \dfrac{\cdot 204}{\cdot 1812} = 1{\cdot}126$

Relative spect. magnification $= \dfrac{\text{Image in corrected Am. Eye}}{\text{Image in Em. Eye}}$

$= \dfrac{\cdot 204}{\cdot 2083} = 0{\cdot}9792$

Example. Repeat the above example for the case when the hyperopia is refractive, all other quantities remaining the same.

Answer. (*a*) Axial length, from P = 22·22 cm. (Fig. 3.8B). Retinal image in this, and in Em. eye, is 0·2083 mm. (from above).

* Ch. XVI.

(*b*) Image formed by correcting lens $\frac{125}{80}$ mm. (as above)

Retinal image in corrected eye $= \left(\frac{3}{4} \times \frac{125}{80 \times 111}\right) \times 22 \cdot 22 = 0 \cdot 2346$ mm.

(*c*) Spectacle magnification $= \frac{\cdot 2346}{\cdot 2083} = 1 \cdot 126$

Relative spectacle magnification also $= 1 \cdot 126$

It will be observed that the spectacle magnification is the same whether the ametropia be axial or refractive.

Example. An eye is axially hyperopic 8 D. Find the size of the virtual image, formed at its far point, of a 2 mm. extent of its fundus.

If a +12 D lens be placed 7·5 cm. from the eye, find the position and magnification of the fundus under these conditions.

Answer. Light starts from fundus (which may be illuminated as in ophthalmoscopy), is incident on eye's reduced surface with vergence $K' = -68$ D and leaves it with vergence $-68 + 60 = -8$ D $= -K$.

If h = size of object on fundus

h' = size of image at conjugate far point

then magnification $m = \frac{h'}{h} = \frac{K'}{K} = \frac{-68}{-8} = +8 \cdot 5$

hence $h' = 8 \cdot 5 \times 2 = 17$ mm.

With +12 D lens in position, light emerging from eye is further refracted and a second image h″ is formed.

Far point is $-(12 \cdot 5 + 7 \cdot 5) = -20$ cm. from lens $= -5$ D (L);

refraction by lens, $-5 + 12 = +7$ D (L')

final image is $\frac{100}{7} = 14 \cdot 28$cm. beyond lens or $21 \cdot 78$ cm. from eye.

Magnification by lens $m_2 = \frac{L}{L'} = \frac{-5}{+7}$

Total magnification by eye and lens $= -8 \cdot 5 \times \frac{5}{7} = -6 \cdot 07$.

Second image $h'' = -6 \cdot 07 \times 2 = -12 \cdot 14$ mm.

This kind of problem finds application in indirect ophthalmoscopy, to be described in Ch. VII.

3.13. **Aphakia.** (Without lens—DONDERS)

An aphakic eye is one in which the crystalline lens is absent. The term is used to include those cases in which the lens, although not entirely missing from the eye, is at any rate (through dislocation or otherwise) absent from the pupillary area and therefore takes no part in the refraction of the eye. The lens may have been lost or dislocated as the result of a wound, or the absence may be congenital; but in the great majority of cases the aphakic condition is due to removal of the lens by operation. Usually the operation is performed in cases of cataract; very rarely in myopia of high degree.

The absence of the lens may be recognised by the deep and conical appearance of the anterior chamber, the receding edges of the iris giving this appearance; by observing the trembling of the unsupported iris as the eye is moved; or, holding a light before the eye, by noting the absence of the two images normally seen by reflection at the front and back lens surfaces.* The ophthalmoscope may show up remnants of the lens capsule left after the operation.

The wound in the cornea after the operation invariably introduces some astigmatism,† which gradually diminishes with the healing of the wound and settles down to an amount varying between 1·50 D to 3·0 D or more, axis horizontal, or thereabouts. On this account no steps are taken to test the eye, preparatory to the provision of an optical correction, until a week or two after the operation. Neglecting this residual astigmatism, the optical result is that the eye has been deprived of an optical element, the lens, of about 21·5 dioptres power in the average case; the cornea is the only refracting element remaining. A previously emmetropic eye will be highly hyperopic, the hyperopia being mainly refractive and wholly absolute since the eye has no longer any power of accommodation. The acuity is often quite good, 6/6 or so.

The aphakic eye can be corrected for distance by a positive lens of appropriate power—see below. If the fellow eye be more or less normal, the two eyes probably cannot be used together in binocular vision‡, mainly owing to the considerably increased size of the retinal image in the corrected aphakic eye which renders fusion of the two retinal images difficult or probably impossible§; and also partly due to the loss of accommodation in that eye. This must be seriously considered by the surgeon when deciding whether a unilateral cataract shall be removed; in many cases nothing is gained by removing the cataract if the subject has one good eye. In some cases, such as those where, the fellow eye being good, it is important to the subject to take advantage of the additional visual field on

---

* §10.2. † Ch. IV and §9.8.

‡ A few cases have been reported in which, in these unilateral cases, both eyes were stated to be used in binocular vision.

§ See Ch. XVI.—*Anisometropia.* Since aphakia is an example of ametropia that is mainly refractive, the retinal disparity is much reduced if a contact glass is used for correction.

the aphakic side, the cataract is removed. Careful consideration must then be given to the question as to whether an optical correction is to be provided for the aphakic eye. Each case has to be considered on its merits, the condition of the other eye and the subject's age and occupation being important factors.

Assuming that the questions of policy have been disposed of and returning to the purely optical aspects of the problem, it will be shown below that an aphakic eye originally of standard emmetropic dimensions requires—if it is to be corrected—a distance correcting lens, placed at the conventional distance of $12\frac{1}{3}$ mm. in front of the cornea, of about $+11{\cdot}25$ D. The lens necessary for correction of an aphakic eye originally ametropic depends upon the amount of the ametropia and whether it were axial or refractive. *Assuming axial ametropia*, the distance correcting lens is given *approximately* by

$$\text{DISTANCE CORRECTING LENS} = +11{\cdot}25 + 0{\cdot}62\ F_1 \text{ dioptres}$$

where F_1 is the spectacle refraction of the originally ametropic eye. From this it follows that an eye previously axially myopic to the extent that it required about $-18{\cdot}5$ D to correct it, will be emmetropic in the aphakic condition.

In most cases the lens required by the aphakic eye, frequently called a *cataract lens*, is fairly powerful and is made in bent form to diminish oblique astigmatism over the peripheral portions of the visual field as the eye rotates. One surface of the lens may even be made aspherical in order to eliminate the astigmatism completely.*

The total loss of accommodation in the aphakic eye may at first be the cause of much inconvenience to the subject in moving about, descending stairs, etc. The indistinctness of reading matter and other close work can be counteracted to a small extent by adopting the common device of screwing up the eyes, which has the pinhole effect of reducing the blur circles on the retina and increasing the depth of focus; and, in those cases where the aphakic distance correction is sufficiently powerful (greater than about 7 D, corresponding to an original myopia of about 6 D), by moving this correction away from the eye, which

---

* *Ophthalmic Lenses*; Ch. XV. It appears to be important, however, to provide reasonably good peripheral vision; and lenses bent to a greater extent than the usual "best form" lenses are found to be superior.

enables near objects to be brought to focus closer to the retina and also increases the size of the blurred retinal image of the near object. With strong distance corrections such as the + 11 D lens required in cases of original emmetropia, and higher powers, it is possible to *focus* objects at the usual reading distance of 33 cm. sharply on the retina by moving the distance spectacles down the nose.

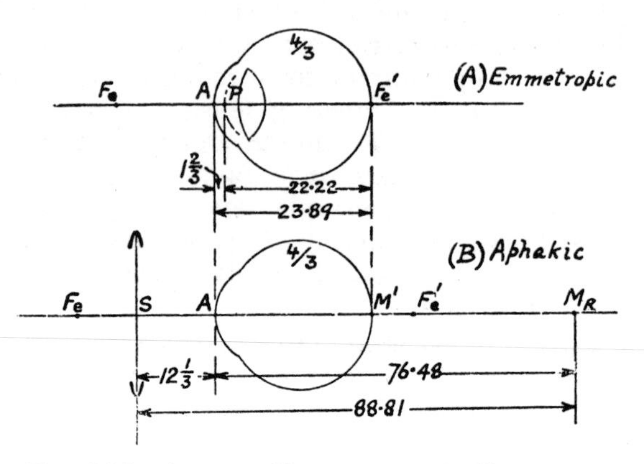

FIG. 3.10—APHAKIC EYE PREVIOUSLY EMMETROPIC.

Apart from makeshift helps of this kind, the aphakic eye requires a separate correction for near work.

We will illustrate the principles of correction by one or two numerical examples.

Example. Calculate the distance correction required by an aphakic eye which was originally emmetropic, the lens to be worn $12\frac{1}{3}$ mm. in front of the cornea. Also find the spectacle magnification when corrected. Use the constants of the standard 60 D eye.

Answer. In Fig. 3.10 (A) indicates the originally Em. eye and (B) the aphakic eye. Note that in the latter the refracting surface at A is the cornea and *not* the equivalent surface of the reduced eye, which is shown at P. The focal points of the eye move out as shown in (B). The problem amounts to finding the position of the far point M_R for which purpose we need to know two quantities : (*a*) the power of the refracting surface (cornea) at A and (*b*) the distance from this of the fovea M′ which is conjugate to M_R.

In the standard schematic eye the radius of curvature of the cornea surface is 7·8 mm. ; hence

$$\text{power of cornea} = \frac{n' - n}{r} = \frac{(\frac{4}{3} - 1)\,1000}{7\cdot 8} = 42\cdot 73 \text{ D}.$$

$$\text{In the Em. eye PM}' = \frac{1000}{60} \times \frac{4}{3} = 22\cdot 22 \text{ mm}.$$

Length of aphakic eye = AM′ = 22·22 + 1·67 = 23·89 mm.

$$\text{Vergence of light in eye} = \frac{1000}{23\cdot 89} \times \frac{4}{3} = 55\cdot 81 \text{ D } (L')$$

Vergence of light incident on eye (L) is given by

$$L = 55\cdot 81 - 42\cdot 73 = 13\cdot 08 \text{ D}.$$

$$\text{Distance AM}_R \text{ to far point} = \frac{1000}{13\cdot 08} = 76\cdot 48 \text{ mm}.$$

Focal length correcting lens = SM_R = 12·33 + 76·48 = 88·81 mm.

$$\text{Power of correcting lens} = \frac{1000}{88\cdot 81} = +11\cdot 26 \text{ D}.$$

Spectacle magnification :

Of a distant object subtending angle w, the unaided aphakic eye forms a retinal image given by

$$-w' \times 23\cdot 89 = -\frac{w}{n'} \times 23\cdot 89 \text{ mm}. \quad (1)$$

When corrected, spectacle lens forms image at M_R of size $w \times 88\cdot 81$ mm.

This subtends at eye an angle

$$\frac{w \times 88\cdot 81}{76\cdot 48}$$

$$\text{retinal image in corrected eye} = -\left(\frac{w}{n'} \times \frac{88\cdot 81}{76\cdot 48}\right) \times 23\cdot 89 \quad (2)$$

$$\text{Spectacle magnification} = \frac{(2)}{(1)} = \frac{88\cdot 81}{76\cdot 48} \doteq 1\cdot 16$$

An emmetropic eye would obtain a retinal image of size $-\frac{w}{n'} \times 22\cdot 22$ mm. ; hence

$$\text{Relative spectacle magnification} = \frac{88\cdot 81}{76\cdot 48} \times \frac{23\cdot 89}{22\cdot 22} = 1\cdot 25$$

Thus if the fellow eye were emmetropic and possessed reasonably good visual acuity, one retinal image would be 25 per cent larger than the other and binocular vision would be irksome if not impossible.

Note.—The hyperopia of an aphakic eye is made up of two parts ; in comparison with the standard reduced Em. eye its globe is long, producing axial myopia ; its power is, however, much reduced giving refractive hyperopia ; the net result is usually hyperopia.

Example. Find the distance correcting lens, to be worn 12 mm. from the cornea, for an aphakic eye that was (axially) myopic 10 dioptres prior to removal of the crystalline lens

Answer. Proceeding in a similar manner :

Vergence within myopic eye = $K' = K + F_e = -10 + 60 = +50$ D.

$$PM' = \frac{1000}{50} \times \frac{4}{3} = 26\tfrac{2}{3} \text{ mm.}; \quad AM' = 26\cdot 67 + 1\cdot 67 = 28\cdot 33 \text{ mm.}$$

Vergence of light incident on cornea of aphakic eye

$$L = L - F = \frac{1000}{28\cdot 33} \times \frac{4}{3} - 42\cdot 73 = 47\cdot 07 - 42\cdot 73 = +\,4\cdot 34 \text{ D}$$

Far point of aphakic eye $AM_R = 230 \cdot 4$ mm.
focal length of correcting lens $SM_R = 230 \cdot 4 + 12 = 242 \cdot 4$ mm.

$$\text{Power of correcting lens} = \frac{1000}{242 \cdot 4} = +4 \cdot 12 \text{ D.}$$

A result in close agreement to this is given by the approximate expression stated in the text above; F_1 is the correcting lens for the originally myopic eye and its power is $-11 \cdot 59$ D; thus the expression gives $11 \cdot 25 - (0 \cdot 62 \times 11 \cdot 59) = +4 \cdot 06$ D.

3.14. Thick Spectacle Lens. Vertex Power.

Up to the present we have assumed the correcting lens to be thin, the equivalent and vertex powers of the lens all being equal. In hyperopia of moderate to high degrees, however, the thickness of the positive correcting lens begins to be appreciable. The vertex of the back surface of the lens will be placed at the spectacle point S and the condition still holds that, for correction of the eye, the second focal point of the lens shall coincide with the eye's far point. The distance from the spectacle point to the far point is then the *back vertex focal length*, or simply back focal length, f'_v, of the correcting lens and the spectacle refraction of the eye is equal to the *back vertex power*, F'_v, of the lens.

Thus in the case of a thick correcting lens we have:

$$f'_v = d + k$$

Equation $(3 \cdot 2)$ becomes

$$F'_v = \frac{K}{1 + dK}$$

Lenses of equal back vertex powers, placed with their back surfaces at the spectacle point, will be equally effective in correcting the eye's refractive error, but they will not produce retinal images of equal size if they differ in form —biconvex, meniscus, etc.* Except in special cases, we will assume correcting lenses to be thin, however. For further particulars of thick spectacle lenses refer to *Ophthalmic Lenses*.

3.15. Clinical Aspect of Spherical Ametropias.

Throughout the chapter we have been considering the eye as an optical instrument and have concerned ourselves only with the optical problems associated with its correction. Although the practical work carried out by the student will already have brought home to him the importance of the fact that the eye is a living organ, we will include here a few remarks on the clinical aspects of hyperopia and myopia.

* See §10.20.

Hypermetropia is usually congenital. It diminishes gradually during childhood. Unless it is of high degree, or the amplitude of accommodation low, the subject obtains good distance vision by accommodating. The continual exercise of the ciliary muscle may, however, cause accommodative asthenopia—frontal headaches. Other possible symptoms are blepharitis, conjunctivitis ; a large angle alpha giving the appearance of divergent squint ; the pupils tend to be contracted, probably due to the continual exertion of accommodation ; since the subject must accommodate for distance vision, for which purpose no convergence of the visual axes is required, there is disharmony between the two functions of accommodation and convergence which, as will be more clearly understood later,* may lead to diplopia and to convergent squint in a child, or to muscular asthenopia with pain in the temples. Even if there is no discomfort in distance vision, there may be in near vision, especially as age advances.

Myopia is rarely congenital ; it is nearly always acquired, mostly about the school age, although there may be a hereditary tendency. It is practically always axial. Generally, the low to medium degrees, say up to −8 D, are stationary in character whilst the higher degrees may be progressive and malignant. That is, we may subdivide myopia into what may be described as *simple* or optical, and *pathological*. The latter includes malignant progressive myopia, keratoconus, incipient cataract accompanied by increase in power of the crystalline lens caused by changes in its refractive index.†

Progressive myopia is to be carefully looked for when the myopia is of moderate or high degree. It progresses fairly rapidly, usually throughout life, and is accompanied by abnormal changes in the media and tunics of the eye, with perhaps a posterior staphyloma. The degree may be 20 D, 30 D, or even 40 D ; the visual acuity (vision with lenses) is usually subnormal and the full correction is rarely prescribed. The changes in the tunics, choroid and sclera, are accompanied by the appearance of a whitish myopic crescent near the optic disc, which can be observed with the ophthalmoscope ; these fundus changes may spread towards the macula ; further progress may lead to detachment of the retina. Cases of progressive myopia require medical attention.

---

* §§ 5.2 and 13.16.

† See §6.3.

A person who is really hyperopic may appear to be myopic—false or pseudo myopia—because of spasm of accommodation.*

In simple myopia, in addition to the provision of glasses for constant wear to enable the subject to see clearly at distance as well as near, attention should be paid to such matters as the prohibition of too much near work such as reading; to good lighting, ventilation, fresh air, rest and outdoor occupation and exercise.

We shall see later that the glasses to be prescribed in both hyperopia and myopia, for distance and for near, depend to some extent upon the condition of the subject's oculomotor system as well as upon the ametropia.

EXERCISES. CHAPTER III.

1. Explain clearly, with the aid of appropriate diagrams, the terms emmetropia, far point, refraction of the eye or ametropia; and make clear the difference between axial and refractive ametropia.

2. Taking the spectacle point as 14 mm. from the reduced eye surface, calculate the ocular refraction and the spectacle refraction of eyes the far points of which are at the following distances from the reduced surface: (*a*) $+2$ metres; (*b*) $+25$ cm.; (*c*) $-1 \cdot 5$ metres; (*d*) $-33\frac{1}{3}$ cm

3. The far point of a certain eye is distant -25 cm. from the eye.† What lens will have to be placed against the eye to enable it to see clearly without accommodation an object (*a*) at infinity, (*b*) at 1 metre? (Assume the reduced eye.)

4. How far from an eye myopic 5 D must a -7 D lens be placed, and how far from an eye hyperopic 6 D must a $+3$ D lens be placed in order that a distant object may be seen clearly?

5. Find the diameter of the retinal blur circle corresponding to each distant object point in the case of a myope of 5 D with a pupil diameter of 4 mm. (*a*) when the myopia is wholly axial; (*b*) when it is wholly refractive.

6. Assuming a 60 D reduced eye and axial ametropia, find the position of the far point in eyes that have the following axial lengths: (*a*) $33\frac{1}{3}$ mm.; (*b*) $19 \cdot 05$ mm.; (*c*) $22 \cdot 22$ mm.

7. It is found that an eye is corrected for distance by a -8 D sphere placed 15 mm. from the eye. If the axial length of this eye is $24 \cdot 1$ mm., what is its dioptric power and the radius of curvature of its reduced surface?

8. An eye is corrected for distance by a $+8$ D lens placed 14 mm. from the cornea. Find the effective power of the lens at the cornea

---

* §6.7.

† Unless the contrary is obvious from the nature of the problem the statement "from or to the eye" will be taken from or to the surface, P, of the reduced eye.

and the power of lens to correct the eye if placed (*a*) 20 mm. and (*b*) 5 mm. in front of the cornea.

9. If the refractive index of the interior of the emmetropic reduced eye of power 60 D were to change from $\frac{4}{3}$ to 1·40, what would then be its refractive condition ?

10. An eye has axial myopia correctable for distance by a −8 D sphere placed 15 mm. in front of the reduced surface or principal point. Find the error in axial length of this eye and the diameter of blur circles on the retina corresponding to distant object points. The pupil diameter is 4 mm. and the eye is uncorrected and unaccommodated.

11. Calculate the size of the retinal blur circle for an axial myope (−2·5 D) uncorrected, with pupil diameter 8 mm. and anterior focal length 16$\frac{2}{3}$ mm., when a distant object point is viewed.

What linear diameter would this blur circle appear when projected on a plane 6 metres in front of the eye ? (S.M.C.)

12. Explain the terms static refraction and visual acuity, and how the former may be defective and the latter good.

Find the V.A. of an eye which is just capable of reading Snellen letters 35 mm. square seen by reflection in a plane mirror which is 3·5 metres from the subject and 4·5 metres from the test chart.

It is found that placing a pinhole before this eye improves vision. Explain this with the aid of a diagram and state what is to be deduced from it.

13. Assuming that the whole eye can be represented by an air chamber provided with two thin lenses, one of +43·0 D for the cornea and another of +20·5 D for the crystalline lens placed in air 4 mm. behind the equivalent corneal lens, calculate the position of the retina in this equivalent air chamber for a case of emmetropia. (S.M.C.)

14. Prove that in axial ametropia the error in axial length is given approximately in millimetres by x where :

$$x = \tfrac{3}{8} K$$

K being the refractive error in dioptres. (S.M.C. Hons.)

15. An object distant 200 metres moves perpendicularly to the line of sight at a speed of 5 metres per second. What is the angular speed in degrees per second and in prism dioptres per second ? At what linear speed does the retinal image move across the retina of the emmetropic eye ?

16. A reduced eye has a radius of 5·5 mm. and refractive index $\frac{4}{3}$. Under certain conditions its axial length alters by a constant amount per dioptre of refractive error. State the conditions necessary and calculate the constant. (S.M.C. Hons.)

17. Prove that each dioptre of ametropia or of fogging with positive lenses produces a retinal blur circle that subtends about 3·5 × a minutes of angle, where a is the pupil diameter in millimetres.

18. Determine graphically the size of the blur circle on the retina using a distant point source of light for pupil diameters of 5 mm. and 2 mm. in each of the following cases : (*a*) an eye axially hyperopic 4·5 D ; (*b*) axially myopic 9 D.

19. What is accommodation ? What is its purpose and how is it supposed to be accomplished ? Mention one theory only. (S.M.C.)

20. By how much will an eye with 3 D of myopia need to accommodate in order to see clearly an object at a distance of 20 cm. from the eye? What accommodation must be exerted by a hyperope of 1 D?

21. Find the position of the near point in each of the following cases: (*a*) eye myopic 3 D, amplitude 8 D; (*b*) eye hyperopic 3 D, amplitude 8 D: (*c*) far point 20 cm. in front of eye, amplitude 7 D.

22. Prove that the amplitude of accommodation is equal to the power of the positive lens which, placed at the eye, forms an image of the near point at the far point.

23. When a +2 D sphere is placed at the eye, the far point is found to be 50 cm. in front; and with a −4 D sphere the near point is 50 cm. in front. Find the positions of the far and near points of the unaided eye and its amplitude of accommodation.

24. What is the range of accommodation of a myope of 5 D whose amplitude of accommodation is 8 D?

A person using two-thirds of his accommodation sees distinctly an object at 50 cm. With the aid of a +2·5 D sphere placed 2 cm. in front of the eye he sees an object clearly at 42 cm. from the eye when exerting one-third of his accommodation. What is his refractive condition and amplitude of accommodation?

25. A hyperope of 4 D has amplitude of accommodation 8 D. What is the nearest position of an object to be clearly seen through a +5 D sphere close to the eye?

26. All the accommodation is exerted when an eye views a distant object through a +2·5 D sphere placed 15 mm. in front of the cornea; with a +5·0 D sphere in place of the +2·5 D only one-half of the accommodation is exerted. What would be the power of the distance correction placed 15 mm. in front of the cornea? (Neglect distance between principal plane of eye and cornea.) (S.M.C.)

27. A hyperope of 3 D has a range of distinct vision up to a point 50 cm. before the eye. If we wish to leave one-half of his accommodation in reserve what lens will he require for distance and what lens for reading at $\frac{1}{3}$ metre?

28. A myope, with accommodation relaxed, can just see distinctly an object 18·6 cm. in front of a −13 D sphere placed 28 mm. from the cornea. Where would be the artificial far point if the distance separating lens and cornea were reduced to 5·5 mm.?

29. An eye has ocular refraction −4 D (myopia) and 6 D amplitude of accommodation. Find the distances from the eye of the artificial far and near points when a +5 D sphere is placed 2 cm. before the eye. What is the distance correcting lens, to correct the myopia fully, and to be worn 12 mm. from the eye?

30. With a certain lens, the power of which is not zero, placed 15 mm. in front of an eye no accommodation is required when an object 20 cm. from the eye is viewed through the lens. Neither is any accommodation required when the same lens is moved forward by 1 cm., the object remaining fixed. What lens placed 15 mm. in front of the eye would correct it for distance? (S.M.C.)

31. When reading at 33·3 cm. a person uses one-quarter of his accommodation when looking through a −1·0 D sphere. What fraction of his accommodation will he exert when reading at 25 cm.

with the aid of a $+1 \cdot 0$ D sphere if the nearest point of distinct vision with this $+1 \cdot 0$ D is apparently $12 \cdot 5$ cm. away ? What is his refractive error ? (S.M.C.)

32. When a person uses one-half of his accommodation he sees an object at one metre distinctly. With the aid of a + 4 D sphere and exerting one-third of his accommodation he sees an object clearly at 25 cm. What is his refractive error and his amplitude of accommodation ? (S.M.C.)

33. Reading at 1 metre with a $-2 \cdot 0$ D sphere requires the exertion of no accommodation. Reading at 20 cm. with the aid of a $+ 1 \cdot 0$ D sphere requires the exertion of maximum accommodation. What fraction of the maximum accommodation is exerted when reading at 25 cm. without any lens ? (S.M.C.)

34. Explain the terms : latent, manifest, total and absolute hypermetropia. Describe the general effect of age on these quantities.

A girl aged 15 on being tested accepts +4 D sphere and still clearly reads the 6/6 line with which she started. Her near point (unaided) is found to be at 20 cm. If her amplitude of accommodation is normal at 12 D, what is the manifest and the latent hyperopia ?

35. In a certain case vision is raised to 6/60 with a $+2 \cdot 0$ D sphere and to 6/6 with a $+4 \cdot 50$ D sphere. It remains 6/6 with a $+5 \cdot 0$ D sphere and becomes 6/12 with a $+5 \cdot 50$ D sphere.

Estimate the degree of (*a*) manifest hypermetropia ; (*b*) facultative hypermetropia ; (*c*) absolute hypermetropia. (S.M.C.)

36. An eye reads 6/18. With a $1 \cdot 50$ D sphere vision is 6/6 ; it remains 6/6 with a $+ 3 \cdot 50$ D sphere. After application of atropine a $+4 \cdot 50$ D sphere is accepted, vision remaining 6/6. Describe this case briefly. State the amplitude of accommodation and probable age.*

37. Find the total, manifest, latent and absolute H. and the amplitude of accommodation in the following cases : (*a*) vision poor at first becomes 6/6, its maximum value, after addition of +5 D.S. Vision remains 6/6 with a $+7 \cdot 50$ D.S. After atropine no further power is accepted ; (*b*) on preliminary test V is poor but becomes 6/6 after addition of + 3 D.S. and remains 6/6 with +6 D.S. After cycloplegic, subject accepts $+ 7 \cdot 50$ D.S., V being 6/6 ; (*c*) subject reads 6/5 and her near point is found to be 40 cm. in front of the eye. A $+3 \cdot 0$ D.S. is accepted, vision remaining unaltered. With cycloplegic $+7 \cdot 50$ D.S. is accepted.

38. Explain with diagrams, the principle of the simple optometer. Why is it not generally used in clinical practice for determining the lenses to be worn ?

Construct the scale of spectacle refraction for an optometer provided with a $+4 \cdot 0$ D optometer lens.

39. Explain briefly how the refractive condition of an eye may be determined approximately with a Scheiner disc.

A disc of this type, with apertures $1\frac{1}{2}$ mm. in diameter separated by 12 mm. between centres, is placed in contact with a +5 D spherical lens facing a distant point source. Find the appearances on a screen placed (*a*) 3 cm. in front of, and (*b*) 4 cm. behind the second principal focus of the lens.

---

* For the relation between accommodation and age see Chapter VI.

40. A Scheiner disc, having apertures 1 mm. in diameter separated 3 mm. between centres, is placed close before an eye that is axially myopic 6 D. The line joining the apertures is vertical and the upper one is covered with a red glass.

Describe, giving dimensions, what is seen when the eye views a bright point of light 6 metres away.

41. Explain the optical arrangement and principle of Young's optometer. Draw the scale of the instrument, assuming the optometer lens to be + 10 D.

42. An astronomical telescope, having an objective of 120 mm. focal length and an eyepiece of 30 mm. focal length, is to be used as an optometer. The eyepiece is kept at a fixed position 15 mm. in front of the eye under test and the objective is moved. Find its movement for each dioptre of refractive error from 5 D of hyperopia to 5 D of myopia; the emmetropia position (infinity adjustment) being the zero position.

43. A Galilean telescope, having an objective of 250 mm. focal length and an eyepiece of focal length 50 mm., is to be used as an optometer (von Graefe's type) with a distant object. The eyepiece occupies a fixed position 20 mm. in front of the eye. Construct a scale showing the position of the objective for each dioptre of refractive error from 5 D of hyperopia to 5 D of myopia.

44. An emmetropic eye views an object placed 50 cm. in front of the objective of a simple telescope which is in infinity adjustment. The objective is a thin +4·0 D sphere and the eyepiece has a power of − 20 D sphere. Calculate the accommodation required when the eye is situated 15 mm. behind the eyepiece. (S.M.C.)

45. A simple optometer consists of a +10·0 D sphere whose focal point coincides with the principal point of an eye under examination. Show how to calibrate the instrument to read directly dioptres of refractive error and explain the precautions you would take in using the instrument. (S.M.C.)

46. A certain form of optometer is so arranged that one focal plane of it coincides with the anterior focal plane of the eye. If x be the distance of the test object from the other focal plane, P the power of the lens and E the error of refraction referred to the anterior focal plane, establish a formula to show that x is simply proportional to E (both P and E in dioptres). Use the same formula to calculate the necessary value of P if the instrument is to be divided into equal divisions of 5 mm. each. (S.M.C. Hons.)

47. Define the terms spectacle magnification and relative spectacle magnification. With the aid of appropriate diagrams prove that the former is greater than unity in hyperopia and less than unity in myopia, whether the ametropia be axial or refractive, except when the correcting lens is placed at the reduced surface (of principal point) of the eye.

48. With the aid of appropriate diagrams prove that the relative spectacle magnification is less than unity in axial hyperopia, greater than unity in axial myopia, when the correcting lens is worn within the eye's anterior focus; and that it is equal to unity when the correcting lens coincides with the eye's anterior focus, the ametropia being axial.

Also show that when the ametropia is refractive, the relative spectacle magnification is always greater than unity in hyperopia and less than unity in myopia wherever the correcting lens may be, except in the particular case when it coincides with the eye's reduced surface or principal point.

49. An eye has axial hyperopia correctable with a $+5$ D sphere placed 14 mm. in front of the reduced eye surface. Find the axial length of this eye and the size of the retinal image, formed in the unaided eye, of a 60 metre letter of the test chart.

Find the size of the retinal image of the same object when the eye is corrected and compare this with the retinal image formed in a standard emmetropic eye.

(Take power of eye 60 D and refractive index $\frac{4}{3}$.)

50. An object 20 feet high is situated at a distance of half a mile. What is the size of the retinal image in an eye myopic 4 D with the correcting lens worn 15 mm. in front of the cornea ? (S.M.C.)

51. The centre of the blind spot is 15 degrees outside the point of fixation which lies in a tangent screen one metre from the cornea. What linear distance on the screen measured from the fixation point will correspond with the blind spot's centre ? (Assume static power of eye $+60$ D ; principal plane of eye $1 \cdot 5$ mm. behind cornea ; media indices $\frac{4}{3}$; $\tan 15° = 0 \cdot 268$.)

Discuss generally the apparent position of the blind spot (on the screen) if the eye were rendered aphakic and provided with a correction (e.g. $+12$ D at 15 mm. from cornea). (S.M.C.)

52. An axially myopic eye is corrected for distance by a $-11 \cdot 75$ D sphere placed 14 mm. from the reduced eye surface. Calculate the error in axial length. (Assume 60 D eye and index $\frac{4}{3}$).

Suppose the far point distance and refraction of the eye are measured from the eye's anterior focal point ; find the relationship between the axial error of the globe and the refractive error (in dioptres) measured in this way.

53. (*a*) An eye with axial myopia is corrected for distance by a -8 D sphere placed 14 mm. in front of the reduced eye surface. Find the axial length of the globe of this eye.

(*b*) Find the size of the retinal image, in this corrected eye, of an object 150 feet high distant 2 miles. Compare this image with that formed in an emmetropic eye.

(*c*) An eye with refractive myopia is corrected for distance by a -8 D sphere placed 14 mm. from the eye. Find the size of the retinal image in this corrected eye of the same object as in (*b*) above.

54. Discuss the effect of correcting lenses on the size of the retinal image in cases (*a*) of axial myopia ; (*b*) of curvature myopia. (S.M.C.)

55. Why do patients sometimes find that they can see better if they draw their glasses further away from their eyes ? What action should be taken in such a case ? (B.O.A.)

56. What changes take place when an eye by operation becomes aphakic ? How can it be demonstrated and compensated ? What approximate power will be required when an eye previous to an operation was respectively emmetropic, hyperopic 5 D., and myopic 12 D ? (S.M.C.)

57. An eye previously axially hyperopic and corrected for distance by the lens + 5 D sphere worn 15 mm. from the eye's principal point, is rendered aphakic. Find the power of the distance correcting lens now required, in the same position. Neglect any astigmatism introduced by the operation and assume the following values: corneal radius, 8 mm.; index of media, $\frac{4}{3}$; power of eye, 60 D; distance from cornea to principal point, $1\frac{2}{3}$ mm.

What lens will be required for reading at 25 cm.?

58. An eye with axial myopia has its crystalline lens removed and is then found to be emmetropic. What was the amount of the myopia? Assume the standard values for the eye.

59. An aphakic person, wearing R. and L. $+11 \cdot 0$ D sphere, is just able to see distinctly print held 40 cm. beyond the lenses, which themselves are 25 mm. in front of the corneæ. What lenses, placed 14 mm. from his corneæ, will enable him to see distant objects distinctly?

60. An eye previously emmetropic is rendered aphakic. Calculate the power of the required distance correcting lens placed 12 mm. in front of the cornea. Assume power of eye 60 D, refractive index $\frac{4}{3}$, cornea-reduced surface separation $1\frac{2}{3}$ mm., corneal radius $7 \cdot 8$ mm.

Find the position that must be occupied by this lens to enable the subject to read clearly at $\frac{1}{3}$ metre from the original position of the lens.

61. Compare the size of the retinal image of a distant object formed by a static emmetropic eye (static power $+60$ D) with that by the corresponding aphakic eye with the correcting lens placed 15 mm. in front of the cornea (corneal radius 8 mm.; position of cornea = $1\frac{1}{3}$ mm. in front of the principal plane of normal eye; refractive index of humours = $1\frac{1}{3}$). (S.M.C.)

62. Draw to scale ($\frac{1}{5}$ inch = 1 mm.) the emmetropic reduced eye. Take two rays from a point on a distant object subtending an angle of 20° to the axis and find the size of the retinal image.

Repeat with an (axially) hyperopic eye corrected with a $+10$ D lens placed 14 mm. in front of the eye. (In this second case it may be necessary to use a smaller scale.)

63. If a lens is moved backwards and forwards in front of the eye, how are the refracting effect and size of the retinal image varied? Describe the effects for both plus and minus lenses. (S.M.C.)

64. Taking the power of the eye as 60 D and the ametropia as axial find the axial length of an eye that is corrected for distance by a $+6$ D sphere placed 12 mm. from the cornea.

What is the equivalent dioptric power of the combination of correcting lens and eye?

65. Find the power of the spherical lens, at 15 mm. from the cornea required by an emmetropic person to enable him to see distant objects distinctly when he is under water. (Take power of cornea normally at $42 \cdot 3$ D; refractive index of the lens as $1 \cdot 523$; refractive index of humours, $\frac{4}{3}$).

66. An eye is corrected for distance by a system consisting of two thin lenses, namely, a $+3$ D sphere at 20 mm. and a $+5$ D sphere at 10 mm., in front of the eye. Find the power of the single (thin) lens, to be placed 15 mm. from the eye, that will correct it for distance.

Compare the size of the retinal image of a distant object formed in the first case, when the two lenses are worn, to that formed in the second case. Assume the ametropia axial.

67. An axial hyperope of 5 D, an emmetrope and an axial myope of 5 D all observe an object placed at the myope's far point. Assuming accommodation is ample, compare the sizes of the retinal images formed in the three eyes.

Comment on the relative mental interpretations of these three individuals as to the size of the object.

68. Calculate the radius of curvature of the reduced surface of the accommodated eyes of the hyperope and emmetrope of the previous question, assuming the principal point remains unchanged in position during accommodation.

69. Calculate the size of the image formed at the far point of an eye axially myopic 10 D, the object being a 2 mm. extent of its fundus.

If K is the refractive condition and F_E the dioptric power of an eye generally, show that the magnification of the fundus is given by $m = 1 + \frac{F_E}{K}$.

70. An opera glass having lenses of powers +6 D and − 18 D is focused for infinity by an emmetrope. How much and in what direction must the eyepiece be moved for a hyperope of 2 D to see distant objects distinctly ?

71. Describe the Scheiner test for refractive errors. Illustrate clearly on medium sized diagrams the pencils of light which reach the retina of a myopic eye when a Scheiner disc, holding two pinholes each 1 mm. diameter with inner edges 1 mm. apart, is placed centrally before (and close to it) the eye whose pupil diameter is 5 mm. A spot source at infinity is observed.

Show in addition on separate diagrams the effect of (*a*) 1 mm. transverse displacement ; (*b*) 2 mm. transverse displacement from the central position.

What effects would you thus expect to see ? (S.M.C.)

72. Compare the size of the retinal image of a distant object formed by a static emmetropic eye (static power +60 D) with that formed by the corresponding aphakic eye when it is corrected with a contact glass. The corneal radius is 7·8 mm. ; position of cornea is $1\frac{2}{3}$ mm. in front of principal plane of normal eye ; refractive index of humours, $\frac{4}{3}$.

73. If the ocular refraction of the eye is represented by K and its spectacle refraction by F_1, the dioptric power of the eye by F_e and its refractive index by n', show that

$$\text{axial error } F_e'\text{M}' = \frac{n'K}{F_e(F_e + K)} \text{ metres}$$
$$= \frac{n'F_1}{F_e F}$$

F being the power of the combination of correcting lens (F_1) and eye (F_e).

REFRACTION OF THE EYE

CHAPTER IV

AMETROPIA. ASTIGMATISM.

4.1. Image Formation in Regular Astigmatism.

WE have now to deal with that class of eyes in which point images are not formed. Sometimes this is due to irregularities of one kind or another producing a poor and quite asymmetrical image; to a small extent this is true of all eyes because of their optical imperfections,* but in

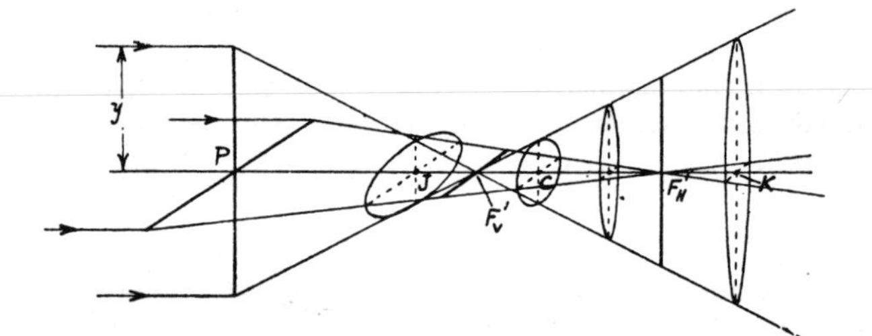

FIG. 4.1—ASTIGMATIC PENCIL: SYSTEM WITH CIRCULAR APERTURE AT P.

some eyes such irregular image formation is present to a marked extent; we will call this condition IRREGULAR ASTIGMATISM and postpone its consideration until later.

Apart altogether from these, however, there are eyes in which the refracted pencil within the eye due to light from each point, including the axial point, of the objects is *regularly* astigmatic, forming two approximate focal lines perpendicular to one another, in the same fashion as those produced by an astigmatic (sphero-cyl. or toric) lens. It is this condition of REGULAR ASTIGMATISM that we are about to consider. It is a condition of refractive ametropia. It is due to one of the refracting surfaces of the cornea or crystalline lens being toroidal instead of spherical; or to tilt of the one element with respect to the other

Wherever the seat of the regular astigmatism may be, the result is a sphero-cylindrical effect such as would be

---

* § 11.1.

caused by the surface of our reduced eye being toroidal. We shall continue to use this concept of the simple reduced eye, still $1\frac{2}{3}$ mm. back from the cornea, only now (in the astigmatic eye) it has a toric surface. The form of the refracted pencil it produces is illustrated in Fig. 4.1; which applies to any $+/+$ astigmatic system, such as the astigmatic eye, in which the principal meridians are respectively horizontal and vertical and the aperture or pupil circular. The aperture is, of course, greatly magnified in the diagram. The pencil of light degenerates to a focal line at F'_V parallel to the weaker meridian of the system, passes through the confusion disc at C on its way to the second focal line at F'_H, parallel to the stronger meridian. Elsewhere the pencil is elliptical in section, the major axis of the ellipse changing from parallelism to the first focal line to parallelism to the second focal line as the pencil passes through the disc of least confusion.

The student is familiar* with the determination, graphically or by calculation, of the positions of the focal lines and confusion disc, which depend upon the principal meridian powers of the system; and of their sizes, which depend also upon the diameter of the pupil aperture.

Using the symbols explained in §2.1 and putting F_1 and F_2 for the powers of the stronger and weaker meridians respectively, L'_c the vergence to the confusion disc, $2y$ for pupil diameter, we have corresponding to an object point at the dioptral distance L from the system:

$$\text{Length of first focal line} = 2y\left(\frac{L'_1 - L'_2}{L'_1}\right)$$

$$\text{Length of second focal line} = 2y\left(\frac{L'_1 - L'_2}{L'_2}\right)$$

$$L'_c = \tfrac{1}{2}(L'_1 + L'_2)$$

$$\text{Diameter of confusion disc} = 2y\left(\frac{L'_1 - L'_2}{L'_1 + L'_2}\right)$$

Fig. 4.1 shows the formation of the astigmatic pencil corresponding to *one* object point lying on the axis. Every point of the object gives rise to a similar astigmatic pencil as indicated, for a near object, in Fig. 4.2. The refracting system is at P, its vertical meridian being more powerful than its horizontal meridian (as in Fig. 4.1). The focal lines, corresponding to the axial object point B, are at B'_V and B'_H. In the plane, perpendicular to the axis, through B'_V lie the horizontal focal lines Q'_V and S'_V corresponding

* *Ophthalmic Lenses*: Ch. XIII.

to the extra-axial object points Q and S; and in the plane, perpendicular to the axis, through B'_H lie the vertical focal lines Q'_H and S'_H.

If the aperture of the lens were square, the confusion disc between B'_V and B'_H corresponding to the axial object point B would approximate to a square. This and the similar square confusion discs corresponding to Q and S are shown in the diagram. In the case of the axial pencil from B four peripheral rays refracted by the lens at 1, 2, 3, and 4 are indicated.

The focal lines and directions of the elliptical or rectangular blurs are parallel to the principal meridians of the astigmatic system; these are indicated as vertical and horizontal in Figs. 4.1 and 4.2 purely for simplicity.

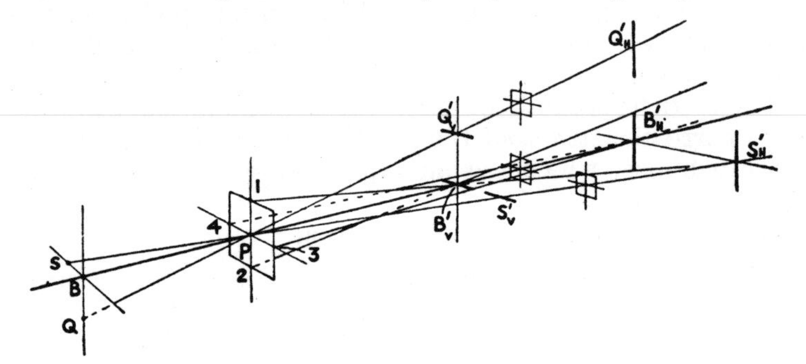

FIG. 4.2—ASTIGMATIC IMAGE FORMATION OF EXTENDED OBJECT.

In the above description of image formation by an astigmatic system, aberrations of the system have been ignored and its aperture assumed small. Actually, each pencil will be more complex in character than here indicated and the focal "lines" of a given direction will not all lie in one plane perpendicular to the axis. But for small obliquities of the incident light and for apertures not too large, the simple astigmatic image formation represented in Figs. 4.1 and 4.2 will apply with sufficient approximation —and these conditions may be taken to apply to the eye.

4.2. The Astigmatic Eye.

We will neglect the irregular astigmatism present to a greater or less degree in most eyes and suppose an eye with regular astigmatism, the principal meridians being vertical and horizontal. We will assume the power to be greater vertically; say 62 D along V. and 60 D along H., giving 2 D of ocular astigmatism. *Every* point of a distant object will be imaged as a short horizontal line 21·51 $\left(=\frac{1000}{62}\times\frac{4}{3}\right)$ mm. from the reduced eye surface at P and a somewhat longer vertical line 22·22 $\left(=\frac{1000}{60}\times\frac{4}{3}\right)$ mm. from P. The disc of least confusion will be 21·85 $\left(=\frac{1000}{61}\times\frac{4}{3}\right)$ mm. from P. We will assume the eye to remain in its unaccommodated state. The appearance of an object to this eye will depend upon the position of the retina. If the axial length be 21·51 mm., in which case the vertical meridian of the eye is emmetropic and the horizontal meridian hypermetropic, the horizontal focal lines are sharp on the retina and a line object such as (a) Fig. 4.3 will appear as shown at (b). The horizontal focal lines corresponding to all the points of the horizontal line in the object overlap one another so that this line appears distinct; all other lines of the object are blurred, the more so as they approach the vertical.

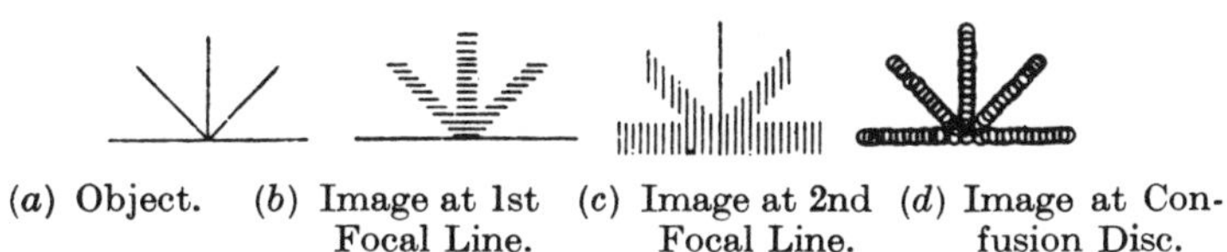

(*a*) Object. (*b*) Image at 1st Focal Line. (*c*) Image at 2nd Focal Line. (*d*) Image at Confusion Disc.

FIG. 4.3—IMAGES FORMED BY ASTIGMATIC SYSTEM.

To an eye of axial length 22·22 mm., emmetropic in the horizontal meridian and myopic in the vertical, the same object will appear as shown at (c), the vertical line being distinct. At 21·85 mm. each point of the object is imaged as a small disc of light, the object appearing as at (d) to an eye of this axial length. All lines of the object appear equally blurred. It is important to observe that lines of the object not lying in one of the principal meridians of the eye are not distinct in any position of the receiving screen or retina. Vision in the astigmatic eye *must* therefore be subnormal. Wherever the retina may be, some lines, if not all, in the object pattern will be blurred.

We must not overlook the fact, nevertheless, that an astigmat may, by experience, recognise familiar objects such as printed letters with surprising facility although possibly at the cost of eyestrain and resultant asthenopia.

By noting which lines are seen by the subject distinctly and which are blurred, we can use an object made up of lines oriented in different directions, such as the well known fan (Fig. 4·5) to determine the directions of the principal meridians of the eye.

It is to be noted that of the two focal lines corresponding to a point object, each line is at the focus of the power meridian perpendicular to it.

The astigmatic eye has two far points, one conjugate to the fovea in one principal meridian and the other conjugate to it in the other meridian. Evidently the correcting lens must be astigmatic (sphero-cyl. or toric), its principal meridians being parallel to those of the eye and its focal lines coinciding with the far points. This will be more clearly understood from the following paragraph.

4.3. Astigmatism and Axial Length of Eye.

The astigmatism is independent of the length of the globe. It may co-exist with a globe of normal length or with one that is longer or shorter than normal. According to the position of the focal lines in relation to the retina, we may have five classes of astigmatic defects. These are shown diagrammatically in Fig. 4.4. We will take the eye of the last paragraph, with 2 D of astigmatism ; the reduced surface of the eye is supposed to be at P. The zero of the dioptric scale in the diagram is the position that would be occupied by the retina of the standard 60 D emmetropic eye. If the retina M′ be to the left of this, we have hyperopia superimposed on the astigmatism due to the optical system ; if to the right, axial myopia.

In case (a) the globe is short by an amount to produce 5 D of hyperopia in the standard eye, the retina being indicated by the vertical dotted line. The horizontal meridian is, then, hyperopic 5 D axial. The vertical meridian is hyperopic 3 D, made up of 5 D axial H and 2 D refractive myopia. The image of a distant object point would consist, in the absence of the retina, of a horizontal line at H and a vertical line at V with a disc of least confusion roughly midway between them. Obviously the patch of light on the retina at M′ will be a comparatively large elliptical blur with its major axis horizontal, and vision will be considerably subnormal so long as the eye does not accommodate.

We will assume the eye to remain unaccommodated throughout.

A + 3 D sphere, supposed placed at P, will impose 3 D of convergence on the refracted pencil in each meridian ; both

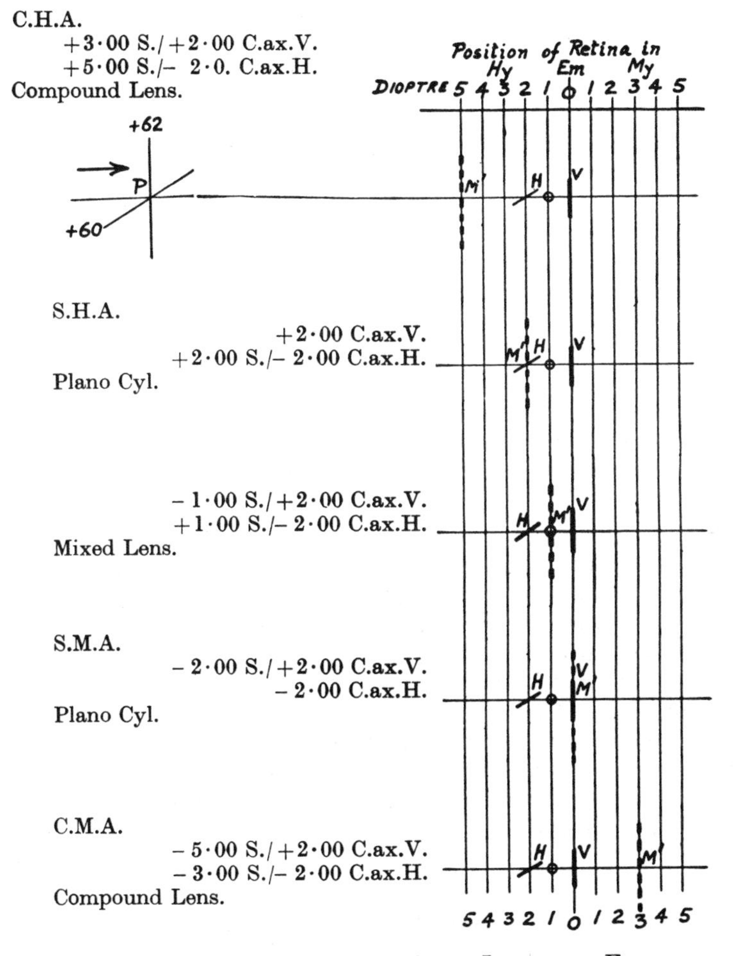

FIG. 4.4—ASTIGMATISM AND AXIAL LENGTH OF EYE.

focal lines will be brought 3 dioptres nearer to the system. The H line will then be on the retina at M′ and the V line two dioptres behind. Horizontal lines of an object will be seen clearly and vertical lines blurred. To bring the V line on the retina without disturbing the H line (in which case the refracted pencil will become stigmatic, the focal lines approaching one another and collapsing to a common *point*), we must clearly add to the + 3 D sphere a + 2 D cyl. with its power meridian horizontal: that is, a + 2 D cyl. *axis* vertical. Thus, when, after supplying the spherical lens, object lines lying in one meridian are seen distinctly and those in the perpendicular meridian blurred, the cylinder for complete correction is added *with its axis parallel to the blurred lines.*

The correcting lens, supposed in contact with the eye at P, is

+ 3·00 D.S./ + 2·00 D.Cyl. ax. V.

This lens corrects the eye's ametropia in both meridians; it so changes the light incident on the eye that the refracted pencil within the latter, corresponding to each point of the object, is brought to a point focus on the fovea at M′.

We might have proceeded somewhat differently. Thus, a + 5 D sphere would place the V line on the retina and the H line 2 dioptres in front of it. The horizontal meridian would be emmetropic and the vertical meridian 2 D myopic. Vertical lines of a test object would be seen clearly and horizontal lines blurred. To correct the vertical meridian and place the horizontal line on M′ we clearly require a − 2 D cyl. *axis* horizontal. The correcting lens is then

+5·00 D.S./− 2·00 D Cyl. ax. H.

It will be seen at once that this is the same lens as the first one, only in the transposed form. Again the cylinder was added *with its axis parallel to the blurred lines.*

The ametropic condition we have just dealt with, the eye being hyperopic in both meridians, is called *compound hyperopic astigmatism* (C.H.A.). The astigmatic correcting lens is a + compound lens.

Fig. 4.4 gives a diagram similar to the one discussed for each of the five classes of astigmatism, namely:

(*a*)	*Compound hyperopic astigmatism,*	C.H.A.
(*b*)	*Simple hyperopic astigmatism,*	S.H.A.
(*c*)	*Mixed astigmatism,*	Mx.A.
(*d*)	*Simple myopic astigmatism,*	S.M.A.
(*e*)	*Compound myopic astigmatism,*	C.M.A.

The student should have no difficulty in deriving the distance correcting lens in each case. All the lenses have

2 D more power in the horizontal meridian than in the vertical.

Although, for simplicity, the principal meridians have been taken as respectively vertical and horizontal, the student must not forget that they may be oblique—but always, in regular astigmatism, perpendicular to each other.

4.4. The Correcting Lens.

In the above, the correcting lens was, for simplicity, assumed to be in contact with the reduced eye, so that the power of the lens in each principal meridian was equal to the ocular refraction or ametropia in that meridian. Actually the lens will be placed some distance in front of the eye and its principal powers will differ from the ocular refractions on that account, as in the case of spherical ametropia (§3.3).

Wherever the lens be placed, its two image space focal points must coincide with the two far points of the astigmatic eye. In case (a) above, the far point for the horizontal meridian is 200 mm. (5 D of H), and for the vertical meridian $333\frac{1}{3}$ mm. (3 D of H), behind the eye. If the lens be placed 14 mm. in front of P, its focal lengths must be 214 mm. and $347\frac{1}{3}$ mm. respectively. Its power is therefore $\frac{1000}{214} =$ $+ 4 \cdot 67$ D in the horizontal and $1000 \div 347\frac{1}{3} = + 2 \cdot 88$ D in the vertical. The cylinder effect of the lens itself is $4 \cdot 67 - 2 \cdot 88 = 1 \cdot 79$ D. Thus an eye with *ocular* refraction expressed by

$$+ 5 \cdot 00 \text{ S.} / - 2 \cdot 00 \text{ C.ax.H.}$$

has *spectacle* refraction, or is corrected by the lens

$$+ 4 \cdot 67 \text{ S.} / - 1 \cdot 79 \text{ C.ax.H.}$$

the lens being placed 14 mm. in front of the eye.

As explained in §3.3, however, the methods of clinical practice aim at determining the prescription of the correcting lens, which is to be placed at the spectacle point. The spectacle refraction is of greater practical importance and is usually understood unless the *ocular* refraction is definitely specified. And unless a problem is on hand in which the proper relationship between the ocular and spectacle refraction is of significance, the two are often treated as equal. This will be done often in the following pages in order to escape the necessity of referring continually to these " effectivity " differences, but the student must keep the correct relationship in mind, to be used whenever circumstances demand.

4.5. Vision in Astigmatism.

As we have seen, vision must be subnormal in the presence of astigmatism—to an extent depending on its degree and, to a smaller extent, on its orientation. A person with oblique astigmatism, the principal meridians of his eye lying along 30° and 120° or 70° and 160°, etc., will not see so well as a person with an equal degree of astigmatism but whose principal meridians are vertical and horizontal. This is so since the main distinguishing features of most objects that we encounter in everyday life are vertical and horizontal, especially vertical.

A person whose astigmatism is associated with hyperopia can improve his vision by the exercise of accommodation; since he thereby brings the focal lines of the refracted pencil into proximity with the retina, and reduces the blurring. Which part of the pencil he places on his retina will vary according to the configuration of the particular object he is scrutinising and the directions of his principal meridians relative thereto. Most natural objects are seen to best advantage when their vertical parts are the best defined. This applies also to printed matter, as the student can verify for himself. If the vertical strokes only of a few printed words are written down, the legibility will be higher than if only the horizontal strokes of the letters are written down.

It is reasonable to suppose that either the confusion disc or one or other of the focal lines will be placed on the retina usually, with a preference for the vertical focal line, or the line most nearly vertical in an eye with oblique meridians, unless the meridian responsible for this line is appreciably more ametropic than its fellow meridian.

Individuals with small amounts of uncorrected spherical error and astigmatism will obtain vision sufficiently good to prompt continuous efforts of accommodation in the attempt to see detail more closely and will consequently be more liable to asthenopia than individuals with large errors who cannot obtain reasonably good vision by such muscular effort, and who do not therefore attempt it.

The above remarks do not apply, or apply with little force, when the astigmatism is associated with myopia;

for in that case the focal lines are already within the retina with the eye in its relaxed condition and accommodation would remove them further away and make vision worse. There is consequently no incentive to accommodate and the eye will tend to remain relaxed.

Probably the chief characteristic of astigmatism as an ametropic defect is its lack of symmetry about the eye's visual axis resulting, as we see, in the vision of the eye being best for those lines of a test object that lie parallel to the eye's principal meridians. This leads at once to the service that can be rendered by test objects of the kind illustrated in Fig. 4.5. The upper part is usually referred to as the FAN and the double set of parallel lines below as the BLOCK; this latter is rotatable around the centre.

Suppose a person with ocular refraction – 0·50 S./ – 1·00 C. ax. 60° were to look at such a " line chart " set up at 6 metres and adequately illuminated. The condition is C.M.A. with principal meridians at 60° and 150°; the 150° meridian is 1 D more myopic than the 60° meridian; the focal line lying along 150° (due to the 60° meridian of the eye's optical system) is nearer to the retina than the 60° focal line. The subject consequently sees the lines of the fan lying along 30° and thereabouts much more distinctly than the lines lying along 120° and thereabouts—*note that the* 30° *line of the fan* (*assuming a direct chart at* 6 *metres*) *is parallel to the* 150° *meridian on the subject's face and the* 120° *line of the fan to the subject's* 60° *meridian.* When specifying the directions of fan and block lines in future we will use the directions of the corresponding meridian of the subject's eye. Thus in our present example the subject sees the " 150° line " more distinctly than the " 60° line."

Thus we obtain immediately the directions of the principal meridians of the eye under test. The lines of the fan will be made all equally distinct by placing before the eye a – 1·00 D.Cyl. axis 60; for this will reduce the myopia of the 150° meridian to that of the 60° meridian, leaving only a *spherical* refractive error of – 0·50 D.

THE FAN CHART.

In trying to detect small amounts of astigmatism in practice, we wish to arrange that the line or lines appearing blurred to the subject shall be made as ill-defined as possible and merge, as it were, into the background and so present the maximum of contrast with the sharper lines perpendicular to them. The difference in visibility between the " best line " and the " worst line " will then be most evident to the subject. The blurredness of the worst line depends upon the size of the focal lines or ellipses by which each

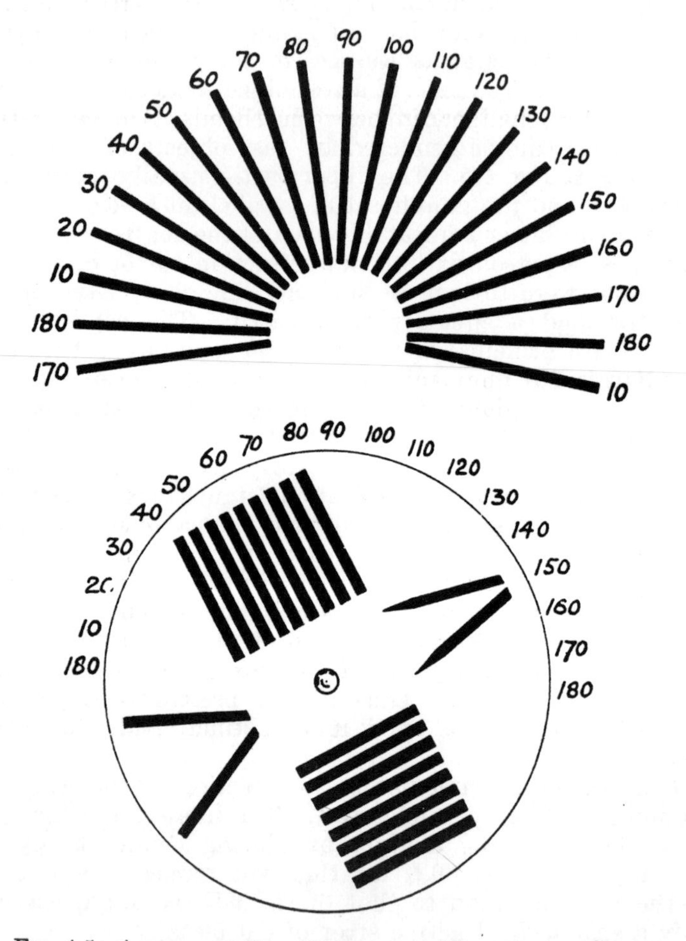

Fig. 4.5—Astigmatic Fan, Blocks and V's. Direct Chart.

point of the line is imaged on the retina, these focal lines or ellipses being perpendicular, or nearly so, to the length of the line. The size of the focal lines or blur ellipses depends on the degree of astigmatism and upon the pupil diameter. The only way to increase this size, in the presence of a given degree of astigmatism, is to increase the pupil diameter ; and this can be done by carrying out the test in low illumination since the pupil then dilates.

Something might also be done to make the worst line disappear rapidly into the background by arranging that this background is not white but grey. With this in mind, astigmatic fan charts have been designed with various thicknesses of the individual lines and with various shades of grey for the spaces between them. An interesting example is the FRIEDENWALD fan chart (1924) which contains narrow (2·3 mm.) black lines with narrow white borders, on a grey background. It is to be remembered, however, that such devices, whilst accentuating the indistinctness of the worst line, also reduce to some extent the distinctness of the best line ; and experiment has shown that for general practice a fan chart consisting of black lines of a thickness about equal to the limbs of the 6/18 test letters (i.e. about 5 to 6 mm.) on a white background, such as the one illustrated in Fig. 4.5, is probably the most satisfactory.

With regard to the assistance provided by low illumination in detecting small degrees of astigmatism, it is to be noted that the dilatation of the pupil uncovers marginal portions of the eye's optical system. Under these conditions the eye may require a correction different from the one needed in ordinary daylight, particularly if the optical imperfections of the marginal portions are irregular in character. The practice of using low illumination for revealing small degrees of astigmatism, or for any other purpose, is therefore to be adopted with some reserve.

If F_1 and F_2 are the dioptric powers of the stronger and weaker meridians of an astigmatic eye and $2y$ its pupil diameter, then corresponding to a distant object point the expressions of §4.1 become

$$\text{length of first focal line} = 2y\left(\frac{F_1 - F_2}{F_1}\right) = 2y\,\frac{Ast}{F_1}$$

$$\text{,, ,, second ,, ,,} = 2y\left(\frac{F_1 - F_2}{F_2}\right) = 2y.\,\frac{Ast}{F_2}$$

$$\text{diameter of confusion disc} = 2y\left(\frac{F_1 - F_2}{F_1 + F_2}\right) = 2y.\,\frac{Ast}{F_1 + F_2}$$

In keeping with the circumstance that spherical refractive errors are mainly axial, we may reasonably presume that the mean of F_1 and F_2 does not depart appreciably from the standard power of 60 D.

We may then employ the *approximate* expressions

$$\text{length of focal lines} = 2y.\frac{\text{Ast}}{60}$$

$$\text{diameter of confusion disc} = 2y.\frac{\text{Ast}}{120}$$

Thus the confusion disc in a given degree of astigmatism has half the diameter of the retinal blur circle in an equal degree of myopia (§3·5). If, therefore, when "putting up" spherical lenses during the preliminary stage of a test for astigmatism (the eye having, say, *A* dioptres of astigmatism) it were possible to arrange with some degree of certainty to put the eye into a condition of mixed astigmatism, with the confusion disc on the retina,* the letter vision recorded at this stage should be about twice as good as that of a myope of *A* dioptres. We should thereby have a rough indication at once of the amount of astigmatism and could proceed expeditiously with the remaining steps of the test. If vision were, for example, $\frac{6}{15}$ or thereabouts we should expect the required correcting cylinder to be roughly 2 D (see Table §3.5).

4.6. Accommodation of the Astigmatic Eye.

It is quite conceivable that the complicated movements of ciliary, lens suspensions and crystalline lens during the act of accommodation may result in a change in the tilt of the lens, or in slight accidental astigmatic deformation of one of its surfaces; in which case more power will be added in one meridian than in another perpendicular thereto and consequently the astigmatism of the whole eye (cornea plus lens) for near work will differ from its astigmatism for distance.† Indeed, in so far as the lens is tilted somewhat with respect to the visual axis, the total astigmatism of the eye *must* change when the power of this tilted component is increased during accommodation, even if the angle of tilt remain unchanged, unless some compensatory astigmatism is introduced in some other way.

However, practical experience shows that the extent of such change of astigmatism during accommodation is in most cases negligibly small; and we shall assume, as is done in clinical practice, that when an astigmatic eye accommodates, positive power is added to its refractive system equally in all meridians, just as if a positive spherical lens had been placed against the eye. Both focal lines are,

---

* e.g. at step 2A in the Table of §4.8.

† The effect here described is not to be confused with the so-called *astigmatic accommodation* by which, it is sometimes claimed, the lens is deformed, even in distance vision, by a *purposeful* irregular contraction of the ciliary muscle in such a manner as to tend to neutralise the corneal astigmatism. This much disputed matter will be ignored here.

in consequence, approached by equal dioptral distances towards P; their dioptral separation is unchanged. The eye of Fig. 4.4 (a) by accommodating 3 dioptres, brings the H focal line on to the retina and the V focal line to a position 2 D behind the retina; the result achieved by the + 3 D sphere. Vision is thereby considerably improved.

The fact that hyperopes can see distant objects distinctly by accommodating and that persons with astigmatism associated with hyperopia can improve vision by so doing, and that they have been in the habit of exerting their accommodation all their lives on this account, introduces considerable difficulty when they are put under test to determine their ametropia and distance correcting lens. In any method, whether subjective or objective, for determining the eye's refractive condition, the result will be too myopic if the measurement is made at a moment when the eye is accommodating. Further: if an objective method be one requiring two separate settings or readings for the two principal meridians in turn, a change in the accommodative state of the eye between the settings will result in an incorrect record of the astigmatism. And in a subjective method where the subject is required to express an opinion as to the relative distinctness of two sets of test lines placed parallel to the principal meridians of his eye, the examiner will receive confusing and contradictory answers if variable accommodation is placing first one focal line and then the other on the retina during the examination. This is particularly the case with young people whose accommodation is active.

So long as the focal lines are behind the retina, or even if one of them is behind, there will be difficulty due to active accommodation when trying to select the appropriate cylinder lens to equalise the clarity of lines on the block or fan; it is desirable to put the eye by some means into a condition of S.M.A. or preferably slight C.M.A. before proceeding to investigate the degree of astigmatism. In so far as this condition can be attained, the incentive to accommodate is largely removed.

Fogging.

A procedure that is sometimes adopted, particularly with young people, to encourage the relaxation of accommodation is to "fog" the eye with sufficient positive spherical power to bring the eye's focal point, or focal lines if astigmatic, well within the retina. Thus in determining the refractive condition in a case of hyperopia, rather than increase the positive spheres gradually when it has been found that positive power will be accepted (§3.8), sufficient plus sphere is immediately added to reduce vision to 6/12 or worse. After allowing the subject to view the letter chart for a few moments and so giving time to encourage relaxation, vision is gradually improved by holding up successive minus spheres before the positive sphere until best vision is attained. A general tendency to accept finally more positive power is found by this method of reducing an originally over-strong positive lens than by the method described in §3.8 of gradually increasing the positive power.

Whether applied in some such manner as this in simple hyperopia or whether, in the case of an astigmatic eye, at the appropriate stage of the test in order to place the focal lines within the retina, this type of procedure is described generally as " fogging " the eye.

4.7. Experiments and Examples.

The student who has access to an organised laboratory will have carried out various experiments concerning vision through cyl. and sphero-cyl. lenses, leading up to the complete testing of astigmatic cases by various subjective procedures. Others should perform for themselves experiments such as the following:

1. Wearing your distance correction, if any, observe a fan chart at 6 metres through a +2·0 D Cyl. axis V., which creates S.M.A. the horizontal meridian being myopic. Vertical lines appear blurred; equality of H and V lines is restored with a − 2·0 D Cyl. ax. V.

2. Wearing your distance correction, if any, make records of your vision on the letter chart as seen through a +3·00 D Cyl. with its axis set successively at 0°, 45° and 90°. Repeat with a − 3·00 D Cyl. Repeat with a pinhole disc in addition to the cylinder.

3. Observe the letter chart through a powerful +/+ sphero-cyl. axis V or H, creating artificial C.M.A. In front of this lens place a stenopaic slit set vertically. Find with what additional spherical lens vision is best. Repeat with the slit placed horizontal. Note vision also when the slit is at other orientations.

The results of these tests should be carefully considered and recorded.

Example. The refractive condition of an eye is − 3·00 D Cyl.ax.H., its axial length is 22·22 mm. and its pupil diameter 6 mm. Find the positions and sizes of the two focal lines when a distant object point is observed.

Answer. Axial length is standard and since H meridian of eye is Em., dioptric power of eye (F_2) in H meridian is 60 D. Since V meridian is myopic 3 D, power of eye (F_1) in V meridian is 63 D.

First focal line, which is H

position : $L'_1 = 63$ D hence $l'_1 = \frac{1000}{63} \times \frac{4}{3} = 21 \cdot 163$ mm. from P.

size $= 2y.\frac{F_1 - F_2}{F_1} = 6 \times \frac{3}{63} = \frac{2}{7} = 0 \cdot 286$ mm.

Second focal line, which is V

position : $L'_2 = 60$ D hence $l'_2 = 22 \cdot 22$ mm. from P ; i.e. on retina.

size $= 2y.\frac{F_1 - F_2}{F_2} = 6 \times \frac{3}{60} = 0 \cdot 30$ mm.

The V focal line on retina extends over about 100 foveal cones and overlaps the boundaries of the foveal pit.

Example. The ocular refraction of an eye is $-1 \cdot 00$ S./$-1 \cdot 50$ C. ax. 30 and its amplitude of accommodation 3 D. A test card containing a small astigmatic fan is moved up towards the eye from a distance. At what positions of the card will certain lines of the fan be seen distinctly and which lines will they be when the eye is (*a*) relaxed, and (*b*) fully accommodated ?

Answer. Far points of eye are at 1 metre (30° meridian) and 40 cm. (120° meridian) in front of eye. Hence when eye is relaxed, the 120° line of fan will be clear at 1 metre and the 30° line at 40 cm. (Note : the 120° line of fan means the line parallel to the 120° meridian of the eye ; and similarly for the other line).

When eye is accommodated, the 120° fan line will be clear at -4 D or 25 cm. from eye and the 30° fan line at $-5 \cdot 50$ D or $18 \cdot 18$ cm. from eye.

Thus range of distinct vision for the 120° line is 75 cm. and for the 30° line, $21 \cdot 82$ cm.

4.8. Determination of Astigmatism with Line Charts.

The subject seeking optical examination will ordinarily have done so because of defective vision or asthenopic discomfort. Assuming that the cause of the trouble is optical and that vision is subnormal, the refractive error responsible for it may be purely spherical. In other cases, which we are now considering, the vision obtained with the best sphere, found as briefly described in the last chapter or by fogging, although the best obtainable with spheres, will not equal the highest vision of which the subject is capable. The cause, under the assumptions made above, will be astigmatism. If the astigmatism be appreciable, the vision recorded with spheres alone will have been definitely below 6/6 ; but in low degrees of astigmatism vision may be as much as 6/6, asthenopia having been a symptom. When the astigmatism is corrected, vision may be 6/5 or even better.

We have now to enquire how the astigmatic error is determined. Postponing objective methods meanwhile, there are several possible subjective methods. Of these, those that are of service clinically involve the use of the trial case and the letter chart—usually, but not always, in conjunction with the line (fan and block) chart. We will deal at present with the type of method in which the letter chart and line chart are both employed in association with the trial case.* The underlying optical principles are quite simple and have already been fully described in this and the preceding chapter, particularly as far as astigmatism is concerned, in §4.3. What may appear to be complications in the practical application of these principles are in the main merely steps to bring about the relaxation of accommodation that we have already discussed. There are many possible variations of detail in this subjective line chart method, and it may require modification or amplification in certain types of cases, but the routine given below in tabular form illustrates the general method applicable to the ordinary case.

We have to determine the nature of the refractive error, the spherical portion of the required distance correction and the cylindrical portion, both in (*a*) direction of axis and (*b*) magnitude; and the lenses are to provide comfortable binocular vision for distant objects. It has been mentioned previously that the lenses determined as the result of this optical procedure may require modification when further tests concerning near vision (Ch. VI) and the binocular functions (Ch. XIII and XIV) are applied; and such factors as the age, temperament and nervous condition of the subject, his symptoms and the kind of work he is called upon to do, all have a bearing on the actual lenses *to be prescribed*.

When carrying out these subjective tests the student should retain a mental picture of the position of the focus or focal lines of the refracted pencil in relation to the subject's retina and of the effect on this position of the various steps of the test. The diagrams inserted in the table are intended to assist in this direction.

The arrow heads or V's on the rotating circular card carrying the blocks of parallel lines (Fig. 4.5) are intended to provide a fine adjustment, as it were, when establishing and checking the direction of the best line. They were introduced by E. E. MADDOX (1912). If, when the arrow

* By which term we include such instrumental adaptations of the ordinary trial case as the *refractor head*, a device whereby the trial lenses, spherical and cylindrical, are conveniently mounted so that they can be rotated, singly or in chosen combinations, into position before the eye.

has been placed at what is believed to be the best line direction (e.g. its direction in Fig. 4.5 is 150°), the two limbs of the arrow are not equally blurred to the subject, a slight rotational adjustment of the chart is called for. If in Fig. 4.5 the upper limb were the clearer, the required rotation would be clockwise. Two arrows are provided, the angles between the limbs being (in the chart of Fig. 4.5) respectively 25° and 50°. It will be necessary to use the narrow arrow when the astigmatism is of high degree; the more widely separated limbs of the other arrow would be too blurred in such a case.

The diagrams in the Table depict an eye with principal meridians vertical and horizontal. This is merely for simplicity; the astigmatism may be at any obliquity in practice.

Measurement of Ametropia.

Subjective—Letter and Line Charts.

	Test Object and Eye Diagram.
1. (*a*) MEASURE AND RECORD UNAIDED VISION, monocular and binocular. If V. normal, may be Em. may be H. or H.A. with active acc. If V. subnormal, may be abs. H., M., H.A., M.A., H. or Em. with spasm of acc.; irregular astig., or may be disease, amblyopia, cloudy media.	Letters
(*b*) Measure and record V. with pinhole. Assuming pinhole reveals optical defect:	
2. DETERMINE NATURE OF ERROR	Letters
A. SPHERICAL ERROR.	
1. Occlude L.E. Add + Sph. to R.F until V. *begins* to blur; or fog and reduce + Sph. to best V. (Diags. 1 and 2). To verify: hold + 0·50 S. which should blur one line and then − 0·50 S. which should *not* improve V.	

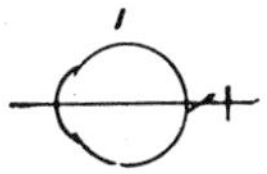

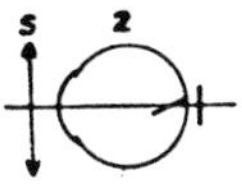

Test Object and Eye Diagram.

2. If any + Sph. blurs, defect is not H. Add − Sph. until V. *ceases* to improve. Power of − Sph. to start with is indicated by record of unaided V. (Diags. 3 and 4).
   Verify as in A1.

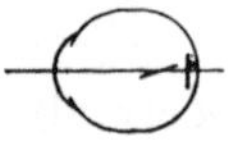

3. Repeat for L.E., with R.E. occluded.

   V. may now be : supernormal—probably no Ast.
   normal—may be weak Ast.
   subnormal—Ast.

   If eye is astigmatic, focal lines will now be in neighbourhood of retina, as shown in diagram No. 2 or No. 4, but subject *may* be accommodating.

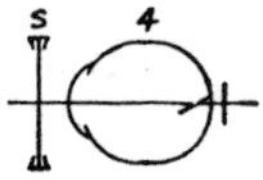

B. ASTIGMATISM—DIRECTION. — Fan

Subject now wearing Sph. found in 2 A.

1. Occlude L.E. Determine clearest line or lines on fan.

   Subject may :

   (*a*) distinguish at once some lines clearer than others.

   (*b*) say all equally clear.

   (*c*) say some clear at one moment and those at right angles at another moment.

   Class (*c*) will probably become class (*a*) on adding +1·0 S. or so to existing sph.

   Direction of best line to be determined as accurately as possible at this stage.

   If Ast. has not been determined and (a) V. is 6/9 or better, error is measured by sph. lens found in 2 A.

   (b) V. is $<$ 6/9, then there is Ast. yet undiscovered or irregular Ast.

   If Ast. has been determined, its direction is now known approximately and its magnitude has to be found.

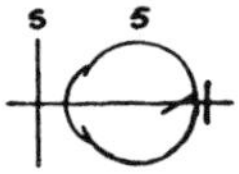

2. Repeat for L.E. with R.E. occluded.

	Test Object and Eye Diagram.
Each eye now has a Sph. lens and is probably in condition of Mx.A., but may be accommodating.	
3. MEASURE ASTIGMATISM (*a*) Occlude L.E. Place block at direction of best lines. Try to improve direction by obtaining equality of limbs of arrow. Use wide arrow if possible; narrow arrow for high Ast. (*b*) Add + Sph. until blurring begins, starting with + 0·50 D or less. Some + Sph. may be accepted.	Block—placed parallel to best line
(*c*) Rotate block through 90° or direct subject to other block and repeat attempt to add + Sph.; this will probably not be accepted. Replace the 2 spheres by one sphere. Eye should now be in condition of SMA or CMA with accommodation relaxed.	Block—through 90°
(*d*) Determine negative cylinder. Return to fan; equalise clarity of lines by adding – cyls. with axis parallel to blurred lines. If V. were high at 2A, start with – 0·25 cyl. Keep amount of – cyl. as low as possible. (*e*) Repeat *a*, *b*, *c* and *d* for L.E. with R.E. occluded.	Fan
4. CHECK OR SUPPLEMENTARY. Turn to letters. V. should now be nearly normal except in high myopia. With subject looking at smallest line of type readable: (*a*) Rotate cyl. in trial frame through ±5° or so to find its position for most acute V. Direction should agree substantially with that found in 2 B, or at 90° thereto.	Letters

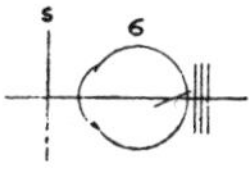

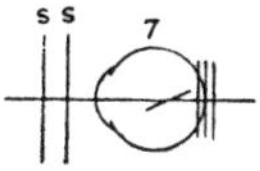

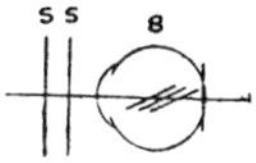

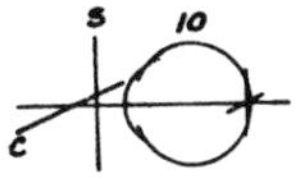

	Test Object and Eye Diagram.
(*b*) Try + 0·50 Sph. which should blur one line. If more can be accepted, repeat test from 2 A.	
(*c*) Turn to block, with one set of lines parallel to cyl. axis. + 0·50 sph. should blur both sets equally. If those parallel to cyl. axis become clearer than others, too much – cyl. was added at 3 (*d*).	Block
(*d*) Repeat for L.E. with R.E. occluded.	
Each eye has now been *separately* provided with the sph. cyl. lens to produce best vision. It remains to compare the V.A. of the two corrected eyes and to test final V.A. when eyes are used binocularly.	
5. BINOCULAR CHECK.	Letters
(*a*) Subject observes letters binocularly, concentrating on lowest line he can read. Occlude first one eye and then other eye in quick succession. Equalise as required (but see below).	
(*b*) Blur binoc. V. up to 6/7.5 or 6/9 by holding R. and L. + Sphs. before trial frame. Reduce this blur gradually until 6/6 line is read well.	
(*c*) Record final prescription, and V.A. attained with it, monocularly and binocularly.	
This completes the investigation of the subject's refractive condition. It has now to be determined whether he has binocular vision and whether there is any motor imbalance (Ch. XI).	

When the routine outlined above has been completed, the distance correcting lenses in situ in the trial frame, and the best vision attained by the subject with their aid (V.A.), are recorded. The direction of the cylinder axes may be read off on the trial frame which is graduated for the purpose in *standard notation;* one type of trial frame is illustrated in Fig. 4.6. The fan and a circle around the circumference of the rotatable card carrying the blocks and arrows are marked in degrees to correspond. In the case of a direct chart to be viewed directly at the 6 metres testing distance, the graduations will proceed from 0° on the left, through 90° to 180° in a clockwise direction, as already explained. The markings will be counter-clockwise in the case of a reversed chart to be viewed by reflection in a plane mirror.

It is important for the beginner to determine carefully the direction of the best line at steps 2 B and 3 (a). For if the negative cylinders are placed before the eye at step 3 (d) at an orientation not agreeing with the principal meridians of the subject's eye, the negative cylinder in the trial frame and the positive cylinder in the eye itself produce a resultant cylinder effect the axis direction of which lies

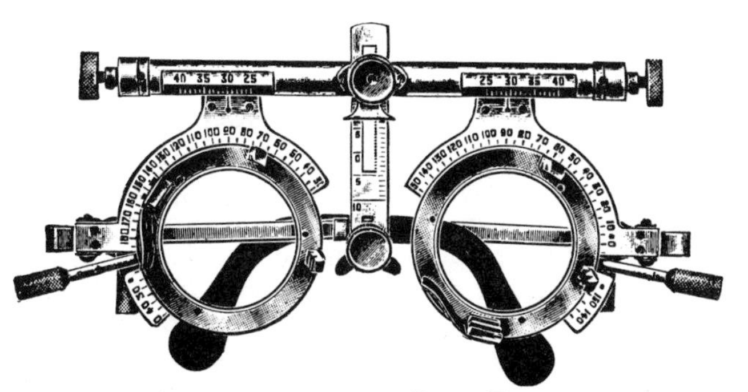

FIG. 4.6—A TYPICAL TRIAL FRAME.

outside the axes directions of the components and the best line is shifted to a new direction altogether; this will lead to confusing answers by the subject subsequently. It is sometimes not an easy matter to decide upon the best line direction at step 2 B—3 (a), especially in cases where a certain amount of irregular astigmatism is superimposed upon the regular astigmatism.

With regard to the binocular check—step 5 (a)—the V.A. may be found unequal in the two eyes. If one is 6/6 and the other, say 6/4·5, a + 0·25 D might be tried before the latter to obtain equalisation; if the + 0·25 D blurs to a state worse than 6/6, it will not be incorporated in the correction

The inequality of vision, if any, may be due to slight amblyopia or high astigmatism in one eye, in which case equalisation probably cannot be attained. In such a case the vision of the better eye will be allowed to remain at its best. In step 5 (b) an effort should be made to have more positive spherical power accepted by both eyes. It may be that + 0·50 D may be accepted. On the other hand, this step might result in a slight final addition of negative power to obtain binocular vision of 6/6.

It would be an advantage if this comparison and balancing of the vision in the two eyes could be carried out while the subject is observing the test letters with both eyes simultaneously. This can be done by presenting an indirect chart through the agency of two plane mirrors, one for each eye. One plane mirror with a central vertical strip blocked out would serve.* Alternatively, three charts placed side by side at the usual testing distance can be viewed by the subject through an aperture placed a metre or two in front of him ; the width of the aperture being such that the left chart can be seen only by the right eye, the right chart only by the left eye and the central chart by both eyes.

4.9 The Cross Cylinder.

This simple instrument may be used to carry out the check adjustments of step 4 in the above line chart method, or it may be employed to determine completely the astigmatism from step 2, no fan or block being required ; only the letter chart (or a Landolt ring chart) is needed.

The cross cylinder is a lens having the effect of two cylindrical lenses, of equal strength but opposite in sign, with their axes at right angles to each other. It is mounted in a ring of trial lens diameter and attached to the ring is a slender handle about four inches long, bisecting the angle between the principal meridians of the lens (Fig. 4.7). If the handle be rolled or " twirled " through 180° between thumb and finger, keeping its direction constant, the lens rotates around the axis XX ; the axis of the plus cylinder and the axis of the minus cylinder change places. The power in the vertical meridian—Fig. 4.7 (A)—changes from minus to plus and in the horizontal meridian from plus to minus.

Cross cylinders may be had in various powers : + 0·50 D with – 0·50 D or + 0·25 D with – 0·25 D, etc. The latter strength is the most useful for subjects with normal acuity.

* These ideas have been incorporated in the Turville Infinity Balance Test.

The axis of the minus cylinder should be clearly marked with two white spots.

Suppose a subject who is emmetropic or truly corrected observes monocularly a distant spot of light which is imaged clearly on his retina. If the + 0·25/ − 0·25 cross cylinder is held before the eye in the position indicated in Fig. 4·7 (A), the point image is changed to two focal lines ; the vertical line is formed a little way in front of the retina and, in the absence of the retina, the horizontal line would be formed at an approximately equal distance behind the retina. On the retina itself the previous point image is replaced by a small circular blur—the disc of least confusion —and vision is worse than before. If now the cross cylinder is twirled through 180°, the power in the vertical meridian becomes +0·25 D and in the horizontal − 0·25 D, the focal lines change places and the circular retinal blur remains unchanged.

Thus if a cross cylinder is applied to an eye with no astigmatism, vision is as good in the first position as in the twirled position. In neither position, be it noted, is vision as good as it is without the cross cylinder.

(a) DETERMINATION OF POWER OF CORRECTING CYLINDER.

Suppose now the cross cylinder is applied to an eye with astigmatism such that the lens − 0·50 D Cyl. axis H. is

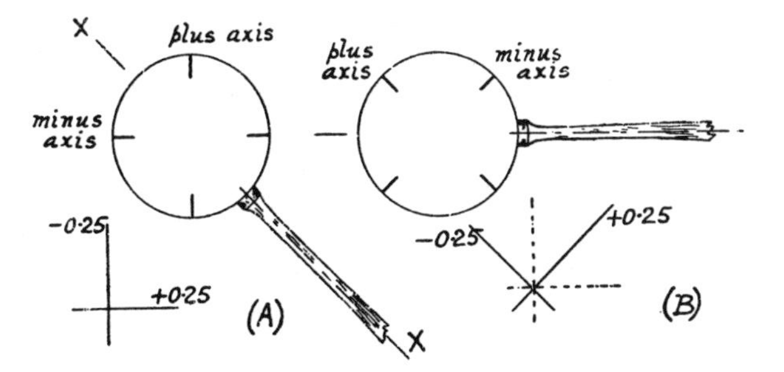

FIG. 4.7—THE CROSS CYLINDER.

needed to correct it, the subject having some accommodation in play so that he accommodates to bring the confusion disc on his retina. The optical system of his eye is more powerful, by + 0·50 D, in the vertical meridian than in the horizontal ; the horizontal focal line is in front of, and the vertical focal line position behind, his retina, by 0·25 D in each case. Application of the $+0{\cdot}25/-0{\cdot}25$ cross cylinder in the first position, Fig. 4·7 (A), will neutralise the eye's astigmatism. The focal lines will approach one another and collapse to a point on the retina. Vision will be improved. When rotated through 180° into the second position, the cross cylinder *accentuates* the eye's astigmatism; the horizontal focal line is moved further forward, away from the retina, and the vertical line further backward, each by 0·25 D, and the confusion disc on the retina is doubled in size. Vision is made worse.

If, during the test, the subject is observing the letter chart, a question to him elicits the reply that vision was better in the first position. In this position the two white spots marking the axis of the minus cylinder would be noted by the examiner as being horizontal. If a negative cylinder with axis horizontal, and of a power indicated by the line of letters the subject is reading, is inserted and the test is repeated, the subject will give the same reply as before but with more hesitation, if the power of the cylinder is insufficient. If the correct strength of cylinder has been exceeded, the second position will be better than the first and the cylinder is reduced until both positions of the cross cylinder give equal vision; or a cylinder of power midway between those on either side of the change-over is prescribed.

(b) DETERMINATION OF DIRECTION OF CORRECTING CYLINDER.

In the test just described, the *direction* of the astigmatism was supposed to be known. If, as will often be the case, we do not know this direction, it can be found by the cross cylinder. It is applied as before with the handle along 135° and then twirled. If astigmatism is present in the eye and the meridians happen to be vertical and horizontal, its presence is at once revealed. Suppose, however, that the meridians of the ocular astigmatism are, say, 30° and 120°. Even so, the rotation of the cross cylinder, with its handle at 135° as in Fig. 4.7 (A) will reveal the astigmatism. Since the 30° meridian does not lie midway between the horizontal and vertical meridians of the cross cylinder, the astigmatic element introduced into the 30° meridian in one position of the cross cylinder will not be the same as that introduced in the other position. The subject's vision will consequently be improved in one position and made worse in the other.

If the first position (minus axis horizontal) is superior, the examiner knows that a minus cylinder is required with its axis either horizontal, or nearer to the horizontal than to the vertical. He inserts in the trial frame a minus cylinder axis H. To check this direction he applies the cross cylinder with the handle not at 135° as heretofore, but horizontal as in Fig. 4.7 (B). The principal meridians of the cross cylinder are now at 45° (minus axis) and 135° (plus axis). The subject observing his best line on the letter chart, the cross cylinder is twirled. In the case under consideration—requiring a minus cylinder axis 30°—the first position will be superior to the second, since in the first position the minus axis of the cross cylinder is nearer to the true axis, 30°. The cylinder in the trial frame is accordingly rotated to move its axis from horizontal towards 45°, say by 20°. With the cross cylinder handle now held at 20° the process is repeated and further adjustment of direction of the trial frame cylinder made until its axis lies along such a direction that the two positions of the cross cylinder produce equal vision; in the case under consideration this direction is 30°.

Having thus located the direction of the required correcting cylinder, its power is finally adjusted by using the cross-cylinder in the manner explained in section (a).

If the meridians of ocular astigmatism happened to lie along 45° and 135°, then the application of the cross cylinder with handle along 135°, Fig. 4.7 (A), would not reveal it. In any such case where the first test reveals no astigmatism, the handle of the cross cylinder is moved round to the horizontal and the test repeated. If ocular astigmatism is present, it will then be revealed and the test can proceed.

In routine testing with the cross cylinder, the spherical portion of the correction is first found approximately—step 2A of Table in §4.8—and, say, – 0·50 D is added to this to allow the subject a little accommodation to place the disc of least confusion on the retina.* The cross-cylinder is then applied to determine first the direction, at least approximately, and then the power of the correcting minus cylinder, as explained above, the letter chart being used

---

* It should be stated that some practitioners claim that it is not necessary in practice to take this step of ensuring some accommodation to the subject.

throughout. A final adjustment of direction will then usually be required. The spherical portion of the correction is then adjusted, with the aid of the letter chart.

The twirling of the cross cylinder should be executed crisply. After the twirl it can be held close to the trial frame so that its direction is easily read off.

The cross cylinder in its present simple form was first suggested in 1894 by the American ophthalmologist Edward JACKSON.

4.10. Other Tests for Astigmatism.

TESTS ON LUMINOUS POINTS.

To an astigmatic eye a small spot of light at 6 metres will appear elongated into a thin streak or elliptical blur in the direction of one of its principal meridians, except in the special case when the disc of least confusion falls on the retina, which may occur in mixed astigmatism or in hyperopic astigmatism if the eye accommodates the appropriate amount. The appearance will be complicated somewhat by the optical imperfections of the eye's optical system. A positive spherical lens placed before the eye will reduce the condition to compound myopic astigmatism ; both focal lines will then lie in front of the retina and the spot will appear as an elliptical blur, an ellipse such as K, Fig. 4.1, lying on the retina. The long axis of this ellipse is parallel to the more myopic meridian of the eye. By reducing the fogging sphere until the spot appears as a streak, first in one direction and later in the perpendicular direction, it is theoretically possible to determine the direction of the astigmatism and its amount.

Earlier experimenters such as AIRY and DONDERS used this kind of method in investigating astigmatism ; TSCHERNING gives an interesting account of the method in his *Physiologic Optics* and a discussion of it is included by GULLSTRAND in the third edition of HELMHOLTZ'S *Physiological Optics*. Under laboratory conditions this method permits of an exhaustive enquiry into the nature of the astigmatic refracted pencil within the eye and yields valuable information. It does not lend itself, however, to clinical measurement except perhaps when modified in a manner the principle of which is illustrated in Fig. 4.8. In this arrangement the test object consists of nine small holes, preferably square in shape, cut in a blackened metal disc, the holes being equally and diffusely illuminated. To an astigmatic eye, which should be fogged to a condition of slight C.M.A., the spots appear drawn out into streaks parallel to the more myopic meridian of the eye. The direction of the streaks indicates this meridian and the metal plate is rotated around its centre until each set of three streaks appear to lie along a straight line, as in (A) or (B) Fig. 4.8. If the astigmatism is sufficiently marked the streaks will be long enough to form a continuous line. Having thus determined the direction of the astigmatism, the streaks are reduced to square spots by applying a

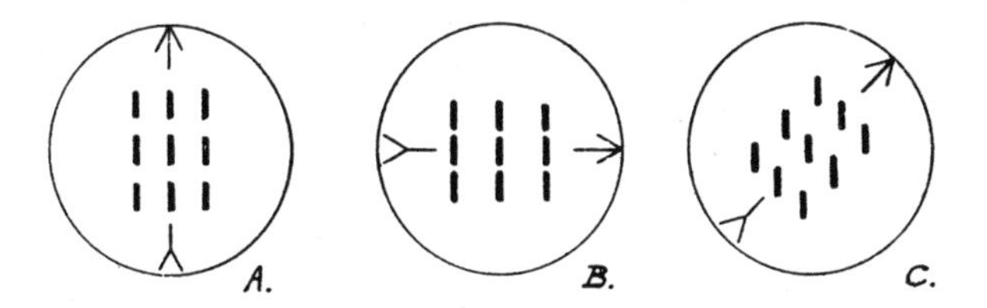

FIG. 4.8—ASTIGMATIC TEST WITH POINT SOURCES (STIGMATOMETER).

negative cylinder with axis parallel to the length of the streaks. The particular arrangement of spots illustrated was suggested by FERREE and RAND (1925), but it might be more convenient clinically to use a simple cross with the square apertures arranged along two diameters at right angles to one another, as had been suggested earlier.

CHROMATIC TESTS.

One or two subjective tests have been proposed based upon the principle of the cobalt glass optometer outlined in §3.10 and depending upon the chromatic aberration of the eye. An interesting example of these was the DUOCHROME TEST introduced by Clifford BROWN in 1927. In this method, test objects in the form of printed letters and sets of parallel lines are presented to the eye in two colours, red and green, chosen so that the dominant wavelengths lie equidistant on either side of the wavelength to which the eye is most sensitive. This wavelength of maximum visibility is 555 mμ (greenish yellow) in photopic vision and 510 mμ in scotopic vision. Hence if the test is to be carried out in a general illumination such that the eye is light adapted, colours of dominant wave length about 500 mμ (green) and 610 mμ (red) would satisfy the requirements.

Suppose a rotatable disc carrying two parallel slits, one illuminated with green light and the other with red light, is presented to the eye. If the eye is emmetropic or properly corrected, the green image will be as far (about 0·42 D) in front of the retina as the red image is behind; both images will appear slightly and *equally* blurred. It is, of course, assumed that the subject's colour vision admits of both red and green being seen. The appearance will remain unchanged as the disc is rotated through 90°. To an eye with simple myopia, or to a hypermetrope suitably fogged, the red line will appear more distinct than the green (Fig. 3.6), the appearance again remaining constant on rotation of the object. A negative sphere of such power as to render the red and green equally blurred corrects the myopia. Green will appear clearer than red to a hypermetrope unless accommodation is active, in which case red and green may be clearer alternately. There is probably not the same urge to accommodate in a test of this kind, however, in which simultaneous comparisons between two colours are being made, as there is in the usual tests. If green is seen clearly the brain will probably be content, rather than make an effort to see red clearly at the expense of green. Nevertheless it would be unsafe to assume that accommodation is passive in these tests.

An eye with astigmatism, directed to observe the green line, will see this line more distinctly in one direction than in any other direction. The same remark applies to the red line, the clearest direction being the same in the two cases. If the eye is myopic in both principal meridians, red will be clearer than green in all directions of the disc. The negative sphere required to produce red and green equality when the lines are in the originally clearest direction measures the myopia of the meridian of the eye perpendicular thereto. The negative sphere to correct the other meridian will be stronger by the amount of the astigmatism. In the case of an eye with C.H.A., which therefore sees green the more clearly, each meridian in turn can similarly be corrected with positive spheres. An eye in a condition of mixed astigmatism will see the green line clearer than the red when the lines are parallel to the myopic meridian of the eye; and red clearer than green when the lines are rotated through 90°.

These observations should assist in understanding the use of the duochrome apparatus which is illustrated in Fig. 4.9. The portions of the letter chart and line blocks shown shaded are red and the unshaded green, the two colours

FIG. 4.9—THE DUOCHROME APPARATUS.*

being of equal intensity. The letters are of the 6/12, 6/9, and 6/6 sizes. The large block within the graduated circle is rotatable. The method of use in ordinary cases is briefly as follows :

(*a*) With the letters illuminated, if the subject reads green letters better than red, the condition is hypermetropic ; if red better than green, myopic. Spherical lenses are added to equalise the letters. If the eye has astigmatism, the condition will now approximate to mixed astigmatism.

(*b*) Leaving the above sphere in position and with the fixed radial blocks illuminated, find which block contains the clearest green lines. The meridian of the eye parallel to this is myopic. The clearest red will be at right angles to this, giving the hypermetropic meridian of the eye.

(*c*) Illuminate the revolving block, rotate it into the direction in which say, the clearest red line was seen and

* In later models of the instrument the astigmatic fan portion is usually omitted.

by slight rotations to one side and the other, locate the meridian more accurately. In this position red is clearer than green and a negative sphere to equalise reduces the perpendicular meridian of the eye to emmetropia. Turn the block through 90° and correct the other meridian.

(*d*) Place the correction thus found, in the form of a sphere and cylinder, in the trial frame ; check on the letters making slight rotations of the cylinder if required.

It will be observed that only spherical lenses are used during the progress of the test, which is a definite practical advantage of the method. Although, as mentioned above, accommodation is probably not so active as usual in tests of this kind, it might be advisable to fog the eye to the C.M.A. condition after step (*a*) above.

A more recent (1952) application of the two-colour principle of testing has been introduced by H. FREEMAN. His apparatus utilises the Landolt ring and a cross-cylinder technique of binocular balance (§4·8) is employed.

4.11. Further Remarks on Astigmatism.

Isaac NEWTON in 1727 made mention of this condition but the term " astigmatism " describing the condition was introduced by WHEWELL (*ca.* 1840–50).* Thomas YOUNG (1801) discovered astigmatism in his own eye in 1793. It appears that he had 1·7 D of astigmatism, more myopic in or near the horizontal, his crystalline lens being mainly responsible. The astronomer, George B. AIRY, who suffered from high compound myopic astigmatism, appears to have been the first to correct the defect with a sphero-cyl. lens, which was made to his instructions by a craftsman named FULLER, of Ipswich (1825).

The introduction of the ophthalmometer† by HELMHOLTZ in 1854 and the valuable work by DONDERS (*ca.* 1864) who was responsible for the introduction of cylindrical lenses into the trial case,‡ drew general attention to the prevalence of astigmatism in the eye. Nowadays, with careful testing, astigmatism is found in probably 80 to 90 per cent of subjects presenting themselves for examination.

---

* It appears from a note in MACKENZIE'S *Diseases of the Eye* that WHEWELL suggested the term to AIRY during this period.

† Ch. IX.

‡ Sets of cylindrical trial lenses were available in England in 1865, manufactured by Messrs. Murray & Heath, Piccadilly.

The astigmatism of the eye may be due to non-sphericity of the corneal or lens surfaces or to a tilt of the cornea or lens relative to the visual axis; or to combinations of these. Usually the greatest contributory cause is the non-sphericity of the anterior surface of the cornea. This is not surprising, for a given difference of curvature between two meridians will produce more effect in this surface than in any other as it separates two media of refractive indices 1 and 1·376, whereas the posterior corneal surface and the lens surfaces are bounded by media more nearly equal in index.* Since there is a general physiological tendency, ascribed to various causes, for the cornea to be steeper in or round about the vertical meridian than the horizontal, ocular astigmatism in which the vertical or nearly vertical meridian has effectively more dioptric power than the horizontal has been called astigmatism "with the rule". Figs. 4.1, 4.2, and 4.4 represent with the rule astigmatism. The opposite case where the vertical meridian has effectively less dioptric power, and is consequently less myopic or more hypermetropic, than the horizontal was described as "against the rule". Thomas YOUNG'S astigmatism was of this type.

These definitions were introduced at a time when the astigmatism was believed to be due in all cases predominantly, and by some people entirely, to the anterior surface of the cornea. There is little doubt, however, that this is not the case and these terms are misleading. They have little meaning in any case when the principal meridians are oblique.

There is ample evidence that the astigmatic error of a given eye is liable to change, in degree or in direction or both, at any period of life, such changes affecting that part of the total astigmatism of the eye that is contributed by the crystalline lens and rarely the corneal astigmatism; the resiliency of the cornea maintains its shape. These changes may be associated with the growth of the crystalline lens, which continues well on into adult life. There is a general tendency for what has been called astigmatism with the rule to change to astigmatism against the rule in later life; that is, the meridian of greatest power lies in or near the vertical in young people and changes to a direction round about the horizontal in later life.

---

* See §10.4 for the constants of the eye.

4.12. Irregular Astigmatism (or Irregular Refraction).

Even in regularly astigmatic eyes with good visual acuity (when corrected) the refracted pencil within the eye will not be of the geometrically clear-cut pattern depicted in Figs. 4.1 and 4.2 because of the aberrations inherent in all eyes and the finite size of the pupil. But many such eyes are sufficiently acute to appreciate the effect of cylindrical lenses as weak as 0·12 D in spite of any aberrations present and so, as already stated, the elementary principles of the preceding paragraphs hold generally for eyes with regular astigmatism.

In some eyes, however, the irregular defects* (caused by local opacities, scars and the crystalline lens structure, etc.) are appreciable and cause marked, and perhaps sudden, variations of ametropia from one part of the pupil to another. Such irregularities will account for a relatively low acuity in eyes having no appreciable refractive error. They will also interfere, in some subjects, with the successful prosecution of the subjective method of examination described in §4.8 and render it difficult for the subject to give precise answers to the examiner's questions. Remembering these facts may sometimes prevent the fatiguing of a subject by lengthy attempts to discover a regular astigmatism that does not exist. These defects, as well as the symmetrical spherical and chromatic aberrations of the eye, will modify the character of the refracted pencils within the eye when the pupil is dilated, in low illumination or otherwise, and may introduce additional astigmatism.

Some individuals possess these irregularities to such an extent that vision is very poor and ordinary methods of examination useless. Evidently the usual spherical and sphero-cylindrical lenses cannot by themselves correct such defects but certain steps can sometimes be taken to assist these people. One general method of examination consists in cutting off, and examining the vision in, isolated local areas of the pupil in turn. A start might be made with a stenopaic slit, rotating it around in the trial frame to the position where letter vision is at its best and improving this vision as far as possible with spherical lenses; this may then be repeated with the slit in the perpendicular position. JACKSON advocates the use of the cross cylinder for this purpose. In some cases the lens representing these two

---

* See §11.5.

powers combined will afford reasonable assistance to the subject.

In others it will be necessary to explore further with a pinhole or with a black spot on a microscope slide, moving the hole or spot about to expose or obliterate different parts of the pupil in succession. Sometimes a correction, rendered opaque by frosting or otherwise except at the small area of good vision, may be of service. Such glasses would clearly need to be carefully fitted and their centring maintained as accurately as possible during wear. Other subjects may at least be assisted to read by the provision of stenopaic spectacles consisting of a blank metal disc with a small hole; or the disc may be held in the subject's hand.

Information concerning irregularities of refraction can sometimes be obtained by examining some vessel on the fundus with an ophthalmoscope through different parts of the pupil in turn.

A special but somewhat rare case of irregularity is *conical cornea* or *keratoconus*, in which the cornea is bulged forward into an approximately hyperboloid form. Such cases exhibit distorted reflex images when examined with the Placido disc, which will be referred to later.* A similar condition of the crystalline lens is known as *lenticonus*. When the irregularity is situated on the anterior surface of the cornea, its effect can be practically neutralised by such devices as contact glasses.

Cases of irregular astigmatism are at best very troublesome to investigate, but the time spent may result in providing some relief to a subject who otherwise would be seriously handicapped.

Subnormal vision that is not sufficiently improved by spherical or astigmatic lenses is frequently dismissed as due to amblyopia without further enquiry, but in many cases irregular astigmatism is responsible. The pinhole disc used at the commencement of a test will assist in clearing up the point since reasonably sharp vision may be discovered over a restricted area of the pupil.

4.13. Remarks on the Clinical Testing of Ametropia.

The ultimate aim of all methods of determining the ametropia of the eyes is to prescribe a distance correction and, when required, a correction for near work, both of which will satisfy the subject's requirements as to clearness of vision and the attainment of unrestricted and comfortable binocular vision. The successful prosecution of a subjective examination requires the co-operation of the subject. His conscious picture or perceptual image of the test object is the result of physiological and psychological actions as well as the purely physical actions leading up to the formation of the retinal image. The examination is therefore conditioned by the physiological state of the subject and, although it must rest upon a sound optical basis, is nevertheless also a matter of applied psychology. These considerations have to be borne in mind when formulating and carrying out a satisfactory clinical procedure, which should consequently meet certain requirements which may be summarised as follows:

1. By some means or other the subject's accommodation must be under control especially when testing for astigmatism. Adequate explanation of this has already been given.
2. The subject must not be unduly fatigued, the test to be carried out as quickly as possible consistent with accuracy.
3. The above condition requires that the steps of the routine shall follow one another in logical sequence, each step eliciting from the subject an answer that carries with it a clear indication of the next step. This is necessary not only in the interests of speed but also to satisfy the condition that the conduct of the test shall be continuously under the examiner's control.
4. Observations required of the subject shall be simple and unambiguous.

Subjective optometer methods and tests on luminous points have already been criticised. The duochrome application of the chromatic test appears to be satisfactory but sufficient evidence has not yet been accumulated since its introduction upon which to base a considered verdict. We are left with the subjective method based essentially upon the use of the trial case and letter chart.

It is to be remembered that we are here discussing subjective methods only. Many practitioners rely upon the objective method of retinoscopy* for determining the

---

* Ch. VIII.

refractive condition, using the letter chart, and maybe the cross cylinder to a greater or less extent, only as a supplementary check to their retinoscopy finding. The objective type of optometer* will probably take its place alongside retinoscopy now that the accuracy of setting has been improved in this type of instrument.

Returning to the subjective method—the line chart method explained in §4.8 is widely employed. There are some cases, however, in the testing of which the line chart is somewhat troublesome. Subjects who have some irregular astigmatism superimposed on the regular astigmatism, or who are hypercritical in comparing the relative blacknesses of the fan lines, may find it difficult to give definite and unambiguous answers to the examiner's questions. Moreover, the fan lines, and more particularly the parallel lines of the block, frequently appear red and green in the presence of small amounts of astigmatism, a phenomenon due to the chromatic aberration of the eye ; they also appear " wavy " to some subjects—additional factors rendering the use of the line chart somewhat troublesome. In cases such as these, if astigmatism has been suspected due to the subnormal vision obtained after the application of spherical lenses, the test must be continued with the aid of the letter chart only. A small cylinder, say 0·75 D, may be " put up " and rotated in the trial frame until a position is found in which letter vision is at its best. Changes in the power of the cylinder at this orientation can then be made until vision has been raised to its maximum value. The cross cylinder method may, of course, be used to great advantage in these cases.

It is of some importance to realise that in all subjective methods the subject is called upon to compare the appearance of an object, such as a test letter, as he sees it at one moment with his *memory* of its appearance a moment previously, through a different lens or the same lens differently orientated. When fine differences of lens power or cylinder axis direction are being sought for, this comparison may not be easy of accomplishment. The time interval between the two appearances should be as short as possible, lens changes being made crisply and quickly. Such devices as the cross cylinder and the refractor head assist towards quick manipulation.

---

* §§7.14 and 7.15.

With regard to the control of accommodation, it might have occurred to the student that this would be conveniently accomplished by means of a cycloplegic such as atropine, which paralyses the ciliary muscle and completely abolishes accommodation. Such a paralysed eye, however, with its dilated pupil, is not in its normal physiological state and the refractive condition may differ in arbitrary fashion from that obtaining in the ordinary everyday life of the subject.

EXERCISES. CHAPTER IV.

1. A parallel pencil of light from a distant object point is incident along the optical axis of the lens $+5 \cdot 00$ D.S./$-2 \cdot 00$ D.C. ax. V. Find the positions of the two focal lines and of the disc of least confusion. State whether the focal line nearer to the lens is vertical or horizontal. Give a diagram.

2. With the aid of a diagram explain the formation of the astigmatic pencil when light is refracted by a lens containing a cylindrical element.

   The lens $+2 \cdot 50$ S./$-1 \cdot 00$ Cyl. is made up in toric form on base -6 D and is set up with the base curve vertical. A small source of light is placed on its axis $1\frac{1}{2}$ metres away. Find the positions, directions and length of the two focal lines and the position of the confusion disc. The diameter of the lens is 40 mm.

3. The dioptric powers of the principal meridians of the reduced surface of an eye with astigmatism "with the rule" are 64 D and 62 D respectively. The axial length, from the reduced surface, is $22 \cdot 22$ mm. Calculate the dimensions of the blurred patch formed on the retina, the object being a distant bright point and the pupil diameter 6 mm. What is the ocular refraction or ametropia of this eye ?

4. The principal meridians of an astigmatic eye are vertical and horizontal, the dioptric powers being 62 D vertically and 65 D horizontally, and the axial length $21 \cdot 68$ mm. A bright circular source, 1 cm. in diameter, is placed 2 metres in front of the eye which remains unaccommodated. Find the dimensions of the patch of light formed on the retina. Pupil diameter is 7 mm. What class of astigmatism does this eye possess ?

5. Explain, with the aid of appropriate diagrams, the terms: compound hyperopic astigmatism, simple myopic astigmatism.

   If eyes with these conditions observe an astigmatic fan at 6 metres, describe the probable appearances of the fan as the eyes accommodate from the relaxed condition.

6. Explain why, in testing astigmatism subjectively, the correcting cylinder is placed with its axis "parallel to the blurred lines."

   What is the main precaution to be observed in the subjective determination of astigmatism and how is the precaution applied ?

7. Explain the meaning of the term "with the rule" in connection with ocular astigmatism. Why is the term unsatisfactory ?

   Assuming accommodation to remain relaxed, explain how the appearance of the fan chart will vary in the different classes of astigmatism with the rule.

8. Find the ocular astigmatism of eyes corrected by the following lenses:

(*a*) $+4\cdot75$ S./$-2\cdot25$ C. ax. 30, placed 14 mm. from the eye (i.e. from the reduced surface).

(*b*) $-5\cdot00$ S./$-2\cdot50$ C. ax. 100, placed 15 mm. from the eye.

(*c*) $-4\cdot50$ S./$+6\cdot50$ C. ax. 135, placed 15 mm. from the *cornea.*

(N.B.—Assume the reduced surface to be $1\frac{2}{3}$ mm. behind the cornea as in the non-astigmatic eyes previously dealt with.)

9. An eye is corrected for distance by the lens $+3\cdot00$ S./$+2\cdot00$ C. ax. H. worn 14 mm. in front of the reduced eye surface. Discuss the amount of accommodation to be exerted by the eye to view an object $\frac{1}{3}$ metre beyond the lens.

(N.B.—Treat each meridian separately. Reference might be made to §6.1 where this problem is discussed.)

10. Find the distance correcting lens, to be worn 14 mm. in front of the reduced surface, in each of the following cases:

(*a*) Ocular ametropia is $+2\cdot50$ S./$+2\cdot00$ C. ax. 45.

(*b*) Ocular refraction is $+2\cdot00$ D along 60° and $-2\cdot00$ D along 150°.

(*c*) The refraction is corrected for distance by the lens $-5\cdot00$ S./ $-1\cdot00$ C. ax. 70 placed 5 mm. from the reduced surface.

11. An eye with 6 mm. pupil shows unaided distance acuity 9/45. When the eye looks through positive spheres of increasing power the highest acuity reached is 9/18 and remains thus for a further increase of two dioptres. When the lenses are tilted forward at the top round a horizontal axis improved acuity is obtained. What inferences of an optical nature may be drawn from these observations? (S.M.C.)

12. An eye views a distant object consisting of horizontal and vertical lines. Viewed through a $+3\cdot00$ D cyl. axis horizontal, the vertical lines only are clear; viewed through the $+\ 3\cdot00$ D cyl. with axis vertical, the horizontal lines only are clear. There is no apparent difference in clarity when the lines are viewed through a $+1\cdot00$ D cyl. axis vertical.

What can you deduce from the above data? (S.M.C.)

13. The refractive condition of an eye is $+3\cdot00$ S./$+2\cdot00$ C. ax. V. The axial length of the eye is $21\cdot5$ mm. Find the dioptric powers of the eye's optical system in its two principal meridians. What are the positions of the two far points?

By exerting one-half of its total amplitude of accommodation the eye sees vertical lines on the distant chart distinctly. What is the amplitude of accommodation?

14. An uncorrected case which actually requires $+\ 1\cdot0$ D sph. combined with $-2\cdot0$ D cyl. axis 90° is equipped in succession with (*a*) a $+1\cdot0$ D cyl. ax. 180; (*b*) a $-1\cdot0$ D cyl. ax. 90; and (*c*) a $+1\cdot0$ D cyl. ax. 90. What would be the approximate Snellen acuity in each case when the testing chart is placed at a distance of 9 metres? Give reasons for your answer. (Assume pupil diameter is about 6 mm.) (S.M.C.)

15. When exerting one-quarter of its maximum accommodation an astigmatic eye requires $+1\cdot5$ D sphere to see the horizontal line of the fan chart distinctly. When exerting one-half of its full accommodation no lens is required. Exerting full accommodation the vertical line of the chart is distinct when seen through a $-1\cdot0$ D. sphere. Find the

amplitude of accommodation and distance correction. What type of astigmatism does this eye possess? (Assume the lenses are in contact with the eye.)

16. An eye which at first sees nothing clearly, sees the vertical line of the fan chart distinctly through a – 1·0 D cyl. Exerting maximum accommodation the eye sees distinctly the vertical line through a – 3·0 D sphere (the horizontal line being blurred) and the horizontal line through a – 6·0 D sphere (the vertical being blurred). Determine the distance correction and state the axis direction of the – 1·0 D cyl. used in the first test above. What is the amplitude of accommodation?

17. When a +6 D sphere is placed 15 mm. in front of a certain eye, completely relaxed, the horizontal line of the distant fan chart is seen distinctly. When the +6 D sphere is moved out to a position 25⅔ mm. from the eye the vertical line of the fan is seen distinctly. Find the distance correcting lens for this eye, to be worn 15 mm. in front of it. Find also the ocular astigmatism.

What is the amplitude of accommodation if the horizontal line is distinct when seen through a 4·00 D sphere placed at the eye, the eye exerting maximum accommodation?

18. A person whose ametropia is corrected by R. and L. +1·75 S./ – 0·75 C. ax. H. uses for reading R. and L. +1·25 D. sph. added to his distance glasses. Explain carefully, with diagrams, how a fan or clock chart should appear to such a person if he were to observe it:

(*a*) without glasses and with accommodation relaxed;
(*b*) without glasses and with 1·75 D of accommodation in use;
(*c*) with his distance glasses only;
(*d*) with his reading glasses only.

19. How can you prove to an intelligent person ignorant of optics that he is astigmatic, by rotating a weak cylinder before his eye? (B.O.A.)

20. Give an account of the requirements to be satisfied by an astigmatic fan chart. A low illumination has been advocated for carrying out the subjective test for astigmatism. State why this should render the rest more sensitive and what, on the other hand, may be the disadvantage of such a procedure.

21. A simple optometer is fitted with a +2 D lens and a fan chart. What will be the positions of the chart when measuring the static refraction of an eye that is correctable by – 2·0 S./ – 3·50 Cyl. ax. 50? What lines will be seen clearly in each position?

22. A person requires for distance R. +1·00 S./+0·50 C. ax. 90 and L. – 0·50 S./ – 0·50 C. ax. 50. Find the positions of the two far points of each eye when the person is provided with an optometer lens of +4 D. If an astigmatic chart be employed for the test, state which line of the chart will first become clear on approaching the chart from a position beyond the more remote far point of each eye.

23. An eye has simple myopic astigmatism of 3 D with the rule. Assuming the reduced eye and the astigmatism is due to the non-sphericity of the reduced surface, give a diagram to scale showing the form of the pencil within the eye, the light having originated at a distant luminous point. What is the length of the line focus on the retina? (Pupil diameter, 4 mm.)

24. Find by graphical construction the image formed on the retina of the eye in the previous question, the object being a circle of 90 mm. diameter situated 6 metres from the eye.

25. What is the principle underlying the Friedenwald chart for testing astigmatism ? What are the probable effects of the size of the pupil in subjective tests, especially in the presence of astigmatism ?

26. Prove that the diameter of the confusion disc (for a distant object) formed in an eye of pupil diameter $2y$ and with astigmatism of A dioptres is given approximately by :

$$\text{diameter} = 2y.\frac{A}{120}$$

Compare this with the blur circle formed on the retina of an eye with A dioptres of myopia ; and comment on the possible practical utility of this comparison.

27. By accommodating, an astigmatic eye can place different parts of the refracted pencil on the retina. Write short notes on the parts of the pencil that will probably be made to fall on the retina in varying conditions.

28. Why is it more important in prescribing glasses to adjust accurately for astigmatism than for the spherical error ? Explain carefully how you effect your final adjustment of the cylinder. (B.O.A.)

29. A subject, aged 20 years, is found to require :

R. +5·0 D.S./+1·0 D. Cyl. ax. 135. L. +5·0 D Sph.

Describe any subjective method of arriving at this result, along with the necessary precautions to be taken, and give an explanation of the appearance of letters, fan, etc., which may be employed.

What extra tests are available to confirm the findings ? (S.M.C.)

30. Describe briefly the steps by which you would ascertain subjectively the correction in the case of an eye which proved to have mixed astigmatism. (B.O.A.)

31. Trace, step by step, the manner in which the following correction +2·00 D.S./+1·50 D cyl. ax. 180°, would be obtained by a routine subjective examination. Explain carefully the object of each of the charts used and describe how each chart should appear at definite stages of the test.

32. Explain, step by step, how the refraction of an eye with mixed astigmatism may be determined subjectively. Assume the astigmatism to be "with the rule" and that the subject's accommodation is relaxed.

Would active accommodation on the part of the subject be liable to affect the accuracy of the results and, if so, what precautions should be taken ?

33. A young man has good distance vision but suffers from asthenopia. He actually requires a correction of +1·00 D.S./+0·50 D.C. ax. H. Describe the progress of the subjective test by which you would arrive at this result, mentioning typical answers which you would expect from the subject at each of the definite stages of the test.

34. A person aged 30 years has uncorrected monocular vision 6/18. Indicate broadly what range of refractive error may be present. If a crossed cylinder, +0·50 D cyl. combined with −0·50 D cyl. (axes at right angles) be placed before the eye referred to, firstly with the negative cylinder axis vertical, vision becoming 6/36 and secondly with

the same axis horizontal vision becomes 6/9, this vision being the highest obtainable with the applied cross cylinder. What will be the possible range of refractive error ? Give reasons for your conclusions. (S.M.C.)

35. Discuss the relative uncorrected visual acuities with hyperopic, mixed and myopic astigmatisms of similar astigmatic differences and the precautions you take when measuring these types subjectively. (S.M.C.)

36. A subjective refractive test reveals +1·0 D sph./– 5·0 D. cyl. ax. 175. Indicate *briefly* your normal routine of measurement by subjective methods and then elaborate additional subjective tests you could apply to confirm. (S.M.C.)

37. Provided with a trial case of lenses, trial frame and Snellen letters only, how would you proceed to measure a case of astigmatism ? (Fan charts, diamonds, objective methods are not allowed.)

Give the optical theory and reasons for your suggested procedure. (S.M.C.)

38. Explain how to test subjectively a subject, aged 20, with a low degree of regular hyperopic astigmatism.

Why should subjects with low degree of uncorrected astigmatism often complain of severe asthenopia whereas, in general, those with a much higher degree do not have asthenopia ?

39. Before final checking in a subjective test, the cylindrical portion of the correction in the trial frame is – 1·50 C. ax. H., and the spherical portion – 2·0 D. When a +0·25 C./– 0·25 C. cross cylinder is held first with the axis of the plus cylinder vertical and then twirled, the second position corrects the outstanding astigmatism and gives the maximum acuity. What kind of modification is required of the lens in the trial frame ?

Give diagrams showing approximately the condition of the interval of Sturm and its relation to the retina (*a*) before the application of the cross cylinder (*b*) in the two positions of the cross cylinder.

40. Distinguish between regular and irregular astigmatism. Describe a procedure for determining the correction required by a subject with regular astigmatism, no cylindrical lenses being used.

41. Describe any method or appliance which utilises the chromatic aberration of the eye in order to determine refractive errors. The theory must also be given. (S.M.C.)

42. Explain the principle and use of the Jackson cross-cylinder for establishing the power and the axis direction of the cylinder portion of the distance correction in subjective testing. Give diagrams.

43. Give a short account of a method for determining the astigmatism of the eye by using a small bright spot as test object.

A method of using a row of such spots is based on the same principle. Explain this method briefly, giving diagrams.

44. Describe the routine procedure for determining the distance correction for an astigmatic eye, using the duochrome test. Make clear, with diagrams, the appearances of the blocks of lines at definite stages of the test.

45. Give brief notes on the work of each of the following investigators in connection with the testing of ocular astigmatism : Whewell, Young, Airy, Donders, Helmholtz, Gullstrand.

46. What are the possible causes of the various subdivisions of refractive spherical ametropia; and the possible causes of ocular astigmatism?

Comment on the non-coincidence of the optical and visual axes of the eye in its bearing on astigmatism.

47. Assuming the crystalline lens to be thin, what kind and amount of astigmatism would be introduced if it were tilted about a vertical axis through an angle of 20° from a position symmetrically disposed on the visual axis? (Take power of crystalline lens as 21·75 D).

48. An eye of standard emmetropic axial length has 5 D of simple myopic astigmatism with the rule, the astigmatism being reckoned at the eye; i.e. ocular astigmatism is 5 D. In attempting to correct the eye for distance, a −4·50 D cylinder is placed with its axis along 160° and (we will assume) in contact with the eye. What is now the refractive condition of the eye and lens combined? Which line of the astigmatic fan will be seen most clearly? What lens, placed 15 mm. from the eye, will be required (in addition to the −4·50 D cyl. ax. 160) to correct the eye?

(N.B.—For compounding obliquely disposed cylinders, see *Ophthalmic Lenses*, XIII.)

49. (*a*) The thin lens +15·0 D.S./+1·00 D cyl. ax. V. is set up facing a distant point source. Find the position of the disc of least confusion and the length of the interval of Sturm.

(*b*) A −0·50/+0·50 cross cylinder is held in front of it with the plus cylinder axis vertical. Find the position of the confusion disc and the length of Sturm's interval now—assume the cross cylinder to be in contact with the lens.

(*c*) The cross cylinder is now twirled into the perpendicular position what is the condition of the refracted pencil now?

50. Give an account of the possible causes, and effects, of the general defect called irregular astigmatism. Describe briefly the kind of procedure that may be adopted in order to arrive at a lens that may provide a measure of correction.

51. Write a short essay showing on what simple optical principle these usual (visual acuity) subjective methods of determining the eye's ametropia are based; and what is the fundamental requirement to be satisfied by the distance correcting lens. What factors, ignored in the methods so simply based, may operate to render the prosecution of the methods difficult or even to vitiate the results obtained by them?

52. When, by some subjective or other method, the ametropia of each eye of a subject has been separately determined, what further kinds of information would you consider it is necessary to obtain in order to provide comfortable binocular vision for both distant and near objects? When everything that can be done by physical or optical means has been accomplished, in what ways may the subject's vision still be defective?

53. Assuming that an objective method is not available for measuring refraction, write down a summary table showing the order of steps taken during a subjective routine.

Some ocular and refractive conditions are more difficult to measure by subjective methods alone; enumerate these and indicate how you would recognise them early during the subjective routine you have just summarised. (S.M.C.)

54. Show that lenses of different form with equal back vertex power, whilst being equally effective for static corrections, are not so equally effective when used in near vision.

Apply this information to discuss the relative accuracies of ordinary trial case measures and of refracting devices using lens batteries with widely separated components. (S.M.C.)

55. You are required to explain to another student exactly what to do, and why, to find the suitable correction lens for an eye with about 5 D myopia. Give a full account of your procedure. (B.O.A.)

CHAPTER V

ACCOMMODATION AND CONVERGENCE

MENTION has already been made* of the power possessed by the eyes to rotate around their centres of rotation and so converge upon a near object that has claimed attention, each eye at the same time accommodating on this object of fixation and varying appropriately the diameter of its pupil. Such associated actions, controlled by the same nerve (in this case the third nerve) are termed SYNKINETIC. The movements of the eyes in binocular vision generally will be considered later,† but it is desirable at this stage to deal with some aspects of the particular movement of convergence and its association with accommodation.

The student should first revise his knowledge of the effects of prisms.‡ A prism deviates light towards its base so that an object seen through it is apparently displaced towards its edge or apex, along the base-apex direction of the prism. In order to receive the image on the fovea the eye behind the prism must rotate, around its centre of rotation, towards the prism apex through an angle equal to the deviation of the prism, when the object is distant. When the object is near, on account of the forward position of the prism in relation to the eye's centre of rotation, the rotation required of the eye is somewhat less than the prism deviation ; in other words, the *effective* power of the prism is less than its true deviating power, for near objecst. The difference is small except in the case of strong prisms and correspondingly large eye rotations, however, and we will keep the following discussion, for simplicity, free from these " effectivity " considerations ; but they must be taken into account in any accurate calculations.

When dealing with the strength or power of prisms, we shall always refer to their *deviating* power, the angle through which they deviate the light ; which may be measured in degrees, although usually in prism dioptres or centrads. Very approximately, 4 degrees equal 7 prism dioptres or

* Ch. I. † Ch. XII. ‡ See *Ophthalmic Lenses* : Ch. VI.

centrads, for *small* angles. One centrad (▽) is one hundredth of a radian.

5.1. Convergence.

In a normal healthy visual apparatus the nervous impulses for producing movements of the eyes are transmitted equally to the associated muscles of the two eyes. Thus both eyes move together as a single organ to the right, to the left, upwards and downwards, each of these so-called conjugate

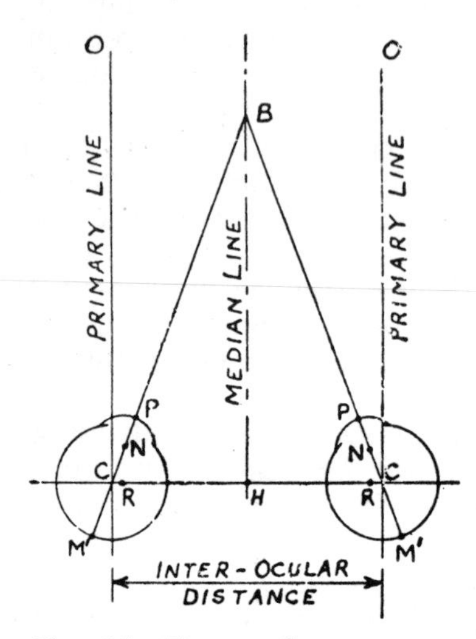

FIG. 5.1—EYES IN CONVERGENCE ON POINT B.

RR Centres of Rotation.

CC Centres of Projection.

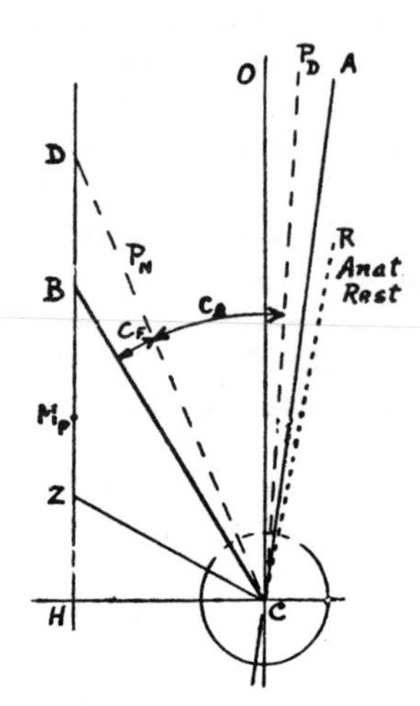

FIG. 5.2—STATES OF CONVERGENCE—RIGHT EYE.

movements* being controlled by one conjugate innervation. In addition, there is an innervation which stimulates mainly the medial recti muscles, enabling the eyes to move in opposite senses and converge upon objects at various distances and so receive their images on the two foveæ. This is necessary in order to maintain *single* vision of the object ; if the visual axes were not swung round so as to intersect at the object of attention, one of the retinal images at least would be formed at a point not coincident with the fovea and double vision would ensue.

* §12.13.

In Fig. 5.1 the points R R represent the centres of rotation of the eyes; they are situated nasally from the primary lines, C O*. When the eyes fix an object, the plane containing that object and the centres of rotation of the eyes is the PLANE OF FIXATION. It rotates around the inter-ocular base line CC, up or down, as the object fixed lies above or below the horizon. It is convenient to refer eye movements to certain axes of reference that are fixed in relation to the head. The eyes are normally situated symmetrically, or approximately so, on either side of the MEDIAN PLANE of the head, which is a vertical plane dividing the head into two lateral halves. When the head is held erect and a distant object lying on the horizon is under view, the plane of fixation is horizontal and it intersects the median plane in a straight line stretching from the mid-point between the eyes to the horizon; this is the MEDIAN LINE of the head, represented by HB in Figs. 5.1 to 5.3. When looking straight ahead at an infinitely distant object on the median line, the visual axes of the eyes are parallel and each eye is in its *primary position*, CO in Fig. 5.1. In dealing with the movements and attitudes of the eyes in binocular vision it will be understood that, except where otherwise specified, the objects of fixation lie *in the median plane.*

To fix binocularly a near object B the eyes, with their visual axes, rotate about the rotation centres RR. For all practical positions of B up to the near point, the successive positions of the visual axes intersect the primary lines in points which all very nearly coincide with the points CC lying at the intersections of the primary lines with the inter-ocular base line RR. We make very little error, therefore, in assuming that the visual axes, on which in all positions lie the points P, N and M′, always pass through the points CC, which we may call the CENTRES OF PROJECTION. The state of convergence of the eyes is expressed by the angle OCB through which each eye has rotated from the primary position. This angle may be measured in any unit of angular measure—the degree, centrad, prism dioptre, etc. It clearly depends upon the distance of the object and upon the inter-ocular distance CC, which is very nearly equal to the inter-pupillary distance, or P.D.

NAGEL proposed that convergence be measured in a unit which he called the METRE-ANGLE (M.A.), which is the

---

* §§ 2.4 and 10.7.

angle through which *each* eye has rotated from the primary position in order to fix an object distant one metre. Each eye rotates through two metre-angles to fix an object distant half a metre; through 10 M.A. to fix an object distant 10 cm.; and so on. Thus the number of metre-angles of rotation is found by dividing the object distance, expressed in centimetres, into 100. The unit is occasionally convenient in that an emmetrope would have accommodated one dioptre and converged one metre-angle to fix binocularly an object at one metre; 3 D of accommodation and 3 M.A. of convergence for an object at one third metre; and so on. In conformity with this association between accommodation and convergence it would seem that the distance of the object should be measured from the principal point of the eye, or the reduced surface P of the reduced eye, along PB. It is probably more convenient, however, to reckon the distances along the median line from the interocular base line, CC; i.e. to take the object distance as HB. It matters little in practice; and we will adopt this procedure of measuring the object distance (HB) from the base line CC. Even so, the actual size of the metre-angle depends not only on the distance HB, but also on the subject's P.D. and so is a variable quantity. One person's metre-angle differs from another person's.

As we shall see, convergence is usually measured actually in prism dioptres or centrads, and it follows from the diagram, Fig. 5.1, that:

$$\left.\begin{array}{r}\text{Convergence of each}\\ \text{eye in } \triangle \text{ or } \nabla\end{array}\right\} = (\text{Number of M.A.}) \times (\tfrac{1}{2}\ \text{P.D. in cm.})$$

Taking an average value of 60 mm. for the P.D. the convergence of each eye to view an object distant 50 cm. is 2 M.A. or 6△. At the reading distance of one third metre, the convergence is 3 M.A. or 9△. In the case of a subject with a P.D. of 68 mm. the convergences would be 2 M.A. or 6·8△; and 3 M.A. or 10·2△. In all cases the actual size of the convergence angle is the angle whose tangent is HC ÷ HB.

If an object be approached towards the eyes along the median line, the eyes accommodate to maintain clear vision of it and also converge upon it in order to maintain single vision. At a certain distance the limit of accommodation is reached—the near point of accommodation,*

*§3.9.

M_P. Nearer than this the object cannot be seen distinctly, but a normal pair of eyes can converge more than this and so continue for a while to obtain single, though indistinct, vision. At a certain nearer point the object will appear double since the limit of convergence of the eyes (under the conditions of the experiment)* will have been passed, and one retinal image at least will no longer fall on the fovea. The nearest point that can be seen *singly*, when both accommodation and convergence are allowed full play, is the NEAR POINT (or punctum proximum) OF CONVERGENCE. It is the intersection of the visual axes when the maximum effort of convergence is made. The object used in the test may be a fine black vertical line on a white card, as suggested in the simple optometer (§3·9). The eyes will not sustain this maximum effort indefinitely, but will diverge after a while, or at any moment that one eye is covered.

We will define the FAR POINT (or punctum remotum) OF CONVERGENCE as the farthest point that can be seen singly: that is, the intersection of the fixation lines when the maximum effort of *divergence* is made. It will usually be beyond infinity, behind the eyes. The eyes will not maintain this position indefinitely, but will converge from it after a while, or at any moment that one eye is covered.

In conformity with the terminology used in accommodation, the distance between the far point and near point is the range of convergence; and the angle turned through by each eye in converging from the far point up to the near point is the AMPLITUDE OF CONVERGENCE. Convergence on a point within infinity will be described as positive; the rotation from the primary position to a point beyond infinity, requiring divergence of the eyes, as negative convergence. The near point of convergence is normally quite close to the eyes, being only 8 cm. or so from the inter-ocular base line CC. For an average P.D. of 60 mm. this is equivalent to 37·5△ for *each* eye, or 75△ both eyes. The maximum divergence from the primary parallel position is normally 3△, each eye. The total amplitude of convergence is thus about 40△ each eye. There is appreciable variation between individuals, especially if ametropic. The near point may be as high as 45△ and the far point appreciably greater than 3△. Moreover, the amplitude in

* See §5.4.

a given individual can probably be extended in both directions, especially the positive direction, by exercise.

When referring to the converging and diverging movements any figures quoted, whether in M.A. or in △, will express the movement of *each* eye, unless otherwise specified.

Convergence is more easily executed when the eyes are depressed below the horizon, as in reading, than when they are maintained horizontal. Convergence is still more awkward when the eyes are elevated, which is to be expected since in nature near objects are mostly below the horizon.

The amplitude of convergence does not decrease progressively with age as accommodation does.* The position of the near point is affected little, if at all, with advancing years.

NOTE ON THE PRISM DIOPTRE AND CENTRAD.

The centrad (▽) is one hundredth of a radian $= \frac{1}{100}$ of $\frac{180}{\pi}$ degrees; it is a definite and constant quantity. The number of centrads in an angle is found by expressing the angle in radians and multiplying by 100. The prism dioptre (△) is the angle whose tangent is $\frac{1}{100}$. The number of prism dioptres in an angle is found by multiplying the *tangent* of that angle by 100: the value of an angle in prism dioptres increases more rapidly than the angle itself and so the prism dioptre is not really a satisfactory unit scientifically though it is simple to measure in practice. The centrad is a sounder unit.

5.2. Accommodation and Convergence.

A primary requirement for complete binocular vision is to obtain reasonably distinct as well as single vision of any chosen object point within the binocular field of vision. This requires that the functions of accommodation and convergence shall operate in close association with one another. In ordinary circumstances they act together without conscious effort of mutual adjustment. The slightest impulse to either makes a difference in the other and, given a healthy visual apparatus, the required amounts of each come into play without difficulty in the ordinary visual tasks of everyday life, even although an error of refraction of moderate degree may be present. As a result the two visual axes meet at whatever point is accommodated for. In the emmetrope the amounts of accommodation in dioptres and of convergence in metre-angles to do this are equal; and

* §6.2.

in the corrected ametrope they are sensibly so.* A small relative adjustment of the two functions is necessary when the subject fixes an object well to the left or right of the median plane, as when reading across the page of a large book or newspaper without moving the head, for the change in the distance of the object is not proportional to the change of convergence demanded.

The uncorrected ametrope, on the other hand, must exert unequal proportions of the two functions. Thus a hyperope of 3 D who wishes to observe an object at 33·3 cm. must use 6 D of accommodation to only 3 M.A. of convergence; and a myope of 3 D, requires no accommodation at all for the same convergence.

Thus, although the two functions are closely inter-related and controlled by the same cranial nerve, and cannot be voluntarily dissociated except under special experimental conditions, they are not linked together rigidly. They have become associated by hereditary habit. They are brought into action to such relative extents as are required to place both visual axes on the one object and to accommodate for it; in which circumstances the retinal images are on the two foveæ and the resulting neural images in the cortex can be *fused*† into a single mental percept. An individual with moderate ametropia apparently grows accustomed to the disparity between the two functions and finds no difficulty in summoning the nervous energy required for the fusion of the two uniocular impressions. His powers of accommodation and convergence develop naturally to deal with the one-sided relationship. A new relationship has to be developed when the refractive error is corrected.

If the disparity to which an ametrope has become accustomed be increased in the performance of some unusual visual task, the extra effort needed to redress the balance will be made in the interests of single vision and to avoid the diplopia which is so disconcerting. A large fusional effort of this kind may be sustained for a while without causing distress; on the other hand, depending upon the individual, it may give rise to considerable strain. If the disparity between accommodation and convergence be too great, the advantage of single vision will be reluctantly sacrificed, monocular vision will be accepted, and one eye may deviate from the fixation point (*squint*).

---

* §12.23.

† §12.6.

In Fig. 5.2 representing the right eye, CO is the primary direction. Each eye will take up this position when the individual is actively observing and fusing an infinitely distant object. CR indicates the position of ANATOMICAL REST of the eyes; the position they would take up in the absence of all innervation, as during sleep, or under an anæsthetic, or at death. The position is one of appreciable divergence and slight elevation. During waking hours, but at moments when no effort is being made to observe and fuse any particular object, the eyes gazing passively with relaxed accommodation into space, they take up a position CP_D which is called the position of FUNCTIONAL REST or the PASSIVE POSITION. This less divergent position is due partly to muscle tone and partly to continuous activity of the converging innervation. It is often slightly divergent as indicated in the diagram, but may be parallel or slightly convergent and still be considered normal, or physiological.

As soon as a distant object claims the individual's attention the visual axes will move round, under the stimulus to fuse the retinal images of it into a single mental impression, until they occupy the primary positions, CO. CA represents the far point position; the extreme position of divergence the eyes can reach and which they will assume only when compelled to do so in order to obtain single vision of a distant object when it is observed under difficulties, as when a base-in prism is placed before one eye or the other, as explained below. Z is the near point of convergence; CZ the extreme position of convergence taken up when the maximum effort of convergence is made. The angle ACZ is the amplitude of convergence.

In the diagram the anatomical rest position CR is shown as lying outside the extreme active position CA, but its position is problematical.

M_P is the near point of accommodation; its position depends upon the age of the individual but it will always be more remote than Z, the convergence near point.

When a given object B has claimed the mind's attention, the position CB that must finally be assumed by the visual axes in order to see the object singly, is called the FIXATION POSITION. If, from the distance passive position CP_D, it is desired to observe a near object B, the total amount of convergence to be executed by the right eye to reach the desired fixation position is the angle P_DCB. The final precise adjustment of the accommodation and convergence is made under the compelling influence of fusion. If the eyes are set the task of observing the point B, but the final fusion of the images is prevented in some way, as by covering one eye,* the fixation lines will be found usually to take up some passive position such as CP_N; and the accommodation in force will probably be the amount proper to the point B or to some point lying between B and the point D where the line CP_N cuts the median line. If now the obstacle to fusion be removed and the eyes allowed to look naturally at B, they will immediately move through the angles P_NCB to intersect in B, and also make any adjustment of accommodation that may be required. (Actually, if the right eye be covered, the left eye will be directed to the point B and the right eye will take upon itself *all* the deviation from the fixation position, CB ; that is, it will deviate by twice the amount P_NCB. But this is equivalent to a deviation of *each* eye equal to angle P_NCB ; in the diagram the left eye is supposed to be deviated from the fixation position by an equal amount. When the cover is removed, whereas only the right eye needs to move, through twice the angle P_NCB, the effect is equivalent to a movement of both eyes, each through the angle P_NCB.) The position CP_N we will call the NEAR PASSIVE POSITION, corresponding to the fixation point B.

The extent by which the distance passive position CP_D differs from the distance fixation position CO may be considered as a zero error, as it were, of the oculo-motor system, just as hyperopia and myopia are in the case of refraction. And similarly the angle P_NCB is a zero error of the motor system at the near working distance.† When the motor system is in perfect balance the distance passive position coincides with the distance fixation position, which is the primary position, CO ; and the near passive position coincides with the near fixation position, CB. We shall see later that such a condition of perfect balance of the oculo-motor system is called ORTHOPHORIA.‡

It is not an easy matter to determine precisely the state of accommodation of an eye. The brain is apparently capable of " seeing " an object distinctly when the eye's optical system is focused for some point nearer or further away

* Various methods of preventing fusion will be discussed in Ch. XIII.

† Ch. XIII. ‡ §§12.14 and 13.2.

than the object. But, as we shall see when discussing *heterophoria* in Chapter XIII, the state of vergence (convergence or divergence) of the eyes at a given moment can be measured with reasonable accuracy.

The fact that the visual axes so frequently fall into a relatively divergent position CP_N, even in emmetropia, when the final act of fusion is prevented from taking place, has led to the view that each dioptre of accommodation is accompanied by less than one metre-angle of convergence, leaving the balance P_NCB to be made up during the final fusional adjustment. This divergent zero error at near is common and has been called *physiological exophoria.**

But it is to be noted that although the test object may be seen with apparent distinctness by the subject, the eyes *may* be accommodated for a point further away. If that is the case, the actual accommodation exerted has been less than it seems.

Accommodative convergence comes into play in proportion to the impulse for accommodation. Conditions that require less of this accommodative effort, such as myopia, will tend to leave the eyes on the divergent side of the object to be fixed, as indicated by CP_N in Fig. 5.2. The tendency in hyperopia, where accommodation has to be excessive, will be to place the eyes on the convergent side of the object to be fixed, leaving a *negative* amount of convergence to be executed under the direction of fusion. That is, the line CP_N in such a case will tend to lie nearer to the eyes than the fixation position CB. If the ametropia be pronounced, the fusion convergence angle P_NCB, whether positive or negative, will tend to be large and in such people the fusion faculty must be well developed if they are to enjoy comfortable binocular vision. Otherwise the exercise of accommodation in excess of convergence in hyperopia may lead to the abandoning of binocular vision in which case only one eye will be used; the other would turn in, producing a convergent squint. The excess of convergence over accommodation required by a myope to obtain single vision may lead correspondingly to a divergent squint.

Since accommodation and convergence can be brought into action to different extents when the need arises, each

---

* Ch. XIII.

function can vary within limits when the other remains constant. The amount by which accommodation can be varied, without change of convergence is called RELATIVE ACCOMMODATION; and the amount by which convergence can be varied without change in accommodation, or at least without the test object becoming indistinct to the subject, is the RELATIVE CONVERGENCE. These quantities may be measured as described in the following paragraphs.

5.3. Relative Accommodation.

The extent of relative accommodation may be measured in the following manner. The subject, made emmetropic with his distance correction, observes with both eyes a card of small type or a fine black line held at the distance for which the information is required. The most useful distance in practice is the near working distance, say 33·3 cm. Negative spheres of equal power are placed before both eyes; the subject must now accommodate, without changing his convergence, if he is to see the object distinctly as well as singly. The strongest negative spheres with which this can be done measure the positive portion of the amplitude of relative accommodation to convergence of 3 M.A. The procedure is repeated with positive lenses, the strongest measuring the amount by which accommodation can be *relaxed* at this fixed degree of convergence; or the negative portion of the amplitude of relative accommodation to convergence of 3 M.A. The amounts of these two portions of the relative amplitude depend upon the subject's age. In a young person of, say, 15 years with ample accommodation, the positive portion will average about 3·5 D, and the negative portion 3 D or so. When exerting the former the total accommodation in force will thus be 6·5 D and with the latter nil; the total relative amplitude being 6·5 D. It is difficult to measure these quantities with any accuracy; the blurring does not take place suddenly and, possibly due to the crystalline lens being in a state of continual variation, the distinctness or otherwise of the object is difficult to assess.

The positive portion will decrease with age, since the near point of accommodation has receded. If the subject's near point is at 33 cm., the positive relative amplitude will be nil. Whatever the age this positive amount will decrease as the test object is approached towards the subject's near point of accommodation.

When the test object is at infinity, the subject wearing his distance correction, there will be no negative relative amplitude, since accommodation is completely relaxed to begin with. The positive amount will be about 3 D.

For the subject to have comfortable binocular vision at the reading distance it is necessary that there be an appreciable amount of positive relative accommodation available, so that he is not working near the limit of his accommodation, but has some in reserve. Otherwise there will be discomfort and strain due to ciliary muscular fatigue. In such circumstances artificial aid in the form of positive lenses is required in order to bring the near point of accommodation nearer to the eyes. (§6.4.)

The extent of the amplitude of relative accommodation for various states of convergence may be represented graphically in the manner illustrated in Fig. 5.3, which applies to the right eye of an emmetrope. The lettering in this diagram has the same significance as in Fig. 5.2. CO is the primary position for the right eye and HB the median line. The circles with C as centre represent lines of constant accommodation. The straight lines radiating from C, and passing through the various fixation points Z, M_p, B, etc., on the median line, are lines of constant convergence. The circle of zero accommodation should really be at infinity but is shown in a conventional finite position for convenience. The point B is shown at the near working or reading distance of one third metre, corresponding to 3 dioptres of accommodation and 3 metre-angles of convergence. The distance Ba along the 3 M.A. line represents the positive portion of the amplitude of relative accommodation for this degree of convergence; Br the negative portion or relaxation. The relative accommodation is also shown for all possible states of convergence between the far point position CA and the near point position CZ. The diagram is supposed to apply to an average emmetrope, or corrected ametrope, with a total amplitude of accommodation of 7 dioptres, the near point of accommodation M_p being distant 7 dioptres, or $\frac{100}{7}$ cm.

Similar diagrams may be drawn, if required, for uncorrected ametropes. It is only necessary to shift the zero of the accommodation scale. Thus for a hyperope of 3 D the circle marked 0 in Fig. 5.3 would be marked 3; the circle through the reading position B would be marked 6, and so on.

5.4. Relative Convergence.

If the relative accommodative amplitude ar, Fig. 5.3, were determined for several states of convergence between the far and near convergence limits CA and CZ, resulting in an accommodation-convergence diagram for the individual under investigation, the amplitude of relative convergence for various states of accommodation could be read off from

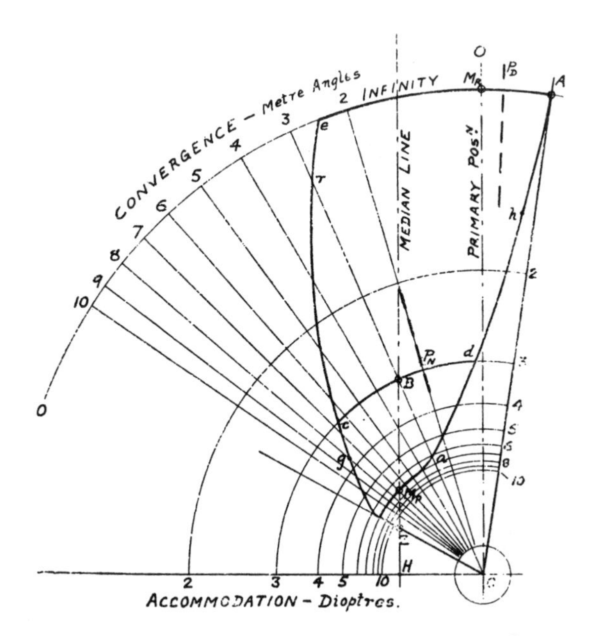

FIG. 5.3—RELATION BETWEEN ACCOMMODATION AND CONVERGENCE—EMMETROPE WITH 7 D AMP. OF ACC., SLIGHT EXO. AT DISTANCE AND 1 M.A. OF EXO. AT NEAR.

CA Far Point of Con.
CZ Near Point of Con.
M_R Far Point of Acc.
M_P Near point of Acc.
CP_D Functional Rest—passive position for distance.
CB Near Working Point—$\frac{1}{3}$ Metre.
CP_N Passive position for Near Work.

the diagram. For example, for the case illustrated in Fig. 5.3, convergence can be altered within the limiting positions Cc and Cd, the object B at the reading distance remaining distinct throughout. The circular arc cBd is the line of constant accommodation, namely 3 dioptres, whilst convergence changes from the position Cc, in which it exceeds 6 metre-angles, to Cd, a position of slight convergence.

Information regarding the interplay between accommodation and convergence is ordinarily required however, if at all, only for distance and the near work position. In the last paragraph we have indicated how the accommodation of the subject around the reading position B may be obtained, and we shall deal further with this matter in the next chapter. The amplitude of relative convergence, ed for near work and eA for distance, may be measured with prisms, or by means of a stereoscopic device called a *haploscope*, an example of which* will be described in Chapter XIII.

DISTANCE VISION.

To test by means of prisms—the subject wears his distance correction, carefully centred.† He observes with both eyes a small but distinguishable test letter at 6 metres. We seek to measure the TOTAL AMPLITUDE OF RELATIVE CONVERGENCE AT DISTANCE. This total relative amplitude consists of a negative portion P_DA and a positive portion P_De, the position P_D being the starting point for the measurements since it is the rest position of the eyes, with no fusional effort in operation.

To measure the negative portion P_DA we place a prism base in before one eye; we will suppose the right eye, Fig. 5.4(a). The immediate effect will be to move the retinal image of the object off the fovea of the right eye nasalwards, thus producing binocular diplopia. In response to this there will arise an innervation for divergence of both eyes. These innervations are shared equally between the two eyes; because of this it does not matter whether the prism be placed before the one eye or the other, or whether two prisms are used, each of half strength, one before each eye—in each case with base in. If, as indicated in Fig. 5.4(a), the prism is too strong, the eyes will be unable to diverge sufficiently to receive the images on the two foveæ and obtain single vision—they cannot diverge beyond the position CA, Fig. 5.3. They will consequently settle down to their passive or functional rest position as indicated in Fig. 5.4(a), the subject seeing apparently two objects, since

* e.g. the synoptophore (§13.11.).

† In experiments of this kind and in measuring heterophorias (Chap. XIII) it is most important to centre the lenses as accurately as possible. With the ordinary trial frame this centring is difficult to obtain and more difficult to maintain during the experiment. Inaccurate results are often obtained on this account.

in the left eye the image is formed on the fovea and in the right eye at a point b removed from the fovea. The object seen by the right eye will be projected, and therefore appear to the right of the one seen by the left eye.* This is UNCROSSED (*or homonymous*) DIPLOPIA. The eyes may make tentative efforts of divergence from this position, the

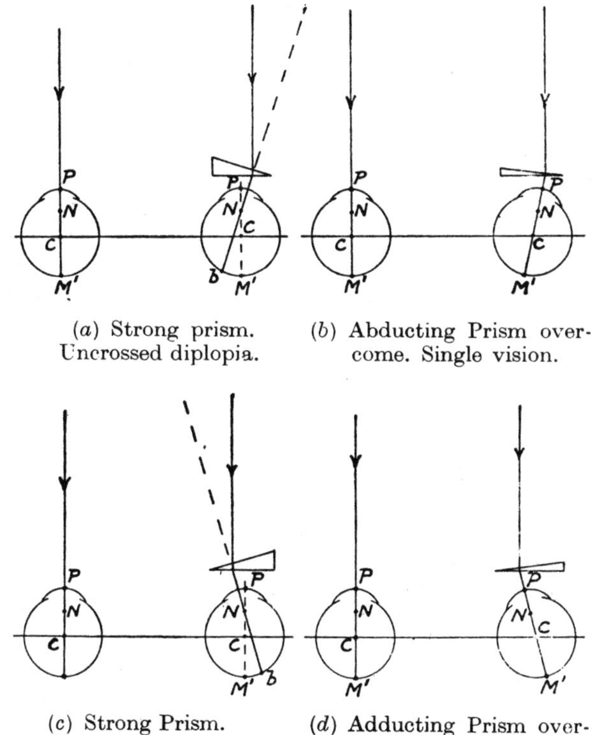

(*a*) Strong prism. Uncrossed diplopia.

(*b*) Abducting Prism overcome. Single vision.

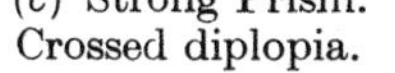
(*c*) Strong Prism. Crossed diplopia.

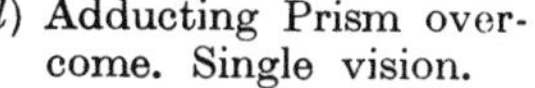
(*d*) Adducting Prism overcome. Single vision.

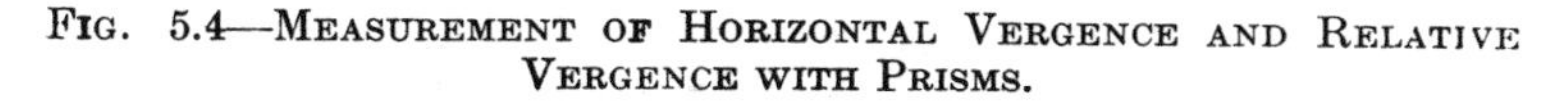
FIG. 5.4—MEASUREMENT OF HORIZONTAL VERGENCE AND RELATIVE VERGENCE WITH PRISMS.

objects in consequence appearing to the subject to approach and recede from one another.

If the right eye is markedly the "dominant" eye,† in spite of the existence of the prism before it, both eyes may range equally to the right until the image is on the fovea of the right eye. The image will then be to the right

* See also §§ 12.3 and 13.4.

† §12.7.

of the fovea in the left eye and the diplopia will be uncrossed as before.

A weaker base-in prism will be overcome by the eyes in the effort to obtain single vision. There will be an innervation to each to diverge through an angle equal to half the prism deviation, plus an innervation to move both eyes together to the right. The final position of the eyes will be as shown in (b), the left eye, under the action of the two innervations, probably not having moved at all. Both images are now on the fovea and single vision is obtained. Since at the commencement of the test both eyes were fixing the distant test letter, and occupying therefore the positions CO, the strongest prism that can be overcome in this way, the object remaining well defined, measures the sum of the angles OCA for the two eyes, Fig. 5.3 ; that is, it measures the negative portion P_DCA of the amplitude of relative convergence at distance, plus any zero error P_DCO of the oculomotor system at distance. If this error (*heterophoria*) be zero, the person being orthophoric, the prism measures directly the negative relative amplitude. Normally the prism will be 4△ to 8△ ; equivalent, say, to 3△ or 1 M.A. of divergence of *each* eye. Since the eyes moved together to the right, the direction of the object will be judged as to the right.

The effects of base-out prism are shown in (c) and (d). When the prism is too strong as in (c), the eyes will remain in their passive position except for the swinging movements made as the effects to fuse persist (unless the right eye is markedly dominant, in which case an equal rotation to the left may take place, bringing the image on to the right fovea and to the left of the left fovea). Of the two objects seen, the one due to the right eye will lie to the left of that seen by the left eye, which is CROSSED (*or heteronymous*) DIPLOPIA.

The weaker prism of case (d) will be overcome, the left eye remaining stationary and the right eye converging under the impulse of the two innervations for converging and conjugate movement to the left. The single object seen will appear to the left of its true position. The strongest prism thus overcome, the object remaining distinct, measures the angle OCe, Fig. 5.3, which is equal to the POSITIVE portion of the amplitude of relative convergence at distance, after a correction has been made for the zero error P_DCO, if any. No such correction is required when the subject is orthophoric. This positive amplitude appears to vary considerably in different individuals, but may be taken as roughly 16△ on the average, equivalent to 8△ or 2·5 M.A. or so, *each* eye.

It is to be noted that in cases (a) and (c), when the prism is too strong, the eyes settle down to their passive position, approximating to parallelism; whereas in cases (b) and (d) the eyes *rotate* into a new active position.

Distinct vision of the test letter is to be maintained throughout each test, so as to ensure, as well as can be done subjectively, that accommodation remains relaxed. As already remarked, however, such distinctness cannot be relied upon as indicating unchanged accommodation. It may change within limits because of the depth of focus of the refracted pencils within the eye,* and the latitude allowed by cortical interpretation. In any case, in such experiments as the above it is not easy to satisfy oneself whether the test object has deteriorated in distinctness; the prisms themselves introduce chromatism and distortion which confuse the issue, especially on the positive side where strong prisms are required. The term relative convergence to accommodation, and diagrams such as Fig. 5.3 purporting to illustrate it, are therefore to be taken as referring to the change of convergence *whilst the test object remains subjectively distinct.*

The degree of *relative* convergence obtained as above must not be confused with the extreme amplitude of convergence attained when accommodation is allowed to operate with it, as in §5.1. Under those conditions the convergence is, of course, much greater. In Fig. 5.3 the *relative* convergence at distance is given by the angle ACe whilst the total amplitude is ACZ.

NEAR VISION.

The subject wears his near correction, if any, the lenses being centred for the near working distance of one third metre. The object may be a vertical row of small test letters or a fine vertical line. Base-in prisms will reveal that the eyes can normally diverge by 2 to 3 M.A. each from this position, the object remaining distinct; this (assuming the subject orthophoric) is the extent of the negative amplitude of relative convergence at near, represented by Bd in Fig. 5.3. The positive portion Bc varies according

---

* §11.3.

to age. (The two portions will be reckoned from P_N if there is a zero error at near.) The amplitude of accommodation decreases with age,* but convergence remains more or less constant. Thus in older people the point M_P recedes from the eyes towards the point B and the boundary cc of the diagram intersects the line CZ at a point more remote from C; the line Bc of constant accommodation will therefore be longer. It would, moreover, be expected that a young person, with appreciable and active accommodation, will not be able to converge very far from the reading position CB without accommodation changing also. Thus the positive portion of the amplitude of relative convergence at near is 3 M.A. or so for a person about 15 years old and accommodative amplitude 10 D, whereas it is in the neighbourhood of 4 to 5 M.A. for a person of 35 years and 6 D amplitude of accommodation. It is shown as about 3·5 M.A. in Fig. 5.3.

When viewing a near object binocularly through prisms, as in the above test, the apparent distance and size of the object are modified.† Seen through a base-out prism it will appear nearer than its true position since the estimate of distance, in the case of a near object, depends to some extent on the innervation for convergence required to see it singly, and an augmented effort of convergence is required in this case. Since it is judged to be nearer, but its retinal image has not actually altered in size as it would have done had the object *really* been nearer, it is also judged to be smaller than its true size.‡ With base-in prisms the subject receives the impression that the object is somewhat further away and larger. It might also be added that in the former case a flat object such as a sheet of paper appears to be concave and in the latter case convex, to the subject.

5.5. Vergence (Horizontal) and Relative Vergence.

We see that, when viewing a distant object, the normal individual can vary his convergence from such a position as Ce, Fig. 5.3, to the extreme position CA, maintaining throughout clear vision of the object, at least in so far as he is able to estimate clearness through the prisms used in the test. If no effort is made to see the object distinctly,

---

* §6.2. † §2.5.

‡ These effects are not so marked as the altered amount of convergence would suggest, since variations of convergence are not a very potent factor in our appreciation of depth—see §§ 12.1 and 12.22.

the subject will be able to converge, on the positive side, through a much larger excursion than the angle OCe and continue to hold *single* vision of the object. Suppose some position such as Cg is achieved at a first attempt; during the increase of convergence from Ce to Cg, accommodation comes into action along with convergence, increasing from zero at e to the value indicated by g, nearly 4 dioptres in the diagram. The object becomes increasingly blurred. The convergence of each eye in this situation is about 8 M.A. and we have therefore about 48△ of base-out prism power before the two eyes. Seen through such strong prisms the object will in any case be blurred and coloured, and although the *attention* is directed to it, attempts to accommodate for it will be feeble.

After one or two trials, no effort being made to accommodate for the test object, the eyes will be able to converge and so hold single vision of the object, over a larger range and will in some cases approach the absolute maximum of convergence, CZ (about 75△, both eyes). We are here measuring the convergence capabilities of the eyes without regard to the state of accommodation. For this purpose the object may be a small light of moderate brightness (the "muscle light") in dark surroundings instead of the test letter used in the tests on *relative* convergence. With such an object there is less incentive to focus accurately on it. In proportion to the extent to which accommodation is left free to operate, we measure simply the converging power of the eyes.

The total prism should be divided equally between the eyes since then the indistinctness introduced by the prisms will be the same in both eyes; unequal distinctness, which would be caused if the whole prism strength were placed before one eye, would lessen the desire for fusion* and so tend to give too low a figure for the convergence we seek to measure.

If divergence be tested in a similar manner, with base-in prisms, the result obtained will be the same as the relative divergence of the previous paragraph (4△ to 8△ on the average for both eyes), since the accommodation cannot relax any further.

If the test be carried out with the muscle light at the point B at the reading distance, the eyes will again converge and accommodate to about the same position Cg

---

* § 12.6.

with base-out prisms, subsequently approaching and maybe practically coinciding with the near point position CZ; and will diverge and relax accommodation to a position such as Ch, approaching the extreme divergent position CA.

As stated before, converging and diverging movements of the eyes are necessary to bring the visual axes to bear upon the object of attention so that the two images thus made to fall on the foveæ can be fused in the cortex. In order that objects from distance up to the reading position may be fixed binocularly with comfort it is necessary that the eyes be capable of diverging to some extent beyond the primary position and of converging to some extent within the reading position, so that there is a reserve of possible further movement at each extremity, especially at the convergent extremity. That is to say, they must possess an adequate amplitude of convergence.

These movements of the eyes in the interests of fusion have been called *breadth of fusion* or *ductions* or *prism-vergences*, but there is considerable confusion as to the precise meaning of these terms. By some writers they are used to define what we have called relative convergence. Others use the terms to describe the strongest prism with which single vision can be maintained irrespective of the state of accommodation, as just explained, the positive portion of the breadth of fusion or the abduction or prism-convergence being obtained by the use of base-out or *adducting* prisms; and the negative fusion breadth or abduction or prism-divergence with base-in or *abducting* prisms. But we have seen that the excursion of the eyes when viewing a distant object, under these conditions is, on the negative side, simply the far point of convergence; and on the positive side approaches, and after a little practice, almost reaches, in some cases, the near point of convergence. Hence it scarcely appears necessary to introduce new terms to designate this capability of the eyes. In many cases where subjects do not approach the near point under these tests it is because the exercise is unusual and the subject is not clear as to what is required.

When measuring the convergence amplitude the subject "holds on" to single vision until the effort is too great, at which stage the single object breaks into two—the "break-point". This does not usually happen suddenly. The eyes will then have moved into their passive position, or approximately so. If now the prism strength is further increased somewhat and then gradually reduced, the widely separated projections of the object will approach one another and presently will be again fused into one. This prism with which single vision is regained, measures what is sometimes called the "recovery point." There is, however, practically no difference between these two prism strengths and the separate terms are not required.

In carrying out experiments or clinical tests on the verging power of the eyes (vergence tests) the indistinctness introduced by the prisms can be avoided and the tests conducted much more conveniently by using an instrument of the haploscope type, such as the synoptophore, to which reference has already been made.

5.6. Supravergence and Cyclovergence.

As we shall see more fully when discussing ocular movements generally in Chapter XII, it is necessary to consider the relative positioning of the fixation lines of the two eyes, and the movements of the eyes with respect to each other, not only in the horizontal direction but also in the vertical direction. To obtain binocular fixation of a given object, both visual axes must be made to lie in the plane of fixation, which we will assume to be horizontal. And further, the eyes must be properly oriented around their visual axes; that is, the meridian of the retina intended to be vertical must be so, within certain limits.

The eyes can move with respect to each other in the vertical direction if they are forced to do so in order to obtain single vision. They cannot move in this manner voluntarily, but if diplopia is produced in the vertical direction in some way, as by placing before either eye a prism with its base-apex line vertical, there will at once arise an innervation to move one eye higher than the other in the attempt to regain single vision. Such movements are not conditioned by accommodation as horizontal movements are; at least, not directly. The strongest prism overcome measures the vertical vergence or SUPRAVERGENCE of the eyes. If the diploma is such that the right eye has to rotate upwards with respect to the left, as would be the case with a base-down prism before the right eye or a base-up prism before the left eye, the movement is one of *right* supravergence. It might alternatively be called left *infra*vergence, but there is no real need to introduce this term. Conversely, if the left eye move higher than the right, the movement is described as left supravergence (or right infravergence). The value of the strongest vertical prism thus overcome is about 2△ to 3△ in the normal case; it is much the same value whether tested with the muscle light at 6 metres or at the reading distance. The sum of the strongest base-down prism overcome before one eye and the strongest base-up prism before the same eye gives the AMPLITUDE OF SUPRAVERGENCE, 4△ to 6△ normally. The same result should be obtained whether the prism is placed before the right eye or the left eye. If a difference is found it may be due to fatigue or to the production of a tonic contraction by the effort that was required to overcome the first prism; this persists for a certain time; or it may be due to the subject gaining more facility after one or two trials, although supravergence is scarcely amenable to extension by exercise.*

The eyes can also rotate around their front-to-back axes in the interests of fusion, such movements, when considering either eye separately, being termed *torsions* or *cyclo-rotations*. The extent to which the eyes can execute these movements with respect to one another when continuing to observe a given object will be described as cyclovergence, and will be dealt with in Chapter XIII.

Convergence in a given individual can often be increased by exercise; divergence, supravergence and cyclovergence are more constant and less amenable to exercise.

5.7. Rotary Prism Devices.

In carrying out the tests described above for eliciting the powers of the visual apparatus to overcome prisms in the effort to obtain single vision of the test object and fuse the images into one mental impression—vergence tests, or fusion tests as they are sometimes called—gradually increasing or decreasing prismatic power has to be put before the eyes. Instead of using single prisms one after another in the trial frame for this purpose, it is more convenient to employ some kind of rotary prism arrangement. Suppose we have two prisms each of strength P prism dioptres mounted face to face in a single holder before the right eye and capable of rotating in opposite directions at equal speeds.† When one prism is base up and the other base down there is no prismatic effect either in the vertical direction or the horizontal; they form a parallel sided slab of glass. If now the prisms are rotated around an axis coinciding with the eye's visual axis, the base-down prism clockwise and the other anti-clockwise,‡ each through an angle θ, we introduce before the right eye a resultant horizontal prism, base out, of strength $2P \sin\theta$. The first prism lies base out and down along $(90 - \theta)$ and the second base out and up along $(90 + \theta)$. Their resolved vertical components annul one another. The resultant horizontal prism gradually increases as the rotation is continued until

* §13.18.

† *Ophthalmic Lenses*: Ch. VI.

‡ As viewed by the examiner standing in front of the subject—the "examiner's view".

it reaches a maximum value equal to 2P when $\theta = 90°$. The two prisms are now horizontal, and base out.

On further rotation the resultant horizontal prism decreases until it becomes zero again when $\theta = 180°$. The prisms have now changed places, the original base-up prism being now base down. On still further rotation the bases of the prisms become respectively base in and up, and base in and down, the resultant effect being a horizontal prism, base *in*, which increases to a maximum value 2P as before. There has been no resultant vertical prism throughout.

If, by further rotation, we bring the two prisms back to their starting position and then turn the complete holder through 90°, the prisms are set respectively base out and base in and again produce no effect in any direction A procedure similar to the one already described introduces before the right eye a resultant *vertical* prism base up and base down, as far as the same maximum value 2P in each case.

Thus, with such a rotary prism device we are able to provide *gradually* increasing amounts of prism power, either horizontally or vertically, according to the starting position adopted. The principle of the rotary prism was introduced by Sir John HERSCHEL for astronomical work and first adapted to ophthalmological requirements by CRÉTÈS of Paris. A form in which the two prisms are mounted in a small circular holder which fits into the ordinary trial frame was introduced by RISLEY of Philadelphia. In the Risley rotary prism, each prism has an apical angle of 15° and therefore produces a deviation, or has a prismatic power of about 15△.

Instruments incorporating the rotary prism principle may be used for carrying out vergence tests such as those described in §§5.4 and 5.5 and for other purposes to be discussed in Chapter XIII. In the so-called variable prism stereoscope,* two rotary prisms of this kind are used, one before each eye. By means of a worm and wheel mechanism, base in or base out prism effect is introduced simultaneously before both eyes.

A rotary prism of the Herschel type just described, of power approaching that of the Risley prism, is marred by considerable chromatism unless the individual prisms are

* Used in connection with testing for motor-balance: Ch. XIII.

made achromatic or a coloured plano glass of good quality is added to them. Even so objects seen through the instrument are blurred and distorted and if used before one eye only, so that the image seen by this eye is blurred in comparison with that seen by the other eye, the impulse to fusion is diminished. This disadvantage is obviated by placing the two prisms one before each eye. This design is adopted in the STEVENS phorometer (1888) and the prism verger of MADDOX.*

THE PHOROMETER.

This instrument is similar to the prism verger in that the two prisms are separated, one being placed before each eye, but they rotate in the *same* direction and in all positions produce a relative prism effect on the two eyes. The apparatus (Fig. 5.5) was designed for the measurement of

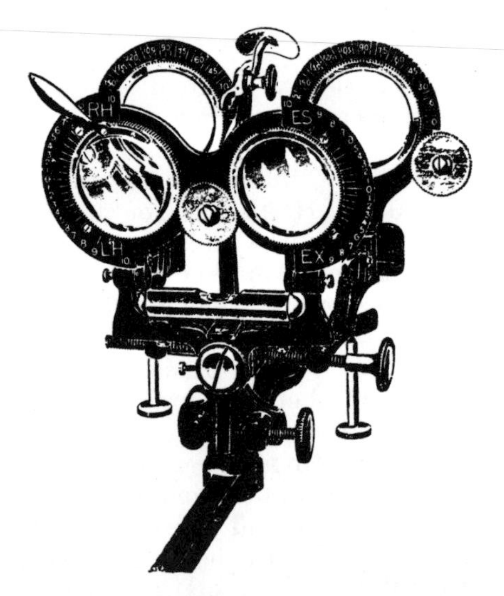

FIG. 5.5—STEVENS' PHOROMETER

heterophoria and is not adapted for determinations of the vergence power. Each prism has a deviating power of 5△. There are two zero positions as in the prism verger. In one

* Described by MADDOX in the first (1889) edition of his book *The Clinical Use of Prisms*, but not commercially available until 1906. The instrument is now obsolete.

of these the prism before the right eye is base up and the one before the left eye, base down. The eyes being unable to overcome this amount of relative prism effect in the vertical direction, they will fall into their passive position and there will be vertical diplopia of the test object; the object as seen by the right eye will be the lower one of the two. In these circumstances fusion of the two images is impossible and any horizontal deviation of the eyes in their passive position will result in the objects appearing not only at different levels vertically, but also displaced horizontally from one another. The subsequent procedure belongs to the subject of heterophoria, and will be discussed in Chapter XIII.

EXERCISES. CHAPTER V.

1. Why is it necessary for the eyes to converge when observing a near object? Explain how the amount of the convergence is usually expressed and the units used.

2. A prism of refracting angle 11° and refractive index 1·53 is placed base in before the right eye of a subject whose inter-ocular distance is 60 mm. An object at 6 metres is viewed with both eyes. What effect is produced? Give the position or positions of what is seen and draw a careful diagram. What will be the angle between the visual axes?

3. A prism is placed before one eye of a subject, the other eye being occluded. Show, giving a clear explanatory diagram, that the rotation of the eye to receive the image on the fovea
   (*a*) is equal to the prism deviation when viewing a distant object;
   (*b*) is less than the prism deviation when viewing a near object.

4. An object lying on the primary line of an eye is observed, with that eye alone. A 6Δ prism is placed base down before the eye, the distance separating prism and centre of rotation being 27 mm. By how much must the eye rotate to maintain direct vision of the object (*a*) when the object is distant; (*b*) when the object lies one-third metre beyond the prism?

5. Define the unit "metre-angle" sometimes used in expressing amounts of convergence of the eyes. Prove that the convergence of each eye in prism dioptres is given by the product of the number of metre-angles of convergence and the semi-interpupillary distance in centimetres. Give a diagram.
   What is the disadvantage of the metre-angle as a unit?

6. Find the value of the metre-angle in minutes of angle in the case of persons of P.D. (*a*) 55 mm.; (*b*) 60 mm.; (*c*) 70 mm. Reckon the object distance as one metre measured from the line joining the centres of rotation of the eyes—the inter-ocular base line.

7. What are the advantages that accrue from the possession of two forward-looking eyes? What prompts the eyes to converge when the attention is directed to a near object?

Describe the unit frequently adopted in expressing the extent of this convergence.

8. Describe the synergic act of convergence-accommodation. (B.O.A. Hons.)

9. With the aid of an appropriate diagram, or diagrams, explain carefully the terms: far point of convergence; near point of convergence; amplitude of convergence; plane of fixation. Give the normal values for the first three of these quantities.

10. A person can converge sufficiently to see singly an object 8 cm. from the inter-ocular base line, and he can diverge under compulsion until his fixation lines intersect in a point 50 cm. behind the base line. His P.D. is 63 mm. Find his amplitude of convergence in metre-angles and in prism dioptres.

Repeat for a second person whose near point of convergence is at 9 cm. and far point at −40 cm., the P.D. being 64 mm.

11. Write an account of the relationship between accommodation and convergence, explaining the condition of the hyperope and the myope in this connection.

12. Explain carefully, with a diagram, the meaning of the following terms: primary position; position of anatomical rest; position of functional rest; near passive position; fixation position; accommodative convergence; fusional convergence.

13. In what manner does the comfort of a person in binocular vision depend on his fusion faculty? What is meant by physiological exophoria?

14. Explain the terms: relative accommodation and relative convergence. State the normal amounts of the positive and negative relative amplitudes for a person 15 years old and draw a careful accommodation-convergence diagram for such an individual who is emmetropic.

15. Describe carefully some method of *measuring* the extent of the relation between convergence and accommodation. (B.O.A. Hons.)

16. Explain the terms: amplitude of convergence; amplitude of relative convergence. The two eyes fix a bright spot of light at 6 metres; explain the effects of the following prisms, giving diagrams showing the path of a typical ray from the object into the eyes:

(*a*) 2△ base in before right eye;
(*b*) 10△ base in before left eye;
(*c*) 10△ base out before right eye.

17. (*a*) A spot of light placed over the zero of a scale of centimetres is observed binocularly from a distance of 6 metres. A 20△ prism is placed base in before the right eye. Explain what will happen. Give a careful diagram of the arrangement, showing the two eyes, their foveæ, nodal points, centres of rotation, and the positions of the two retinal images.

(*b*) The first prism is replaced by one of 5△ base in before the right eye. Give the same information as that required in (*a*).

18. Explain the effects on the apparent distance and size of a near object when observed binocularly through prism (*a*) base out; (*b*) base in.

19. Explain carefully the difference between convergence and relative convergence of the eyes. How can these two quantities be measured ?

What are the disadvantages attendant on the use of prisms for measuring such quantities as these ?

20. Draw an accommodation-convergence diagram for an emmetrope whose amplitude of accommodation is 5 dioptres. Mark the diagram to show up clearly the amplitude of relative convergence, positive and negative, both at distance and at near.

21. The terms breadth of fusion, ductions and prism vergences are sometimes used in connection with vergence movements of the eyes. Write a short account of the two meanings given to these terms by different people.

A subject fixes binocularly a bright spot of light at 6 metres. Explain the effect of placing before the right eye :

(*a*) an abducting prism of 3△

(*b*) an abducting prism of 12△

(*c*) an adducting prism of 12△. Give diagrams.

22. Explain the terms : supravergence and cyclo-vergence. State the average extent of the former and describe how it may be measured.

A spot of light at $33\frac{1}{3}$ cm. is observed binocularly and an 8△ prism is inserted before the right eye, base down. Explain what will occur and what, giving dimensions, will be seen.

23. Explain how to ascertain whether a subject's " vergences " are normal or not. Define the term normal in this connection and describe how to measure each of the lateral and vertical vergences. State any precautions that need to be observed during the tests.

24. Discuss the relative accommodations and convergences, before and after correction, of a case about 20 years old whose manifest correction is +4 D sphere, R. and L. eyes. (S.M.C.)

25. What relative amplitude and range of convergence would be indicated if an emmetropic subject, with a P.D. of 64 mm., could just see an object 80 cm. away distinctly and singly, on observing it through either a pair of 16△ adducting prisms or a pair of 4△ abducting prisms.

26. How is the relation between accommodation and convergence affected by (*a*) uncorrected hypermetropia, (*b*) uncorrected myopia ? What would happen in such cases, as regards distance and near vision, if there were no elasticity in the relationship between accommodation and convergence ?

27. A 3·5 D hyperope with a P.D. of 58 mm. wishes to see distinctly and singly an object 40 cm. away without his accommodation having to be assisted. He desires also to maintain the same relationship between accommodation and convergence as an emmetrope. What glasses, if any, would enable him to do this ?

28. Explain the terms : homonymous diplopia and heteronymous diplopia. Describe a method of exhibiting these conditions to a subject.

What kind of diplopia would be observed by a person viewing a distant object through a 12△ prism base down before the right eye and a 4△ prism base down before the left eye ?

29. Describe, with diagrams, the optical construction and mode of action of a rotary prism of the Herschel type. For what purpose are these rotary prisms used?

If the strength of each component prism is P prism dioptres and the starting position is vertical, show that after a rotation of θ from this position, the deviation produced is horizontal and given by 2P sin θ.

30. Two prisms, each of apical angle 6° and refractive index 1·667 are mounted in contact as in a rotary prism device. They are set in the zero position with their base-apex lines vertical. Find the magnitude and direction of the resultant prism effect after rotations of 15°, 30°, 60° and 90°; and hence indicate on a diagram the calibration of the scale to read in prism dioptres of deviation.

31. Explain the principle involved in the construction and use of the Stevens' phorometer. Give a sketch of the essential parts of the instrument, indicating the scales. What precautions should be observed in practice to obtain reliable readings?

32. Describe three optical phenomena which occur when an observer, after looking at a distant object, looks at one near to his eyes. Give a brief account of the muscular activities associated with each of these. (B.O.A.)

33. A Risley rotary prism, consisting of two prisms of 15° apical angle and made of spectacle glass, is set at zero with the front prism base in and the two base-apex lines exactly horizontal before the subject's right eye. What would be indicated if the prisms could be rotated just 6° on either side of the horizontal meridians without producing diplopia?

34. Explain briefly, with diagrams, the optical construction of the phorometer of Stevens. What disadvantage of the Herschel type of rotary prism is obviated in this instrument?

35. A double prism (or bi-prism) of spectacle glass, having apical angles of 6°, is placed with base-apex line vertical before an eye viewing a small spot of light 6 metres away. Explain exactly what will be seen. The subject's other eye is occluded.

If the fellow eye of the subject be provided with a base-in prism of 5Δ and the light now observed binocularly, what will be seen?

36. If a hyperope of, say, 6 D has his attention directed to an object distant one-third metre and one eye is occluded, whereabouts in relation to the fixation position will be the passive position tend to lie? Where will it lie in the case of a myope of 6 D? Give reasons. If the cover is removed from the occluded eye, what happens and why?

37. Hyperopes with ample accommodation nevertheless frequently suffer discomfort in carrying out close work. Explain why this is so. Why does the provision of lenses correcting the ametropia generally alleviate the discomfort?

38. Describe and give the optical theory of two forms of variable prisms. If a deviation of 5Δ base up is required, assume suitable elements for each device, and calculate precisely the conditions necessary to give this deviation. (S.M.C. Hons.)

ACCOMMODATION AND CONVERGENCE

CHAPTER VI

ACCOMMODATION. NEAR CORRECTION.

6.1. Accommodation referred to the Spectacle Point.

WHEN discussing the range and amplitude of accommodation in Chapter III, the positions of the far and near points of accommodation were referred to the eye itself. As we shall see, however, there is some practical convenience in making measurements from the spectacle point; and usually the pre-determined distance correction is in position when the measurements are made. It is necessary to be clear at the outset as to the relationship between the quantity thus measured and the actual accommodation exerted by the eye. For although an ametropic eye is rendered emmetropic by its distance correction, the amount of accommodation it has to exert in order to see distinctly an object at a given distance through that correction is not the same as the accommodation exerted by the emmetropic eye when observing the same object.

EMMETROPIC EYE.

To explain this, consider first an emmetropic eye, Fig. 6.1. The far point M_R is at infinity and the near point at

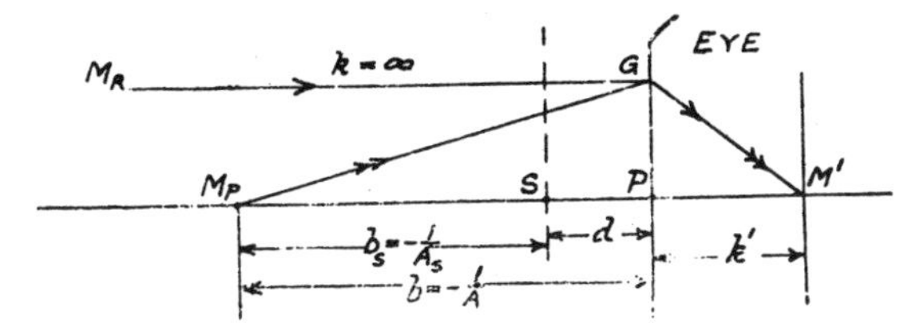

FIG. 6.1—TO ILLUSTRATE OCULAR ACCOMMODATION IN RELATION TO SPECTACLE ACCOMMODATION; EMMETROPIC EYE.

M_P, distant b metres from the eye at P. When the eye is relaxed, a ray M_RG incident parallel to the axis from the far point, is focused on the fovea M′; when the eye is fully accommodated, a ray M_PG from the near point is focused at M′. The eye increases its dioptric power by an amount equal to the difference between the dioptral distances of M_R and M_P. That is :

$$A = 0 - B = -B \qquad \text{(see also §3.6)}$$

If the individual is called upon to do close work such as reading at a point nearer to the eye than M_P, he must evidently be assisted by a positive lens ; and the power of the lens required depends upon three factors, namely :

(*a*) the accommodative amplitude possessed by the subject, or the position of the near point M_P;

(*b*) the distance at which the close work is to be carried out ;

(*c*) the position that is to be occupied by the aiding lens ; whether, for example, it is to be placed at the spectacle point S, or nearer to the eye.

We will consider a numerical example.

Example. The near point of accommodation of an emmetropic eye is found to be 40 cm. in front of the spectacle point, which we will take as 14 mm. from the eye. If the person is to use only two thirds of his full amplitude for continuous near work, what lens will he require for near work at 33·33 cm. from the spectacle point (*a*) if the lens is to be placed at the eye ; (*b*) if the lens is to be placed at the spectacle point ?

Answer. Refer to Fig. 6.1.

When eye is relaxed, parallel light is focused at M′.

When eye is fully accommodated, near point M_P is − 400 mm. from S, or − 414 mm. from P, light reaching eye with divergence

$$\frac{1000}{-414} = -2{\cdot}415 \text{ D} = B$$

Accommodation of eye is therefore + 2·415 D.

Eye is to use only two thirds of this, that is 1·61 D ; in this partially accommodated state of eye, light must reach it with divergence − 1·61 D in order to be focused on M′.

When near work is held − 333.3 mm. from S. or − 347.3 mm. from P, light from it reaches eye with divergence.

$$\frac{1000}{-347{\cdot}3} = -2{\cdot}879 \text{ D.}$$

(*a*) Hence power of lens placed at P to change this divergence to − 1·61 D is

$$-1{\cdot}61 - (-2{\cdot}879) = +1{\cdot}27 \text{ D.}$$

(*b*) Now suppose the aiding lens is to be placed at S ; even so, the light must reach the eye with divergence − 1·61 D, coming from a point distant

$$\frac{1000}{-1{\cdot}61} = -621{\cdot}1 \text{ mm from P; or } -607{\cdot}1 \text{ mm. from S}$$

Divergence in plane through S is consequently

$$\frac{1000}{-607\cdot 1} = -1\cdot 647 \text{ D}$$

Power of lens at S to convert divergence -3 D of light from the near work into $-1\cdot 647$ D is

$$-1\cdot 647 - (-3) = +1\cdot 353 \text{ D}.$$

A rather stronger lens is required at S than at P.

We do not wish, nor is it necessary, to make calculations of this kind in practice. We shall obtain practically the same result by referring everything to the spectacle point, Measurement gave the near point as 40 cm. in front of S. and so the amplitude reckoned from this point is $2\cdot 5$ D, as against $2\cdot 415$ D actually exerted by the eye.

Allowing two thirds of the amplitude referred to S to be exerted

$$\text{i.e. } \tfrac{2}{3} \times 2\cdot 5 = 1\cdot 67 \text{ D}$$

the lens at S to convert the divergence of -3 D from the near work into $-1\cdot 67$ D is

$$-1\cdot 67 - (-3) = +1\cdot 33 \text{ D}$$

which is very nearly the same result as that obtained above.

We thus find that in the case of an emmetropic eye possessing insufficient accommodative amplitude to carry out near work comfortably, the positive power required is obtained very approximately by basing it upon the accommodation referred to the spectacle point, which is the quantity that is measured in practice. The reason for the suggestion that the subject be required to exert only two thirds of the full amplitude for continuous near work, will be discussed later.

The accommodation A measured from, and actually exerted by, the eye is the quantity we dealt with in Chapter III. If we represent the distance of the near point M_P from the *spectacle* point by the symbol b_S, the reciprocal of this, B_S, is equal and opposite to the accommodation referred to S, which we will represent by A_S. Thus

reckoned from P, $A = -B$ in emmetropia

" " S, $A_S = -B_S$ " "

and from Fig. 6.1 $b_S = b + d$

The accommodation, A, referred to the eye we will call the PRINCIPAL POINT or OCULAR ACCOMMODATION. The quantity A_S, referred to the spectacle point, we will call the

SPECTACLE ACCOMMODATION. The former is the amount actually exerted by the eye; the latter is the quantity measured in practice.

AMETROPIC EYE.

When the eye is ametropic an additional factor, the power of the distance correcting lens, enters into the relationship between ocular and spectacle accommodation. Consider Fig. 6.2 (A) which represents an unaided myopic eye, the far and near points of which are at M_R and M_P, distant k and b metres respectively from the eye at P. When the eye is relaxed, a ray M_RG is focused on the fovea M′; when the eye is fully accommodated, a ray M_PG is focused at M′. The eye increases its dioptric power by an amount equal to the difference between the dioptral distances of M_R and M_P. That is (§3.6)

$$A = K - B$$

Fig. 6.2 (*B*) represents the same eye, but provided now with its negative distance correction, of power F_1, at the

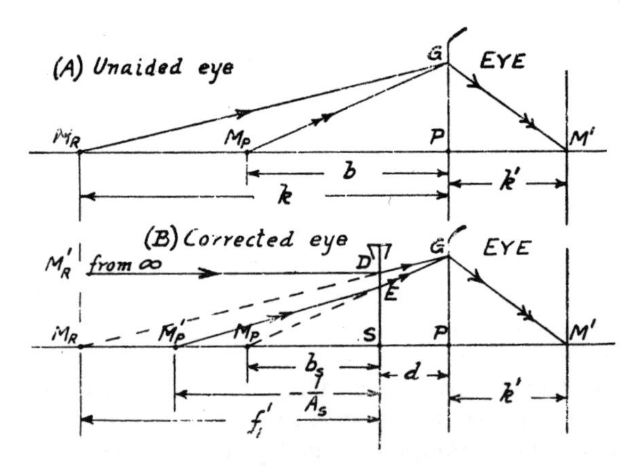

FIG. 6.2—TO ILLUSTRATE OCULAR ACCOMMODATION IN RELATION TO SPECTACLE ACCOMMODATION; MYOPIC EYE.

spectacle point S. The far point of the eye and lens combined, that is the *artificial* far point as it is sometimes called, is at infinity; the combination is emmetropic. A ray M'_RD parallel to the axis is diverged by the lens by such an amount that it enters the eye at G as if coming from the *true* far point M_R. The light leaves the lens with divergence F_1 which becomes K when it reaches the eye; and

$$K = \frac{F_1}{1 - dF_1} \qquad \text{from (3.2)}$$

The eye being relaxed, this light is focused on the fovea.

When full accommodation is exerted, the light must enter the eye as if coming from its *true* point M_P. To be seen distinctly an object must therefore be placed at a point M'_P, which is imaged by the lens at M_P. The ray $M'_P E$ is diverged by the correcting lens into the direction EG, which enters the eye as if from M_P. The point M'_P is the near point of the eye and lens combined, or the *artificial* near point; the true near point is the image of this formed by the correcting lens, just as the true far point M_R is the image of the artificial far point M'_R (at infinity) formed by the lens.

If we were to determine the amplitude of accommodation of the unaided eye, we should have to find the true far point distant k from P and the true near point distant b from P; and so obtain the *ocular accommodation* $A = K - B$. But in practice the accommodation is usually investigated with the distance correction in position. In that case our measurements are made from the spectacle point S and, as just explained, it is the artificial near point that we obtain. (Methods employed to determine this point will be discussed in §6.5). Thus, with the lens in position, the far point is at infinity and the near point at M'_P; and the amplitude of the combination of eye and lens is given numerically by the dioptral distance of M'_P *reckoned from the spectacle point, S*. This quantity is the *spectacle accommodation*. It differs from the ocular accommodation, which is the amount actually exerted by the eye, by reason of the separation d of the distance correction from the eye and of the modifying effect of the power F_1 of this correction.

Example. (*a*) The nearest point seen distinctly by a myope wearing his distance correction of -6 D is found to be 40 cm. in front of the spectacle point; the latter is 14 mm. in front of the eye. Find the ocular accommodation of the eye and the spectacle accommodation.

(*b*) If this person is to use only two thirds of his full amplitude for prolonged near work, what lens will he require for near work at 33·33 cm. from the spectacle point ?

Answer. Refer to Fig. 6.2.

(*a*) Far point M_R is $\frac{1000}{-6} = -166 \cdot 67$ mm. from S

or $-(166 \cdot 67 + 14) = -180 \cdot 67$ mm. from P

When eye is relaxed, parallel light from infinity is diverged by the -6 D lens, leaves this lens with divergence -6 D and reaches the eye at G with divergence

$$\frac{1000}{-180\cdot67} = -5\cdot536 \text{ D}.$$

This is the ocular refraction, K.

When eye is accommodated, light from M'_P, after refraction by the spectacle lens, is received by the eye and focused at M′; and $SM'_P = -40$ cm. Hence light leaves lens with vergence

$$-2\cdot5-6 = -8.5 \text{ D, as if coming from } M_P.$$

Thus

$$SM_P = \frac{1000}{-8\cdot5} = -117\cdot6 \text{ mm. and } PM_P = b = -131\cdot6 \text{ mm.}$$

and light reaches eye with vergence $\dfrac{1000}{-131\cdot6} = -7\cdot60 \text{ D } (=B)$.

The eye must have accommodated by an amount $(K-B)$ equal to $-5\cdot536-(-7\cdot60) = +2\cdot064$ D.

This is the ocular accommodation, A.

The spectacle accommodation is simply the dioptral distance of the artificial near point M'_P subtracted from zero;

i.e. $$0-(-2\cdot5) = 2\cdot5 \text{ D}.$$

(b) For continuous near work the eye is to use only two thirds of its full amplitude, that is

$$\tfrac{2}{3}\times 2\cdot064 = 1\cdot376 \text{ D}.$$

Since, when the eye is relaxed, light must reach it with vergence $-5\cdot536$ D in order to be focused on M′, the vergence of the incident light must now be $-5\cdot536-1\cdot376 = -6\cdot91$ D, diverging from a point at a distance

$$\frac{1000}{-6\cdot91} = -144\cdot7 \text{ mm. from P, or } -130\cdot7 \text{ mm. from S.}$$

Thus when the eye is engaged in near work the light must leave the spectacle plane S with vergence

$$\frac{1000}{-130\cdot7} = -7\cdot654 \text{ D}.$$

Hence, if the near work is 33·33 cm. in front of the spectacle point, the lens for such near work must have power

$$-7\cdot654-(-3) = -4\cdot654 \text{ D}.$$

The lens for distance correction is -6 D; the lens for near work at one third metre from S is $-4\cdot654$ D; thus, the *additional* power for the near work is $-4\cdot654-(-6) = +1\cdot346$ D or, say, $+1\cdot35$ D.

There is no need to carry out such calculations as this in practice when we wish to prescribe additional power for near work. Referred to the spectacle plane the accommodation is 2·5 D. If we take two thirds of this to be in active use, then to read at one third metre the distance lens of -6 D must have added to it an amount

$$3-\tfrac{2}{3}\times 2\cdot5 = +1\cdot33 \text{ D}$$

which is very nearly the same as the more accurately calculated result above, and the same as the result obtained for the emmetropic eye.

Example. As in the previous example, but for a hyperope corrected for distance by a +6 D sphere.

Answer. Proceeding in the same manner:

(*a*) with eye relaxed, light from infinity reaches eye with vergence +6·55 D.

With eye accommodating: light leaves correcting lens with vergence −2·5+6=+3·5 D travelling towards M_P (Fig. 6.3), at a distance 285·7 mm. from S, or 271·7 mm. from P. On reaching P its vergence is therefore

$$\frac{1000}{271\cdot 7} = +3\cdot 68 \text{ D}$$

and ocular accommodation required = 6·55 − 3·68 = 2·87 D.

The spectacle accommodation = 2·5 D.

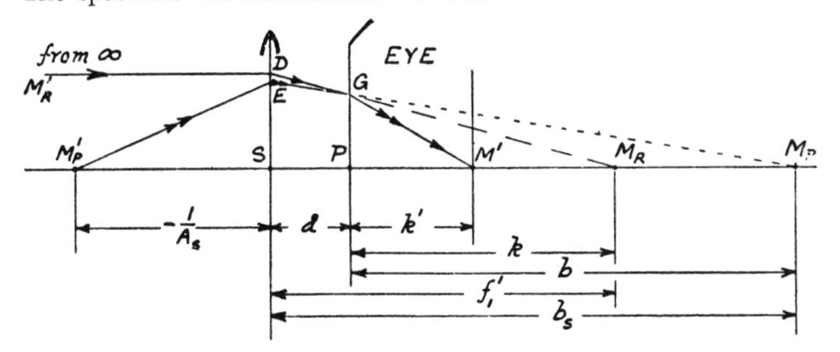

FIG. 6.3—TO ILLUSTRATE OCULAR ACCOMMODATION IN RELATION TO SPECTACLE ACCOMMODATION; HYPEROPIC EYE.

(*b*) If only two thirds of the ocular accom. is to be used, i.e. 1·91 D, the light must reach P with vergence 6·55 − 1·91 = 4·64 D, travelling to a point 215·5 mm. behind P or 229·5 mm. behind S. Light leaves lens at S with vergence

$$\frac{1000}{229\cdot 5} = +4\cdot 355 \text{ D}.$$

It reaches the lens from the near work with vergence −3 D. Hence power of lens required

$$= 4\cdot 355 - (-3) = +7\cdot 355 \text{ D}$$

or, the *additional* power for near work at $\frac{1}{3}$ metre = +1·355 D.

Had we taken the measured spectacle accommodation of 2·5 D and allowed two thirds of this, the extra power for near work at one third metre would have been

$$3 - \tfrac{2}{3}\ 2\cdot 5 = +1\cdot 33 \text{ D}$$

as in the emmetropic and myopic cases.

We find that corrected hyperopic eyes have to exert more accommodation, and corrected myopic eyes less accommodation, than the emmetropic eye in order to see clearly a near object at a given distance. To carry out near work at a specified distance (such as one third metre) the additional lens required (if any) is, however, practically the same in all cases; and its power may be determined, to a close approximation, directly from the measured spectacle accommodation. If two thirds of the subject's full amplitude of accommodation is to be used, for continuous near work at a dioptral distance L from the spectacle point, and if we represent the *spectacle* accommodation by A_S and the additional power required by F_A, then

$$F_A = -L - \tfrac{2}{3} A_S \qquad (6 \cdot 1)$$

The following table connects ocular accommodation with the corresponding spectacle accommodations for ametropes of varying degrees, corrected for distance. The spectacle point is assumed 14 mm. from the eye's principal point. The student should check some of the values in the tables in the manner indicated in the above examples. The first column of the table, giving the age of the subject, will be dealt with in the next paragraph.

TABLE. MONOCULAR ACCOMMODATION AND AGE. (Based upon DUANE)
Separation of spectacle point and principal point of eye, 14 mm.

Age Years.	Ocular Accom. A Dioptres.	A_S = spectacle accommodation in dioptres when distance correction worn is								
		+10	+6	+3	0*	−3	−6	−10	−15	−20
10	**11·0**	9·4	10·75	11·8	**13·0**	14·25	15·5	17·3	19·8	22·5
15	**10·25**	8·7	9·9	10·9	**12·0**	13·1	14·25	15·9	18·2	20·6
20	**9·5**	7·9	9·1	10·0	**11·0**	12·0	13·0	14·5	16·6	18·8
25	**8·5**	7·0	8·0	8·8	**9·6**	10·5	11·5	12·8	14·6	16·5
30	**7·5**	6·1	7·0	7·7	**8·4**	9·1	10·0	11·1	12·6	14·2
35	**6·5**	5·2	6·0	6·5	**7·1**	7·8	8·5	9·4	10·7	12·0
40	**5·5**	4·35	5·0	5·5	**6·0**	6·5	7·0	7·9	8·9	10·0
42	**5·0**	3·9	4·5	4·9	**5·4**	5·9	6·3	7·1	8·0	9·0
43	**4·5**	3·5	4·0	4·4	**4·8**	5·2	5·6	6·3	7·2	8·0
44	**4·0**	3·1	3·5	3·9	**4·2**	4·6	5·0	5·5	6·3	7·1
45	**3·5**	2·7	3·1	3·4	**3·7**	4·0	4·3	4·8	5·5	6·1
46	**3·0**	2·3	2·6	2·9	**3·1**	3·4	3·7	4·1	4·6	5·2
47	**2·75**	2·1	2·3	2·6	**2·8**	3·1	3·4	3·75	4·25	4·8
48	**2·37**	1·75	2·0	2·25	**2·4**	2·7	2·9	3·2	3·6	4·1
50	**2·0**	1·5	1·7	1·9	**2·1**	2·2	2·4	2·7	3·0	3·4
52	**1·75**	1·25	1·5	1·6	**1·8**	1·9	2·1	2·3	2·6	3·0
55	**1·5**	1·1	1·3	1·4	**1·5**	1·7	1·8	2·0	2·25	2·5
60	**1·25**	0·9	1·1	1·2	**1·25**	1·4	1·5	1·7	1·9	2·1
65	**1·12**	0·8	1·0	1·1	**1·12**	1·25	1·3	1·5	1·7	1·9
70	**1·0**	0·75	0·9	1·0	**1·0**	1·1	1·2	1·3	1·5	1·7

* Up to age 45 a spread of ± 2 D is allowable; at 50 years ± 1 D; and from 55 upwards, ± 0.5 D.

6.2. Accommodation and Age.

The capability of the eye to increase its refractive power in order to see near objects diminishes steadily as age advances. Thus the amplitude of accommodation decreases, the near point receding gradually further and further away from the eye. Although a complete understanding of the cause of this recession of the near point is impossible until we have fuller knowledge of the processes involved in the act of accommodation,* there is little doubt that the main cause is the sclerosis or hardening of the crystalline lens with age. As a consequence, the contraction of the ciliary muscle and the moulding action of the lens capsule are able to produce less change of shape in the hardening lens of the adult than they could in the softer, almost semi-fluid, lens of youth. In §2.14 attention was drawn to the physical accommodation, or the actual change in refractive power brought about in the lens, and the physiological accommodation or power of the ciliary muscle. Clinical observations show that the adult appears to be under as much strain in maintaining his full three or four (or fewer) dioptres of accommodation as is the youth in holding his considerably greater amplitude. Hence a considerable body of opinion is in favour of the view that the middle-aged adult exerts his maximum effort of physiological accommodation, even although the physical result of it in the hardened lens is small. It may be, however, that the strain is partly the result of the changed relationship between accommodation and convergence. For although the amplitude of accommodation decreases with advancing years, the amplitude of convergence remains comparatively unimpaired, and it may be that the full innervation for accommodation tends to be accompanied by a large amount of convergence, in which case a considerable demand will be made upon the fusion faculty in order to maintain binocular single vision.

In any case the main cause of the sequence of events is the loss of resiliency in the lens. There may also be some diminution in the physiological accommodation due to weakening of the ciliary muscle with age, but this does not appear to be appreciable.

The loss of accommodation is a normal physiological accompaniment of senility and takes place at more or less

* §2.14.

the same rate in all normal individuals, whether emmetropic or ametropic. DONDERS first published a table giving average figures for the amplitude at all ages from 10 to 70 years or so. Careful observations have been made since by Dr. Alexander DUANE. The figures given in the first two columns of the table on p. 202, connecting age and ocular accommodation, are derived from his results. We see that the youth of 20 years has normally an amplitude of 9·5 dioptres. If he is emmetropic his near point lies, therefore, 105 mm. from the eye's principal point P. If he is a myope wearing a distance correction of – 10 D, then his amplitude measured from the spectacle point is 14·5 dioptres; his artificial near point is only 69 mm. $\left(=\frac{1000}{14\cdot5}\right)$ from the spectacle point, when measured with his distance correction in position. The amplitude of which the eye is capable has dropped to 3·5 D at age 45, and the near point has receded to a position 285 mm. from P in an emmetropic subject. It will be observed that, according to DUANE, the rate of decline of the amplitude is somewhat accelerated between the ages 40 to 55 years, after which the decrease is much more gradual.

The figures in the table refer to *monocular* accommodation and were measured for each eye separately, the fellow eye being occluded. If both eyes are allowed to observe the test object, the near point of accommodation then obtained is somewhat nearer the eyes than when one eye is occluded, probably because in the former case the operation of the convergence function is accompanied by some slight extra accommodative innervation not operating in the absence of convergence. Thus DUANE gives the excess of binocular over monocular accommodation as follows:

Below 17 years	0·6 to 0·7 D
18—31 years	0·5 D
32—53 years	0·4 D
Above 53 years	0·3 D

We see that the young eye possesses remarkable powers of accommodation; at age 15 it can change from its focus so as to see distinctly at all distances from infinity up to 9·75 cm.—in the emmetrope. A corresponding focusing adjustment in a camera would require a large movement of the plate.

DONDERS made his observations mostly on emmetropic eyes and referred his measurements of the near point distances to the eye's nodal point. This he took as 3 lines, or 0·25 Paris inch, or 6·77 mm. behind the cornea ; which is thus 5·1 mm. back from the reduced surface, P, of our simple eye. The figures given in the table in the Appendix have been obtained by subtracting 5·1 mm. from the emmetropic near point distances given by DONDERS, so as to refer the amplitudes to the principal point of our standard eye. DUANE, on the other hand, used the spectacle point* as his origin for measurements, " the near point being determined . . . either with the full distance correction, or with such determinate addition to that correction as would bring the range within measurable limits ". Thus the figure given by DUANE is the quantity we have designated by A_s, except that he took the spectacle point as being 14 mm. in front of the *cornea* whereas in our standard eye it is 14 mm. in front of P. This slight adjustment has been made and all figures for amplitude somewhat rounded off in the table. It is not clear from DUANE's published papers that he made any allowance for the effect of the correcting lens on the accommodation actually exerted by the eye. His figures are the result of observations on over 4,000 eyes.

Both DONDERS and DUANE obtained their results subjectively. As already mentioned, we are never quite sure that the optical system of a subject's eye is really in accurate focus on the test object, even when the subject feels quite definitely that he is accommodating on it and is seeing it distinctly. It would be interesting to determine the refractive condition of the eye by some objective method, such as the objective optometer,† when seeking to measure amplitudes of accommodation.

It is probable that the near point of accommodation is affected by the illumination of the test object. FERREE and RAND have found that it is situated somewhat nearer to the eye at higher illuminations, especially in old people.

6.3. Recession of the Far Point. Acquired Hypermetropia.

After the early years of bodily growth, the static refraction of the eye, and hence the position of the far point, remains substantially stationary in the normal individual. At about the age of 55 years there commences, however, a slowly progressive tendency to hypermetropia, this so-called ACQUIRED HYPERMETROPIA being due to changes taking place in the crystalline lens.

The growth and development of the lens continue into adult life. Not only does it become less elastic, resulting

---

* He assumed the anterior focal point of the eye to be 14 mm. in front of the cornea and adopted that as the spectacle point.

† §§ 7.14 and 7.15.

in the loss of accommodation already described, but the refractive index of the newer cortical layers that are continuously laid down as it develops is less than the index of the older and more sclerosed portions within. The lens thus consists of a series of thin lamellæ which increase in refractive index the nearer they are situated to its centre or nucleus. Optically, therefore, the lens is somewhat complicated but its effect may be approximately represented by considering it as a biconvex lens of a certain index ($n_2=1{\cdot}386$), the central nuclear portion of which has a higher index ($n_3=1{\cdot}406$), the whole being surrounded by the aqueous and vitreous humours of index $n_1=\frac{4}{3}$ (Fig. 6.4). Each of the four surfaces of this compound lens has positive power.

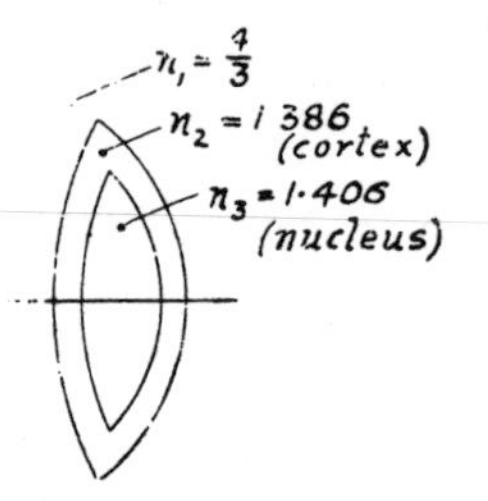

FIG. 6.4—THE CRYSTALLINE LENS (SCHEMATIC).

As it develops, the total power of the lens changes because of (A) decrease in curvature of its surfaces as it increases in size and (B) increase in the refractive index of the cortex and nucleus. The former results in a gradual loss of dioptric power. Whether the latter effect produces a gain or loss of power depends upon the proportionality between the increase of n_2 and the increase of n_3. The power will be raised under heading (B) unless the increase of n_2 is much more pronounced than the increase of n_3.

The net result due to both causes (A) and (B) is normally a loss of power which begins to be noticeable from age 55 or thereabouts; thus hyperopia (of the refractive variety) is acquired, approximately according to the following table.

Age	55	60	65	70	75	80
Acquired H. in D. ..	0·25	0·5	0·75	1·25	1·75	2·25

Sometimes, however, in a case tending towards nuclear cataract the index of the nucleus is raised sufficiently for the gain in power under (B) to prevail over the loss of power due to (A), in which case myopia is acquired.

Returning to the normal case: a myope will tend towards emmetropia. An emmetrope who has acquired, say, one dioptre of hyperopia at age 65 to 70, will experience some difficulty in distance vision since he must exert all his then amplitude of one dioptre to see distinctly. In the case of a person who has been hyperopic throughout life, the hyperopia acquired in the above manner may be accompanied by a further apparent increase due to the change over from latent to manifest error caused by loss in ciliary muscle tone (§3·7). Thus a person whose manifest hyperopia was, say, 1·25 D at age 30, will be hyperopic to the extent of about 2·50 D or 2·75 D at age 65; the latent hyperopia of about 0·50 D to 0·75 D at 30 years, has become manifest and a further 0·75 D has been acquired due to lens changes.

6.4. Optical Correction for Near Vision.

The distance correction is determined as the result of tests carried out with the eye very nearly in its state of relaxed accommodation. (It may be observed in passing that during such distance tests, at 6 metres, the visual apparatus is not quite in a static condition; a small amount of accommodation is in force and the eye with its correction is finally in a condition of slight myopia—one sixth dioptre.)

A considerable proportion of the daily lives of many people is spent with the visual apparatus concentrating on work distant only about one third of a metre, the visual mechanism being in an appreciably active or *dynamic* condition. To reach this state, changes have been brought about in the shape and power of the crystalline lens and in the oculo-motor system of the eyes. It is conceivable that the refractive conditions of the eyes have changed not only in spherical power, but also in the degree of astigmatism; and possibly to different extents in the two eyes. (When the distance correction is astigmatic, the cylinder portion of it produces a different effect in near vision, as we shall see in §6.6). The condition of equilibrium of the oculo-motor system may also be different as between distance and near vision. Whereas the passive position of functional rest may coincide with the distance fixation position so that the eyes take up fixation for distance without effort, there may be a want of balance in near vision which has to be overcome by the individual's fusion resources.*

* §§ 5.4 and 5.5.

It would appear to be desirable, then, to investigate both the ametropic condition and the oculo-motor balance at the near working distance just as they are investigated at 6 metres. The motor balance is so examined, as we shall see. The refractive condition, however, is not completely re-determined at near; the procedure adopted is to accept the distance correction as a foundation upon which to add a certain amount of spherical power, usually equal in the two eyes, determined in accordance with the amplitude of accommodation possessed by the subject. This practice is adopted because of the difficulty of controlling the subject's accommodation when the eyes are in the appreciably dynamic condition necessary to observe a near test object; and because experience shows that the astigmatism does not change, or changes by an amount insufficient to be appreciated by the subject. when the eyes accommodate. It is to be noted that in the accommodated state the pupil contracts and so reduces the cross section of the refracted pencils in the neighbourhood of the retina; any blurring there may be as the result of astigmatism is thereby diminished and vision improved. For this and possibly other reasons, a degree of astigmatism that would render distance vision definitely subnormal can be much more easily tolerated in near vision.

Consequently, the majority of ametropes when corrected for distance enjoy comfortably clear vision at all distances provided their accommodation is adequate. Were it not for the loss of accommodation with increasing age, the distance correction would ordinarily serve for all purposes. It would be necessary only to make sure that the spectacle lenses themselves did not introduce some cause of discomfort in near vision. In anisometropia, for example, the right and left lenses might introduce different vertical prismatic effects when the visual axes intersect the lenses at points considerably below their optical centres, as in reading; in which case a separate pair of spectacles, although of the same power, would be required for near work, suitably decentred to different extents in the two eyes.

As the loss of accommodation and the consequent recession of the near point proceeds, however, it becomes increasingly difficult to see near objects distinctly, and extra positive power has to be added to the distance correction for near work. The subject is then said to have arrived at the condition called PRESBYOPIA (old eye) by DONDERS. It is not possible, nor is it of importance, to give a precise definition of this condition; individuals differ as to the distance at which they hold their reading matter and other kinds of near work, so that, of two persons with the same amplitude of accommodation and corrected for distance, one will become "presbyopic" and require additional power for near work before the other. This working distance depends upon the physical proportions and habits of the individual and, of course, upon the nature of the work to be done. The watch-maker and engraver carry out their fine work at a distance of 20–25 cm.; whereas for playing the piano the distance is 40–50 cm. or more. We will take the average distance as 33·33 cm. beyond the spectacle point.

A person of 45 could see an object at this distance clearly but would have to exert nearly the whole of his full amplitude of accommodation (3.5 D) to do so. Continuous work under such conditions would be very fatiguing, however, for two reasons. Strain would arise from the continued efforts of the ciliary muscle to maintain the full accommodation; and secondly, the innervation for convergence would be in proportion to the accommodative effort, tending to place the visual axes in too convergent a position; a tendency that would be held in check by the fusion faculty, necessitating the expenditure of further nervous energy. Such an individual would suffer from blurred and perhaps double vision of small print, especially in poor illumination when the pupils are dilated and the retinal blur circles large. In due course eyestrain and headache—ACCOMMODATIVE ASTHENOPIA—would set in. Some relief can be obtained by holding reading matter further from the eyes, in a position where it can be focused with less effort. Middle-aged people are frequently observed resorting to this expedient.

As with any other muscle of the body, so with the ciliary muscle it is necessary for comfort that only a certain proportion of its maximum power be called upon for prolonged periods. Only a proportion of the total accommodative amplitude is to be exerted, leaving the remainder in reserve. The proportion to be used is variously given as one half or as two thirds, LANDOLT having suggested the latter figure, which we will adopt for ordinary cases.* Assuming that the amplitude of accommodation has been determined, by

---

* It may be necessary in practice to reduce this proportion to one half in certain cases, such as individuals in poor health, etc.

methods to be described below, if two thirds of this amount falls short of the dioptral distance of the working point agreed upon, the difference is to be made up artificially by means of positive spherical power added to any distance correction the subject may need.

Thus if the full amplitude of an emmetrope or a corrected ametrope, measured from the spectacle point, is found to be 2·25 D, two thirds of this is 1·5 D, hence for near work at one third metre (3 D) the extra power or *near addition* required is 3·0 − 1·5 = 1·5 D. For work at 40 cm., the near addition would be 2·5 − 1·5 = 1·0 D.

We have seen (§6.1) that although the ocular accommodation actually exerted differs from the spectacle accommodation, which is measured in practice, by an amount depending upon the distance correction worn when the test is made, the near addition is nevertheless obtained with sufficient accuracy by subtracting two thirds of the "spectacle amplitude" (A_S) from the working distance L expressed in dioptres, that is

$$\text{Near Work Addition} = \boldsymbol{F_A} = -\boldsymbol{L} - \tfrac{2}{3}\boldsymbol{A_S} \qquad (6{\cdot}1)$$

$$= 3 - \tfrac{2}{3}A_S \text{ for the usual near work}$$

distance.

If, as appears to be the case,* the full amount of physiological accommodative effort has to be exerted by the middle-aged person in order to read, etc., whereas the convergence effort remains unchanged, it would appear that the relationship between the innervations for accommodation and convergence is gradually changing with age, necessitating increasing calls on the fusion faculty. When an ametrope is first corrected for distance, the accommodation-convergence relationship to which he has become accustomed is suddenly changed, and a new relationship has to be developed. The corrected hyperope now requires less accommodation than before; the corrected myope more. Moreover, when later on a presbyopic addition is first worn, the amount of accommodative effort required for near work is suddenly diminished; and again a new relationship between the two functions in near work has to be met. Consequently, unless there are other special conditions to be satisfied, the distance correction and later on the near addition prescribed should be kept as low as possible consistent with the provision of reasonably clear

* §6.2.

and comfortable vision. With regard to the near addition, there is the additional point that the greater the amount of accommodation we leave for the subject to use, the larger is his range of distinct near vision.

6.5. Determination of Amplitude of Accommodation.

To determine the amplitude of accommodation we must, in effect, find the far and near points. If distances, or their reciprocals, are referred to the eye, we have (§6.1)

$$A = K - B \quad \text{dioptres.}$$

If the quantities are referred to the spectacle point, S, we have $A_S = F_1 - B_S$ dioptres.

$B_S = \dfrac{1}{b_S}$ being the dioptral distance to the true near point from the spectacle point (Fig. 6.3). When the subject is rendered artificially emmetropic with his distance correction, it is only necessary to find A_S and from this the near addition, directly. We will assume that the visual acuity of the subject is not too low; only rough determinations can be made if vision is poor.

As laboratory tests, we could employ the concave lens method, or the Scheiner disc. In the former, the distance-corrected subject views a test chart letter; negative spheres added to this correction force the subject to accommodate in order to see the letter distinctly. Each eye would be tested separately. The strongest negative sphere thus overcome measures the spectacle accommodation.

Through a Scheiner disc (see §3.10) the emmetrope or corrected ametrope will see an object, such as a fine line, singly through the two apertures so long as the object is beyond or up to the near point. Within this point, however, the power of the eye's optical system cannot be increased sufficiently to bring the refracted pencils within the eye to a common focus on the retina, so that monocular diplopia results.

A more direct method is to use the *near point optometer*, with which a test object is approached along the visual axis of the distance-corrected eye to the nearest point at which it can still be seen clearly, maximum accommodative effort being made. The distance of the object from the spectacle plane may then be read off on a rule, or "pointer" as it is sometimes called, graduated in cm. and in dioptres. The zero of the cm. scale should commence at the spectacle plane. In the case of young people a concave sphere, say –4 D, should be added to the distance correction in order to remove the near point to a reasonable distance. A positive lens should be added similarly in cases of low amplitudes. In both cases allowance must be made for the added lens, using the conjugate foci relation $L' = L + F$.

With any of the above methods the value obtained for the amplitude should be checked against the subject's age, using the table of §6.1. In doing this, the effect of the distance correction should be borne in mind.

The student must realise that the table of age and accommodation gives only the *averages* of a large number of cases, and represents therefore the amount of accommodation that might reasonably be expected in a subject of the stated age. The figures are to be used only as a general guide. At ages up to about 45 years, the amplitude found may differ from the tabulated figures by as much as 2 to 3 dioptres above and 2 dioptres below and yet be considered as normal; at 50 years the spread is about 1·5 D above and 1 D below; from 55 years onwards $\pm$ 0·5D. If, however, the subject's amplitude is found to fall outside these limits, more especially outside the lower limit, there is revealed an anomaly of accommodation which should receive careful consideration.*

Although young people will not ordinarily require correction for close work, their accommodative amplitude should nevertheless be measured, as it sometimes occurs that young people do not possess the normal reserve of accommodation and will then have trouble with near vision, although corrected for distance.

When the measured amplitude shows that the subject is presbyopic, the near addition may be prescribed according to the rule already given (equation 6.1). It is usually about age 45 years that the need begins to be felt for such presbyopic addition, but this general statement must not be used as a basis for dealing with a given case. Each must be treated on its own merits and corrected in accordance with the accommodation actually measured.

It would be necessary to check a new correction determined in the above manner by adding the extra spherical power to the distance correction in the trial frame and presenting the reading types (§2.12) to the subject for trial.

---

* § 6.7.

It is, in fact, the most common practice to determine the presbyopic addition directly by means of these types, as follows.

READING OR HAND TEST TYPES.

The subject, wearing the distance correction that has already been determined, is asked to hold the card containing the types at his usual reading distance and to read binocularly the smallest line of type he can manage. A person not more than 40 years of age should have no difficulty in reading the smallest (J1 or J2) types in good illumination, unless his acuity is somewhat sub-normal, in which case all but the smallest line or two should be read. People of 45 years and over will probably show a tendency to hold the types further away and will experience difficulty when asked to hold them closer.

In such cases spheres of equal power are added to the right and left distance lenses in the trial frame, the P.D. of the latter being adjusted to about 4 mm. less than the distance P.D. The power of the spheres will depend upon the subject's age or, if the amplitude of accommodation has already been measured with the near point rule or other device, upon the known amplitude. Assuming the case is one in which presbyopic symptoms are just commencing, the spheres will be 0·5 D to 1·0 D. With such lenses added to the distance correction the subject should be able to maintain comfortable vision at his usual reading distance and, further, should see the types clearly when approached to within 20 or 25 cm. of the eyes, indicating that a reasonable proportion of accommodation remains in reserve. If the subject fails to accomplish this, the examiner will first suspect the possibility that too much negative spherical power is present in the distance correction. If this and the possibility of an incorrect age having been given are ruled out, we have evidence pointing to subnormal accommodation, or perhaps to unequal accommodation in the two eyes. In the latter event, confirmed by testing the accommodation of each eye separately, it may be necessary to try different reading additions for the two eyes. Near points at different distances for the two eyes are to be expected in such a condition as anisometropia.

Assuming that no accommodative abnormality is discovered, slight adjustments of the additional spheres may be found necessary in order to provide comfortable near vision with some accommodation in reserve. The tendency should be to undercorrect somewhat in order to interfere as little as possible with the accommodation-convergence relationship, a matter already referred to in §6.4.

If the near work for which the subject requires optical assistance is special in character, the near test must be carried out at the appropriate distance.

The results of the motor balance tests at distance and near and the vergence tests, may lead to a modification of the near work addition arrived at as above ; this will be referred to in Chapter XIII.

The correction finally decided upon may be prescribed, according to circumstances, in the form of separate spectacles for distance and near, or as bifocal lenses, or double (hinged) spectacles.*

Except in special circumstances, the presbyopic addition for the average working distance of 33·33 cm. should never exceed 3 dioptres whatever the age of the subject may be. The average amounts of additional power to be expected at various ages are indicated in the accompanying table. The student should check the figures, which have been calculated on the basis of leaving one third of the accommodation in reserve, the results being rounded off to the nearest quarter dioptre.

TABLE. ACCOMMODATION AND NEAR ADDITION.

(One-third of accommodation in reserve.)

Spectacle Amplitude Dioptres	Age (in Em) Years.	Approximate spherical addition in dioptres for near work at the stated distances, measured from the spectacle point.		
		40 cm.	33⅓ cm.	25 cm.
6·0	40	—	—	—
5·0	42—43	—	—	0·50
4·0	44—45	—	0·50	1·25
3·0	46—47	0·50	1·00	2·00
2·0	50—51	1·00	1·50	2·50
1·5	55	1·50	2·00	3·00
1·25	60	1·75	2·25	3·25
1·0	70	2·00	2·50	3·50

* *Ophthalmic Lenses* : Ch. VIII.

6.6. Effect of Astigmatic Distance Correction in Near Work.

The cylindrical effect produced at the eye by an astigmatic lens, that is the ocular astigmatism, differs from the cylinder effect of the lens itself, the spectacle astigmatism, because of the forward position of the lens (§4.4). Such a lens, correcting the eye for distance, does not correct the eye's astigmatism for near work. Even if the eye accommodates equally in all meridians and therefore remains astigmatic by a fixed amount in all states of accommodation, the cylinder correction required for near work differs theoretically from

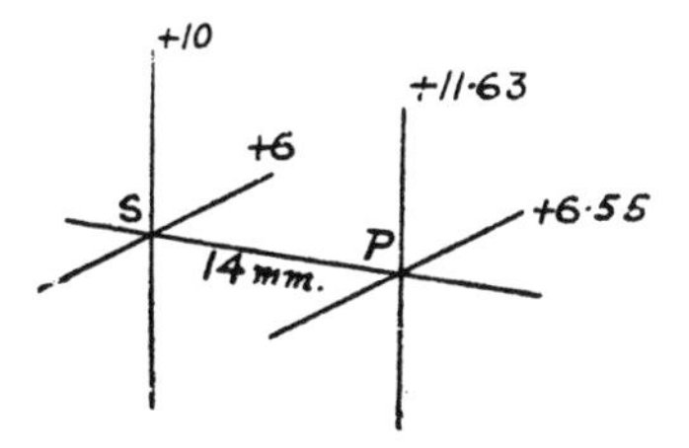

FIG. 6.5—SPECTACLE AND OCULAR ASTIGMATISM.

that required in distance vision. When the astigmatism is of moderate amount, the failure of the distance correction to provide the proper astigmatic correction, for near work gives rise to no discomfort; and the usual clinical procedure of adding only spherical power to the distance correction in presbyopic cases is accepted by most subjects without complaint. The near vision of subjects with higher degrees of astigmatism may, however, be unsatisfactory unless the cylinder prescribed for near work differs from that in the distance correction, in power and perhaps in orientation.

Consider a case of compound hypermetropic astigmatism corrected for distance by the (thin) lens +10 S/ − 4 C. ax. V. placed at our standard position S distant 14 mm. from the reduced surface, P (Fig. 6.5). The effect at the eye is +11·63 D in the vertical meridian and +6·55 D in the horizontal. The spectacle astigmatism is 4 D and the ocular astigmatism 11·63 − 6·55 = 5·08 D. Suppose now the eye, having sufficient accommodation, observes an object 33·33 cm. from the spectacle plane. The light leaves the lens with vergences V. +7 D and H. + 3 D and arrives at P with vergences V. + 7·76 D and H. +3·13 D. The astigmatic effect produced at the eye is only 7·76 − 3·13 = 4·63 D when the near object is observed. In order to obtain a completely sharp retinal image, it would be necessary for the eye to accommodate by different amounts in the two principal meridians, namely:

$$11\cdot63 - 7\cdot76 = 3\cdot87 \text{ D in the vertical.}$$
$$6\cdot55 - 3\cdot13 = 3\cdot42 \text{ D in the horizontal.}$$

(Compare Table §6.1.)

If we assume that the eye accommodates equally in all meridians,* the problem arises to determine the modification to be made to the distance correction so as to satisfy the eye's requirements in near vision. Clearly the cylinder portion should theoretically be changed.

We will consider first a young subject possessing adequate accommodation. If he accommodates the full amount, 3·87 D, proper to the vertical meridian, the power of the lens in this meridian will remain unchanged, for the 3·87 D ocular accommodation is equivalent to 3·0 D spectacle accommodation at S which exactly counterbalances the 3 D of divergence from the near object. In the other meridian, the light reaching P must have a vergence $6\cdot55 - 3\cdot87 = +2\cdot68$ D and must therefore leave the lens at S with a vergence given by

$$\frac{2\cdot68}{1+\dfrac{14\times2\cdot68}{1000}} = +2\cdot58 \text{ D}$$

Power of lens needed in this meridian is therefore

$$3+2\cdot58 = +5\cdot58 \text{ D}$$

and the complete lens for near vision is

+10·00 S./– 4·42 C. ax. V.

If the subject were to accommodate the amount, namely 3·42 D, proper to the horizontal meridian, similar calculations would give the powers of the lens as H. +6·00 D, and V. +10·37 D or

+ 10·37 S./ – 4·37 C. ax. V.

The accommodation of the eye in practice would depend on circumstances, including the configuration of the object being observed (§4.5), but in any case we see that the distance cylinder component should be increased by about 10 per cent. in the example quoted.

Turning to the case where the subject is presbyopic, the increase required in the distance cylinder will be found to depend upon the available accommodation and therefore upon the amount of spherical addition required. Starting with a case in which we will suppose there

TABLE. CHANGE OF DISTANCE CYLINDER FOR NEAR WORK.

Spherical addition in D when near work distance in D measured from spectacle point is :			Increase distance cylinder by
2·5	3·0	4·0	
		0	12 per cent.
	0	+0·50	10 ,, ,,
0	+0·50	1·25	7·5 ,, ,,
+0·50	1·00	2·00	6 ,, ,,
1·00	1·50	2·50	4·5 ,, ,,
1·50	2·00	3·00	3 ,, ,,
2·00	2·50	3·50	1·5 ,, ,,
2·50	3·00	4·00	No change.

* See §4.6.

is no accommodation, the vergences at the eye must be 11·63 D and 6·55 D. and at the lens, therefore, 10 D and 6 D. Hence the additional power for near work at $\frac{1}{3}$ metre will be 3 D in each meridian, and the distance cylinder remains *unchanged*.

Suppose now the maximum accommodation is measured, as explained in §6.5, and the spectacle accommodation, A_S, found to be 2 D. In the vertical meridian, the principal point accommodation corresponding to this is 2·62 D (Table §6.1). Allowing the eye to exert two thirds of this, which is 1·75 D, the light arriving at P is to have vergences of $11 \cdot 63 - 1 \cdot 75 = 9 \cdot 88$ D in the vertical and $6 \cdot 55 - 1 \cdot 75 = 4 \cdot 80$ D in the horizontal. Hence the meridian powers of the lens at S, for work at $\frac{1}{3}$ metre, are to be

$$\text{Vertical,} \quad 3 + \frac{9 \cdot 88}{1 + \dfrac{14 \times 9 \cdot 88}{1000}} = 11 \cdot 68 \text{ D.}$$

$$\text{Horizontal,} \quad 3 + \frac{4 \cdot 80}{1 + \dfrac{14 \times 4 \cdot 80}{1000}} = 7 \cdot 50 \text{ D.}$$

The addition required is 1·68 D in the vertical and 1·50 D in the horizontal, the complete correcting lens for near work being

$$+11 \cdot 68 \text{ S.}/-4 \cdot 18 \text{ C. ax. V.}$$

A somewhat different lens would have been obtained had we assumed the eye's full amplitude to be 2·37 D which is the amount corresponding to the measured spectacle amplitude of 2 D, in the horizontal meridian. The cylinder proves to be −4·16 D in that case.

The near work addition obtained from the simple expression (6.1) is

$$-L - \tfrac{2}{3} A_S = 3 - \tfrac{2}{3} \times 2 = 1 \cdot 67 \text{ D.}$$

which is practically the same as that obtained for the vertical meridian.

If calculations are carried out as above for distance corrections with various spherical and cylindrical powers, including negative values for compound myopic astigmatism, and for different values of the amplitude of accommodation, it will be found that the distance cylinder should be increased according to the foregoing table. Thus the spherical addition may be obtained in the ordinary way by one of the procedures outlined above, and the cylinder then increased by the percentage stated in the table. The correcting lens has been assumed thin in the calculations.

6.7. Anomalies of Accommodation.

If the amplitude of accommodation of either eye falls outside the upper and lower limits stated in §6.5 for the age in question, the case is to be considered as abnormal. Accommodation may be subnormal because of:

(*a*) insufficiency of accommodation
(*b*) paralysis of accommodation
(*c*) spasm of accommodation.

Insufficiency of accommodation may be due to the fact that the crystalline lens does not respond to the ciliary muscle, the lens being sclerosed more than the amount proper to the subject's years. The physiological accommodation may be normal but the physical accommodation is reduced, creating in effect a premature presbyopia. The condition is met by prescribing as for ordinary presbyopia. Alternatively, the insufficiency may be due to loss of physiological accommodation brought about by weakness of the ciliary muscles. In such cases the amplitude is not only subnormal but variable; the subject finds near work troublesome and complains of eyestrain and headaches. The condition may be due to excessive use of the eyes in near work, probably in poor or badly arranged illumination, but general debility or ill-health in some form are usually present also. The efforts of accommodation may be accompanied by excessive convergence, but most frequently there is an insufficiency of convergence. The refractive error should be corrected and, in cases where near work is difficult, additional power given for such work. The accommodation may be improved by exercise, the subject bringing up the accommodation test card (fine black line) towards one eye until it blurs, the other eye being occluded, and repeating this process in the attempt to bring the near point closer to the eye. The exercise is repeated for the other eye, and then with both eyes open.

A sub-division of this latter type of insufficiency occurs in which the subject possesses the normal amplitude for his age but the accommodation cannot be sustained, except for short periods. The subject should be referred for medical treatment.

Loss of amplitude due to paralysis of accommodation is usually accompanied by an enlarged pupil and defective pupillary reaction to light. It is due to paralysis of the ciliary muscle or some region of the oculo-motor nerve. Near vision is blurred and objects often appear smaller than their proper size (*micropsia*) since the extra effort of accommodation required to see them distinctly leads to the delusion that they are nearer than they really are; since the retinal image is of a size proper to the true distance, they appear reduced in size. Distance vision may be normal except for the tendency of the enlarged pupil to produce dazzling. The subject should be referred for medical treatment.

Spasm or cramp of accommodation is comparatively rare. It arises from excessive contraction of the ciliary muscle outside the control of the subject, so that when it occurs in distance vision (*tonic* spasm) it causes emmetropia and low hypermetropia to appear as if the condition were myopia. The excess of accommodation may arise only in near vision (*clonic* spasm). In any case vision, especially for near work, is subnormal, troublesome and fluctuating, which symptoms should prevent the examiner from confusing the condition with genuine myopia. Further evidence is afforded by the apparently diminished amplitude of accommodation obtained. The pupil may be small and sluggish in action. The spasm is completely relaxed by atropine, which is necessary to determine the proper refractive condition.

The few cases of spasm are found usually in young people, excessive close work under bad conditions and marked motor imbalance (exophoria) figuring amongst the several possible causes.

Whereas in accommodative paralysis objects tend to appear smaller than their true size, the opposite phenomenon of *macropsia* is associated with spasm. In this case the voluntary effort of accommodation required to see a near object distinctly is small, leading the subject to the conclusion that the object is further away ; the retinal image, however, is of a size proper to the near distance and hence the object appears enlarged.

Treatment should be undertaken in conjunction with medical opinion. Near work should be limited and carried out under good conditions of illumination, etc.

Unequal accommodation in the two eyes, already mentioned in §6.5, should be included as an anomaly of accommodation.

EXERCISES. CHAPTER VI.

1. Explain carefully what is actually measured when the near point of an eye wearing its distance correction is determined in practice. Establish a relation between this measured quantity and the accommodation actually exerted by the eye. Give a ray diagram.

2. An eye wears its distance correction of -12 D placed 14 mm. in front of the eye's principal point or reduced surface. The near point of accommodation is found to be 50 cm. in front of the lens. Find the actual accommodation exerted by the eye, i.e. the principal point accommodation. What should be the approximate age of the person ?

3. Explain the terms far point and near point of accommodation. How is amplitude of accommodation measured, and why ?

The furthest point of distinct vision is 52 cm. from the eye when a $+10{\cdot}0$ D sphere is placed 20 mm. in front of the cornea. The nearest point is at 12 cm. from the cornea with the same lens. Calculate the refractive error, the amplitude of accommodation and the position of the near point when the correction is worn.

Indicate roughly how the form and thickness of lenses would affect the values given in the question. (S.M.C.)

4. Discuss the advantages and disadvantages of measuring accommodation (*a*) from the anterior focal plane of the eye; (*b*) from the principal plane. Illustrate by solving the following rider:

A person is fully corrected by means of a $+6 \cdot 0$ D sphere placed in the anterior focal plane of the eye (assume static power $+60 \cdot 0$ D). If a $+3 \cdot 0$ D sphere be substituted for the full correction what accommodation is exerted by the eye (*a*) referred to its principal plane; (*b*) referred to its anterior focal plane? (S.M.C.)

5. Criticise the existing methods of measuring the amplitude of accommodation and discuss the effects of high power distance corrections on the apparent amplitude. (S.M.C.)

6. Two eyes, the one corrected by a $+8 \cdot 00$ D.S. and the other with a $-8 \cdot 00$ D.S., show the same near point of 20 cm. from the cornea. If the lenses are worn at 15 mm., calculate in each case the amplitude of accommodation existing in the principal plane. (Ignore the distance between the principal plane and cornea.)

Comment on your results, and state their significance from a practical point of view. (S.M.C. Hons.)

7. A myopic eye is corrected by a -6 D sphere placed at the spectacle point S, 14 mm. in front of the eye's principal point P. With this lens in position the near point is found to be at M'_P, 40 cm. from the spectacle plane, S. Find the actual (principal point) accommodation exerted by the eye.

If only two-thirds of this full accommodation is to be used, what lens will be required for near work at $\frac{1}{3}$ metre from the spectacle point?

8. Account for the loss of amplitude of accommodation with increasing age. Explain why a presbyopic person cannot maintain his full accommodation although the change effected in the form of the lens is small.

9. What is meant by physical and physiological amplitude of accommodation? Account for the loss of amplitude of accommodation with increasing age and discuss the influence which this change may have upon the relation of accommodation to convergence.

10. Plot a graph showing the variation of the amplitude of accommodation with age.

Explain the optical consequences of the onset of presbyopia and find the power of the lens required in the average case, by an emmetrope 50 years old (*a*) for reading at $\frac{1}{3}$ metre; (*b*) for work at $0 \cdot 5$ metre; one-third of the amplitude of accommodation being held in reserve in each case.

11. A young subject is found to require for distance: R. $+1 \cdot 00$ D sphere and L. $+4 \cdot 00$ D.S. Assuming that the principal point accommodation is $4 \cdot 25$ D in both eyes, where will the near points of accommodation be found to be situated when the distance correction is worn 13 mm. from the cornea?

Comment on the practical significance of this.

12. What is the meaning of the term: acquired hypermetropia? Explain carefully how the condition arises. In the case of a subject in whom the refractive changes with age are normal and who was hyperopic 1·50 D at, say, 30 years of age, where will the far and near points be approximately situated at age 60?

13. An equibiconvex lens of refractive index 1·50 has a central portion, also of equiconvex form, of index 1·60. The radii of curvature of the outer surfaces are +10 and − 10 mm., and of the inner surfaces +5 and − 5 mm. Calculate the total power of the compound lens assuming it to be thin and to be surrounded by air.

Calculate the total power also after the following changes have occurred:

(*a*) the index of the outer portions has increased to 1·60, so that the lens is homogeneous;

(*b*) the outer portions increase in index to 1·60, the index of the central portion increasing at the same time to 1·65.

14. Assuming that the distance correction and the spectacle accommodation of a subject have been determined, give a brief account of the factors to be taken into consideration in arriving at the additional power, if any, required for near work.

If the distance correction were − 1·50 S./+1·75 C. ax. 30 and the spectacle accommodation 1·50 D, what lens would ordinarily be prescribed for reading at 33⅓ cm.?

What assumption is made in the usual method of arriving at the near addition?

15. Explain the meaning, causes and symptoms of presbyopia. Discuss the considerations governing the prescribing of glasses in cases of presbyopia.

16. Give reasons why asthenopia is liable to be experienced by a presbyope who, for near work has been ordered lenses in which too strong an addition to the distance correction has been made.

17. What factors should be taken into consideration in arriving at the lenses to be prescribed for near work in a case of presbyopia? Of what symptoms might the subject complain if the presbyopic addition prescribed were (*a*) too weak, (*b*) too strong?

18. What are (*a*) the range, (*b*) the amplitude of accommodation of a subject whose near and far points are distant 13 and 26 cm. from the eye respectively? What glasses would you prescribe for reading and for distance? (B.O.A.)

19. What factors influence your decision to provide a correction for near work only? (S.M.C.)

20. Find the size of, and construct, a Snellen letter H that would be read at a distance of 24 metres by an eye the visual acuity of which is 6/12.

The vision remains 6/12 on adding +4 D sphere before the eye and also with a − 1·0 D sphere, but deteriorates with +4·25 D or with − 1·25 D. By independent means the full amplitude of accommodation is found to be 7 D. Determine the refractive condition of the eye and the lens required for near work at 25 cm.

21. What are meant by range and amplitude of accommodation? Explain carefully how these may be measured.

With a – 5·0 D sphere the near point of a person is found to be at 40 cm. while with a +6·0 D sphere his far point is at 10 cm.—before the eye in each case. Find his refractive condition, amplitude of accommodation and probable age.

22. Taking the diameter of a foveal cone as 0·0025 mm., what is the size of the Snellen letter on the test chart at 6 metres the image of which just covers one cone in the standard emmetropic eye ? What is the visual acuity of the eye if a letter covering ten such cones can just be read ?

What will be the probable effect on the vision of this letter of putting a – 5 D sphere before the eye in the case of a person of age (*a*) 20 years, (*b*) 55 years ?

23. An eye is corrected for distance with a + 10 D sphere placed 14 mm. in front of the reduced surface. With this lens in position the near point is found to be 40 cm. from the lens. Find the amplitude of accommodation, reckoned at the reduced surface.

Repeat for an eye the distance correction of which is – 10·0 D sphere. In each case find the correction for near work at $\frac{1}{3}$ metre from the spectacle point, one-third of the eye's accommodation being left in reserve.

24. When the eye is completely relaxed and looking through a +4 D optometer lens placed 15 mm. from the eye's principal point, a test object is seen distinctly when 50 cm. from the lens. When the eye is fully accommodated the object is seen distinctly as 12·5 cm. from the lens. Find (*a*) the distance correction ; (*b*) the ocular refraction ; (*c*) the principal point accommodation exerted by the eye ; (*d*) the spectacle accommodation. Assume the correcting lens to be worn 15 mm. in front of the eye's principal point.

25. Assuming that a static emmetropic eye can be represented by an air chamber with thin lenses, one of +43 D for the cornea and another of + 20·5 D for the crystalline lens placed in air 4 mm. behind the equivalent corneal lens, find the alteration in power of the crystalline lens when the eye accommodates for its near point at 20 cm. in front of the cornea. Assume the crystalline lens is stationary in position. Compare the crystalline accommodation with the nominal amplitude (S.M.C.)

26. By means of an optometer the near point of accommodation is found to be at 16·5 cm. with a – 3·0 D sphere and the far point is at the same distance with a +1·0 D sphere. Find the refractive condition, amplitude of accommodation and approximate age. What lenses are required for distance and near vision respectively ?

27. A hyperope possesses an amplitude of accommodation of 3·25 D reckoned at the eye. If the position of his near point is determined when he is wearing his distance correction of +8 D at a position 14 mm. in front of the reduced surface of the eye, what will be the distance of this artificial near point from the correcting lens ? What will be the position of the near point in the case of an emmetrope with the same amplitude ?

28. A young person looks at a fan chart through a +1·0 D sph./ – 2·00 D cyl. When the axis of the cylinder is vertical, the vertical line of the chart appears clear and the horizontal blurred. When the cyl. axis is horizontal, the vertical line is blurred and the horizontal clear.

For what range of refractive error is this possible ? At what age roughly would the above observation cease to be possible ? (S.M.C.)

29. If a +6·0 D Cyl. axis V. be placed 16·7 mm. in front of an eye it corrects distance vision. What lens placed in the same plane will correct near vision for an object one-third metre in front of the eye plane ? (Assume ocular astigmatism constant and accommodation possessed ample.) (S.M.C.)

30. A person aged 25 years requires for distance :
R +0·50 D.S./+0·50 D.C. ax. 90 and L. – 0·50 D.S./– 0·50 D.C. ax 180.

Find the positions of the far points when provided with an optometer lens of +4 D. Find also the approximate corresponding near points.

If an astigmatic chart be employed for the test, state which line of the chart will first become clear on approaching the chart from a position beyond the more remote far point, for each eye.

31. Explain how the near point of accommodation of a subject may be determined (*a*) using concave spheres, (*b*) using a Scheiner disc. Give reasons why these methods are not used in ordinary clinical practice.

32. Describe the near point rule or optometer and explain how to determine with it the near point of (*a*) a high hyperope, (*b*) a young myope. Show how the principal point accommodation of the subject is determined from the readings taken, and how this amplitude is checked against the accommodation-age table.

33. Describe the method of determining the near work correction of a subject, using the reading types. State any precautions that should be taken and mention reasons why the near addition determined monocularly may need modification in the final prescription.

34. Explain why, in cases of high astigmatism, the lens adequately correcting the eye in distance vision does not provide the correct astigmatic correction in near vision.

Illustrate your answer by finding the correct lens for near work, at $\frac{1}{3}$ metre beyond the spectacle plane, in the case of a subject whose distance correction is – 10·0 D.S./ – 5·00 D.C. ax. V. worn 14 mm. in front of the eye's principal point (*a*) when the subject is young and has adequate accommodation ; (*b*) when the spectacle amplitude of accommodation is 2 D.

35. Write an essay on the theoretical shortcomings of the usual clinical procedure of determining the correction for close work, in which this correction is based upon the distance correction. In particular, explain why the cylindrical portion of the distance correction may be unsatisfactory for near work.

36. State the anomalies of accommodation that may occur in practice and discuss briefly the possible causes of each.

37. What is spasm of accommodation and how would you establish its presence ? (S.M.C.)

OPHTHALMIC INSTRUMENTS

CHAPTER VII.

OPHTHALMOSCOPY.

7.1. Illumination of the Eye. Field of View .

FOR many reasons it is necessary to examine the internal media of the eye and the fundus, especially the area of the latter containing the macula and optic disc ; or, as in retinoscopy, to utilise light emerging from the eye for the purpose of measuring its refractive condition objectively. Difficulties arise on account of the smallness of the pupil, which is the only entrance fcr the light required to illuminate

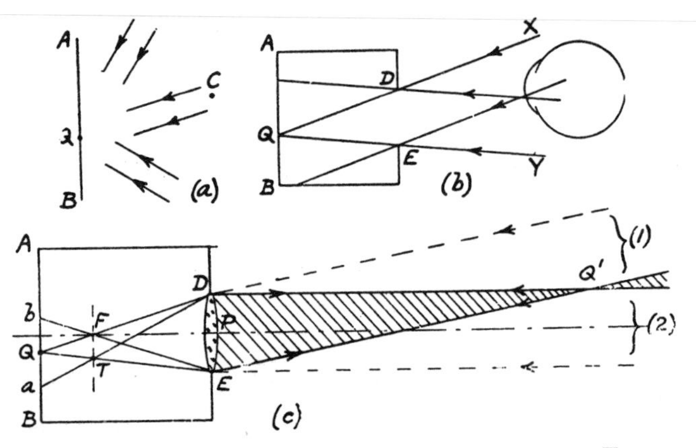

FIG. 7.1—ILLUSTRATING THE ILLUMINATION OF THE EYE.

the otherwise dark interior and the only aperture through which observations of it can be made.

If a surface AB, Fig. 7.1, is set up in ordinary daylight, any point Q on it is illuminated by light reaching it in practically parallel pencils from all directions, as from the sky. If the surface is of a nature to reflect light diffusely, Q will be visible under good illumination to an eye placed at C. If the surface be enclosed in a box, as at (b) Fig. 7.1, with an aperture DE, the light able to reach Q is considerably restricted. It is illuminated by light contained within the cone XQY, which cone at the same time limits the light reflected from Q that can emerge from the enclosure. In order to observe Q an eye must be placed within the region XY and so blocks the entering light necessary for the illumination of Q. Hence if the dimensions of the eye and head are comparable with those of the aperture DE, this and the interior appear very dark. The pupil of an observed eye appears black for the same reason.

If the aperture contains a lens, the illumination and observation of AB are further circumscribed. We will make a brief enquiry into the conditions as they are illustrative of the principles underlying the observation of the eye by means of ophthalmoscopy and retinoscopy. If the lens has a focal length PF, a point Q receives light from all pencils lying between (1) which focuses at T and forms a blur circle Qa on AB, and (2) which similarly produces a blur patch Qb. The light illuminating Q all lies within the cone Q′DE, Q′ being the intersection of the extreme rays of the pencils (1) and (2). Q is evidently the image of Q′ with respect to the lens and all light issuing from Q must also lie within this cone. The pupil of an observing eye must lie, wholly or partially, within the cone in order to receive light from Q.

The diagram serves to represent a myopic eye. It will be evident that the pencil from Q will be strongly divergent as it emerges from an eye with high hyperopia; it will be divergent also beyond a point Q′, situated close to the eye, in high myopia. In these conditions, therefore, an examiner's eye some distance from the subject's eye can be placed within the required cone without intercepting *all* the light necessary for the illumination of Q.

Fig. 7.2 represents an emmetropic eye, JK being the examiner's pupil or the sighthole of an instrument through which observations are being made. If the image J′K′ of the sighthole formed by the subject's eye is constructed by the usual graphical methods, the pencils JDEJ′ and KEDK′ mark out an out-of-focus patch ab on the subject's retina. Considering points between a and b as the origins of pencils returning from the diffusely reflecting retina, we have a parallel pencil (1) emerging parallel to the line aN, from a and pencil (2) parallel to bN, from b. All points between a and b, assuming they can be illuminated, send light through the opening JK and are therefore visible through the apertures JK and DE. Hence the blurred image ab of the sighthole on the subject's retina defines the FIELD OF VIEW.

The examiner's head would prevent the ordinary illumination of the room reaching ab. If we could arrange to provide a small source of light just outside the edge of the sighthole at K, the patch bc would be illuminated, forming the FIELD OF ILLUMINATION. The two fields would be laterally displaced in relation to one another, the portion ac of the field of view being unilluminated. If a second source were placed at J, the whole field of view would be bright. Any extension of the sources laterally beyond J and K would increase the intensity and enlarge the illuminated patch beyond the limits a and b.

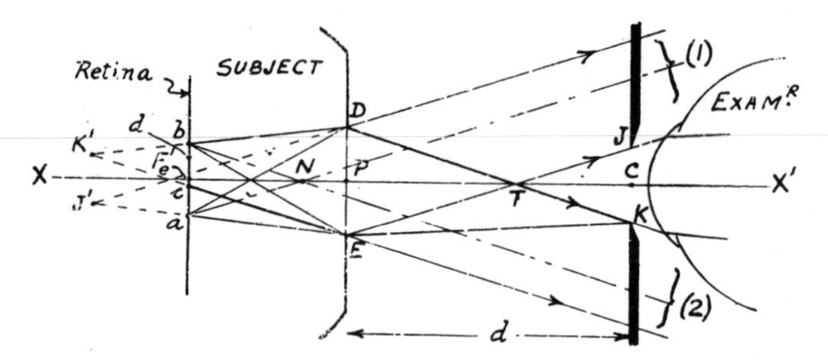

FIG. 7.2—FIELD OF ILLUMINATION AND FIELD OF VIEW.

It is common practice to specify the field of view of optical instruments in angular measure. Thus, with respect to the axis XX′ of the arrangement, the extreme point b is seen under an angle determined by the pencil (2), which is angle DTP or bNF′$_e$. It is the visual angle of the " object " F′$_e$b. We see from the diagram that the tangent of this angle is given by

$$\frac{DP + CK}{PC} = \frac{p_1 + p_2}{d}$$

where p_1 and p_2 are the radii of the pupils at P and C.

It is to be noted that whereas it is only the mere edge of the pencil from a or from b that succeeds in entering the pupil JK, the latter is filled by the light issuing from a central point of the field, such as F′$_e$ (if p_1 is not less than p_2). Thus even if the whole extent of ab be adequately illuminated, it will appear at its maximum brightness only over a central area, outside of which the brightness will decrease gradually to zero at a and b.* There is a point d in such a position in the field that the extreme ray of the pencil emerging from it passes along the direction DC, the pencil thus filling half of the aperture JK. It is usual and reasonable to consider this as the limit of the field, since regions outside it are inadequately illuminated. With respect to the axis, this point is viewed under the angle DCP which we will represent by w, hence

$$\tan w = \frac{p_1}{d}$$

gives half the angular field. If we take the subject's pupil DE as 4 mm. in diameter, the sighthole as 3 mm. and the separation d as 35 mm. we obtain

$$w = \tan^{-1} \frac{2}{35} = 3^\circ\ 16'$$

or, field of view = 6·5 degrees, approximately, which is very nearly the angular size of the optic disc.

The extreme field is

$$2 \tan^{-1} \frac{3 \cdot 5}{35} = 11 \cdot 5 \text{ degrees, approx}$$

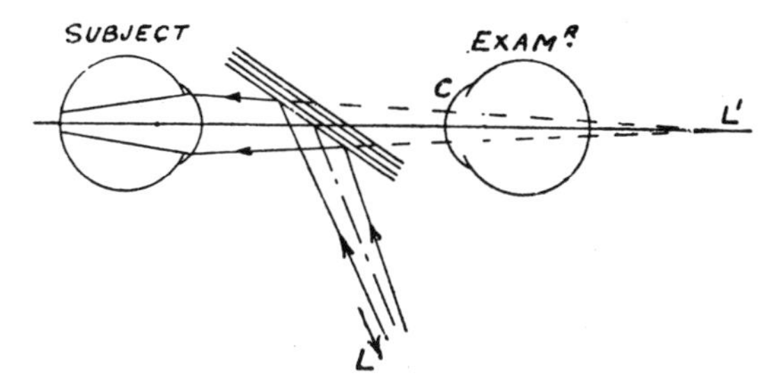

FIG. 7.3—HELMHOLTZ'S OPHTHALMOSCOPE (DIAGRAMMATIC).

Since the eye's interior is invisible under ordinary conditions, artificial means must be employed for its illumination. Fig. 7.3 illustrates the method adopted by HELMHOLTZ, in which light from a source L is reflected into the subject's eye by means of an inclined plane glass plate, or several such plates. A certain area of the fundus is thereby illuminated and can be viewed through the plate by an examiner at C. Much light is lost in this arrangement and,

* The decrease in the apparent brightness will scarcely be appreciated, however, because of the "averaging" property the eye seems to possess. See §20.5.

although it has some advantages, it has been discarded in favour of a silvered mirror provided with a central clear aperture forming a sighthole through which the examiner makes his observation. For certain purposes a plane silvered mirror is used; for others, including observation of the fundus with which we are mainly concerned, the mirror is concave, its curvature depending upon the method of ophthalmoscopy employed. Instruments of this kind are called ophthalmoscopes (=ocular mirrors).

DIRECT OPHTHALMOSCOPY

7.2. The Illumination System.

The fundus can be viewed directly, as in Fig. 7.2, provided we arrange for its illumination. The concave mirror used

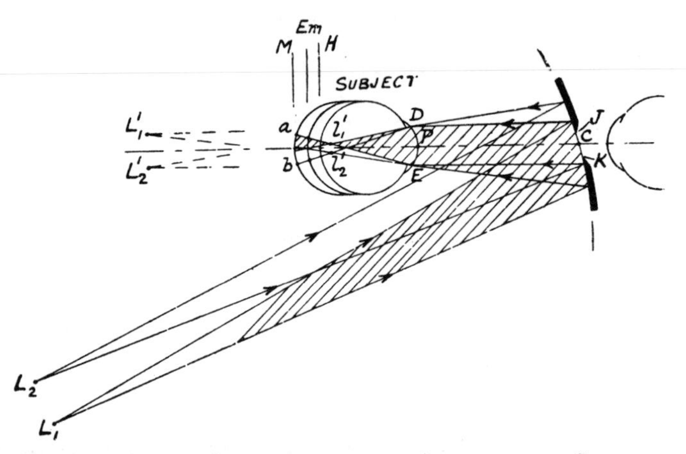

FIG. 7.4—DIRECT OPHTHALMOSCOPY. ILLUMINATING SYSTEM.

for this purpose in this, the *direct method*, varies in focal length from 6·25 to 25 cm. As illustrated in Fig. 7.4, the source of light L_1 L_2, somewhat behind and to one side of the subject's head, is about 25 cm. from the mirror, the focal length of which we will take to be 10 cm. To increase the field of view the examiner must approach as near as practicable to the subject's eye, the separation PC being about 3·5 cm. The sighthole in the mirror will be 2 to 3 mm. in diameter and the subject's pupil under these conditions about 4 mm. The examiner's pupil just behind the sighthole will generally be larger than the latter, but in any case as it is usually in continual motion, the sighthole is the determining aperture. In the absence of the subject's eye the mirror, tilted the appropriate amount, would form an inverted image of the source at L'_1 L'_2 about 13 cm. behind P and about two thirds the size of the source. The eye intercepts these convergent pencils and forms a small image l'_1 l'_2 about $\frac{1}{13}$ the size of the source, 20 mm. or so behind P (taking the power of the eye as 60 D). Each pencil passes through its focus and forms a blur circle on the fundus, the extent of the complete field of illumination ab depending directly upon the position and size of l'_1 l'_2 and the blur circle diameter. These quantities in turn are governed by :

(*a*) the source, its size and distance
(*b*) the mirror, its power and position
(*c*) the subject's pupil
(*d*) the subject's refractive condition.

The diameter of the subject's pupil decreases by reflex action as the brightness of the source is increased, the more so as the light is directed to the macular area. The diminution of pupil size proceeds at a slower rate than the increase in brightness, however ; the intensity of illumination on the patch ab depends mainly on the brightness of the source and the refractive condition.

It can be seen from the diagram that the extent of the diameter of the mirror actually effective is limited by the subject's pupil and the size of source. In practice the diameter of the mirror does not exceed 20 mm. or so. The pencil from each point of the source reflected by the mirror is robbed of some light at the sighthole, especially if this is in the form of a hole drilled through the mirror and not merely an aperture made by removing the silvering from the glass surface.

An average size for the diameter of the source is 25 mm., in which case l'_1 l'_2 becomes about 1·5 mm. Hence with the above arrangement the patch ab varies from a size roughly equal to that of the optic disc in (axial) hyperopia of about 5 D, about two discs in emmetropia, to three discs or more in (axial) myopia of 10 D or so, the intensity of illumination being less in the latter case since the same quantity of light is spread over the larger area. An adequate extent of field therefore is illuminated except perhaps in high hyperopia.

The light is reflected diffusely in all directions by the retina with its choroid backing, so that each point illuminated becomes in effect the source of a returning pencil the convergence or divergence of which on emergence from the eye depends *only* upon the latter's refractive condition.

7.3. The Observation System: Direct Method.

Assuming the fundus illuminated, it is viewed, as in Fig. 7.2, under conditions analogous to those obtaining in the use of the simple magnifying glass, the "glass" in this case being the subject's optical system, of power 60 D. The fundus is thus seen erect and magnified. If the examiner be emmetropic or corrected, then with accommodation relaxed he sees the fundus of an emmetropic subject clearly, provided the subject does not accommodate, since the light leaving the subject's eye is parallel in these circumstances. The ophthalmoscope is provided with a battery of tiny positive and negative spherical lenses which can be rotated, in turn, into position just behind the sighthole. Thus the fundus of a hyperope or myope can be seen distinctly by the relaxed examiner by rotating into the aperture the appropriate positive or negative sphere. In hyperopia the light emerging from the subject's eye is diverging as from his far point, and a positive lens is required to restore the light to the parallelism necessary to the relaxed examiner. A negative lens produces the same effect upon the convergent light emerging from a myopic eye.

The lens required for a clear view of the fundus is thus a measure of the subject's ametropia. For the purpose of measuring ametropia the method is inaccurate and unsatisfactory, however, for the following reasons:

(*a*) Accuracy depends upon complete relaxation of both subject and examiner; the former is very unlikely and the latter not to be relied upon except after long experience.

(*b*) For accuracy the observation should be made on the subject's macula; but when the light is directed to this region the pupil contracts and the corneal reflection obscures the field of view. If observation is made on the optic disc, which is less sensitive to light and contains prominent blood vessels upon which to focus, the estimation of the refraction may be in error since the globe length here may differ from that at the macula.

(*c*) The ophthalmoscope lens swung into position in the sighthole is a considerable distance from the subject's spectacle point. The sighthole is 35 mm. or so from P and the spectacle point 14 mm. from P. Hence the positive lens in hyperopia will be too weak and the negative lens in myopia too strong; very much so in high degrees of error.

(*d*) The difficulties in astigmatic cases are very great. The axis direction especially can be obtained only very roughly.

For measuring ametropia objectively, the method of retinoscopy to be described in the next chapter is much

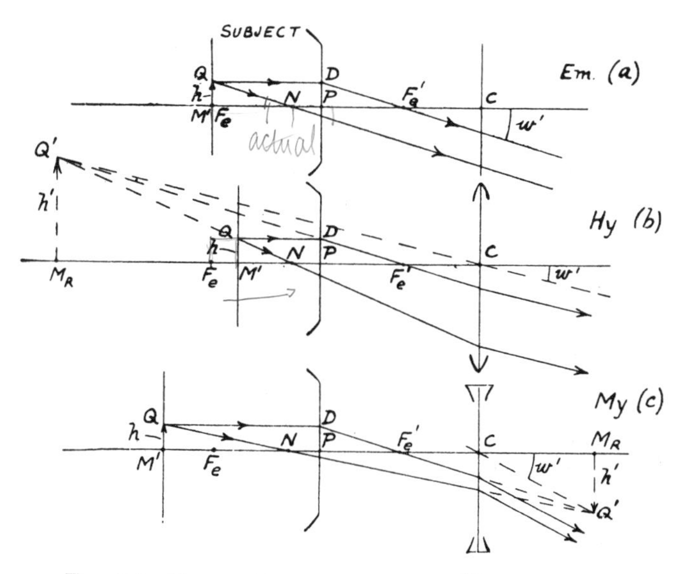

FIG. 7.5—DIRECT OPHTHALMOSCOPY—MAGNIFICATION.

more accurate than ophthalmoscopy, the main purpose of which is to explore the regions in and around the optic disc and macula for signs indicative of disease.

If the examiner be appreciably astigmatic, to obtain a clear view of the fundus it will be necessary for him either to wear his correction or, alternatively, have fitted into the supplementary lens disc of his ophthalmoscope a small cylinder of appropriate power oriented so that its axis will be in the correct meridian when it is rotated into position behind the sighthole. If the subject be astigmatic, vessels of the fundus running in a direction parallel to one of the eye's principal meridians will be clearer than vessels running in a perpendicular direction; the magnification will also differ in the two meridians, so that a distorted view will be obtained.

The corneal reflection, to which reference has been made, arises since the anterior surface of the cornea acts as a powerful convex mirror and forms a bright virtual image of the source and mirror 4 mm. or so within the eye. The reflected light enters the examiner's eye and interferes with his view of the fundus unless the reflected image can be shifted to one side by slight tilting of the mirror. This reflex is particularly troublesome when making observations of the macular area, since when light is directed to this sensitive region the pupil contracts under the increased reflex stimulation. The field of view is thereby diminished and the corneal reflex occupies a larger proportion of it. This matter of the reflex will be discussed later.*

7.4. Magnification and Field of View: Direct Method.

Consider first an emmetropic subject, Fig. 7.5(a). P is the reduced surface of the subject's eye, M′ his fovea. C is the centre of the sighthole through which the examiner is observing. The conditions are those of the simple magnifying glass, the subject's optical system at P acting as the glass and the extent of fundus M′Q as the object. The magnification obtained is given by the quotient†

$$M = \frac{\text{Angle under which fundus is viewed actually}}{\text{(Angle under which it would be viewed if placed alone at the distance of distinct vision, } q = 25 \text{ cm.)}}$$

$$= \frac{h}{F_e N} \div \frac{h}{q} = \frac{q}{f_e} = \frac{250}{16 \cdot 67} = 15.$$

Fig. 7·5(b) represents a hyperopic eye the far point of which is at M_R, a positive lens of focal length CM_R having been introduced into the instrument at the sighthole position C in order to render parallel the divergent pencils emerging from the subject's eye. A given extent of fundus, $M'Q = h$, is imaged by the subject's optical system at $M_R Q'$, which is viewed by the examiner under the angle $Q'CM_R$. This angle is seen to be smaller than the angle DF'_eP or $Q'F'_eM_R$ under which the same extent of fundus is observed in the

* See §7.13.

† See Ch. X for a fuller statement of the magnification provided by optical instruments and systems.

emmetropic case. Hence the magnification is less in hyperopia than in emmetropia. It follows from the diagram that

$$\frac{\text{Magnif. in H.}}{\text{Magnif. in Em.}} = \frac{\angle Q'CM_R}{\angle Q'F'_eM_R} = \frac{F'_eM_R}{CM_R}$$

which is less than unity when the sighthole C is back from the focal point of the subject's eye. When examining an eye that is 10 D hyperopic, the eye-sighthole separation PC being 35 mm., a positive lens of focal length 135 mm. or power 7·4 D is required and the magnification obtained is 12·96.

When the subject's eye is myopic as in Fig. 7.5(c), its optical system forms an image M_RQ' of the fundus at its far point M_R, which is now in front of the subject's eye. A negative lens of focal length CM_R is required and the fundus image is viewed under the angle $Q'CM_R$, which is larger than the corresponding angle in emmetropia, since the proportion $F'_eM_R \div CM_R$ is now greater than unity with the sighthole in the usual position. Thus, as in hyperopia, we have

$$\frac{\text{Magnif. in M.}}{\text{Magnif. in Em.}} = \frac{F'_eM_R}{CM_R}$$

In myopia of 10 D a minus lens of focal length 65 mm. or power −15·4 D is required and the magnification obtained is 19·23.

FIELD OF VIEW.

We have already discussed (§7.1) the field of view obtained in direct ophthalmoscopy when the subject is emmetropic. If diagrams similar to Fig. 7.2 are constructed for hyperopic and myopic eyes, it will be found that the angular extent of fundus visible in the former case is larger and in the latter case appreciably smaller than in emmetropia. This will be seen also from Fig. 7.5 taking account of the fact that the examiner's pupil is situated behind the ophthalmoscope lens at C. In high degrees of myopia the field is very much less than the optic disc; and in large amounts of hyperopia the extensive field of view obtainable may not be adequately covered by the field of illumination.

If, however, as is likely, the hyperopic subject accommodates until the refractive condition is approximately emmetropic (the subject having been requested to gaze at a distant object during the examination), the linear field of view on the fundus will be considerably reduced, being then somewhat less than the standard emmetrope's field. This reduction due to the change from the hyperopic to the emmetropic state is enhanced by the contraction of the pupil which accompanies the accommodation. The figure derived above for magnification in hyperopia will also be affected in practice if the hyperope accommodates; it will be rather more than the 15 obtained in emmetropia.

From the above and Fig. 7.2 we find that the field of view in direct ophthalmoscopy depends upon:

(*a*) the sizes of the subject's pupil and sighthole
(*b*) the separation of these
(*c*) the refractive condition of the subject.

INDIRECT OPHTHALMOSCOPY

7.5. The Illumination System.

In the direct method the field of view is limited, especially in cases of high myopia. To increase the field, pencils such as (1) and (2) of Fig. 7.2 and others still further inclined to the axis, from points of the fundus outside a and b, must be made to enter the examiner's eye. This can be done by means of a strong positive condensing lens held at O, a short distance in front of the subject's eye, as in Figs. 7.6 and 7.7. Light from widely separated portions of the fundus a and b is then collected by this lens and directed towards the sighthole JK in a mirror held some distance away. At the same time this condensing lens forms a real inverted aerial image AB, Fig. 7.7, of the fundus in the region between itself and the sighthole. When the subject's eye is emmetropic this aerial image will be formed at the focal point F′ of the condenser; in myopia and hyperopia it will lie within and beyond F′ respectively.

This is the arrangement for *indirect* ophthalmoscopy. In comparison with the direct method it possesses the definite advantage of a larger field: on the other hand the magnification is correspondingly reduced, and the fundus is seen upside down. The fundus is illuminated by a concave mirror as before, the condensing lens being held in position in the examiner's left hand, the fingers of which may rest on the subject's forehead for steadiness. The distance separating the subject's eye and the mirror is thus a short arm's length, say 60 cm. To provide a reasonable field and produce the aerial image at a convenient distance from the examiner, and having in mind also the illumination of the subject's fundus, the power of lens required is about 13 dioptres. In highly hyperopic subjects a stronger lens may be better.

The source L_1L_2 placed, as before, behind and to one side of the subject's head, is roughly 75 cm. from the mirror at C, Fig. 7.6. The latter has conveniently a focal length of 25 cm., a diameter of 30 to 40 mm. and a sighthole of 4 mm. aperture. As indicated in the diagram, a real inverted image of the source is formed at L'_1 L'_2 where, with an arrangement of the given dimensions, the distance from the

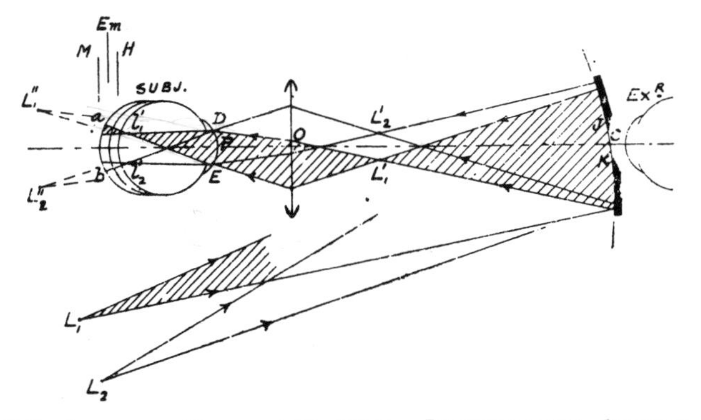

FIG. 7.6—INDIRECT OPHTHALMOSCOPY. ILLUMINATING SYSTEM (NOT TO SCALE).

mirror to the image is 37·5 cm. We shall find when considering field of view below that the condenser is to be held very nearly 9 cm. from the eye or 51 cm. from the mirror. The image L'_1 L'_2 being therefore 13·5 cm. from the condenser, this lens would in the absence of the eye, form a second real image L''_1 L''_2 9 cm. behind the eye (P). Finally, the eye forms an erect image of the source at l'_1 l'_2 very nearly 19 mm. behind P. The size of this image is approximately one eighth of the size of the source. The patch ab formed on the fundus by the overlapping blur circles is about twice the size obtained in the direct method, with same sized source. To cover the comparatively large field of view obtained in the indirect method, a larger source can be used. If the light is supplied by a pearl electric lamp, enclosed in an asbestos chimney provided with a circular aperture, it is an advantage to make the latter large enough to take an iris diaphragm, which can be regulated as required for the two methods, and for other purposes.

To the factors controlling the field of illumination in the direct method, we have the condensing lens as an additional factor. It will be gathered from Fig. 7.6 as compared with Fig. 7.4 that the more extensive illuminated field in the indirect method requires a larger mirror than in the direct, a diameter of 30 mm. being usual.

7.6. The Observation System. Indirect Method.

The light returns from each illuminated point of the fundus and emerges from the eye in parallel pencils in emmetropes (Fig. 7.7) or diverging from or converging to the far point in H. and M. respectively. The real inverted image AB formed by the condensing lens in the neighbourhood of its focal point in all these conditions is viewed

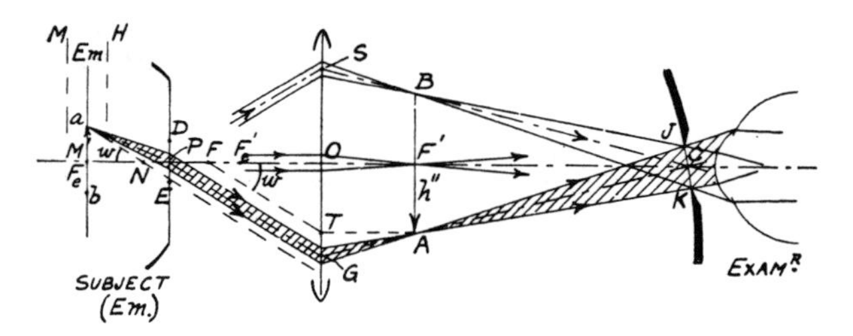

FIG. 7.7—INDIRECT OPHTHALMOSCOPY. OBSERVATION SYSTEM (NOT TO SCALE).

by the examiner, who will either accommodate the necessary amount or preferably, especially in cases of hypermetropia, rotate a plus 1·5 D lens into the sighthole. To obtain a good view of the portion of the fundus it is desired to examine a certain amount of care must be exercised, especially with undilated pupils, and facility is attained only after practice. The condensing lens must be held approximately centrally on the line joining the two eyes and moved longitudinally towards or away from the subject until the mirror and sighthole are imaged on the latter's pupil, a condition necessary for obtaining a wide field of view, as we shall see below. It will be understood from Fig. 7.7 that a lateral movement of the condenser moves the aerial image in the same direction. Thus if, with the optic disc in the centre of the field when examining the right eye, the condenser is moved to the examiner's left, the macula will come into the centre. Different portions of the fundus may be brought into central view also by requesting the subject to move his eye. To examine the lower part of his fundus he must rotate his eye downwards; the fundus moves upwards and the aerial image of it downwards, bringing a lower region of the fundus into view.

A cause of considerable annoyance to the beginner is the presence of three bright reflexes, which are the images of the source and mirror formed by reflection at the two surfaces of the condenser and at the anterior surface of the cornea. Those formed by the lens can be removed from the centre of the field by slightly tilting the lens; this moves the reflexes in opposite directions since, with the usual biconvex condenser, one image is formed by reflection in the convex surface and is virtual, the other is formed by the concave surface and is real, so that they move in opposite directions when the lens is tilted. The corneal reflex may be displaced somewhat by the lateral movement of the condenser mentioned above, which shifts the fundus image relatively to the reflex.

By means of these manœuvres a comparatively clear view of the fundus can be obtained except that it is extremely difficult when attempting to view the macula. The subject's eye is then looking straight into the mirror and the pupil further contracts, so that the view, hampered by the corneal reflex, is unsatisfactory unless the pupil is dilated with a suitable mydriatic.

The indirect method is useful in that it provides a general view of a large extent of fundus. Isolated portions of the fundus can be examined erect and under higher magnification by the direct method. In some cases the direct method is unsatisfactory (e.g. high myopia because of the small field) or impossible (e.g. nystagmus) and the indirect method is then particularly serviceable.

7.7. Field of View: Indirect Method.

Consider first the observation of an emmetropic eye, which is represented in Fig. 7.7. It will be observed that in this diagram the condensing lens has been placed in such a position O that the centre of the subject's pupil at P*

* It is assumed for simplicity that the pupillary plane passes through P (see §10.8.)

and the centre of the sighthole at C are conjugate points with respect to the lens. The sighthole JK is therefore imaged, on a reduced scale since the distance OP is much less than OC, within the pupil DE. Hence *all* rays passing through this small area of DE must pass through JK after refraction by the lens. Consequently the inclination to the axis of marginal pencils such as aPG and bPS, and therefore the extent ab of fundus observed, is limited only by the aperture of the condenser. If this lens were shifted nearer to or further from P, the pencils referred to would not enter the sighthole and the field ab would be diminished. Light refracted by the marginal portions of a lens as powerful as 13 dioptres will be affected by spherical aberration, however, if the aperture be too great, and the peripheral portions of the field near a and b will be indistinct. Hence, although for practical convenience in enabling the posturings of the lens (mentioned above) to be carried out, the lens is usually of about 6 cm. diameter, we will take 4 cm. as the *effective* aperture limiting the field in any one position of the lens.

We can now proceed to obtain an expression for the size of the field of view. The angular dimension of half the field is given by the angle w subtended at the nodel point N by the linear extent M′a, which angle is equal to angle OPG, the tangent of which is OG ÷ OP. OG is 2 cm. To find OP : the distance separating P and its image C is 60 cm. and the lens is + 13 D.* Calculation shows that OP is very nearly 9 cm. Hence

$$\tan w = \frac{OG}{OP} = \frac{2}{9}; \quad w = 12\tfrac{1}{2}°$$

or field of view = 25° ≡ about 4 discs ; including, therefore, a linear extent ab of about 7·5 mm. on the fundus, in emmetropia. We thus obtain a reasonably well defined field about four times larger than that obtained by the direct method. Since in the calculation we have used only 4 cm. of the total aperture of the condenser, the field will extend still further, but the outlying portions will probably be ill-defined. To obtain sharp definition up to the extreme margin of the field of which the full aperture of the condenser is capable, the biconvex form of the lens used in ordinary

* i.e. We have $-l + l' = 0.60$ m. and $\frac{1}{l'} - \frac{1}{l} = F = 13$ D. which gives us a quadratic equation for l or l' and hence two positions of the lens, one 9.06 cm. from P and the other an equal distance from C.

practice would have to be replaced by a form specially designed to be free from aberration, an aspherical curve being necessary for one surface of the lens.* Failing an aspherical lens (which is expensive) the + 13 D could be made up with surfaces of approximately + 11 D and + 3 D the steeper surface facing the examiner. Allowing for the lens thickness the total power would be about 13 D.

The positions of the retina in axial myopia and hypermetropia are indicated in dotted lines at M and H in Fig. 7.7. Although the emerging pencils PG, etc., will be convergent and divergent respectively, the *angular* field of view is still limited as before by the inclination of PG and PS. The *linear* extent of fundus included within this angle is, however, larger in myopia and smaller in hypermetropia, than in emmetropia.

To cover this large field with illumination, especially in the myopic case, it will be necessary to increase the 25 mm. diameter source used in the direct method to 40 mm. or more.

The pencils emerging from the eye are very narrow and do not fill the whole of the subject's pupil. The size of the image of the sighthole formed at P by the condenser is given by

$$\frac{OP}{OC} \times JK = \frac{9}{51} \times 4 = 0 \cdot 7 \text{ mm.}$$

for a 4 mm. sighthole. It is for this reason that the sighthole in the mirror used for indirect ophthalmoscopy should be larger than the 2 to 3 mm. used in the direct method. A smaller sighthole would further reduce the width of the pencils leaving the eye at P and so reduce the brightness of the subject's fundus. The narrowness of the emerging pencils is of importance in connection with the elimination of reflections, to be discussed later.

7.8. Magnification : Indirect Method.

In emmetropia the fundus image AB is formed at the second focal point F′ of the condenser, at a distance of rather more than 43 cm. from the sighthole in our arrangement (Fig. 7.7). For our present purpose consider the half fundus M′a = h and its image F′A = h'', which is viewed under an angle F′CA = w'. Adopting the usual definition

* §7.13 and *Ophthalmic Lenses*; Ch. XV.

of magnification, or magnifying power, of an optical instrument (used for near objects);

$$M = \frac{\text{angle under which image is seen with the instrument}}{\text{angle subtended by object at distance of distinct vision}}$$

$$= \frac{h''}{F'C} \div \frac{h}{q} = \frac{h''}{h} \times \frac{q}{F'C}$$

i.e. the magnification obtained is equal to that produced by the subject's eye and the condenser, reduced in the proportion of the distance of distinct vision to the distance at which the image is actually viewed. From the diagram*

$$\frac{h''}{h} = \frac{OT}{M'a} = \frac{OF}{NM'} = \frac{-f}{f_e} = \frac{-F_e}{F} = \frac{-60}{13} = -4\tfrac{1}{2}$$

(The minus sign signifying that the image is inverted.)

Thus with the dimensions we have adopted

$$M = -\frac{60}{13} \times \frac{25}{43} = -2{\cdot}7$$

as compared with a magnification of 15 in the direct method.

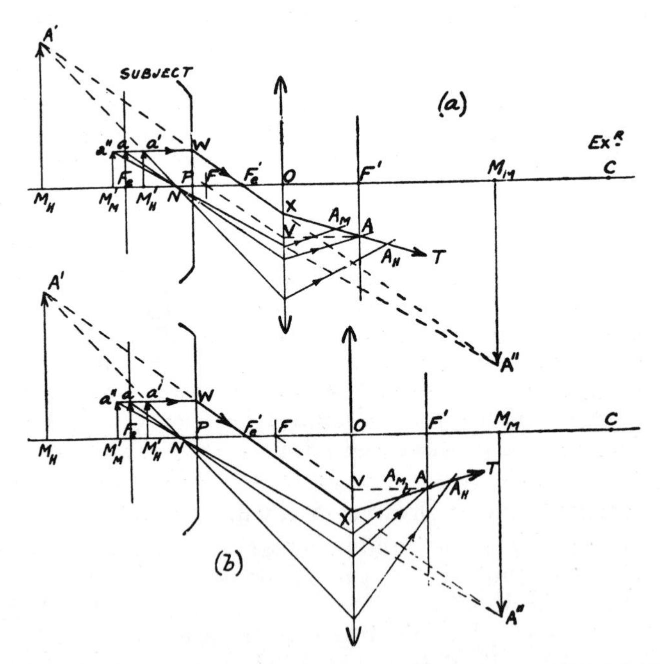

FIG. 7.8—INDIRECT OPHTHALMOSCOPY. EFFECT OF MOVEMENT OF CONDENSER ON MAGNIFICATION OF FUNDUS.

* FT is parallel to PG and hence TA is parallel to the axis.

The magnification is greater in hyperopia and less in myopia than it is in emmetropia, with the condenser in the above position, 9 cm. from the subject's eye. Fig. 7.8(a) is intended to illustrate this. In the emmetropic case the extent of fundus $F_e a$ is imaged at $F'A$ as in Fig. 7.7, the image point A in the F' plane of the condenser being fixed by the usual graphical constructions. For example, a line FV drawn parallel to the ray aN proceeds parallel to the axis as VA in the image space to the right of the condenser, cutting the F' plane in A. The ray aW parallel to the axis within the eye passes after refraction through the focal point of the eye F'_e and hence along the direction XAT after refraction by the condenser. In hypermetropia with the retina at M'_H and far point at M_H, the same extent of fundus $M'_H a'$ is imaged by the eye at $M_H A'$. A' in turn is imaged by the condenser at A_H, which point must lie on the ray XT and also on $A'O$ produced. Similarly in myopia, the fundus $M'_M a''$ is imaged by the eye as $M_M A''$ in the plane through the myope's far point; the image of A'' formed by the condenser lies at A_M on the ray XT where it is intersected by the line OA''. It is thus clear from the diagram that the image is smaller in myopia than in emmetropia and, in addition is further from the examiner at C, which further reduces the visual angle under which it is observed. On the other hand, in hypermetropia the image is larger and nearer to the examiner.

The results we have derived for the field of view and magnification in the two methods may be summarised in tabular form.

	Magnification.			Field of View.		
	Em.	H.	M.	Em.	H.	M.
Direct Method ..	+15	less	greater	6·5°	greater	less
Indirect Method	− 2·7	greater	less	25°	less	greater

7.9. Estimation of Refractive Condition : Indirect Method.

The indirect method of ophthalmoscopy is less satisfactory than the direct in estimating the refractive condition of the eye under examination (unless some special contrivance is added to the arrangement of mirror and condensing lens described). An idea of the state of refraction of the eye can be obtained, however, in the following manner. With the condenser at such a distance from the eye that its first focal point F is within the eye's focal point F'_e as depicted in Figs. 7.7 and 7.8(a), we find that the ray XT slopes away from the axis as it proceeds and consequently the aerial image is smaller in myopia and larger in hypermetropia than it is in emmetropia. If the condenser were removed a little further from the eye until F and F'_e coincide, then the ray A'WX would proceed as XT *parallel* to the axis after refraction by the condenser, and the aerial image would be the same size in all refractive conditions.* If the condenser be removed still further from the eye as in Fig. 7.8(b) the ray XT approaches the axis as it proceeds; the aerial image at A_M in myopia becomes larger than the image at A in emmetropia and the hypermetropic image at A_H becomes smaller. The emmetropic image formed at A remains unchanged in size although, of course, it approaches the examiner. If, therefore, when the condenser is first approached to a position within the 9 cm. distance from the subject's eye and is then withdrawn a few centimetres, the aerial image of some part of the fundus such as the disc increases in size, the condition is myopia. If the image decreases, the condition is hypermetropia.

Here again, however, the hypermetrope may be accommodating, in which case, being approximately emmetropic, the above described diminution of the image will not take place.

The field of view will be reduced when the condenser is removed from its best position.

It may be of assistance to work out a numerical example.

Example. Find the position and size of the aerial image of the optic disc formed in indirect ophthalmoscopy, using a +13 D condensing lens held 5 cm. from the subject's eye, the subject being (*a*) emmetropic; (*b*) hypermetropic 5 D and unaccommodated; (*c*) myopic 5 D.

Find the image sizes also when the condenser is withdrawn a further 8 cm. from the eye. Assume the optic disc to be 1·75 mm. in diameter.

Answer. The refractive errors are assumed axial.

(*a*) *Emmetropia.*

Let h = size of disc; h'' = size of final aerial image

$$\text{Magnification} = \frac{h''}{h} = -\frac{f}{f_e} = -\frac{F_e}{F} = -\frac{60}{13}$$

$$\therefore \text{Size of image} = h'' = 1 \cdot 75 \times \frac{-60}{13} = -8 \cdot 08 \text{ mm.}$$

* Compare §3.12.

which remains constant in all positions of condenser, at a distance $\frac{100}{13} = 7 \cdot 69$ cm. from the condenser O.

(*b*) *Hyperopia of* 5 D.

Eye itself forms image $M_H A'$, at dioptral distance L'_1 from P, of fundus $M'_H a'$, at dioptric distance L_1; and $L'_1 = -5$ D.

$$\text{Magnification produced} = m_1 = \frac{L_1}{L'_1} = \frac{L'_1 - F_e}{L'_1} = \frac{-5 - 60}{-5} = +13.$$

Image $M_H A'$ is first -25 cm. from condenser. Final image A_H is produced at dioptral distance L'_2 from condenser at O.

$$L'_2 = L_2 + F = -\frac{100}{25} + 13 = +9\text{ D}; \quad l'_2 = 11 \cdot 11 \text{ cm. from O.}$$

$$\text{Magnification} = m_2 = \frac{L_2}{L'_2} = \frac{-4}{9}$$

Size of final image $= h'' = 1 \cdot 75 \times 13 \times (-\frac{4}{9}) = -10 \cdot 11$ mm.

When condenser is moved into second position:

$$L'_2 = L_2 + F = -\frac{100}{33} + 13 = +9 \cdot 97\text{ D}; \quad l'_2 = 10 \cdot 03 \text{ cm. from O.}$$

$$\text{Magnification} = m_2 = \frac{L_2}{L'_2} = \frac{-3 \cdot 03}{9 \cdot 97}$$

$$\text{Size of final image} = -1 \cdot 75 \times 13 \times \frac{3 \cdot 03}{9 \cdot 97} = -6 \cdot 91 \text{ mm.}$$

(*c*) *Myopia of* 5 D.

By similar calculation we obtain

1st position: image from O $= 5 \cdot 08$ cm.; size $= -6 \cdot 53$ mm.

2nd position: image from O $= 3 \cdot 66$ cm.; size $= -10 \cdot 08$ mm.

Thus in hypermetropia of 5 D the aerial image of the disc decreases from $10 \cdot 11$ mm. to $6 \cdot 91$ mm. as the condenser is withdrawn; whereas in myopia of 5 D it increases from $6 \cdot 53$ mm. to $10 \cdot 08$ mm. In emmetropia it remains constant at $8 \cdot 08$ mm.

Example. If, in the previous example the examiner observes with the sighthole held 60 cm. from the subject's eye, find the magnification of the whole system in each case.

Answer.

$$\text{Magnif.} = \frac{\text{Angle subtended by final image at observing eye}}{\text{Angle subtended by object at dist. of distinct vision } q.}$$

$$\left.\begin{array}{l}\text{Angle subtended by} \\ \text{object at distance } q\end{array}\right\} = \frac{1 \cdot 75}{250}$$

(*a*) *Emmetropia.*

1st position of condenser:

$$\text{Angle subtended by image } h'' = \frac{8 \cdot 08}{(600 - 50 - 76 \cdot 9)} = \frac{8 \cdot 08}{473 \cdot 1}$$

$$M = \frac{8 \cdot 08}{473 \cdot 1} \times \frac{250}{1 \cdot 75} = 2 \cdot 44.$$

2nd position :

Angle subtended by image $= \frac{8\cdot08}{(600-130-76\cdot9)} = \frac{8\cdot08}{393\cdot1}$

$$M = \frac{8\cdot08}{393\cdot1} \times \frac{250}{1\cdot75} = 2\cdot94.$$

(*b*) *Hypermetropia* 5 D.

1st position : Image angle $= \frac{10\cdot11}{(600-50-111\cdot1)} = \frac{10\cdot11}{438\cdot9}$

$$M = \frac{10\cdot11}{438\cdot9} \times \frac{250}{1\cdot75} = 3\cdot29$$

proceeding in a similar manner we obtain 2nd position : M = 2·67.

(*c*) *Myopia* 5 D.

1st position : M = 1·87. 2nd position : M = 3·32.

The magnification of the whole arrangement increases in emmetropia and in myopia but decreases in static hypermetropia. In practice the hypermetrope may accommodate to the emmetropic state, in which event the magnification will increase in his case also.

7.10. Observation of the Eye Media.

The previous paragraphs have been concerned with the conditions governing the observation of the fundus. Although this is, in general, of major importance, the routine examination of the eye must include observation of the media anterior to the fundus. After a general survey, in good general illumination, of the facial characteristics of the subject, the external appearance and movements of his eyes and an estimation of the intraocular tension ; followed by the determination of the refractive and accommodative condition, the performance of the eyes in binocular vision, and (where necessary) other functional tests dealing with the field of vision, light perception and colour vision ; a systematic examination is undertaken in a darkened room.

External parts of the eye and the anterior portions of the media are observed under focal illumination using a positive lens, such as the + 13 D condensing lens of indirect ophthalmoscopy, to concentrate the light from a lamp successively on to the different parts, and a magnifying glass or " corneal loupe " to obtain magnification. By means of light reflected into the eye from a concave or plane mirror, a preliminary inspection is made of the transparency of the media and a rough idea may be gained of the refractive condition* if this has not already been determined. This may be followed

* See Chapter VIII.

by indirect ophthalmoscopy and in any case by a closer scrutiny of the iris, lens and vitreous for evidences of scars, adhesions, opacities, etc., using the direct ophthalmoscope.

The order of sequence and technique of these operations are explained in the laboratory and in books on clinical routine. It is necessary here merely to include a word on the manner of determining the approximate position in the eye of any opacities that may be discovered. The method of parallax may be adopted to estimate the depth in the eye of an opacity, using the edge of the pupil as the point of reference. Consider opacities at various depths A, B, C, etc., Fig. 7.9 along the subject's visual axis. If an opacity lie in the pupillary plane at B there will be no relative movement of B and the pupil margin as the examiner shifts his position laterally from Ex. (1) to Ex. (2); or, alternatively, as the subject rotates his eye upwards. In

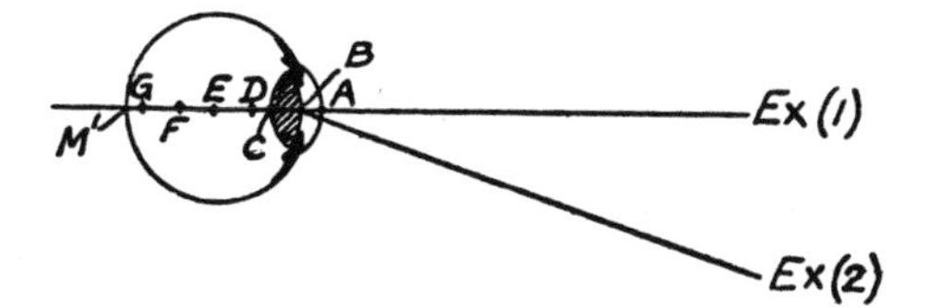

FIG. 7·9—OBSERVATION OF OPACITIES IN EYE MEDIA.

positions such as A, anterior to the pupil, the opacity will move apparently towards the upper edge of the pupil; and if it be farther back than the pupil, its apparent movement will be towards the lower pupillary margin. Opacities such as F and G well back in the vitreous will disappear from view.

The power of the positive lens it is necessary to move into the sighthole of the ophthalmoscope in order to see an opacity distinctly also gives an indication of its depth in the eye. The cornea may conveniently be examined with the + 20 D lens functioning as a magnifying glass, from a distance of 50 mm. if the examiner is emmetropic and relaxed. The same lens will suffice for observation of points B and C by slightly approaching the eye. With, say, a + 12 D in the sighthole a point D, 15 mm. in front of the retina would be seen distinctly from a position about 75 mm. from the cornea. Points E, F and G, respectively 10, 5 and 2 mm. ahead of the retina, would become clear with lenses of power + 10 D, + 7·5 D and + 4 D, the examiner's position and accommodation remaining unchanged.

DEVELOPMENT OF THE OPHTHALMOSCOPE

7.11. The Non-Luminous Ophthalmoscope.

As early as 1823 PURKINJE obtained a view of the interior of the eye by means of candle light reflected from his concave spectacles. Wm. CUMMING, of the London Hospital, succeeded in viewing the fundus in 1846, making his observations to one side of the source of light as explained in §7.1. This method was also used by BRÜCKE of Vienna in 1847. The first mirror for illumination purposes, a silvered glass mirror with a portion of the silvering scraped away to serve as a sighthole, appears to have been made by the Cambridge mathematician Charles BABBAGE in 1847. It remained, however, for HELMHOLTZ, who constructed his first ophthalmoscope (Fig. 7.3) in 1851, to realise the importance of the instrument and to explain with his usual brilliance the underlying optical principles. Great interest was aroused by his exposition of the new instrument and its potentialities, and many different optical arrangements were tried, the indirect method being devised by RUETE early in 1852. By 1856 or so the direct and indirect methods were generally understood and put into practice with instruments that were rather crude; after which there followed a period of gradual mechanical improvement leading to the neat portable instruments of the present day.

A typical example of a non-luminous ophthalmoscope to be used with a separate source of light as explained in the previous paragraphs, is illustrated in Fig. 7.10. Two silvered glass concave mirrors are provided, of different focal lengths and diameters for the direct and indirect methods respectively. Either mirror can be swung round into position before the sighthole, the smaller one for the direct method being tilted so that the instrument itself may be held square-on to the eye and the observations made normally through the lens at the sighthole. Sometimes a plane mirror is fitted in addition.

For clear examination of the fundus and the media of the eye anterior thereto, and especially for the determination of ametropia which was practised by ophthalmologists on the direct method before retinoscopy became generally available, a selection of plus and minus lenses is required. The original disc of four lenses fitted to HELMHOLTZ'S instrument by REKOSS was gradually elaborated into the wheel and chain-drive magazines of the present day, whereby the tiny lenses can be moved into position successively into the sighthole as required. The chain drive head illustrated in Fig. 7.10, generally known as the Morton head, was introduced by COUPER and is usually preferred because of the larger selection of lenses and the greater facility with

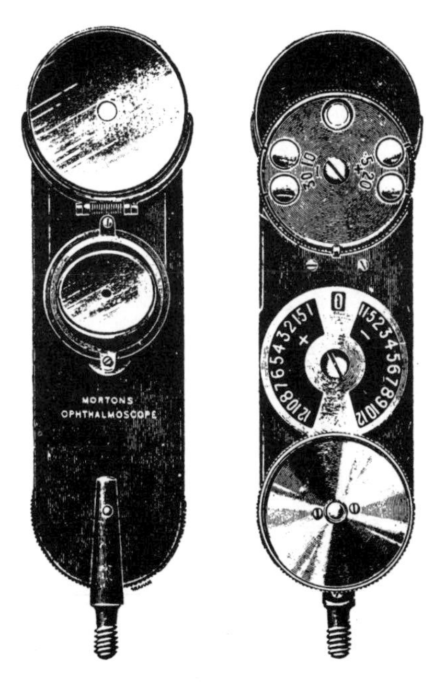

FIG. 7.10—A TYPICAL NON-LUMINOUS OPHTHALMOSCOPE WITH "MORTON HEAD."

which it can be snugly fitted alongside the examiner's nose when in use. On the other hand, the wheel type of head is of simpler construction and less liable to derangement.

7.12. Self-Luminous Hand Ophthalmoscopes.

The close approach to the subject's eye necessary to obtain a reasonable field in the direct method is rather awkward with a non-luminous ophthalmoscope; the light from the source situated beside the subject's head has to be reflected at a considerably oblique angle into the eye.

Efforts to lead the light into the subject's eye from a source contained within the body of the instrument were given a great impetus by the introduction of small low voltage electric lamps, which enabled DENNETT, of New York, to construct the first electric ophthalmoscope in 1884. Since that time various arrangements of the optical system to conduct the light into the eye, and many different types of reflector—glass and metallic—with sightholes of different

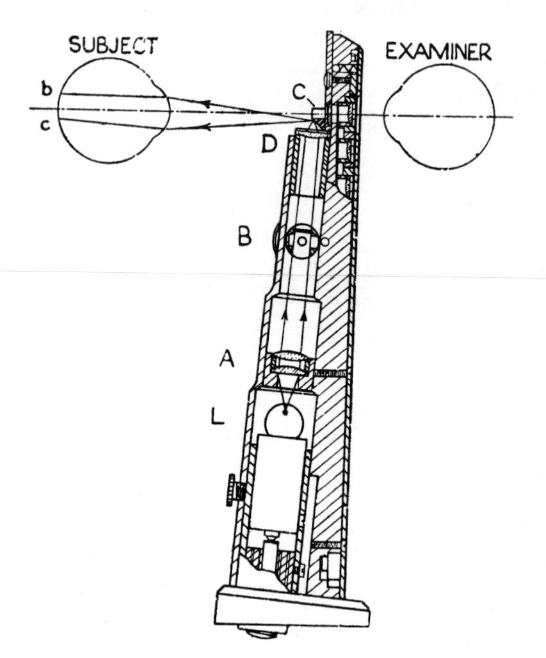

FIG. 7.11—MODERN SELF-LUMINOUS OPHTHALMOSCOPE (EMSLEY).

sizes and shapes, have succeeded one another. The later development of these self-luminous instruments has been in the direction of attempting to improve their optical performance.

Although the corneal and condensing lens reflections encountered in the indirect method can be circumvented by proper posturing of the mirror and condenser in relation to the subject's eye, the reflections make the method more troublesome than direct ophthalmoscopy, at least with the usual type of hand instrument. Most self-luminous hand ophthalmoscopes are consequently used almost exclusively on the direct method and we will describe them first in relation to that method. It is possible to design a hand instrument such that the trouble caused by the reflections in the indirect method is to a large extent eliminated; the principle of the design differs in an important respect from the design required for the direct method and we will postpone its consideration to the next paragraph.

Confining ourselves at the moment, then, to the direct method; it is desirable to provide a clear, uniformly illuminated patch of the required size and intensity on the subject's fundus, including a means of reducing the size

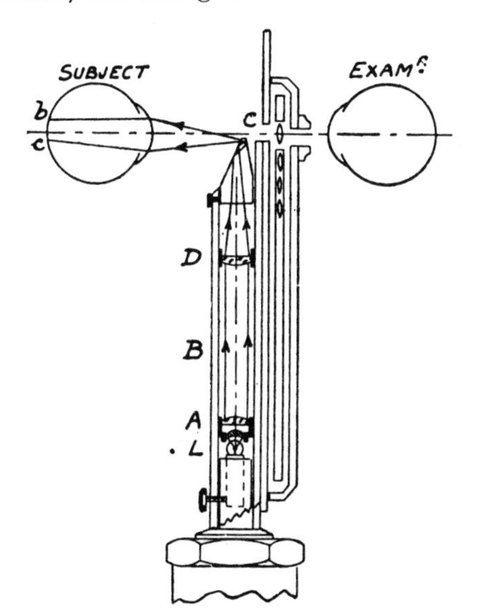

FIG. 7.12—MODERN SELF-LUMINOUS OPHTHALMOSCOPE (ANUMBRA).

or intensity when examining the macula, so as to prevent too much contraction of the pupil: to secure a field of view as nearly concentric as possible with the illuminated patch so that dark areas such as the portion ac of Fig. 7.2 shall be reduced to negligible proportions; to remove flare from the sighthole; and to remove the troublesome corneal reflex from the centre of the field.

Figs. 7.11 and 7.12 illustrate the optical construction of two modern instruments designed with these requirements in view. Light from the filament of a small lamp L passes through the condenser A and the projecting lens D, an image of the filament being thereby formed on the reflector *immediately* below the sighthole at C. In the first instrument, Fig. 7.11, the reflector is a plane silvered glass, or a stainless steel, mirror whereas in the second, Fig. 7.12, it takes the form of a small prism,* the light being reflected from its *two* surfaces, the second (back) one of which is silvered. The image of the filament is formed in the tip of the prism. The light proceeds as a slightly divergent beam in a nearly horizontal direction from this source image towards the subject's pupil. The current for the lamp is supplied either by a dry battery in the handle of the instrument or by means of leads connected to a low voltage supply.

The corneal reflex is an image, formed by reflection at the anterior surface of the cornea, of the source image and surrounding illuminated portion of the reflector. It is reduced in size and displaced from the centre of the field by employing a small source the image of which lies to one side of the sighthole. As indicated in §7.1 and Fig. 7.2, however, this arrangement results in a small portion ac of the field being unilluminated. To reduce this dark area and make the fields of view and illumination more nearly concentric with one another, the source image should be as close to the edge K of the sighthole as possible. And if, further, the source image is nearer to the subject's eye than is the sighthole, the illuminated patch bc will be enlarged. The condition for freedom from corneal reflection and the condition for concentricity of the fields of view and illumination are seen to be opposed to one another. They are satisfied, as far as is practicable in a small handy instrument, and a uniformly illuminated bright field provided, by such designs as those illustrated in Figs. 7.11 and 7.12, in which the optical system—condenser and projector—is designed to be reasonably free from spherical aberration, so that the instrument provides a well defined cone of emergent light and a clear uniform circle of light focusing a few centimetres from the reflector.

It is held by some practitioners that the retinal blood vessels may be studied to better advantage if the illumination of the ophthalmoscope is deprived of red light, in which case the vessels appear black in a fundus

---

* This prism reflector, the origin of which is in doubt, was incorporated by May in his ophthalmoscope, and has since been improved.

of greenish tinge. This effect is achieved by introducing at some point in the optical system of the instrument a red-absorbing filter, of good quality glass or gelatine, called a red-free filter.

Because of their greater convenience, self-luminous ophthalmoscopes have almost entirely superceded non-luminous instruments in practice. Nevertheless, all students should use the latter before proceeding to continuous use of his chosen type of the former, since the knowledge thereby gained of the illumination of the eye and of the effect of reflections, is valuable.

7.13. Reflex-Free Ophthalmoscopy.

In the direct method we have to contend only with the corneal reflex (reflections from the crystalline lens surfaces are present, but they are of far less intensity); and we have seen that we can at least shift this reflection from the centre of the field of view with a well-designed luminous hand ophthalmoscope. In the indirect method the two reflections from the condensing lens are added to the corneal reflex, making this method more troublesome unless steps, such as those about to be described, are taken to eliminate them or diminish their effect.

Several methods have been proposed from time to time to obtain complete freedom from reflections. Most of these are clumsy in practice, but the polarisation method, in which a polariser and analyser are introduced into the illumination and observation systems, is fairly satisfactory. Suggested by HELMHOLTZ, it was put into practice by FUCHS (1882), THORNER (1889) and SALOMONSON (1920).* The most

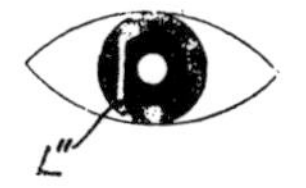

FIG. 7.13—IMAGES OF SOURCE AND SIGHTHOLE IN SUBJECT'S PUPIL IN REFLEX-FREE OPHTHALMOSCOPY.

successful method, however, is the one in which the illuminating beam on its way to the subject's fundus and the observation beam returning therefrom are completely separated from one another as they pass through the subject's cornea, pupil and crystalline lens. In this way, no light reflected by these parts of the eye can enter the observation system. In order to be separated, the two beams must be extremely narrow in the region of the subject's pupil, especially when the latter is of small diameter. To achieve this, the source must be small, and a small image of it must be formed in the subject's pupil and near its margin, leaving the remainder of the pupil in which to form an image of the sighthole, or of the entrance pupil of any observing telescope that may be used. To form an image of the sighthole (or entrance pupil) at the subject's pupil requires a lens between the two,† which leads us to the indirect method of ophthalmoscopy. It has already been explained (§7.7) that in the indirect method the condensing lens O is placed in such a position as to image the sighthole in the subject's pupil on a reduced scale. The source, or a small image of it, must therefore be placed at the same distance from the lens as

* A SALOMONSON ophthalmoscope in the Northampton Polytechnic laboratories gives quite good results.

† A concave mirror *can* be used, as in the reflecting ophthalmoscope introduced by SCHULTÉN, and mentioned below.

the sighthole. To sum up: to view the fundus without reflections, the subject's pupil must be conjugate both to the sighthole or the entrance pupil of the observation system and also to the source or the entrance pupil of the illumination system.

THORNER began a careful enquiry into the problem in 1895, being specially interested in obtaining stereoscopic observations and photography of the fundus, which are practically impossible in the presence of reflections. He produced a large table instrument and remodelled a small hand instrument due to SCHULTÉN (1883) in which the condenser lens is replaced by a concave mirror.* The work was continued by GULLSTRAND (1911) who finally designed a large table ophthalmoscope, completely free from reflections, in which the field of view of three or four discs is observed with remarkable distinctness under a magnification of 40 X. The illumination and observation systems are entirely separate and so arranged that a narrow image, L″, Fig. 7.13, about 1 mm. wide, of the illuminated slit is formed near the edge of the subject's pupil, while a circular image of the entrance pupil of the observing telescope is formed, centrally if the size of the pupil permits, in the remainder of the pupil.

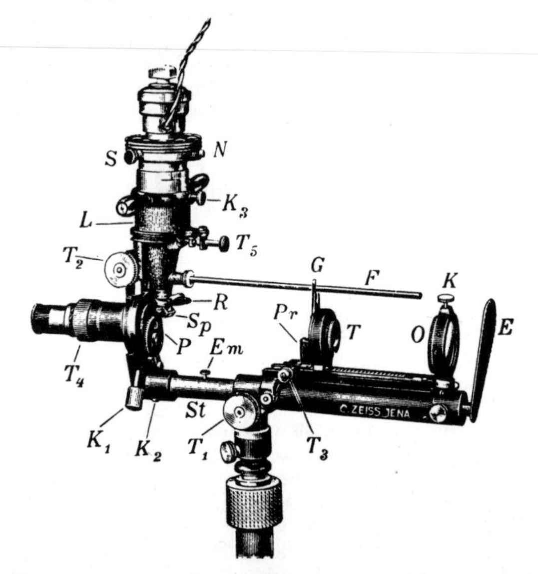

FIG. 7.14—THE LARGE SIMPLIFIED GULLSTRAND OPHTHALMOSCOPE ARRANGED AS A PARALLAX REFRACTIONOMETER.

This ophthalmoscope is somewhat elaborate and costly and has been simplified in a later table instrument illustrated in Fig. 7.14. Ignoring the test disc or target T and the guide rod F (which are additions necessary for adapting the instrument to measure the refractive

* THORNER's small reflecting ophthalmoscope can still be obtained and is quite serviceable.

condition objectively, as explained later), the observation system consists of the ophthalmoscope lens O and the telescope at T_4. The vertical tube in the illustration is the illumination tube. The optical system is shown in Fig. 7.15 (*a*). Light from the lamp at L is condensed by the condenser A on to a slit at L′, just below which is a prismatic reflector R (S_p in Fig. 7.14) which directs the illuminating beam on to the lens O which forms a narrow image L″ of the slit near the margin of the pupil. An extent bc of the fundus is thereby illuminated. The stop at C near the observing telescope is also imaged in the pupil at C′. The illuminating and observation systems are thus separated in this region. The opthalmoscope lens O forms two reflected images of the slit, but they are so small, as well as displaced from the centre of the field, as to be no hindrance to a clear view of

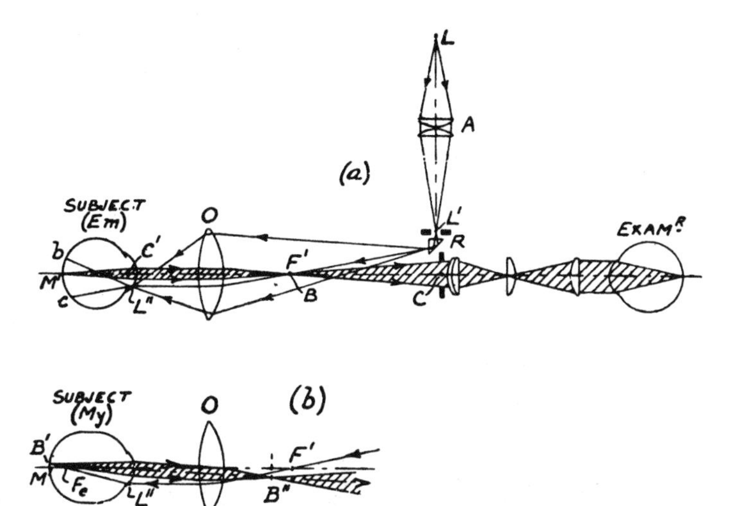

Fig. 7.15—Zeiss Parallax Refractionometer—Optical System.

the fundus. Even with a normal pupil a uniformly bright field of about four discs is clearly seen, the magnification being variable, by different eyepieces, between 5 and 40 diameters. The apparatus can be adapted for binocular vision. It is necessary that the single lens O have an aspherical surface in order to cover the wide field without aberration.

The instrument just described is a large one ; in using it the subject's head is supported firmly in a headrest fixed to a table on which the ophthalmoscope is mounted. The indirect method can be carried out reasonably free from reflections, with a *hand* luminous ophthalmoscope if the latter is suitably designed. Referring to Fig. 7.12, it will be recalled that to satisfy the requirements of the direct method the source image had to be formed close to the sighthole, as otherwise a portion of the field of view would be unilluminated. In the indirect method the ophthalmoscope lens O, Fig. 7.7, when held at the proper distance from the subject's eye, forms a small image of the sighthole and of the source image in the subject's pupil. To keep the illuminating and observations beams separated as they pass through the cornea and crystalline lens, we desire to separate these two images as much as possible, so long as they are both contained within the subject's pupil. Hence we require the source image to be formed some distance (4 to 6 mm. or so) from the sighthole.

OBJECTIVE MEASUREMENT OF AMETROPIA OBJECTIVE OPTOMETERS

7.14. Direct Ophthalmoscopy adapted to Optometry.

To determine objectively the eye's ametropia we must employ some arrangement for measuring the vergence of the light which having its origin at the fundus (assumed to be adequately illuminated), emerges from the subject's eye, on its way to or from the far point. In direct ophthalmoscopy this can be achieved by rotating into the sighthole a lens of such power as to render the emergent light parallel, the parallelism being recorded by the examiner's eye when he sees the details of the fundus distinctly. This method is inaccurate, however, for reasons given (§7.3). We could receive the light issuing from the subject's eye and ophthalmoscope lens, placed at or as near as possible to the spectacle point, in a telescope provided with a crosswire. The lens in the sighthole necessary to make the telescope image of the fundus focus sharply on the crosswire would then measure the ametropia, the examiner's state of accommodation being of no consequence. The reading would depend upon the subject's accommodation, however, as before.

The fundus does not contain detail sufficiently well defined upon which to focus, however, especially around the macula where we wish to make our determinations. It becomes necessary, therefore, not merely to illuminate the fundus, but to project on to it the image of a well defined object of some kind, this image to be viewed by the examiner through the sighthole and an ophthalmoscope lens of appropriate power to enable it to be seen distinctly. The object, with the lens used to project it into the eye, then form an optometer as described in §3.9, only here the object is not to be observed and commented upon by the subject, but its image on the latter's fundus is to be viewed *objectively* by the examiner. Fig. 7.11 or 7.12 will serve to illustrate the arrangement diagrammatically. If the object or target—a black crossline or other geometrical figure on a transparent glass plate—be introduced into the illuminating system at B, the focal point of the projecting lens D, parallel light will be incident on the subject's eye from each point of the target, and an image of it formed sharply on the fundus, if the eye be emmetropic. This image may then be observed by the examiner through the sighthole. If the subject be ametropic, the fundus image of B will be out of focus and blurred. Means are provided for sliding the target along the axis of the illuminating system, towards the projector in myopia and away from it in hypermetropia, until its image is in sharp focus on the retina. The position of the target is read off on a dioptric scale.

The light returning from the image will be divergent in H. and convergent in M., and to see it distinctly, the appropriate plus or minus lens must be rotated into the sighthole at C. This lens is not being used for measuring the ametropia, however, but merely to observe the distinctness or otherwise of the fundus image, and the examiner's state of accommodation does not affect the matter.

The subject must be prevented from accommodating, for which purpose some kind of fixation mark, actually or virtually at distance, should be provided. If the particular type of luminous ophthalmoscope depicted in Figs. 7.11 and 7.12 were thus adapted for ametropic measurements, the dioptre scale of ametropia would not be uniform since, for reasons concerned with displacement of the corneal reflex already described, the second focal point of the projecting lens is at or near the sighthole and thus removed some 23 mm. or so from the spectacle point. The scale could, however, be calibrated for a projector of given focal length and for a fixed distance of the instrument from the spectacle point.

If the subject be astigmatic, a position can be found for the target when one meridian of it is in sharp focus on the retina ; and a second position for the other principal meridian. Each reading can be taken separately and the refractive condition thereby measured.

The optometer principle is in this way introduced into the direct ophthalmoscopic method in such instruments as the "*Keeler Decagon*" ophthalmoscope and in the *Rodenstock* and *Astron* "refractometers," which latter are table instruments. The accuracy of the results obtained depends upon correct positioning of the instrument in relation to the subject's eye, which is not too easy of attainment in the direct method. The corneal reflection is rather troublesome when working on or close to the fovea.

Depth of focus when observing the fundus image also mitigates against accuracy ; and finally, there is a serious tendency for the subject to accommodate when the observing appliance is close to him.

7.15. Optometers using the Indirect Method

The arrangement of indirect ophthalmoscopy is more suitable for the purpose. In this case the target moves over a scale in the region of the focal point F′ of the condensing lens O (Fig. 7.7), being all the time within the illuminating beam and so adequately illuminated. When it occupies a position B, Fig. 7.15, which is conjugate to the far point M_R of the subject, with respect to the lens O, an image of it is formed on the latter's retina at M′. Light returning from the retina thus forms a sharp aerial image of the fundus image at the position B coincident with the target. A scale giving dioptres of ametropia can be constructed along the axis of the system, the zero for emmetropia coinciding with the focal point F′ of the ophthalmoscope lens O ; the myopia and hypermetropia divisions lying respectively within and outside this point.

An early attempt thus to adapt the indirect ophthalmoscope to measurements of refraction was made by SCHMIDT-RIMPLER (1877). The condensing lens O, of power +10 D, was held on a bar at a distance of 10 cm. from the principal point of the subject's eye (the point P of the reduced eye). The concave mirror at C (Figs. 7.6 and 7.7) produced an image at its focal point, 20 cm. from the mirror, of a distant illuminated coarse grating. The mirror, and hence the grating image, was moved towards or away from the subject's eye until the aerial image of the grating image formed by light returning from the fundus was seen in sharp focus by the examiner through the sighthole. The latter could be provided with a +5 D lens and the examiner could remain relaxed. The position of the mirror was obtained from a spring tape which was fixed to the ophthalmoscope lens O, its free end being attached to the mirror handle. Thus, if the reading were 30 cm. when sharp focus was obtained the aerial image, 20 cm. from the mirror, must lie at the focal point F′ of O, since the focal length of the latter is 10 cm. The eye being tested is therefore emmetropic. A reading of 25 cm. would be obtained with an eye the ocular refraction of which is 5 D of myopia. The scale, for ocular refractions, would be uniform, each centimetre corresponding to one dioptre of error. Relaxation of accommodation on the part of subject and examiner is necessary for accuracy in this arrangement and reflections at the cornea and ophthalmoscope lens are troublesome.

In modern instruments of this kind, variously called *optometers* or *refractionometers*, the reflections are eliminated as described in §7.13. The method of doing this, by forming images of the source and the entrance pupil of the observing eyepiece or telescope side by side in the subject's pupil, ensures that the lens O occupies with some accuracy the proper position in relation to the eye. The aerial image is observed through a telescope provided with a crosswire, so that the setting is independent of the examiner's accommodation. Fixation marks are provided for the subject, arranged so as to assist relaxation as much as possible, but this matter of his accommodation always introduces an element of doubt. The result given by these instruments depends upon the accuracy with which the position of the aerial image is determined, and it is in the method adopted for making this determination that the various models differ from one another. Although the field of view in the indirect method is large, each point of the fundus image is imaged in the observation system by a narrow pencil and there is consequently appreciable depth of focus. An instrument in which the setting depends upon focusing the image in the observing telescope, is thus liable to some inaccuracy on that account, especially in view of the fact that the image of the target formed on such a screen as the subject's living retina can never be very crisp.

In the ZEISS parallax refractionometer the setting is made in an interesting manner. The instrument consists of the simplified GULLSTRAND ophthalmoscope, as already described, with the addition of a target T, Fig. 7.14, or Fig. 7.15 (b), capable of movement, over a dioptre scale, along the axis of the ophthalmoscope lens O. This target lies within the illuminating beam emerging from the illumination tube at L′, Fig. 7.15, and also within the observation beam returning from the subject's fundus. The setting consists in racking the target along the instrument until its aerial image is sharp and coincident with it. If the target does not occupy the proper position, conjugate to the eye's far point with respect to the ophthalmoscope lens O, the fundus image and consequently the aerial image will be blurred. But in addition to this, the aerial image will be laterally displaced from the target. This arises from the fact that whereas the axis of observation, which is the main axis of the whole instrument, coincides with the subject's visual axis, the illuminating pencil, by which the target at B, Fig. 7.15 (a), is imaged on the retina, is oblique to the axis, since it enters the eye through the laterally disposed slit at L″. Thus if the subject be myopic and the target at F′ (the focus of the lens O, the proper position for emmetropia), the image is formed in front of the retina at F_e and the out of focus image B′ on the retina will be displaced to the side of the axis. The aerial image B″ of this decentred retinal image will also be decentred and will be seen by the examiner as out of focus and laterally displaced relative to the original target. A movement of the target towards O, until it is conjugate with the retina with respect to O and the eye, will restore the aerial image to sharp focus and to super-position with the target on the axis.

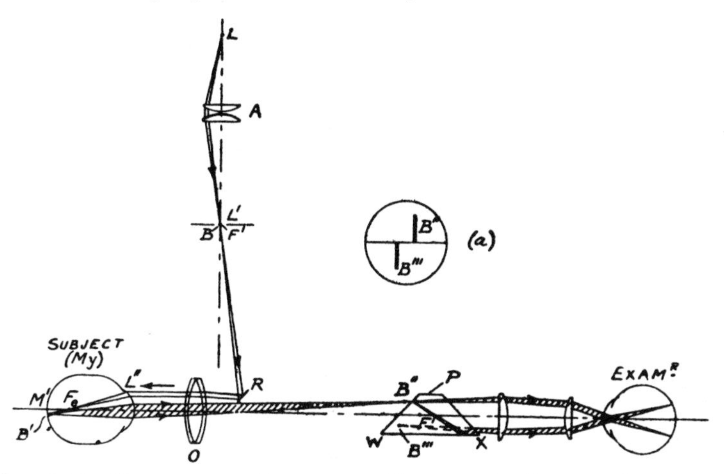

FIG. 7.16—COINCIDENCE OPTOMETER (FINCHAM). OPTICAL PRINCIPLE (DIAGRAMMATIC).

There is an appreciable range of uncertainty in setting even with this arrangement, however, due in large measure to the difficulty of *superposing* the inevitably somewhat fuzzy image on the original object. In the instrument recently designed by FINCHAM, at the Northampton Polytechnic, London, the coincidence method* of setting is incorporated in the design.

THE COINCIDENCE OPTOMETER (FINCHAM).

The general principle of this instrument is represented in Fig. 7.16 in which the lettering corresponds to that of Fig. 7.15. The light from the source L, condensed on to an aperture at L′, enters the eye as a narrow parallel beam at L″ and is brought to focus at the focal point of the eye F_e; the subject's eye shown is myopic, as in Fig. 7.15 (b). It reaches the retina to one side of the fovea in such an eye. The target is not on the axis of the observation system as it is in the previous instrument, but is removed to the side, to a position B, between the

* §2.8.

condenser A and the reflector R. It is therefore not seen by the examiner, who has an uninterrupted view of the image formed by the light returning from the subject's eye. In the diagram the target B is shown at the focus F′ of the optometer lens O, the correct position for an emmetropic subject. In the myopic eye, however, the image of it on the retina (B′) is blurred and displaced laterally from the fovea M′. By means of the light returning from this fundus image, the optometer lens O forms an aerial image B″ of the target to one side of the axis of the observation system, again as in Fig. 7.15 (b).

Before entering the observing eyepiece, however, this observation beam is divided into upper and lower halves by the prism P, which is

FIG. 7.17—THE COINCIDENCE OPTOMETER (FINCHAM).

inserted only in the lower half of the system. One half of the beam misses the prism and enters the eyepiece and thence the examiner's eye; the other half is reflected once at the face WX of the prism, producing a reversed copy of B″, on the other side of the observation axis, at B‴. The separation of the two halves is twice the displacement of the original aerial image B″. The target is a fine vertical line, so that in the case of a myopic eye the appearance of the images B″ and B‴ is as indicated in the circle at (a), the upper and lower halves of the image, one on each side of the horizontal separating line, being blurred and *separated laterally*. The lateral separation of these two half images depends upon the retinal separation M′B′ and is thus a measure of the subject's ametropia. The separation produced by a refractive error of one eighth dioptre may be definitely detected.

To measure the ametropia the target B is moved from the emmetropic zero position F′ along the axis of the illumination system, towards the condenser O in a myopic case, until the illumination beam enters the subject's eye with the necessary amount of divergence to be focused on the retina at M′ instead of F_e. The retinal image B′ of the target is then sharp and coincident with the axis at M′. The resulting aerial image B″ also becomes a sharp image and moves laterally on to the axis ; the other half of it, formed by reflection in the prism P, similarly sharpens and moves in the *opposite* direction until it lies in coincidence with the first half. Thus the setting consists in aligning the two vertical half images, which can be done with considerable accuracy. The position of the target B is read off from the dioptric scale provided along the axis of the illumination system, F′ being the zero of this scale.

The instrument is adapted also for determining the principal meridians of an astigmatic eye and the degree of astigmatism. These measurements are also made by bringing the separated halves of the aerial image, B″ and B‴, into coincidence alignment. The adjustments necessary to execute the measurement are described in the manufacturer's literature.

Fig. 7.17 is an illustration of the complete instrument. The subject's headrest is seen on the left and the examiner's eyepiece on the right. The vertical circular disc A carries a scale of degrees for recording the axis direction in astigmatic eyes. The dioptric scale giving the ametropia is engraved on the horizontal disc R and is viewed by the examiner by means of a small mirror on the other side of the instrument. It is the rotation of this disc that, in effect, moves the target B along the axis of the arrangement. The small lever just above the ametropia disc R brings into position an auxiliary lens system enabling the examiner to see the subject's pupil and so to centre the instrument before proceeding to take readings.

EXERCISES. CHAPTER VII.

1. Show on a diagram, drawn approximately to scale, the observation of the fundus of an emmetropic eye by direct ophthalmoscopy.

Prove that the magnification of the fundus is about 15 times and the field of view (reasonably illuminated) about 7 degrees, or about the size of the optic disc.

2. Explain with careful diagrams, the factors upon which depend (*a*) the field of illumination ; (*b*) the field of view, in direct ophthalmoscopy, using a concave mirror and a source alongside the observed eye.

Obtain an expression for the magnification obtained when the observed eye is emmetropic.

3. In examining a 10 D myope by direct ophthalmoscopy, the sighthole being 3 cm. from the subject's cornea, what lens will be required in the sighthole to see the fundus clearly ? What will be the effect on the field of view in comparison with that seen in the case of an emmetrope ? Give a diagram.

4. Explain with diagrams the field of vision and the field of illumination in direct ophthalmoscopy. What are their comparative sizes ? (S.M.C. Hons.)

5. Explain with the aid of a diagram the factors upon which the field of illumination depends in direct ophthalmoscopy.

Calculate the magnification under which the fundus is seen in the following case: eye axially hyperopic 10 D; distance of mirror from eye 35 mm.; power of eye 60 D.

6. Draw a careful double scale diagram to show image formation and extent of fundus visible using a stationary direct ophthalmoscope, when an unaccommodated emmetropic eye observes the fundus of a similar emmetropic eye. Assume that the distance between the eyes is three times the front focal length of either eye and that the diameter of the pupil of the observing eye is twice that of the observed eye. Give a brief explanation of the construction. (S.M.C.)

7. The eyes of observer and observed in direct ophthalmoscopy are 5 cm. apart and the lens battery lies 2 cm. in front of the observer's eye. What single lens in the battery would be required if the spectacle corrections of observer and observed, when measured 15 mm. in front of the eye in each case, were +5 D? Assume that neither eye accommodates. (S.M.C.)

8. If the fundus of an eye, whose axial length is 26 mm., is to be seen clearly in the direct method by an emmetropic unaccommodated observer, what lens of the ophthalmoscope battery will be required? Also compare by calculation the apparent magnification of the image seen with that from the same eye when of normal length. Assume a reduced eye, refractive index $4/3$, radius $5 \cdot 2$ mm.; distance of lens from cornea of observed eye 28 mm. (S.M.C. Hons.)

9. A reduced eye has a radius of $5 \cdot 5$ mm. and index $4/3$. Its axial length is increased 50 per cent. beyond the normal. Calculate the necessary correcting lens, assuming the latter to be placed 25 mm. in front of the cornea.

What numerical change of magnification would result under these conditions in direct ophthalmoscopy, to an emmetropic observer? (S.M.C. Hons.)

10. Explain, with the aid of careful diagrams, how the field of illumination in direct ophthalmoscopy is governed by:

(*a*) the size and distance of the source
(*b*) the power and position of the concave mirror
(*c*) the size of the subject's pupil
(*d*) the subject's refractive condition,

and how the field of view is governed by:

(*a*) the sizes of the subject's pupil and the sighthole
(*b*) the separation of sighthole and subject's eye
(*c*) the subject's refractive condition.

11. Describe the reasons why the direct method of ophthalmoscopy does not lend itself to an accurate determination of the subject's refractive condition.

12. Compare the direct and the indirect methods of ophthalmoscopy making particular reference to the magnification and field of view obtained by the two methods. Give diagrams.

13. Taking the optic disc as an illuminated object $1 \cdot 5$ mm. in diameter, find the position and size of its image formed by the eye's

optical system (of power 60 D) when the eye is (*a*) axially myopic 5 D and (*b*) axially hyperopic 5 D.

Repeat for the same amounts of ametropia when this is not axial, but refractive.

14. With the aid of careful diagrams explain what quantities are involved in determining (*a*) the area of subject's fundus illuminated; (*b*) the field of view on the subject's fundus, when the unaccommodated eye is illuminated and observed by means of a plane mirror containing a sighthole.

Explain the effect on (*a*) when the eye accommodates on the sighthole.

15. Calculate the magnification obtained in direct ophthalmoscopy of an eye axially myopic 20 D, the observation position being 35 mm. from the subject's eye.

16. Find by calculation the best position for field of view of the ophthalmoscope lens of +13 D when, in indirect ophthalmoscopy, the separation of the subject's eye and the observation point is 60 cm.

17. Find the size of the aerial image of the optic disc, which has a diameter of 1·5 mm., as formed in indirect ophthalmoscopy, the condensing lens being +13 D placed 10 cm. from the subject's eye, which is (*a*) emmetropic; (*b*) hyperopic 5 D and (*c*) myopic 5 D.

18. With the aid of an accurately drawn ray diagram explain how a detail in a fundus is observed in indirect ophthalmoscopy. Indicate the positions of salient focal points and shade in a pencil of rays from the observed detail to the observing eye. (S.M.C.)

19. Draw the course of rays from two points on the retina of the observed eye to two points on the retina of the observer's eye in an observation of the fundus by indirect ophthalmoscopy. (B.O.A.)

20. Draw the course of two rays to each of two points on the retina, by which the retina is illuminated in indirect ophthalmoscopy. Omit entirely the returning rays by which the retina is observed. (B.O.A.)

21. Explain with the aid of diagrams how the lens and corneal reflexes can be thrown aside in an ophthalmoscopic examination of the fundus. (B.O.A.)

22. Show graphically (ray diagram) that the aerial image of the fundus obtained in indirect ophthalmoscopy increases in myopia, decreases in hyperopia and remains unchanged in emmetropia as the ophthalmoscope lens is withdrawn from the subject's eye, the starting position being close to that eye.

23. In indirect ophthalmoscopy some indication of the ametropia of an eye may be obtained by noting the change produced in magnification as the ophthalmoscope lens is moved to or from the subject's eye. Find the change in magnification of the aerial image that occurs as a +13 D ophthalmoscope lens is moved from 10 cm. to 15 cm. away from an eye (*a*) hyperopic 3 D; (*b*) myopic 3 D.

24. The examiner in an indirect ophthalmoscopy test uses a +13 D ophthalmoscope lens and holds the concave mirror (of focal length 10 inches) 22·5 inches from the subject's eye. Show on a diagram drawn to scale the paths of two pencils from the extreme retinal points that can be seen and the aerial image of them, the useful aperture of the condenser being 1·5 inches.

Prove that the magnification of the fundus is approximately 4·5 times and the field of view about 25°.

25. In an indirect ophthalmoscopy assume that a source (10 cm. diameter) and condensing lens (aperture 10 cm., power +12 D) are placed 10 cm. in front of an eye whose far point is 20 cm. in front of the eye. A concave ophthalmoscope mirror (50 cm. radius, aperture 4 cm.) is placed 50 cm. from the condenser. Discuss, with the aid of a diagram drawn ¼ scale, the field of illumination and the factors affecting field of view and magnification. (S.M.C.)

26. Give a clear diagram showing the passage of a pencil of light from a point, not on the axis, of the subject's fundus to the examiner's eye in indirect ophthalmoscopy.

In a given case the ophthalmoscope lens was a +12 D sphere, the separation of subject's eye and examiner's eye 60 cm. Find the position of the lens to give maximum field of view; and calculate the angular size of this field if the aperture of the lens is 5 cm.

27. Briefly compare the direct and indirect methods of ophthalmoscopy.

Upon what does the field of view depend in the latter method? What will be, approximately, the maximum field of view in the following case: emmetropic eye; condensing lens +13 D and aperture 6 cm. held 9 cm. from subject's eye.

At what distance from the subject's eye should the mirror be held in this case.

28. In indirect ophthalmoscopy, find the extent of fundus illuminated under the following conditions:

(*a*) subject: 10 D myopic (axial); pupil diameter 4 mm.
(*b*) concave mirror of $f = 25$ cm.
(*c*) source: 4 cm. diameter at 75 cm. from mirror.
(*d*) working distance, eye to mirror, 60 cm.
(*e*) ophthalmoscope lens +13 D placed 9 cm. from subject's eye.

What diameter of mirror is required?

29. In indirect ophthalmoscopy a concave mirror of 25 cm. focal length and condensing lens of about 13 D power and 5 cm. effective aperture are frequently used. Explain why these dimensions are adopted and draw a careful diagram (not necessarily to scale) showing the paths of two pencils from the extreme retinal points that can be seen with your arrangement.

Show clearly the aerial image of the fundus and prove that the magnification and field of view obtained are respectively about 4·5 times and 25°.

30. In an imaginary case an eye 20 D axially hyperopic is observed by indirect ophthalmoscopy using a 40 D ophthalmoscope lens of aperture 40 mm., the working distance, eye to sighthole, being 20 cm. Give a careful diagram to scale showing the course of a pencil of light from the most outlying point of the fundus that can be seen.

31. Explain the factors upon which the magnification of the fundus depends in the indirect method of ophthalmoscopy.

Supply the data required and calculate the magnification on the assumption that both subject and examiner are emmetropes with accommodation relaxed. Give a diagram.

32. Give a ray diagram to scale showing the observation of the fundus in direct ophthalmoscopy, the sighthole being 30 mm. from the subject's eye, in the case of (*a*) emmetropia ; (*b*) myopia of 20 D, a lens correcting the myopia having being rotated into the sighthole. What will be the power of this lens ?

Show all necessary focal points, far point, etc. Assume the reduced eye of power 60 D.

33. Explain with the aid of a diagram how the image of the optic disc seen in indirect ophthalmoscopy appears to vary in size when the condensing lens is moved axially away from an observed highly hyperopic eye. (S.M.C.)

34. Indirect ophthalmoscopy may be carried out entirely by means of mirrors. Describe and show in a careful diagram the necessary arrangement of mirrors and source. Discuss any advantages or disadvantages such a system possesses as compared with the usual method. (S.M.C. Hons.)

35. Presuming the reduced eye, of radius 5·5 mm. and refractive index $4/3$, to have a length of 23 mm., calculate the magnification of the image formed by indirect ophthalmoscopy if a +16 D condenser is used at a distance of 75 mm. from the observed eye.

Illustrate your answer by a carefully drawn diagram. (S.M.C. Hons.)

36. Explain parallax, and illustrate with carefully drawn diagrams how an emmetropic unaccommodated eye, looking towards the illuminated fundus of a similar eye, will observe parallax displacement of a small opacity which lies one millimetre in front of the fundus of the second eye. (S.M.C.)

37. Using the constants of the schematic eye set out in Column 1 of Table §10.4, check the powers of the lenses, required to view opacities at distances 2, 5, 10 and 15 mm. in front of the retina of the subject's eye, that are stated in §7.10, the observer's eye being 75 mm. from the subject's eye.

38. Write a short account of the historical development of the non-luminous ophthalmoscope, giving approximate dimensions of the mirrors used in modern instruments for both the direct and the indirect methods.

39. With the aid of carefully drawn diagrams illustrate how the light is condensed and directed into an eye when any chosen form of self-luminous ophthalmoscope is used for direct examination. Give reasons for any adjustments or precautions taken in practical application. (S.M.C.)

40. Draw the course of two rays from the illuminating lamp of a self-luminous ophthalmoscope, to each of two points on the retina, when an eye is being examined by the indirect method. The returning rays are to be omitted. (B.O.A.)

41. Describe a hand luminous ophthalmoscope of the type employing a prismatic reflector. Give a diagram of its optical construction. What precautions are necessary in the design of the instrument to ensure that the field of view is evenly illuminated and that the reflection from the cornea does not obstruct the view of the fundus in a case with a small pupil.

42. Give particulars of four types of ophthalmoscope with which you are familiar, emphasising their points of difference, and your opinion of their respective merits and demerits. (B.O.A. Hons.)

43. Explain and give a diagram of the optical system of a luminous ophthalmoscope necessary to give an even field of illumination in the direct method. Describe particularly the conditions which are required for the examination of the macular region in a case with contracted pupils.

44. What are the ideal conditions of illumination to be fulfilled, in the indirect method of using the ophthalmoscope, to avoid the corneal reflex ? Why are they difficult to satisfy in the use of the simple mirror and hand lens ? Why are they more easily fulfilled with a luminous ophthalmoscope ? Explain how they are fulfilled in some self-contained rigid type of mechanical ophthalmoscopes. Why is a large pupil an advantage ? (B.O.A.)

45. Different methods have been suggested for the complete elimination of reflections in ophthalmoscopy. State the principle of one method and give the general design of an instrument incorporating the method. Give a diagram.

46. Describe, with a diagram of the optical construction, a table ophthalmoscope for the indirect method in which the corneal reflex is eliminated and the condenser lens reflexes rendered unobtrusive.

47. Explain how the optometer principle may be incorporated in the luminous ophthalmoscope, using the direct method, providing thereby an objective method of measuring ametropia.

State the precautions that must be observed in order to obtain an approach to accuracy.

48. Explain how the optometer principle may be incorporated in the luminous ophthalmoscope, using the indirect method, providing thereby an objective method of measuring ametropia.

Describe the optical construction of one instrument of this type, giving a diagram showing the course of the illuminating and observation beams of light.

49. Describe the principle and optical arrangement of an objective optometer in which the setting depends on the coincidence principle. Give a diagram of the optical construction and the paths of significant pencils of light.

50. Describe with careful diagrams, the optical principles of two instruments (not the retinoscope) for the objective determination of the refraction of the eye. Explain why the results which they give may differ from the subjective findings.

51. Describe, with the aid of carefully drawn diagrams, the optical construction and give the underlying theory of any instrument of the refractometer (optometer) class for measuring the refraction of an eye objectively. (S.M.C.)

52. A vitreous opacity lies axially 4 mm. in front of the retina of an unaccommodated axial hyperope of 5 D. Assuming a schematic eye with power + 60 D and relative index 4/3, calculate where the opacity would appear to lie during an objective examination. Describe also how the parallax test would reveal its position relative to the retina. (S.M.C.)

OPHTHALMIC INSTRUMENTS

CHAPTER VIII

RETINOSCOPY

8.1. Introductory.

THE process of retinoscopy is an objective method of determining the refractive condition of the eye. A small illuminated patch is formed on the subject's retina, as in ophthalmoscopy, by reflecting light into the eye from a mirror (usually plane or weak concave) which is provided with a sighthole. Some of the light is reflected back from this retinal patch and emerges from the subject's eye in a state of convergence or divergence depending upon the ametropia of the eye. The examiner, observing through the sighthole and concentrating his attention on the subject's pupil, receives this light and sees the pupil completely or partially illuminated; this illumination within the pupil is called the "reflex". By tilting the mirror the patch is made to move laterally across the subject's retina, as a result of which the reflex moves across the pupil "with" or "against" the patch, and slowly or rapidly, according to the kind and degree of the subject's ametropia. Observation of these reflex movements thus provides information about the ametropia, which can be determined with some accuracy in the manner to be explained in this chapter.

This "reflex" seen within the pupil appears to have been first noticed in 1859 by Sir William BOWMAN when investigating conical cornea; but not until 1873–4 was a serious attempt made, by the French ophthalmologist CUIGNET, to utilise the movements of the reflex in the determination of refractive errors. At first the underlying principles of this new objective method were not understood, but in the hands of various investigators, notably LANDOLT, PARENT and PRIESTLEY SMITH, the technique was developed and the principles clarified. According to the views held as to the nature of the process, it has been given various names, such as keratoscopy, pupilloscopy, skiascopy (shadow test), retinoscopy, none of which suitably describes it. We shall use the last term, however, since it has become firmly established in this country.

In the application of retinoscopy certain discrepancies and difficulties arise so that its findings do not quite agree with those obtained subjectively. Nevertheless, retinoscopy is an extremely useful and simple objective method for measuring the eye's refractive condition. As this came to be realised during the years following its introduction, retinoscopy quickly supplanted direct ophthalmoscopy as a means for determining ametropia objectively. The simplest of apparatus, a plane or concave silvered mirror, suffices for its operation and in expert hands it is rapid.

STATIC RETINOSCOPY

8.2. The " Reflex " Movement.

The principle of retinoscopy is simple ; its main phenomena are not peculiar to the eye but arise in any optical system. It is essentially the same process as that introduced by TOEPLER for the examination of striæ in glass and extended into the knife-edge test by FOUCAULT for testing the focus and aberrations of mirrors and lenses. The neutralisation of spectacle lenses is a similar process and we will adopt the analogy of neutralisation in explaining retinoscopy.

A useful idea of the optical principle involved is obtained by performing the following experiment, in which a positive lens replaces the optical system of the subject's eye. Take a positive sphere of 10 D to 15 D power and about one cm. aperture (a trial case lens stopped down with a paper diaphragm will serve) and observe through it an object in the form of a narrow (2 mm. or so wide) strip of white paper on a dark background. In Fig. 8.1 (*a*) the lens, of aperture DE, is at P, its focal point at F, the object (paper strip) at M′ and your (the examiner's) eye at C. Hold the lens near to the object so that the latter is within the focal point and the image consequently virtual and further away, with its centre at M. Place your eye 12 to 18 inches from the lens, at the observation point C. Instead of moving the lens laterally, as when neutralising, move the object laterally from M′ to *a*, keeping lens and eye stationary. Concentrate your attention on the lens aperture (pupil) so that you are looking, not at the virtual image which moves from M to A, but at the projection of this image within the pupil, the centre of which moves from P to A′. This observed projection, the reflex, is slightly blurred since it is out of focus; and it is magnified. It moves "with" the object and at a greater speed: the movement PA′ exceeds M′a.

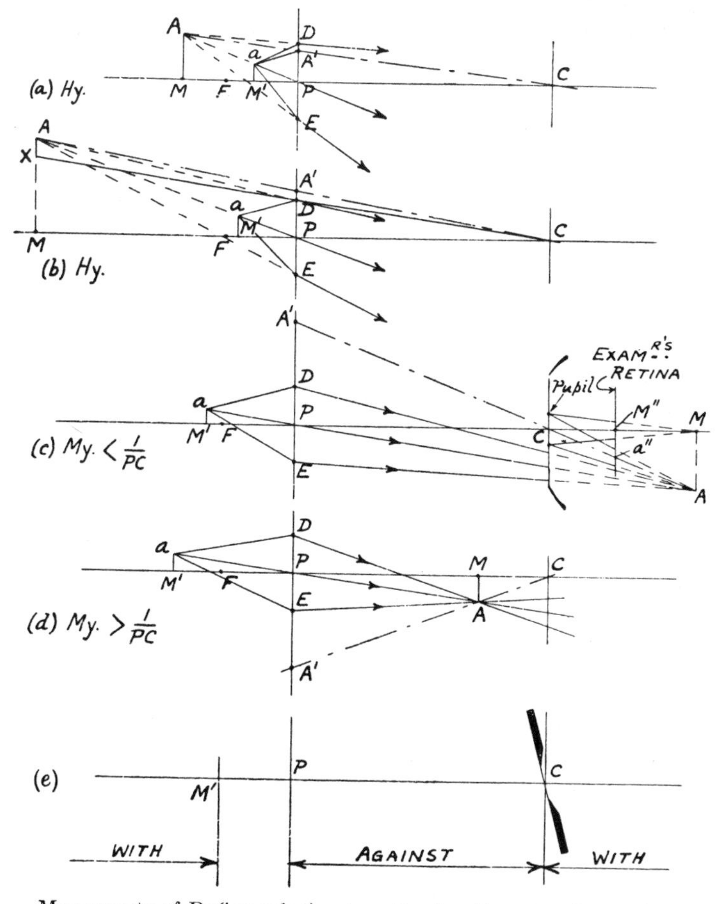

Movements of Reflex relative to retinal path or to plane mirror.

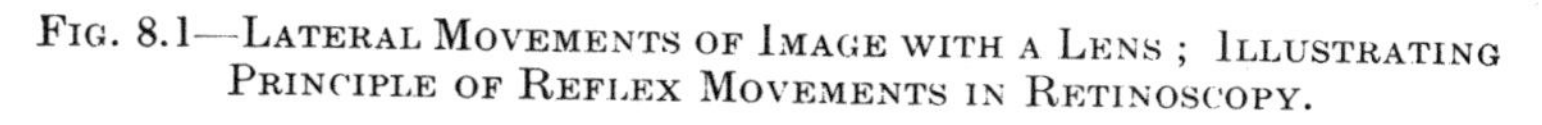

FIG. 8.1—LATERAL MOVEMENTS OF IMAGE WITH A LENS; ILLUSTRATING PRINCIPLE OF REFLEX MOVEMENTS IN RETINOSCOPY.

Increase the separation of object and lens a little, Fig 8.1 (b). The reflex is seen to be larger and more blurred and its movement, PA′, for the same movement M′a of the object is greater than before: it moves more rapidly. Upon increasing the lens-object separation further, a position will be reached in which the reflex of the object (paper strip) completely fills the lens aperture when the strip is in its central position ; we have what is called in technical optics a "complete flash". When the object is laterally displaced, from M′ to *a*, the movement of the reflex across the lens pupil is extremely rapid. On still further increasing the lens-object separation, a position will presently be reached, Fig. 8.1 (d), in which the previous "with" movement gives place to an "against" movement. The object M′ is now beyond the focal point F of the lens ; the images M and A of the object at M′ and *a* are real and lie between the lens and your eye: MA and PA′ are in the opposite direction to cases (a) and (b).

Between cases (b) and (d) lies case (c) in which the object is slightly beyond F so that the image MA is real as in (d) but lies behind your head. Examination of diagram (c) will show that the movement of the reflex PA′ is "with" the object. Observe that the light patch formed on the examiner's retina, which is shown in this diagram, moves down from M″ to *a*″, which by mental projection (§1.4) is interpreted as an upward movement of the reflex, from P to A′.

Between cases (c) and (d) there is a *critical* position in which, in the experiment, the reflex fills the lens pupil in the central position and its movement, on displacing the object laterally, is so rapid that it appears to vanish instantaneously. This occurs when the image M is formed *at the examiner's eye* at C ; the distance PA′ and hence the reflex movement are then infinite, even for a very small movement M′*a* of the object. In the experiment the object is the white paper strip ; in actual retinoscopy it is the small patch of illumination formed on the subject's retina by the light directed into his eye by the mirror.

Since the direction of movement PA′ of the reflex in the pupil DE is reversed as the image MA moves from one side, as in (c) to the other, as in (d), of the critical point C, this latter is sometimes called the POINT OF REVERSAL, or the *neutral* point ; and the phenomenon of the instantaneous disappearance of the reflex is similarly termed REVERSAL of the reflex. Note that since the point A′ is determined in every case by a line joining the point C to the image point A, the size PA′ and consequently the speed of the reflex movement increase as the image MA approaches the neutral point C, whether from the " with " side or the " against ".

It will be observed that the total extent of the optical axis of the arrangement is divided into two main regions. When the image formed by the lens lies within the region PC between lens and examiner, the reflex movement is " against " ; when the image lies anywhere in the region extending from M′, through infinity, up to the observation point C from behind the examiner, the movement is " with ". When the image *coincides with the observation point*, the critical or neutral condition of reversal is obtained. Fig. 8.1 (e) represents these two regions diagrammatically.

It is to be noted that the state of refraction of the examiner's eye at C is not involved in the process described. It is only necessary that he see clearly what is happening within the pupil, DE.

8.3. Reversal of the Reflex Movement.

The lens of Fig. 8.1 will serve to represent the optical system of a subject's eye. The plane M′*a* represents the retina, on which the small illuminated patch moves laterally from M′ to *a* when the mirror is tilted. Cases (a) and (b) then illustrate hyperopia ; case (c) myopia of amount less than the dioptral distance PC ; and case (d) myopia exceeding this amount. If the eye be in its static condition, MA is its far point plane.

In practice the dimensions and movements across the axis are very small and may justifiably be represented by straight lines perpendicular to the axis ; and the elementary paraxial relations of image formation are applicable.

Suppose an unaccommodated eye of unknown refractive condition is to be examined. Light is reflected towards the subject by means of a mirror. As the mirror is rotated, reflected light will first appear somewhere on the subject's face, moving towards his eye. Presently, when some of this light enters his eye, a small illuminated patch is formed in his retina. If, on causing this patch to move laterally over the fundus by small rotations of the mirror, the reflex movement is observed to be " against ", then we know that the subject's far point lies between our observation position and the subject. If the " working distance " PC has been chosen as one metre, the subject's refractive condition is myopia of an amount exceeding one dioptre. If the movement is rapid the myopia is not much in excess of 1 D ;

whereas a slow movement indicates high myopia. If a "with" movement is observed, indicating that the far point lies within the other main region P ∞ C, the refractive condition is either hypermetropia, emmetropia, or myopia of amount less than 1 D. The speed of the movement supplies a further clue to the condition; if slow, we have hypermetropia of appreciable degree; whereas a rapid movement indicates that the far point is not far removed (dioptrally) from the observation position and the refractive condition is low hypermetropia, emmetropia or myopia less than 1 D.

The mirror is swung slowly and deliberately and the direction of movement of the edge of the reflex carefully watched as it passes the centre of the pupil.

We thus gain very rapidly an approximate estimate of the unknown ametropia. To complete the operation we must bring the subject's far point into coincidence with the examiner's eye, which state the examiner knows he has reached when instantaneous disappearance of the reflex, or reversal, is observed. This may be done in two ways:

(a) the examiner maintaining a fixed position, the far point is brought artificially to the observation point by adding a lens of appropriate power before the subject's eye. A positive lens is required to reverse a "with" movement and a negative lens an "against" movement;

(b) the examiner shifts his observation position towards or away from the subject until reversal is obtained, the far point having first been brought to a convenient position in front of the subject by means of a lens of appropriate power.

The working distance most commonly used is one metre, this being more satisfactory than a shorter distance from the point of view of accuracy, and yet sufficiently close to enable the seated examiner to place test lenses in the subject's trial frame. When, during a test, it is thought that reversal has been obtained at this distance, a check is afforded by leaning back, say to 125 or 133 cm., when the reflex should move against; and then by leaning forward, say to 80 cm. when the movement should be with. Practice will enable one to alter the observation position by these amounts. It is probably a good plan to commence a test at a distance less than one metre (say 66 cm. or 80 cm.) for greater convenience in changing the trial lenses, until reversal is nearly obtained, and then to lean back to one metre distance to complete the test.

Whether the method adopted be (*a*) or (*b*) or a combination of the two as just suggested, when reversal is finally obtained, *the combination of eye and lens is myopic by an amount equal to the dioptral distance of separation, PC.* The lens producing this condition is the REVERSING LENS.

If, in method (*a*), a fixed working distance PC of one metre is chosen and the neutral condition of a certain eye is obtained by adding a $+3$ D sphere, then the eye alone is hypermetropic 2 D and the distance CORRECTING LENS is $+2$ D. If the lens to produce reversal is found to be $-1\cdot50$ D sphere, the correcting lens is $-2\cdot50$ D. If, using method (*b*), reversal is obtained with a $+1\cdot50$ D sphere, the final separation PC being 50 cm., the eye *plus* lens is myopic 2 D and the eye alone myopic $0\cdot50$ D.

Putting

$$\left.\begin{aligned} PC &= e \text{ metres} \\ \frac{1}{PC} &= \frac{1}{e} = E \text{ dioptres} \end{aligned}\right\} \text{always reckoned positive}$$

$F =$ power of lens to produce reversal at the distance e; the reversing lens;

then

$$\left.\begin{array}{l}\text{Refractive condition or} \\ \text{Distance Correcting lens}\end{array}\right\} = (\boldsymbol{F} - \boldsymbol{E}) \text{ dioptres} \qquad (8\cdot 1)$$

$$= (F - 1) \quad ,, \quad \text{for } e = 1 \text{ metre}$$

$$= (F - 1\cdot 50) \quad ,, \quad \text{for } e = \tfrac{2}{3} \text{ metre}$$

etc.

In practice the reversing lens occupies the spectacle point position and to obtain from it the correcting lens as explained above the working distance, *e*, should be reckoned from the same point.

The student, having carried out the experiment of the previous paragraph, should at this stage obtain some preliminary retinoscopy practice on a model eye, which can be obtained from optical firms or made by the student himself from a small box or tin and a spherical lens of about 5 cm. focal length and, say, 1 cm. aperture. Skill in the art of retinoscopy can be achieved only by assiduous and regular practice, first on the model eye and then on living eyes. Moreover, the student is advised to proceed with such practice systematically, first familiarising himself with the appearance of the reflex on the model eye when this is put into conditions of hypermetropia and myopia and the critical position of reflex reversal, using various working distances. The student should not proceed to cases of astigmatism until he has grasped the main principles of spherical errors as described above, and has acquired reasonable skill in the practice of the method.

8.4. Illumination for Retinoscopy. Plane Mirror.

In the experiment of §8.2 adequate illumination of the object was derived from the surroundings. In actual retinoscopy the light required to produce the patch on the subject's retina has to be projected into his eye through his pupil. Ignoring self-luminous retinoscopes for the present, the illumination is ordinarily provided by means of a lamp, placed to one side of or above the subject's head, and a mirror, as in ophthalmoscopy. The mirror may be plane or concave ; we will confine ourselves at present to the plane mirror, which is usually employed. For a working distance of one metre, and assuming the source of light lies in the plane of the subject's eye, the image of the source is 2 metres from the eye. This will be in sharp focus on the retina of an eye that is myopic 0·50 D and if the source is about 1 cm. in diameter, this retinal patch will be about 0.1 mm. in

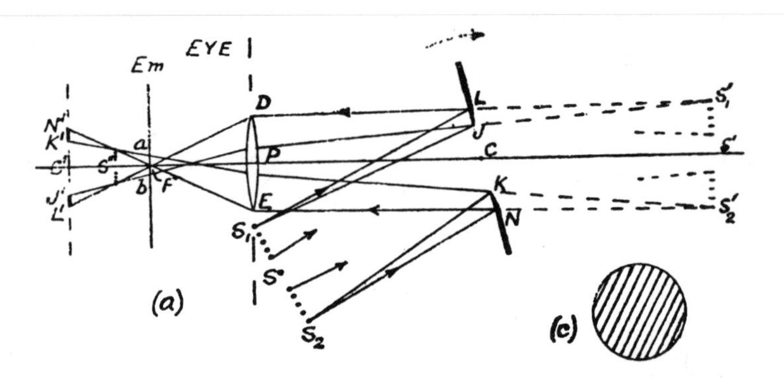

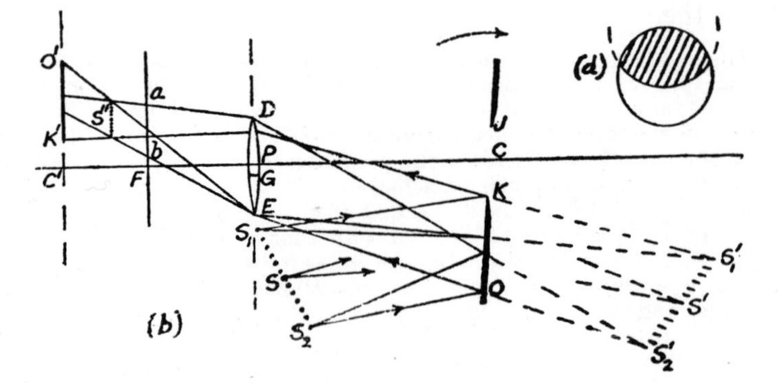

FIG. 8.2—ILLUMINATION FOR RETINOSCOPY. PLANE MIRROR.

diameter. In other refractive conditions it will be blurred and somewhat larger.

The conditions are illustrated in Fig. 8.2 in which the subject's eye is represented by a positive lens of aperture (pupil) DE, the plane mirror with sighthole JK is at C and the source is represented by its central point S and edges S_1 and S_2. An image of the source (sometimes called the *immediate* source) is formed at S'_1, S', S'_2. The retina of an emmetropic eye is simulated by a diffuse white screen placed at F, the focal point of the lens. In the first diagram (a) the mirror is so placed that the source image S'_1 S'_2 is centrally disposed on the optical axis. As no light is reflected by the sighthole, pencils of light as shown enter the eye from points S_1 and S_2 of the source; no light enters the eye from S nor from a certain area around S. A blurred patch *ab* is formed on the screen (retina). Some light is reflected back in all directions and emerges from DE as parallel pencils, light from all parts of DE entering the sighthole. To an examiner's eye placed behind the sighthole the pupil DE thus appears filled with light as indicated at (c).

If now the mirror is rotated upwards as indicated by the arrow until it occupies the position shown in the second diagram (b), the source image moves down and the illuminated patch *ab* on the screen at F moves up. Light reflected back from the screen (retina) emerges from the pupil in a general downward direction; no light enters the sighthole from the portion GE of the pupil. To an examiner at C, the pupil thus appears as indicated at (d), the reflex having moved upwards, i.e. in the *same* direction as the rotation of the mirror, the "eye" being emmetropic. The reflex movements described in the preceding paragraphs can thus be related now to the tilt of the mirror. That is, *with a plane mirror, the reflex movement is against the mirror when the far point lies within the region PC; and with the mirror when the far point lies anywhere outside this region.* Fig. 8.1 (e) still applies.

There are some subsidiary effects that should be noted. In the first position of the mirror, diagram (a), only the portions JL and KN of the mirror are effective in reflecting light into the eye. If the screen were withdrawn to the position C′ which is conjugate to C, no light could fall on the area J′K′ which is the image of the sighthole JK. Consequently none of the light reflected from the screen can enter the sighthole after emerging from the lens DE ; it all falls on the regions JL and KN. The pupil DE would therefore appear quite dark. This state of affairs arises in retinoscopy when the condition of reversal has been reached ; theoretically, there should be no reflex at reversal. The fact that there *is* a reflex in practice is referred to later (§8.11). If the screen were placed somewhere in the region between S'' (the image of S') and C', the reflex seen by the examiner would be dimmed in its central portion.

When the mirror is rotated to the second position, the light is reflected into the " eye " by a different portion of the mirror, namely KO ; light from *all* points of the source now enter DE and the patch *ab* on the screen placed at F is larger than before, as well as shifted upwards. If the screen were moved to position C', the portion $K'O'$ would be illuminated, the portion $J'K'$ still remaining dark ; hence there would still be no reflex visible, theoretically, to an examiner at C. The effects of these conditions on the appearance of the reflex as an eye is approaching reversal in a retinoscopic test are discussed in §8.11.

8.5. The Concave Mirror.

It is possible to use a concave mirror to reflect the light into the eye. If the focal length of this mirror be short, say 25 cm. or so, the image of the source will be real and situated between the mirror and the subject's eye. An upward tilt of the mirror will produce an upward displacement of this source image, as against a downward displacement with the plane mirror (Fig. 8.2). The fundus patch *ba* will move *downwards. The reflex movements with a short focus concave mirror will thus be exactly opposite to those obtained with a plane mirror :* that is, " with " the mirror for myopia exceeding E dioptres and " against " the mirror for hypermetropia, emmetropia and myopia less than E dioptres (E = reciprocal of working distance, e).

The factors that may be affected by the curvature of the mirror are the size and brightness of the reflex and the disturbing appearances, caused by aberration, around the margin of the pupil, particularly if it be a wide pupil. The short focus concave has little advantage in brightness and opinions seem to differ as to the last mentioned effect. It possesses the disadvantage, however, that it may lead to difficulties if the examiner, during a test, approaches the eye in his search for the critical position of reversal. Thus, assuming the source to be in the eye plane, a mirror of 33·33 cm. focus will produce an image of the source 50 cm. in front of the eye when working at 1 metre; and the reflex movements will be opposite to those obtained with a plane mirror. If the examiner approach to 66·67 cm., the source image will be formed practically at the subject's nodal point, in which case no reflex movement will result when the mirror is tilted whatever the refractive condition may be; the play of light within the pupil will simulate the appearance of genuine reversal.* On a still closer approach to the subject, the source image will be formed behind the subject and the reflex movements will change to those of a plane mirror. Effects such as these will be confusing and misleading.

A concave mirror of longer focal length, greater than 75 cm., may be used such that the image of the source is formed behind the subject when the working distance is one metre or a little in excess of this. A wider cone of light from each point of the source will thereby be concentrated upon and enter the pupil (provided the diameter of the mirror is sufficient) and the fundus patch, and consequently the reflex, will be brighter. A closer approach to the subject with such a mirror will result in the source image being formed either still farther behind the subject or in the region behind the examiner. In all working positions (within one metre or so) the reflex movements will be the same as those obtained with a plane mirror. Although the plane mirror reveals opacities in the media better than a concave mirror, for purposes of retinoscopy alone the long focus concave is probably superior. Since the reflex movements are the same with either, we will continue to use the term " plane mirror " to include both.

8.6. The Subject's Accommodation and Fixation.

We utilise this objective method of retinoscopy in order to determine the static refraction, or distance correction, of the eye. The process is consequently referred to as STATIC RETINOSCOPY.

If and when retinoscopy is practised with the subject *purposely* accommodated on a near object, the procedure is called *dynamic retinoscopy*, which will be discussed later.†

* See §8.10.

† §8.14.

In static retinoscopy, with which we are at present concerned, we wish the subject to remain, if possible, in a completely relaxed condition. Actually, the accommodative state of the subject is an unknown quantity during the test and it is not too easy to control it. The room is usually darkened to some extent so that the reflex can be more easily seen in contrast to the darker surroundings. The usual procedure consists in directing the subject to gaze binocularly at some fixation mark such as a spot of light or the illuminated test chart, some metres away. The hyperope will accommodate to see the fixation object, but as the examiner increases the power in the trial frame in order to neutralise the with movement, some of this accommodation will be relaxed; the examiner will put up the strongest positive lens with which reversal can be obtained. A myope of more than E dioptres cannot see the fixation object clearly at any stage of the test. As negative lenses are put up to neutralise the against movement, the artificial far point moves gradually nearer to the observation point C. The examiner will take care to use the weakest negative lens with which reversal can be obtained.

In either case, on obtaining reversal the subject's retina is conjugate to the mirror; but evidently the subject's accommodative state at the moment of reversal is an uncertain quantity.

Various devices have been suggested in the attempt to secure relaxed accommodation. These introduce a certain amount of complication and inconvenience into an otherwise beautifully simple method, however; and in view of the fact that the retinoscopy finding will be checked subjectively on the test chart, it is not of vital importance that the spherical portion of the correction determined by retinoscopy should be exact. But the astigmatism, if any, should be estimated as carefully as possible and so reduce the time required in its subjective verification; we have seen that this sometimes tends to be a somewhat lengthy and troublesome process.

Assuming, then, that we are content to rely on the subject fixing a distant fixation mark, another consideration arises. His visual axis must of necessity be oblique to the examiner's axis of observation since he must look to one side or the other of the examiner's head. This obliquity was mentioned as one of the drawbacks of direct ophthalmoscopy as a means of testing refraction and is equally a disadvantage in retinoscopy. It leads to two possible sources of error. Firstly, the refraction is being determined along a line and at a part of the retina not coincident with those used by the eye subjectively; and secondly, the obliquity may produce oblique astigmatism in the emergent beam, which may falsify the findings. Whereas reliable experimental data as to the magnitude of these effects is lacking, experience shows that in general they are not serious. Nevertheless, they are potential causes of error.

The use of a cycloplegic would enable the subject to look directly at the mirror without accommodating and without pupil contraction and so permit observations on the macula; but the result so obtained is subject to the disadvantage already mentioned that the eye is not in its normal physiological state. Wherever possible, and except in certain special circumstances, the test should be performed without cycloplegia.

8.7. Astigmatism.

It will be understood in a general way that the *circular* reflex obtained in the case of spherical errors of refraction will be replaced, in the case of an astigmatic eye, by an oval reflex, the long and short axes of which are parallel to the principal meridians of the eye. Thus the edge of the reflex seen passing across the pupil as the mirror is rotated will be some portion of the circumference of this oval. Its oval nature may not at first be apparent, except to the experienced, unless the astigmatism is appreciable in relation to the spherical refractive error, but will become more so as the examiner proceeds to put up the spherical lenses required to approach reversal in one meridian or the other.

We will first deal with the procedure to be adopted, leaving the explanation of the appearances to the following paragraphs. By means of spherical lenses one meridian is made to approach reversal. The existence of astigmatism then becomes more apparent, in three main ways: firstly, because of the drawn-out appearance of the reflex, so that the longer edge of it approximates to a straight line; secondly, because the speed of movement of the reflex is greater in the meridian approaching reversal than in the other perpendicular to it; and thirdly because the direction of the reflex movement does not in general coincide with the direction along which the light is driven by the rotation of the mirror. The greater the degree of astigmatism, the more pronounced are these characteristic appearances. In high degrees of astigmatism the reflex may appear almost as a straight band of light across the pupil. In mixed astigmatism the reflex movements are in opposite directions in the two meridians.

When astigmatism is established, either at the beginning of the test or after a certain amount of spherical power has been put up in the approach towards reversal in one meridian the rotations of the mirror are subsequently carried out along one of the two meridians revealed by the extended appearance and direction of movement of the edge of the reflex. From the standpoint of the control of accommodation it may be preferable to attend first to the more hyperopic of the two meridians. Having produced reversal in this meridian with a spherical test lens, attention is directed to the perpendicular meridian, along which the mirror rotations are now performed. There are one or two possible variations of the procedure at this stage.

The reversing sphere of the first meridian may be removed and the second meridian treated in exactly the same way, using spherical lenses. This is probably the best way for the novice. It has the advantage that there is only one lens in the trial frame at one time. Alternatively, the reversing sphere of the first meridian may be left *in situ* and reversal in the second meridian obtained by adding cylindrical lenses with axis parallel to the first meridian. This method has the disadvantages that it is more difficult to observe the reflex through two lenses because of possible confusing reflections from the four surfaces; and that extra care and time are required to ensure that the cylindrical test lenses are each inserted in the trial frame at the proper orientation.

When, by one of these procedures (or by a third to be described presently) the complete astigmatic reversing lens is known and reversal obtained in all meridians when this lens is in position, the combination of eye plus this lens is myopic by an amount equal to the dioptral distance of the observation point C, which is the far point of the combination. If the final working distance were one metre, the distance CORRECTING lens is obtained, as in the case of spherical errors, by subtracting one dioptre from the reversing lens; for a working distance of $\frac{2}{3}$ metre, 1·50 D is subtracted; and so on.

For example: in a given case the principal meridians are found to be 60° and 150°, the reversing lens for the former meridian being + 2·75 D sphere and for the latter + 1·50 D sphere (or − 1·25 D cylinder *added* to the first sphere). The reversing lens is:

+ 2·75 D along 60°/ + 1·50 D along 150°
or + 2·75 D Cyl. axis 150/ + 1·50 D Cyl. axis 60
or + 2·75 D Sph./ − 1·25 D Cyl. axis 60

If the test were carried out at one metre, the correcting lens is:

+ 1·75 D Cyl. ax. 150/ + 0·50 D Cyl. ax. 60
or + 1·75 D Sph./ − 1·25 D.C. ax. 60.

Had reversal with *the same eye* been obtained with a working distance of 50 cm. the reversing lens in sph.-cyl. form would have been:

+ 3·75 D Sph./ − 1·25 D Cyl. axis 60

the subtraction of 2 D for this working distance giving the same correcting lens.

It is to be noted that the meridian being measured is the one along which the light is driven and the reflex movements observed.

It is important in retinoscopy of an astigmatic eye to determine the axis direction of the cylinder lens required as accurately as possible; not only because this is desirable in the final correction but also because an error in the estimation of the direction during the progress of the test tends to complicate matters.* With this in mind, the second of the two procedures described above may be modified in the following manner, which depends upon the principles of obliquely crossed cylinders. The reversing sphere of the first meridian is left in position and reversal in the second meridian approached by adding further *spherical* power. When nearing reversal, this second sphere is replaced by a cylinder of equal power with its axis along the first meridian, or along what is estimated to be the first meridian. If this cylinder has not been correctly placed, it and the cylinder element of the eye together form a pair of obliquely crossed cylinders nearly equal in power but of opposite sign, producing a new cylinder power along a resultant direction which lies outside the two constituent cylinders. As the examiner swings his mirror along the power meridian of the cylinder he has placed in the trial frame, the reflex will appear to move along a meridian determined by this new resultant direction.

Suppose, for example, that the two principal meridians of the eye are actually 30° and 120°, that reversal along the former has been

* See also §4.8.

obtained with a – 3 D sphere and that the examiner, incorrectly estimating the meridians, has added a – 1·75 D Cyl. axis 20°. If the eye really requires, say, – 2·00 D Cyl. axis 30°, then as the mirror is swung slowly along the 110° meridian, the edge of the reflex will apparently move along a meridian approximating to 150°. This warns the examiner that his cylinder lens is incorrectly placed and he will rotate it from the 20° direction its axis occupies to, say, 25° and try again, eventually finding 30° as the correct axis. He will now be swinging his mirror along 120° and the reflex will be moving along the same meridian. Its movement will be quick and against the mirror, and will be stopped by a further – 0·25 D cylinder power, giving the cylinder as – 2·00 D Cyl. ax. 30°. With the complete reversing lens, – 3·00 D.S./– 2·00 D.C. ax. 30°, now in position, there should be reversal in all meridians.

8.8. Astigmatism. An Experiment.

The characteristics of the reflex in astigmatism are: its oval shape; the different speeds of its movement in the principal meridians; and the non-coincidence of its direction of movement with the direction in which the light is driven, except when the latter is along one or other of the principal meridians. An explanation of these characteristics is best preceded by one or two simple experiments, which the student should carry out for himself.

1. Arrange for a second observer to place himself in position to carry out a retinoscopy on a model eye in the front cell of which has been placed a sph.-cyl. lens, say + 3·00 D Sph./ + 2·00 D Cyl. axis 30°. Remove the back of the eye and replace it with a ground glass screen or a piece of tissue paper. Observe the small patch of illumination on this screen. Its shape depends upon the position of the screen, but is generally oval, the long and short axis of the oval lying along 30° and 120°. If the second observer swings the mirror so as to drive the light horizontally, the fundus patch is seen to move practically in a horizontal direction.* When the mirror is rotated along 30° or 120°, the patch moves along the same meridian.

2. Cut out of white paper a tiny oval piece about 4 mm. by 6 mm. and stick it on to a dark coloured piece of cardboard or the cover of a book. This represents the fundus patch. Take the + 12 D sphere and + 4 D cylinder from the trial case and hold them in contact, placing between them a piece of paper with a central circular hole to limit the aperture to about 1 cm. in diameter. Observe the fundus patch, placed with its long axis along 120°, through

* Refer to §10.17.

this sph.-cyl. combination held with the cyl. axis along 30°, the eye being about half a metre from the patch. The view of the latter through the lenses represents the reflex seen in retinoscopy. When the lens combination is held only a few centimetres from the patch and the latter is moved along the principal meridians (30° and 120°), the movement of the reflex is " with " in both meridians, but quicker in the 120° meridian. The arrangement represents an eye with C.H.A. Withdraw the lens slowly and presently reversal will be obtained in the 120° meridian. Withdrawing the lenses a little farther towards the eye, we have a condition of mixed astigmatism and the reflex movement will be " with " in the 30° meridian and " against " along 120°. On still farther withdrawal of the lenses we pass through a position in which reversal is obtained in the 30° meridian, to one of C.M.A. in which the reflex movement is " against " in both meridians, but quicker in the 30° meridian.

With the lenses at this distance, move the fundus patch in a *horizontal* direction and observe carefully that the reflex moves bodily along a meridian lying between 30° and the horizontal but that the advancing or following *edge* of it appears to be moving along the 30° meridian. Similarly if the patch is moved along the vertical direction, the reflex moves along a direction approximating to 70° or 80°, but the long edge of the reflex appears to cross the pupil along the 120° meridian.

Thus when the light in retinoscopy is driven along a meridian that does not coincide with one of the principal meridians, the reflex moves along a new direction which depends upon the amount of astigmatism, the position of the retina in relation to the focal lines (i.e. the refractive condition of the eye) the working distance, *e*, and the direction of rotation of the mirror. The *edge* of the reflex appears to slide across the pupil along a principal meridian. Further information on these movements can be gleaned from the following experiments.

3. Observe a crossline through the + 12 D S./+ 4 D C. combination, the crossline being vertical and horizontal and the cylinder axis, as above, along 30°. When the combination is but a few centimetres from the crossline, as when neutralising, the lines show the well known " scissors effect " and appear to lie along the directions X′X′ and Y′Y′ in Fig. 8.3 (a). Slide the crossline horizontally

and the lines appear to move along the direction X′X′, which does not coincide either with the direction of movement or with either of the principal meridians. Withdraw the lens slowly towards the eye (the eye being half a metre or so from the crosslines) and observe the changes that take place in the directions of the two lines* until, having passed through the critical focal line (reversal) positions, the appearance is as shown in Fig. 8.3 (b). The (astigmatic) images of the lines are now real whereas in the first case they were virtual; the lines are now indistinct since they are near to the eye.

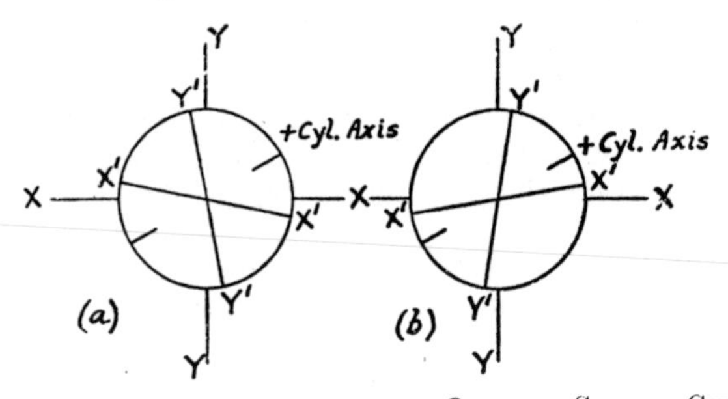

FIG. 8.3—VIEW OF CROSSLINE THROUGH OBLIQUE SPHERO-CYL., ILLUSTRATING MOVEMENT OF REFLEX IN RETINOSCOPY OF AN ASTIGMATIC EYE.

The reason for the obliquity of the crosslines, or of the oblique direction of movement of the reflex in the second experiment, will be understood by considering the prismatic effect produced by the sph.-cyl. combination on a ray of light incident from an object point displaced from the optical axis of the combination. The ray is refracted by a decentred portion of the lens.†

8.9. Astigmatism—continued.

The oval shape of the fundus patch results from the fact that the pencil of light from *each* point of the circular source is reflected by the mirror and is refracted by the subject's eye so as to form a pair of mutually perpendicular focal lines in front of, or behind, or one on each side of, the retina, according to the refractive condition. Consider the case of an eye with C.M.A., myopic 1·5 D in the 30° meridian and 3·0 D in the 120° meridian; working distance

* These are described in §10.16.

† See also §10.16.

one metre, circular source of diameter 1 cm.; subject's pupil 4 mm. The blurred fundus patch is oval, the long axis being about 0·25 mm. in length, along 120°; and the short axis about 0·16 mm., along 30°. The exact dimensions depend upon how much of the myopia is axial and how much refractive.

This somewhat elongated small patch, the outer portions of which are already ill-defined, forms the object for the returning observation system. The far point for the 120° meridian lies $\frac{1}{3}$ metre from the subject's eye and $\frac{2}{3}$ metre from the observation point; the far point for the 30° meridian lies $\frac{1}{3}$ metre from the observation point. The fundus patch will be imaged by the returning light as a patch consisting of focal lines lying along 30° in a plane $\frac{2}{3}$ metre from the observation point and a larger patch of focal lines lying along 120° in a plane $\frac{1}{3}$ metre from this point. When, by swinging the mirror, the fundus patch is made to move along the 30° meridian, the aerial patch nearer to the examiner will also move in this meridian and so, consequently, will the reflex seen within the pupil, since the latter is the projection of the former from the observation point (§8.2). And since in this meridian the aerial image of the fundus patch moves in a plane that is nearer to the observation point than is the case for the 120° meridian, the projection of it on the subject's pupillary plane, and hence the speed of reflex movement, will be greater.

This matter of the oval shape of the reflex and the greater speed of its movement in the meridian that is approaching reversal may be considered finally from a point of view somewhat different from that adopted in §8.2.

Returning for a moment to purely spherical errors of refraction, Fig. 8.4 (a) represents a myopic subject whose far point is at M. Considering one point *a* of the fundus patch, this has been moved, by rotating the mirror, to such a position that of the total pencil of light emerging from the subject's eye, only a portion Dg enters the sighthole and examiner's pupil at Jq. The portion Dg of the subject's pupil, therefore, appears bright and the portion gE dark (the "shadow"). If the mirror be rotated upwards until the point *a* lies on the axis at M′, the aerial image A will move down to the axis at M, the whole pencil from DE will enter the examiner's eye and the pupil DE will appear filled with light; a complete flash. As the point *a* continues to move upwards, the subject's pupil will continue to appear fully illuminated until the ray from D just grazes the sighthole at K, as shown in diagram (b). From this moment the "following" edge of the reflex will cross the pupil downwards from D to E, and, for a given speed of rotation of the mirror, the time it takes to cross the pupil depends

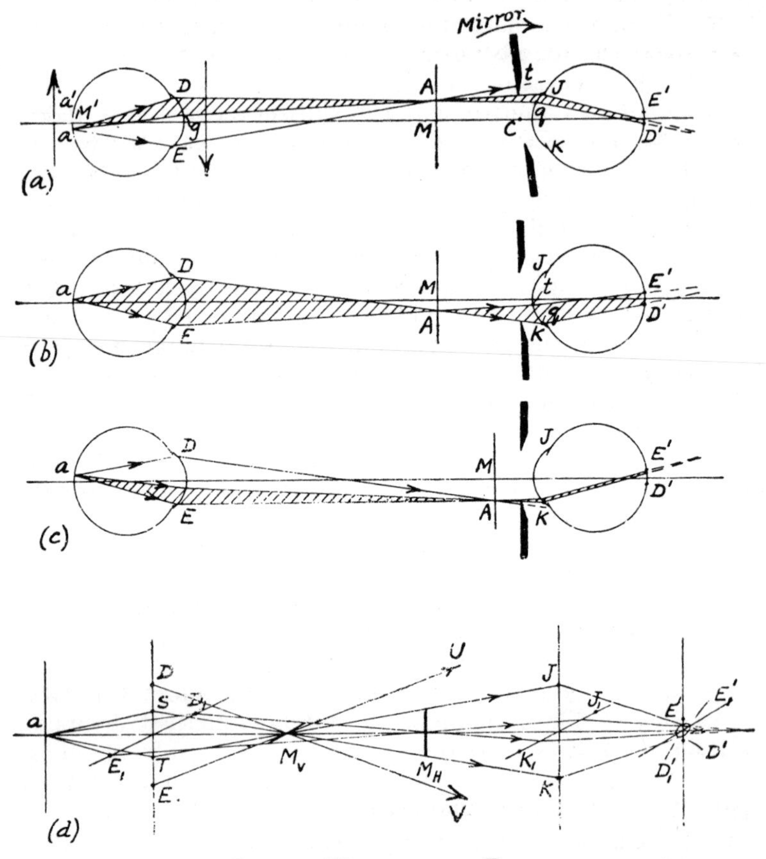

FIG. 8.4—REFLEX MOVEMENT IN RETINOSCOPY.

upon the width tq of the pencil as it enters the examiner's eye. The total size of the reflex (taking all points of the fundus patch) does not affect the speed with which the *edge* of it crosses the pupil.

In diagram (c) the far point M is supposed to have been brought closer to the observation point C (by putting up negative spheres in the trial frame); the state of affairs depicted is just before the disappearance of the following edge of the reflex at the border E of the subject's pupil. It will be clear that for the same speed of mirror rotation, the narrower pencil of this case will pass the edge K of the sighthole much more rapidly. And in the critical case when the far point lies *in* the plane of the sighthole, all the light from DE will enter the latter at one moment and will have been cut off instantaneously at the next moment as the edge K is passed.

Since the examiner is accommodating on the pupil DE, this is imaged sharply as D′E′ on his retina. What the examiner perceives must be the result of light falling within this area. It will be noticed that only a portion of it is filled in diagrams (a) and (c), but the whole of it in (b).

To turn now to the astigmatic eye, which is represented in (d), the principal meridians being vertical and horizontal for simplification of the diagram; the far points are at M_V and M_H. Only one point *a* of the fundus patch is represented, in its central position. Tracing those rays in each principal meridian that can enter the examiner's pupil JJ_1KK_1, it will be seen that the blurred image formed on his retina, within the sharp image $D'D'_1E'E'_1$, of the subject's pupil, is oval in shape with the short axis vertical. This must be the appearance to him of the reflex, which is also seen to be the case from the fact that, in the vertical meridian, only rays at an aperture ST can enter his pupil. It will be clear that when the mirror is rotated in the horizontal meridian, in which meridian the pencil is narrow as it enters the examiner's pupil, the edge of the reflex will move across the pupil D_1E_1 more rapidly than is the case along the vertical meridian, in which the pencil is considerably wider, as indicated by UV.

8.10. Speed of Reflex Movement.

Useful information as to the condition of the reflex with respect to its speed of movement under varying conditions can be derived from expressions obtainable from the elementary laws of geometrical optics. We will begin by working out a numerical example.

Example. Compare the angular rate of movement of the reflex with the angular rate of rotation of the mirror in retinoscopy with a plane mirror under the following conditions: working distance, subject to mirror, 1 metre: distance of source from mirror, 50 cm.; firstly for a subject myopic 5 D; secondly for one myopic 2·5 D.

Discuss the effect of varying the distance of the source from the mirror.

Answer. Refer to Fig. 8.5. The plane mirror is at C: the subject's eye at PM′, nodal point N; subject's far point at M; source at $\bar{S}$ and its image in the mirror, the immediate source, at S where SC = C$\bar{S}$. We place the source on the axis in the diagram for simplicity, and assume it to be a point.

When mirror is perpendicular to axis, fundus image (blurred) is at M′. When mirror is rotated upwards through, say, 2°, into the position shown by full line, source image moves from S to S′ where $\bar{S}$S′ is perpendicular to mirror. For small angles SS′ is sensibly perpendicular to $\bar{S}$S.

$SS' = \bar{S}S \tan 2° = 100 \times \cdot 035 = 3 \cdot 5$ cm.

Light enters eye along direction S′N to point a on fundus.

$\angle CNS' = \tan^{-1} \frac{3 \cdot 5}{150} = 1\frac{1}{3}°$, i.e. $\frac{2}{3}$ of mirror tilt.

By light returning from subject's eye, image of a is formed at A, in far point plane through M.

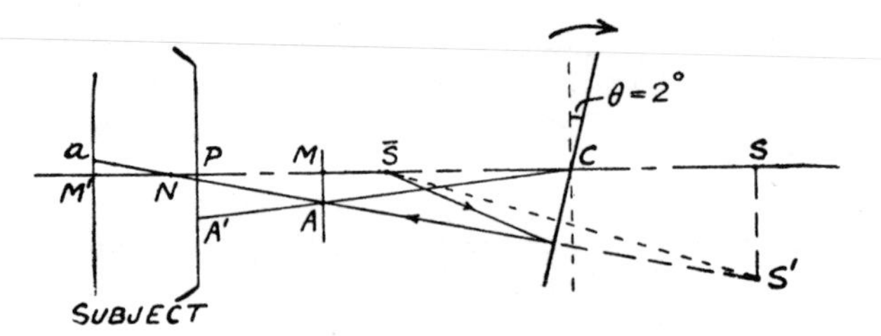

FIG. 8.5—ILLUSTRATING RATE OF REFLEX MOVEMENT FROM P TO A′ COMPARED WITH MIRROR ROTATION, θ.

To examiner at C, reflex appears to have moved *down* from **P** to A′. Since, neglecting the small separation of N and P, (a) NM = $\frac{1}{5}$ metre and MC = $\frac{4}{5}$ metre,

we have $\angle PCA' = \frac{1}{4} \angle CNS' = \frac{1}{4} \cdot \frac{4}{3} = \frac{1}{3}$ degree (down).

$$\text{Hence } \frac{\text{angular movement of reflex}}{\text{angular movement of mirror}} = \frac{-\frac{1}{3}}{2} = -\frac{1}{6}$$

reflex moves at one sixth speed of mirror in opposite direction.

(b) NM = 40 cm. and MC = 60 cm.

$\angle PCA' = \frac{40}{60} \angle CPS' = \frac{2}{3} \cdot \frac{4}{3} = \frac{8}{9}$ degree (down).

$$\text{Hence } \frac{\text{angular movement of reflex}}{\text{angular movement of mirror}} = \frac{-\frac{8}{9}}{2} = -\frac{4}{9}$$

The reflex speed has increased when the far point approaches nearer to the observation point C.

Now suppose the source $\bar{S}$ to be moved nearer to the mirror at C. Its image S′ in the tilted position of the mirror approaches the mirror and the axis. The student should draw a diagram for this case. The angle CNS′ at which the light enters the eye is less than before and so the angular movement of the reflex for a given rotation of the mirror is less; i.e. the reflex movement is slower. Conversely, if the source $\bar{S}$ is moved away from the mirror, the reflex speed is increased.

Expressions may be derived for the more general case when the mirror is concave. In Fig. 8.6 light from the central point $\bar{S}$ of the source $\bar{S}_1\bar{S}\bar{S}_2$ is shown reflected from the mirror after this has been tilted down through angle θ, through the real image S′ to a small blur on the subject's retina at a. The subject is supposed to be relaxed. The image of a is at A in the far point plane and to the examiner at C the reflex has moved from P to A′ For simplicity we will consider only the central point of the source. We wish to find the ratio between the angular movement PCA′ of the reflex and the angular tilt, θ, of the mirror. The eye represented is hyperopic. Let

K = refractive condition of subject's eye (supposed relaxed) – dioptres.

$L = \frac{1}{l}$ = dioptral distance of light source from mirror.

F = power of mirror in dioptres; F = o for plane mirror and is positive for a concave mirror.

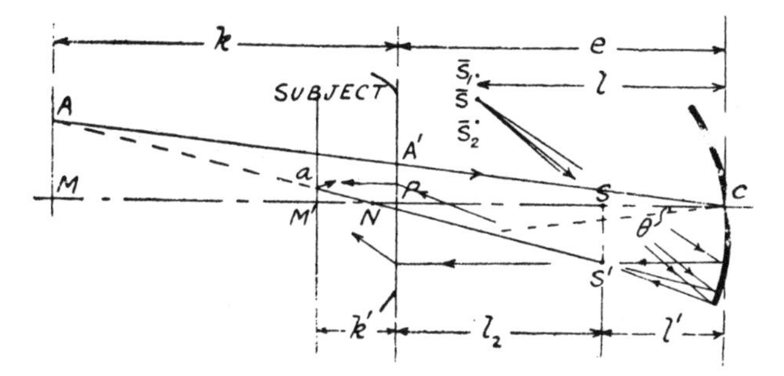

FIG. 8.6—RATE OF REFLEX MOVEMENT.

$L' = L + F$ = diop. distance of immediate source from mirror
L_2, L'_2 = diop. distance of immediate source and its image from subject's eye.

$E = \frac{1}{e}$ = diop. distance from subject's eye to mirror; always positive.

θ = rotation of mirror.

F_e = power of subject's eye – dioptres.

If, in a given time, the mirror is rotated through an angle θ, the spot of light on the subject's face moves through a linear distance $\frac{2\theta}{E}$.

The immediate source S, corresponding to $\bar{S}$, moves from S to S′ through a distance $-2l'\theta$.

Angle subtended by SS′ at nodal point N $= \frac{-2l'\theta}{l_2}$ where $l_2 = -(e + l')$

Movement MA on far point plane $= -\frac{2l'\theta}{l_2} \times k$ (neglecting small separation of P and N).

$$\left.\begin{array}{l}\text{Projection of this, or move-}\\ \text{ment on pupillary plane}\end{array}\right\} = PA' = \frac{-2l'\theta}{l_2}k \times \frac{e}{e+k}$$

$$= \frac{-2l'\theta}{-(e+l')} \times \frac{ke}{e+k}$$

$$= \frac{2\theta}{1+\frac{e}{l'}} \times \frac{1}{\frac{1}{k}+\frac{1}{e}} \qquad \left[\text{Note}: \frac{1}{l'} = -L' = -(L+F)\right]$$

$$= -\theta\frac{2E}{(L+F-E)(K+E)} \tag{8·2}$$

Angular movement

$$= -\theta\frac{2E^2}{(L+F-E)(K+E)}$$

in which a positive result refers to a " with " movement and a negative result to an " against " movement.

For a plane mirror $F = 0$, and

$$\left.\begin{array}{l}\text{linear movement on}\\ \text{pupillary plane}\end{array}\right\} = -\theta\frac{2E}{(L-E)(K+E)} \tag{8·3}$$

If, in addition, the source lies in the pupillary plane, so that **L** $= -E$, then

$$\left.\begin{array}{l}\text{linear movement on}\\ \text{pupillary plane}\end{array}\right\} = \frac{\theta}{K+E} \tag{8·3a}$$

Returning to the general case, the small patch of light on the subject's fundus moves through a distance $\frac{-2l'\theta k'}{n'l_2}$ remembering that the ray incident at P is refracted according to the law of refraction: hence

$$\left.\begin{array}{l}\text{linear movement of}\\ \text{fundus patch}\end{array}\right\} = -\theta\frac{2E}{(L+F-E)(K+F_e)} \tag{8.4}$$

Applying equation (8·3) to the previous example, we have $E = 1$ D; $L = -2$ D; $F = 0$; $K = (a) -5$ D, and $(b) -2·5$ D.

$$\frac{\text{Angular movement of reflex}}{\text{Angular movement of mirror}} = \frac{-2E^2}{(L+F-E)(K+E)}$$

$$(a) \quad = -\frac{2}{-3\times-4} = -\frac{1}{6}$$

$$(b) \quad = -\frac{2}{-3\times-1·5} = -\frac{4}{9}$$

the results obtained above.

From these expressions we learn that the speed of reflex movement is low for high values of K, positive or negative; that the speed increases as K diminishes until when $K = -E$, that is at reversal, the speed is infinite. When $(K+E)$ is positive, in which case the refractive condition K is more positive than $-E$ dioptres, the result of equations 8·3 for a plane mirror is positive, signifying a " with " movement. Equation 8·2 gives a positive result if F is less than $(E-L)$ which is the case for a long focus concave mirror; and a negative result for a short focus mirror of F greater than $(E-L)$; compare §8.5. Similarly, when $(K+E)$ is negative, the refractive condition then being myopia of greater amount than E dioptres, the result is negative or " against " for a plane or long focus mirror and positive or " with " for a short focus mirror of $F > (E-L)$.

In the particular case of a mirror for which $F = (E - L)$, equation 8·2 gives an infinite value for the speed, irrespective of the value of K. This is due to the fact that in these circumstances the immediate source is formed at the subject's eye. This fictitious "reversal" has already been referred to (§8.5) and is to be avoided in practice.

The expressions show that for a fixed working distance E the reflex speed depends on the position L of the source. When $(L + F)$ of equ. 8·2, or L of equ. 8·3, has a high numerical value, the speed remains low for all values of K except those approaching closely to the critical value $K = -E$. When K approaches this value, the speed increases rapidly to infinity. Other things being equal, the condition of reversal will consequently stand out more prominently and the retinoscopy be more sensitive. From this it appears to be advantageous, in the case of a plane mirror, to have the source of light near to the mirror. This arrangement will at the same time have two further advantages. The reflex will be somewhat brighter since more light will enter the eye from each point of the source, even allowing for the slight contraction of the pupil caused by the closer proximity of the source. Moreover, the immediate source being nearer to the point of observation, which becomes conjugate to the subject's retina as reversal is attained, the fundus patch will be more sharply defined and the edge of the reflex consequently sharper.

8.11. Difficulties in Retinoscopy.

In practice the determination of the point of reversal by retinoscopy is by no means so clear cut as the purely geometrical considerations of the previous paragraphs would imply. Due to several causes there is some uncertainty in deciding when reversal has been achieved. In the case of a fixed optical system such as the model practice eye, the initial difficulties are soon overcome ; but when dealing with the living eye, with its possibly irregular optical system and its many unconscious adjustments, the most we can positively say is that the point of reversal lies within a certain neutral region in the neighbourhood of the sighthole. And when the decision as to reversal has been made we cannot be sure of the optical condition of the eye at that moment. Different examiners do not interpret the reflex appearances in quite the same way so that experienced retinoscopists have been found to differ appreciably in their findings.

In addition to this lack of precision, in consequence of which individual tests on a given eye may vary round about a certain average value, a curious discrepancy is found to exist between this mean retinoscopy result and that obtained by subjective methods. There appears to be a general tendency for the subjective correction for distance to be more hypermetropic, by an amount averaging half a dioptre or so, than the correction obtained by retinoscopy, as if the subject were accommodating somewhat during the retinoscopy test.

We will first examine briefly possible reasons contributing to the uncertainty of the method. In the first place the edge of the reflex is usually badly defined; partly because it is, after all, derived from a fundus patch which itself is not sharp since the immediate source is not conjugate to the retina; and again, the fundus image is situated an appreciable distance from the subject's pupil upon which the examiner is accommodating. The edge of the reflex will become sharper the nearer the immediate source is to the sighthole and the smaller the source.

The sighthole in the mirror is responsible for two more disturbing effects. According to whether the mirror is one in which the hole is formed by merely removing the silvering, or one in which the hole is pierced right through the glass, little or no light is reflected from the sighthole area. The fundus patch consequently contains a dull central area which becomes more defined as reversal is approached since the retina is then not far from being conjugate to the immediate source. This dark central area shows up in the reflex. As the mirror is rotated, and varying portions of its surface become effective (§8.4 and Fig. 8.2) the dark centre moves relatively to the fundus patch and the dull portion of the reflex apparently moves across the pupil in the opposite direction to the reflex proper. This may produce misleading appearances, especially in astigmatism.

As reversal is closely approached, the dull central portion becomes progressively more prominent until at reversal the whole reflex is quite dim. The subject's retina and the sighthole are then conjugate with respect to the subject's optical system and a sharp image of the mirror with its sighthole is formed on his retina. In these circumstances the only light that can enter the sighthole from the subject's eye is that which originates at the sighthole image on the retina; and this is dark in the case of a pierced mirror. We should therefore, theoretically, see no reflex at all at reversal, even with the mirror in the central position. The reason that, with such a mirror, we do see the reflex at reversal, although a dim one, must be due partly to the light that "creeps" over the retina from neighbouring illuminated portions and partly due to aberrant light from such portions. If the hole in the mirror is formed by removing the silvering, some light is then reflected from the sighthole area; but then some of the returning light is also reflected by the glass, and is lost.

If this diminution in the brightness of the reflex occurred suddenly at reversal, it might be an advantage, but its progressive onset causes some difficulty in watching the reflex at the most important stage of the test. An arrangement whereby the immediate source could be kept at a distance from the sighthole during the commencement of the test and then brought suddenly near to the sighthole at reversal would, if practicable, appear to be an advantage.

It is perhaps not surprising that opinions differ as to the most favourable diameter of the sighthole, some maintaining that 2 mm. should not be exceeded and others advocating a sighthole of 7 mm. diameter. On account of the somewhat conflicting effects it produces, a mean value of 3 to 4 mm. for its diameter is probably most satisfactory with ordinary retinoscopes.

Troubles arising from the sighthole disappear if a metallic reflector be used. This consists of a plane or concave disc of glass on one surface of which has been deposited a thin film of a metal such as gold, platinum or preferably silver; the thickness of the film being such that about half of the incident light is reflected and half transmitted.* An appreciable amount of the light from the source is lost with such an instrument, however. These retinoscopes have not come into general use.

The aberrations of the eye, especially irregular imperfections, also contribute to the confusing appearances of the reflex as it moves across the pupil. Because of them the speed of movement will vary somewhat at different parts of the pupil and the point of reversal for one region will not be so for another region. These effects will be marked towards the margins of a wide pupil, as the student will have observed, even with a model eye. With such a pupil they are countered to some extent by concentrating attention upon the central portion of the pupil.

Discrepancy between Retinoscopy and Subjective Results.

To come to the question of the discrepancy between the retinoscopy and subjective findings, the cause is still

* Metallic reflectors of this kind are used as protective glasses: see *Ophthalmic Lenses*; Ch. IX.

obscure.* Certain factors can be advanced as being possibly operative in contributing to the difference:

1. In the first place we have no positive knowledge of the state of accommodation of the subject at the moment of reversal and it may be that herein lies an important contribution towards the discrepancy.

2. It has already been mentioned that in ordinary practice the test is carried out along a direction oblique to the subject's visual axis.

3. Aberrations of the subject's eye may play an important role. In both subjective and retinoscopy methods steps are taken to encourage the subject to relax accommodation for an object at 6 metres. The differences between the eye when being tested subjectively and by retinoscopy appear to be:

(*a*) The pupil may not be of the same diameter in both cases. (The ratio between the pupil diameters in the two cases will depend upon the general illumination of the room and the illumination of the test chart.) Marginal rays will then be admitted to the eye in one case that are excluded in the other and the subject may therefore need to accommodate by slightly different amounts in the two cases in order to place the most favourable cross-section of the pencils on his retina.†

(*b*) At the conclusion of the test the lens or lens combination in the trial frame is one dioptre more positive in the retinoscopic case—assuming a working distance of one metre. This may produce a slight difference in the aberration effects, but it can only be small.

(*c*) Irregular aberrations of the eye may quite likely be a contributory factor. Subjectively the best defined and brightest part of the composite retinal image seems to be selected, whereas light reflected back from the whole of the image will be used in retinoscopy.

4. The percipient layer of the retina acting as the receiving screen for the images when the subject is observing an object, such as the test chart, subjectively may not lie at the same distance from the eye's optical system as the effective *reflecting* surface in ophthalmoscopy or retinoscopy.

Whatever may be the cause of the discrepancy between the subjective and retinoscopy results, it is a common

* See also §8.15. † §11.3 and Fig. 11.6.

practice to make a certain "allowance" at the conclusion of the retinoscopy test, in addition to the amount E dioptres that must in any case be subtracted from the reversing lens. Each individual must assess this allowance, if he find it necessary, as the result of his own experience in comparing his retinoscopic and subjective findings. The allowance to be made, if any, depends upon how the examiner interprets the phenomenon of reversal. The question of an allowance scarcely arises, however, if the examiner bases his final decision on a subjective test carried out after the retinoscopy, using the findings of the latter method as a guide to the former. But he should use every endeavour to achieve accuracy in his retinoscopic determination of any *astigmatism* there may be present.

In spite of the difficulties described, retinoscopy is a most valuable method of measuring ametropia. Being objective it can be applied to illiterate or unintelligent or amblyopic subjects and to malingerers, in which cases a subjective test would be difficult or impossible. It is simple in its main principles ; to an expert it is rapid in operation and consequently not fatiguing to the subject and is sufficiently accurate to require very little modification in the cylindrical portion of the correction when subsequently checked subjectively.

It is probably sound to look upon retinoscopy as a rapid objective method of arriving at an approximation to the distance correction introductory to checking this finding subjectively on the test chart, and making such modification to the spherical portion of the correction as is then indicated. Some slight modification may also be required to the axis direction or magnitude of the cylinder portion of the correction. It has already been pointed out that to arrive at reversal, either the examiner can move his observation position or he can maintain a fixed position and bring the subject's far point artificially to the sighthole by appropriate lenses ; or he may combine the two. He could, for example, adopt the following procedure : after noting the direction and speed of the reflex movement, insert a lens of appropriate power to place the artificial far point at a convenient distance in front of the subject's eye, in the region 60 to 100 cm. ; the exact distance is not of importance. Move up to the position where reversal is obtained in the more hyperopic of the two principal meridians. Add a negative cylinder, with axis along this direction, to the lens in the trial frame ; in doing this the examiner's position will have changed. Move up again to the same position and see whether the movement in the second meridian is approaching reversal. Increase or decrease the negative cylinder until reversal is obtained in the two meridians simultaneously. The complete reversing lens is now in the trial frame and the cylinder portion is determined with some accuracy. Estimate approximately the working distance (PC = e) at which reversal was obtained ; subtracting the dioptral value of this from the reversing lens will give also the spherical portion of the distance correction with sufficient accuracy to check subjectively.

8.12. Self-luminous Retinoscopes.

Self-luminous hand ophthalmoscopes are a great convenience, particularly in direct ophthalmoscopy. Although there is not quite an equal gain in retinoscopy, self-luminous instruments have been introduced. Their optical arrangement is very similar to the luminous ophthalmoscope ; indeed we have seen that it is only necessary to modify the power of the projecting lens D, in such an ophthalmoscope as that illustrated in Fig. 7.11, to adapt it for retinoscopy. Since in retinoscopy we have to swing the immediate source of light laterally in relation to the subject's eye in order to obtain movement of the reflex across the pupil, the image of the original source L (Fig. 7.11 and 7.12) must be formed, not on the reflector in which situation it would remain more or less stationary as the reflector is tilted, but at some other position nearer to or farther from the eye. For reasons concerning the speed of the reflex explained in §8.10 it would be preferable to form the immediate source not too far from the observation point C. If, therefore, the instrument is to function as a plane mirror retinoscope, the pencil of light leaving the projector D should be slightly divergent.

The source of light and its image, the immediate source, are much smaller with a luminous retinoscope than with the ordinary retinoscope mirror used in conjunction with an external source. The appearance of the reflex in a given ametropic condition will therefore be different in the two cases, a fact to be realised by a practitioner changing over from an ordinary to a luminous retinoscope. With the latter the reflex will be better defined if the instrument is well designed.

A point arises in connection with the use of a luminous retinoscope on subjects with high refractive errors. The reflex movement is slow with a high error ; a comparatively large rotation of the reflector is required to produce a given extent of reflex movement. Since the reflector is of comparatively small dimensions in these instruments, the beam of light passing from it to the subject is narrow and the light may fail to enter the subject's eye after an appreciable tilt of the instrument. This may happen before the edge of the reflex circle makes its appearance within the pupil ; thus the direction of movement is not ascertained. When the subject's refractive error has been reduced with a spherical lens, however, this difficulty disappears.

DYNAMIC RETINOSCOPY

8.13. Objective Examination of the Accommodated Eye.

We have seen that in the customary subjective methods of arriving at the correction required for near work, it is assumed that any astigmatism there may be in the relaxed eye remains substantially unaltered when the eye accommodates ; and that the near correction consists of the distance correction plus a certain amount of additional spherical power determined in a rather empirical manner on the basis of the subject's accommodative amplitude.*

Small changes of astigmatism as the eye accommodates are of little moment because of the tolerance of the eye in near vision ; but this very tolerance may allow an appreciable change of astigmatism, which may produce symptoms of strain under *prolonged* near work, to pass unnoticed when examined subjectively at the near working distance. An objective method capable of checking the astigmatism when the eyes are accommodated for the near working distance would therefore be of service.

With regard to the spherical portion of the near correction : comfortable near vision requires that there shall be no ciliary strain and also no nervous strain due to marked disharmony between accommodation and convergence. The subjective procedure,† allowing as it does a reserve of both functions, appears to be a rational one. Its accuracy is probably adequate, allowance being made for the fact that the nervous system can adapt itself to appreciable variations of the

---

* §6.5.

† §6.5.

accommodation-convergence relationship—it has to do so as the physical accommodation of the individual declines with advancing years.* Nevertheless, objective methods of *measuring* the amplitudes of accommodation and convergence would be useful as alternatives to the subjective methods, particularly if they were more accurate.

Retinoscopy, carried out with the eyes accommodated on a fixation object situated at the near working distance, might be expected to provide some information concerning the astigmatism and the accommodation. It has been given the name DYNAMIC RETINOSCOPY, since the visual apparatus is in an active dynamic condition during the test. A. J. CROSS, to whom we are indebted for the first observations on the method, set out his views concerning its principles in 1902.

8.14. Observations on Dynamic Retinoscopy.

On the basis of geometrical optics, the phenomenon of reversal or infinitely rapid movement of the reflex occurs when the point conjugate to the subject's retina is brought into coincidence with the observation point. The point conjugate to the subject's retina we will call the FOCUS POINT; when the eye is completely relaxed, the focus point is the far point. When a relaxed emmetrope is examined by retinoscopy with a plane mirror at a finite working distance e, a " with " movement of the reflex is obtained. If the subject were to accommodate by such an amount that his focus point coincided with the observation point, reversal of the reflex would be obtained. The result is as if the subject had remained unaccommodated and a positive lens of power equal to the dioptral working distance had been inserted before the subject's eye.

Suppose the examiner places himself with his retinoscope at a distance of 33·33 cm. from the subject's eye (we will ignore the separation of eye and spectacle point). In the case of a young emmetrope accommodating 3 dioptres, reversal would be obtained. If he exerted his maximum accommodation of, say, 6 dioptres, the examiner would observe an " against " movement which would be converted into reversal if he approached to a working distance of 16·67 cm. Working at 33·33 cm. a myope of 2 D accommodating 1 D, or a hyperope of 2 D accommodating 5 D

---

* §6.4.

would produce reversal. With a presbyope whose near point of accommodation is at 50 cm., the with movement obtained at 33·3 cm. would become reversal if the examiner receded to 50 cm.

DISCREPANCY IN DYNAMIC RETINOSCOPY.

In practice the decision as to whether reversal has been obtained is subject to the same kind of uncertainty as arises in the static method, though not necessarily to the same extent. And just as in the latter method there is a discrepancy between the subjective and retinoscopy results, so in dynamic retinoscopy it does not follow that the point that is seen distinctly by the subject coincides with the focus point at which reversal of the reflex would be obtained.

Suppose a target containing some fine printed letters or geometrical designs is set up in the plane of the retinoscope mirror and just above the sighthole. Assuming a subject with ample accommodation, if the examiner takes up a position at 3 D (33·33 cm.) from the subject, who is asked to concentrate his attention upon the target and read or describe the characters on it, using both eyes, almost invariably a *with* movement of the reflex is obtained. Although the subject is accommodating on the target with sufficient exactness to distinguish very small objects, the *focus point* conjugate to his retina (more particularly, conjugate to the effective retinal reflecting surface) is situated further away. If the target is left in the same position but the examiner moves backwards with the retinoscope, away from the subject, reversal will be obtained at some point lying between 36 cm. and 50 cm. from the subject's eye. The fixation distance is 3 D, but the distance at which reversal is obtained, the *reversal distance* we will call it, is only 2·75 to 2·0 D, depending upon the subject. The with movement obtained when the working distance and target (fixation distance) coincide at 3 D thus varies between 0·25 D and 1·00 D with different subjects.

Theoretically, that is to say on purely geometrical grounds, there should be no such discrepancy; reversal should be obtained at 3 D when the subject is accommodating on a target at 3 D. The rather unexpected "with" movement, which the student can easily observe for himself, has not been satisfactorily explained. It occurs generally with subjects of all ages and refractive conditions. It persists at various working distances, gradually decreasing in amount as the target is moved farther away from the subject. That is to say, if with a given subject reversal is obtained at 44·4 cm. (2·25 D) when the target of fine characters is at 3 D, giving a difference between fixation and reversal of 0·75 D, the difference when the target is moved to a new position at 50 cm. declines a little to, say, 0·5 D; with the target in this situation a "with" movement is at first observed and reversal is obtained when the examiner recedes to, say, 1 metre.

The phenomenon may be stated thus: the subject accommodates on the target; because of aberrations in the eye's optical system the refracted pencil of light from each point of the target will not come to a "point" focus anywhere, but the most favourable cross section of the pencil,* under the conditions of the experiment, will be placed on the percipient layer of the retina, which is situated somewhere along the length of the foveal cones. The pencil of light returning from each point of the small illuminated patch on the fundus (the centre of which patch is a little higher than the fovea since the subject is fixing objects situated above the sighthole) will likewise be subject to aberrations of the eye's optical system, but the mean position of the "focus", at which reversal is obtained, does not lie in the same plane as the fixation target; it is more remote from the subject.

The factors that may be operating in producing this discrepancy are similar to those already cited in §8.11 as contributing to the difference between the static retinoscopy and subjective findings.

1. *Accommodation:* even small print can be read at the reading position when the eye is accommodating for some other distance.† Thus if in an experiment or test the conditions are such that the eyes tend to accommodate for a point within or beyond the test object, the latter may nevertheless be seen sufficiently clearly to be discriminated. But in the above test by dynamic retinoscopy there does not appear to be any adequate reason why the subject should not accommodate with precision on the target. It makes no measurable difference to the speed of the "with" movement of the reflex whether the target is well illuminated or not. It might be expected that accommodation may wander somewhat if the target is not illuminated except

* See §11.3. † §§ 5.2 and 5.4.

by the poor general illumination of the surroundings; but if the target is rendered very bright by light from a separate lamp, the subject's eyes being shielded from direct light from this lamp, little appears to happen except a contraction of the subject's pupils.

The "with" movement has been attributed entirely to this accommodation factor. According to this view, the subject converges on the target and obtains binocular fixation of it, but his accommodation is exerted to a smaller extent, for a point beyond the target. The difference between this accommodation and the dioptral distance of the target was called by SHEARD the "accommodation lag". It is supposed that the convergence exerted is the amount proper to the target distance, 3 M.A. if the test is carried out with the target at 33·3 cm., but that accommodation lags behind. In this connection the following experiment is instructive.

With the retinoscope and target in the same plane, one third metre from the subject, and the target unilluminated except by the general illumination, the subject is directed to concentrate his attention on the characters on the target, both eyes being in use. We will suppose that the examiner observes the reflex in the subject's right eye. With this eye the subject can scarcely distinguish details on the target because of the comparatively bright light flashed into it from the retinoscope mirror; indeed no detail whatever may be seen by this eye. Vision is consequently practically monocular, the left eye only being effective. It is quite possible that under such conditions the right eye diverges somewhat; but the effort to discriminate the target details with the left eye should prevent accommodation from departing far from the fixation distance. As we have seen above, a "with" movement of the reflex is observed by the examiner. It seems a little unsafe to attribute this "with" movement entirely to a lag of accommodation behind convergence, since it is by no means certain that binocular fixation of the target takes place. If the left eye is now occluded so that monocular vision is definitely taken up by the right eye, and the target details discriminated as well as can be under the disadvantage of the glare from the mirror, then usually no observable change in the reflex speed can be detected. In some cases there is a slight indication of an increase in the speed of the "with" movement. That is to say, the general effect of the "with" movement occurs in monocular as well as in binocular vision.

Now when the left eye is occluded, the eyes would be expected to take up their near passive position, usually a divergent position in relation to the object of fixation. In such cases, if binocular fixation obtained before occlusion, it would be expected that accommodation would tend to relax somewhat, if it changes at all, because of the association with the convergence function. The result of such a change would be a *decreased* speed of the " with " movement, indicating a further removal of the focus point from the fixation point. That such does not take place, any change that can be observed being in the opposite sense, is an indication that we cannot assume binocular fixation with both eyes of the subject in use, when the target is not well illuminated.

When the target is well illuminated to such an intensity that the right eye alone can easily distinguish the details in spite of the glaring effect of the retinoscope mirror, the same effect is observed when, after the subject has been allowed to view the target binocularly, his left eye is accluded. That is to say, there is no observable change in the speed of the reflex movement. Under these conditions there is more likelihood of binocular fixation being obtained when both eyes are in use, since the right eye can see the detail. But here also, if the " with " movement were due simply to the eyes being accommodated for a point more remote than the target, occluding the left eye, if it is to cause any change at all, would be expected to produce a relaxation of accommodation in most individuals, and consequently a slower reflex movement. Experiment shows that this does not usually occur, and we are led to accept the probability that the " with " movement is due, in part at least, to the other factors mentioned.

2. As in static retinoscopy, the test is carried out along a direction oblique to the subject's visual axis. The light returning from the eye may possibly possess a degree of convergence, with maybe some slight astigmatism, differing from its theoretical amount.

3. It will be evident from the statement of the phenomenon earlier in this paragraph that the aberrations of the subject's eye are most definitely to be considered as contributing to the discrepancy we are dealing with. The part of the refracted pencil selected by the eye for most distinct vision may quite likely not coincide with the part of the

pencil that acts as origin for the returning pencil. Any longitudinal separation of these two portions of the pencil is bound to result in the mean focus point of the returning light being displaced from the target on which the subject is accommodating.

4. The mean position of the percipient layer of the retina lies somewhere along the length of the cones; its position may conceivably vary under different conditions of seeing. The effective diffusely reflecting surface, which acts as the origin of the light returning from the subject's eye, may be situated in some other plane in the thickness of the retina. The separation of these two planes can only be a small fraction of a millimetre, however, so that this factor alone would hardly account for the discrepancy.

The fact that the static retinoscopy result generally errs on the myopic side and that the discrepancy we obtain in the dynamic test consists of a "with" movement, indicating hyperopia relative to the fixation point, might possibly be explained by the fact that the spherical aberration of the eye is positive when relaxed and decreases, even becoming negative in some eyes, when the eye accommodates. But the matter requires further investigation.

Effect of Lenses.

With the subject observing an illuminated target binocularly, the target and retinoscope situated 3 D from the subject, suppose the "with" movement corresponds to a discrepancy of 0·5 D. Upon inserting equal positive spheres before both eyes of the subject, the "with" movement persists until after putting up, say, + 1·50 D.S. before each eye, the movement ceases and reversal is obtained. The addition of further spherical power produces an "against" movement of the reflex. The same sequence of events occurs, and lenses of practically the same power are required, when the subject's vision is made monocular by occluding the eye not under test.

When the positive power is inserted, the subject can continue to see the details on the target by relaxing his accommodation. Presently a stage is reached beyond which no further relaxation occurs; at this point the relaxation is effectively* equal and opposite to the spherical lens in position. The discrepancy still exists, though probably its

* We cannot be certain that this is the case, however.

amount has changed somewhat due to the altered degree of aberration of the eye in this less accommodated condition. It requires further positive power, equal to this near value of the discrepancy, to neutralise the "with" movement. Ignoring for a moment the variation in the discrepancy, the eye in the above example has relaxed 1·0 D. When the test is carried out with the subject using both eyes, if we could be certain that he is obtaining binocular fixation throughout, this amount of one dioptre would represent the negative portion of his relative amplitude of accommodation, under the existing conditions, which include a stimulation of one eye by the light from the mirror. But we have seen that the maintenance of binocular fixation is problematical; and this doubt is strengthened by the fact that the same power of lens is required to produce reversal when the subject's view of the target is monocular.

The amount of positive power required to neutralise the reflex movement varies with different individuals, but usually appears to be in the neighbourhood of + 1·25 to 2·0 D in individuals possessing sufficient accommodation for the target distance. Why the subject does not relax more than the 1·0 D or 1·50 D or so, especially when the test is monocular, is not clear; for we have seen earlier* that even assuming binocular vision, the negative portion of the relative amplitude of accommodation, as determined by subjective methods, is usually found to be about 3 D at the near working distance of 3 D.

8.15. Dynamic Retinoscopy and Near Correction.

If the subject's astigmatism has changed, in direction or magnitude, during the act of accommodating, this will be observable with the retinoscope used at 3 D, the subject wearing his distance correction and fixing the target, also placed at 3 D. Instead of neutralisation or the usual "with" movement of equal degree in all meridians, the movements in two mutually perpendicular meridians will be unequal. Such evidence of astigmatism is not usually obtained however; but even in those few cases where it may be observed, it will be a matter of some difficulty to measure it since there is little or no control over any fluctuations of the subject's accommodation during the test.† A negative cylinder might be tried to obtain reversal at an

---

* §5.3.

† § 4.6.

observation point back from the target, but any changes of accommodation will render the test unreliable.

In seeking to measure the amplitude of accommodation by dynamic retinoscopy, whatever procedure may be adopted, the result ultimately depends upon the subject's seeing the details of the target distinctly. Whether the examiner attempts the measurement by shifting his and the target's position toward the subject, or by the use of lenses, positive or negative, the subject is required to exercise his judgment as to the sharpness or otherwise of the target details at the final moment when the examiner decides that the near point or artificial near point has been reached. Thus the method scarcely differs in principle from the usual subjective near point determinations and has no advantage over these.

It appears then that dynamic retinoscopy offers no particular assistance in investigating the refractive condition of the eyes at near and is in any case subject to the peculiar discrepancy we have described, which renders its use for any purpose uncertain, at least in the present state of our knowledge concerning it.

Within the last twenty years or so many attempts have been made to establish dynamic retinoscopy as a useful method of investigating certain of the ocular functions when the eyes are in the accommodated state and ingenious explanations have been advanced for interpreting the results obtained by it. Most of this work has, however, been based on faulty, or at least doubtful, assumptions as to the state of accommodation and convergence of the eyes during the test.

EXERCISES. CHAPTER VIII.

1. With the aid of an appropriate diagram explain the terms: immediate source, reflex circle, reflex, point of reversal or critical position, reversing lens and correcting lens, in relation to retinoscopy.

If, using a plane mirror, the "working distance" is 75 cm. and the reversing lens is found to be – 1·25 D, what is the distance correcting lens ?

2. Explain, with carefully drawn diagrams, the with or against movements of the reflex in retinoscopy with a plane mirror according to the position of the subject's far point in relation to the examiner's observation position.

In a test with a plane mirror at one metre, the reflex movements were neutralised with a + 2·25 D sphere along the 70° meridian and a + 1·00 D sphere along 160°. Find the distance correcting lens in toric form on +6 D base.

3. A subject with compound myopic astigmatism of 8 D along the vertical and 5 D along the horizontal is examined by retinoscopy with a plane mirror, the working distance being 50 cm. What lens, expressed in toric form on a + 4 D base, will neutralise the reflex movement ?

If the source of light is circular what will be the shape of the light patch on the subject's retina ?

4. In a retinoscopy test the plane mirror is placed 1 metre from the source of 30 mm. diameter and 1 metre from the subject's eye. Find the size of the illuminated patch on the subject's retina when he is myopic 5 D (axial) and has a pupil diameter of 5 mm.

Find the direction and extent of movement of this patch when the mirror is rotated 5° upwards about a horizontal axis.

5. In a retinoscopy carried out at 50 cm. on a subject myopic 1 D, explain with a careful diagram that the reflex movement is with the patch of light on the subject's fundus.

Extend the diagram to the examiner's fundus and show how the image of the reflex moves over it.

6. Explain with the aid of diagrams the movement of the shadow in the retinoscopic examination of a hyperopic eye. (B.O.A.)

7. Explain with the aid of diagrams how the light in retinoscopy appears cut off from the whole area of the pupil simultaneously at the "point of reversal". (B.O.A.)

8. Explain the optical relation of the observer's pupil to the fundus of the observed eye at the "point of reversal" in retinoscopy. (B.O.A.)

9. Explain why the speed of movement of the shadow should indicate the amount of the error to be corrected in an observation of an eye with a retinoscope. (B.O.A.)

10. Explain, with the aid of a ray diagram, the apparent movement of the reflex in retinoscopy.

When a plane mirror retinoscope is used a − 3·00 D sphere is the weakest concave lens to give neutralisation, fixation being for a distant object and the working distance is 50 cm. What movement would a − 4 D give ?

If fixation be changed for an object in the plane of the mirror, what alterations of movement would you expect in each case ? (S.M.C.)

11. For one eye a person requires the correction +2·0 D.S./− 4·00 D.C. ax. 50°. Describe and explain, with diagrams, the appearance and movements of the reflex in a retinoscopy test using a plane mirror at a distance of one metre.

How will these be modified if a short focus concave mirror be used, and why ?

12. In a retinoscopy test with a concave mirror of focal length 25 cm. and working at one metre, what are the directions of reflex movements and what lenses will annul them in each meridian, when the eyes have the following refractive errors :

R.E. M. of 0·50 D along 45° and M. of 1·50 D along 135°
L.E. H. of 0·50 D along 90° and H. of 1·50 D along 180°.

13. Explain how the reflex movements and appearance, as obtained in retinoscopy with a plane mirror, are modified when the plane mirror

is replaced by (*a*) a short focus concave; (*b*) a long focus concave mirror.

What disadvantage has the short focus concave mirror?

14. What causes of potential error arise when the subject is required to fix a distant object in retinoscopy?

What means have been proposed with the intention of securing relaxed accommodation on the part of the subject during a retinoscopy examination? Discuss these proposals briefly.

15. In what ways does the subject's astigmatism reveal its presence during a retinoscopy examination? Explain how these appearances characteristic of astigmatism arise. What alternative retinoscopy procedures for determining the astigmatism are possible?

16. If, by retinoscopy with a plane mirror, the points of reversal for the vertical and horizontal meridians of an eye with relaxed accommodation were found to be at $66\frac{2}{3}$ cm. and 22·22 cm. respectively from the subject's eye, what would be the distance correction indicated?

If, in the above case, the mirror were used at 1 metre from the subject, who was accommodating 2 dioptres, what lens would be needed just to reverse the reflex movement in each of the principal meridians?

17. Explain how the with or against movement of the reflex is brought about in retinoscopy. Illustrate your answer by carefully drawn ray diagrams making clear the course of the light from the subject's fundus to the examiner's fundus; indicate the position of the subject's far point and explain the effect of this position on the speed of the reflex movement.

The determination of the refraction of an astigmatic eye by retinoscopy could be made by using a single spherical lens before the subject's eye. Explain this.

18. Using a concave mirror (1 metre radius of curvature) retinoscope and a small intense source of light, the following values are to be assumed: (*a*) source-retinoscope distance = 1 metre
(*b*) working distance = 1 metre.

Draw to scale an accurate diagram to indicate the rate of reflex movements in a case of uncorrected myopia of − 10·0 D.

Comment on any peculiarity observed with regard to this problem. (S.M.C.)

19. Show graphically or by mathematical reasoning how the rate of reflex movement will be related to the rate of movement of a plane mirror when the far point of the observed eye lies midway between the mirror and the subject. (S.M.C.)

20. Compare the subjective (visual acuity) and objective (retinoscopy) methods of determining the distance correction of an eye. Comment on the relative accuracy of the two methods, their relative convenience in routine practice, having regard to the ultimate aim of providing the subject with a comfortable correction.

21. Explain how the fictitious appearance of "reversal" arises, irrespective of the refractive condition of the subject, when the arrangement in a retinoscopy test is such that the image of the source is projected into the pupillary plane of the subject, or close to that situation.

22. Show, with an appropriate diagram, that when reversal has been obtained in a retinoscopy examination no light, according to the laws of geometrical optics, enters the sighthole of the mirror.

Why is the reflex nevertheless seen at this stage of the test ?

23. In retinoscopy with a plane mirror show that the angular speed of the reflex movement as observed by the examiner is given very approximately by :

$$\theta' = \theta . \frac{E}{(K+E)}$$

the source of light being assumed in the same plane as the subject's eye. The quantities in the expression have the following meanings :

$E =$ dioptral distance from subject to examiner, always positive
$K =$ refractive condition of subject, + for H. and − for M.
$\theta =$ rotation of mirror
$\theta' =$ corresponding rotation of reflex about observation point.

Hence discuss the speed of the reflex when K is small, large and when $K = -E$.

24. A retinoscopy test is carried out with a plane mirror at a distance of one metre. If the subject is myopic 4 D, compare the angular speed of movement of the reflex with the angular speed of rotation of the mirror. Work from first principles and give a clear diagram. The light source is in the subject's pupillary plane.

25. Find graphically or by calculation the degree of myopia in which the apparent angular rate of reflex movement with a plane mirror retinoscope is equal and opposite to the angular rate of rotation of the mirror. Assume distance of mirror from both source and observed eye is 100 cm.

How will the apparent rate be affected if the source be moved to a position two metres from the mirror ? (S.M.C.)

26. In the case of a subject hyperopic 4 D, find the angular speed of the reflex in retinoscopy with a plane mirror used at a working distance of one metre, when the light source is (*a*) in the subject's pupillary plane ; (*b*) midway between subject and examiner ; (*c*) 75 cm. from subject. Take the angular rotation speed of the mirror as 1 radian per second.

27. Using the expression for speed of reflex movement in retinoscopy with a plane mirror, viz. :

$$\text{Linear movement of reflex} = -\theta \frac{2E}{(L-E)(K+E)}$$

plot the linear movement against K as abscissæ for the case when the working distance is one metre ($E = 1$ D) and the source is (*a*) in the plane of the subject's eye (i.e. $L = -1$ D) and (*b*) 10 cm. from the observation point (i.e. $L = -10$ D).

From the curves obtained comment on the effect of the position of the source on the speed of the reflex movement.

28. Explain possible causes for the uncertainty of deciding upon the movement of reversal in retinoscopy, as the result of which the point of reversal lies, as it were, within a neutral range or range of uncertainty in the neighbourhood of the observation point.

What suggestions can you offer to reduce the uncertainty ?

29. Write an account of possible causes for the disrepancy between the results obtained in the subjective and retinoscopy tests.

Is this discrepancy of great importance in practice ?

30. Give a diagram of the optical system, and the path of the illuminating pencil from one point of the source, of a self-luminous ophthalmoscope adapted for retinoscopy.

Has the position of the " immediate source " relative to the reflector of the instrument any bearing on the effectiveness of the instrument ? Give reasons.

31. Discuss the modifications needed to convert a self-luminous ophthalmoscope into a self-luminous retinoscope, including any changes necessary in the mirror.

32. Explain the disturbing effects that are due to the sighthole in an ordinary retinoscope mirror.

33. Describe the behaviour of the reflex when retinoscopy with a plane mirror is performed at one-third metre distance, the subject accommodating on a test object in the same plane. Give possible reasons for the appearance you describe. Does it make any difference whether the subject views the test object binocularly or monocularly ? Explain.

34. Compare the utility of subjective methods and a retinoscopy method of measuring the amplitude of accommodation. Would you use retinoscopy for this purpose ? Give full reasons.

35. A concave mirror retinoscope is silvered on the wrong side so as to make a convex mirror with radius of curvature 1 metre. On a good diagram show how the reflex appears to move when the distance between the mirror and observed eye is 1 metre, and between the mirror and source is 50 cm. Assume that the observed eye is 2 D myopic. (S.M.C.)

36. What do you understand by " the point of reversal " in retinoscopy ? What optical events take place when such a point is reached ? (S.M.C. Hons.)

37. Calculate the radius of the area of illumination on the fundus of an axial myope of -1 D (static power $+60 \cdot 0$ D) into which light from a circular source of 3 cm. diameter is reflected by a concave mirror of radius 1 metre and aperture diameter 3 cm. Assume source and eye are in the same plane and distant one metre from the mirror. Discuss the effect of (*a*) alteration of pupil diameter, (*b*) rotation of the mirror. (S.M.C.)

38. On a line ABC an eye is situated at A, a small source at B and a plane mirror at C. The mirror is perpendicular to ABC and AB = BC. If the mirror rotate through a small angle α about the point C, show that the reflected light enters the eye making an angle $\frac{2}{3}\alpha$ with the line ABC.

If the rotation be continued, show that the successive images of the source lie on a circle of radius BC ; and that the light enters the eye at an inclination to ABC given by θ where

$$\tan \theta = \frac{\sin 2\alpha}{2 + \cos 2\alpha}$$

39. When a $+1 \cdot 0$ D sphere is placed before an eye employing one half of its accommodation, vertical lines appear clear at 40 cm. from the eye. In order to obtain clear vision for horizontal lines at the same distance, and using the same accommodation, a $-0 \cdot 50$ D sphere must be used in place of the $+1 \cdot 0$ D sphere. One meridian shows reversal of movement in static retinoscopy when using a plane mirror at 40 cm. from the eye, together with a $+1 \cdot 0$ D sphere placed in position. Describe the possible refractive errors and the corresponding accommodation; and explain your argument (S.M.C.).

OPHTHALMIC INSTRUMENTS

CHAPTER IX

KERATOMETRY

9.1. Introductory.

THE ophthalmometer is another instrument the early development of which we owe largely to the genius of HELMHOLTZ, who used it first in 1854 for the purpose of obtaining measurements of the optical constants of the eye. Rough measurements of the radius of curvature of the anterior surface of the cornea were made by SCHEINER who compared the image formed by reflection in this surface with those of the same object reflected in the convex surfaces of a series of marbles of different sizes. KOHLRAUSCH attained greater accuracy in 1839, but his experimental procedure lacked the device of "doubling" the image, without which it is an extremely troublesome matter, indeed in clinical work practically impossible, to obtain satisfactory results on the living eye. The doubling principle, already used in astronomical instruments, was incorporated by HELMHOLTZ in his instrument, with which he proceeded to determine the radii of curvature and positions of all the refracting surfaces of the eye, a branch of the subject which is usually termed "ophthalmometry".* Before long the use of HELMHOLTZ's ophthalmometer by various ophthalmologists and physicists drew general attention to the prevalence of astigmatism in the human cornea; ocular astigmatism had up to this time received little notice.† To render the instrument suitable for everyday clinical practice in measuring this corneal astigmatism, it was necessary to modify HELMHOLTZ's original design which, being a laboratory instrument, entailed a number of readings and some calculation. A satisfactory clinical instrument, simple in use and obviating any calculation on the part of the examiner, was designed in 1881 by Emil JAVAL of Paris in collaboration with Dr. SCHIÖTZ of Christiania.

The Javal-Schiötz instrument and the many that have followed it are designed expressly to determine the curvature,

---

* §10.5. † §4.11.

and particularly the astigmatism, of the cornea only. It would thus appear appropriate to call them keratometers (cornea measurers), leaving the terms ophthalmometer and ophthalmometry for the wider field of investigation of the refracting surfaces of the eye generally. In this chapter we shall be concerned only with measurements of the cornea and will further restrict ourselves to the adaptation of such measurements to clinical purposes, so far as this is possible.

Of the total refracting power, 60 dioptres, of the eye, the cornea contributes about 43 dioptres. Small changes in its curvature produce much greater effects on the total power than do equal changes in any other surface.* Hence, although the information provided by the keratometer is insufficient by itself upon which to write out a prescription for the eye, the study of the cornea is of some importance and in special circumstances, to which we shall refer, the keratometer may be of real service.

9.2. Theory of Ophthalmometer or Keratometer.

When a luminous object is placed before the eye a portion of the light incident on the anterior surface of the cornea is reflected. This surface, with its extremely thin film of tear fluid, thus acts as a polished convex mirror and an image is formed by reflection, the size (h') of which depends upon the size (h) of the object and its distance from the cornea, and upon the radius of curvature (r) of the latter. This reflex image, which is a source of annoyance in ophthalmoscopy and retinoscopy, is made use of in the keratometer for obtaining the corneal radius. We will limit ourselves to the central optical zone of the cornea, extending over a diameter of 3 to 4 millimetres, over which the curvature is approximately regular, either spherical or toroidal, in a normal eye. The radius of curvature varies for different individuals between the limits of approximately 7·0 to 8·5 mm., the majority being round about the average figure of 7·80 mm. With a convex mirror of such steep curvature the virtual, erect image formed by reflection will be of small dimensions.

In Fig. 9.1, A is the vertex of the cornea; the object $BQ = h$ is imaged by reflection at $B'Q' = h'$, two typical paraxial rays being indicated. Actually the image will be curved with its concavity towards the centre C, but we

---

* §4.11.

may neglect aberrations and consider the image to be perpendicular to the axis.* The magnification is given by the usual expression

$$m = \frac{h'}{h} = -\frac{f}{x} = -\frac{r}{2x}$$

which is in any case evident from the diagram, AF being the focal length f and FB $= x$ the distance of the object from the focal point. The image formation on one side of

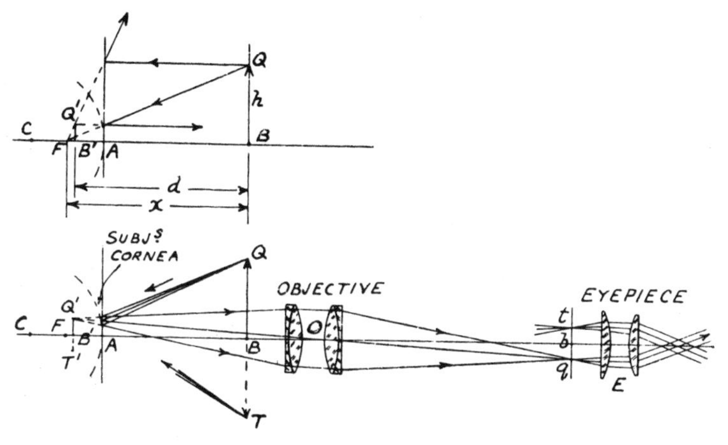

FIGS. 9.1 AND 9.2—PRINCIPLE OF KERATOMETER.

the axis only is indicated. Actually the object extends to T an equal distance on the other side, as shown in Fig. 9.2.

Thus
$$r = -\frac{2x}{h}h' = -2mx \qquad (9.1)$$

and three quantities (h, h' and x) are involved in the measurement of r. To obtain accuracy it is necessary to magnify the small image h', for which purpose it is observed through a long focus microscope (or short focus telescope), the objective of which is at O and the Ramsden eyepiece at E, Fig. 9.2. The microscope is approached towards the subject's eye, until the corneal image B′Q′ is imaged as bq on a crosswire or graticule fixed in the instrument. Thus the objective O is always brought to the same distance from the corneal image, when the latter is in focus; and if the object BQ is fixed to the body of the instrument, the distance

* The following expressions apply when the object is relatively large if such distances as x, d, etc., are measured obliquely to the surface along QC.

BB′ = d is then also a constant quantity. Provided this object distance is not made too small, the image B′Q′ is formed very near to the focus F and we can substitute d for x in the above formula. We have then

$$r = -\frac{2d}{h} \cdot h' = -2md \quad \text{(very approximately)} \qquad (9.2)$$

Thus for an object of given size h, *the size of the image is directly proportional to the corneal radius* r. Since d is a constant, we may determine r either (A) by keeping h constant and measuring the size of h' in some way; or (B) by varying h to produce an image of constant size, h'.

Kohlrausch had two fine vertical threads in the focal plane qbt of the eyepiece; these he could move laterally towards or away from one another by screws. He adjusted

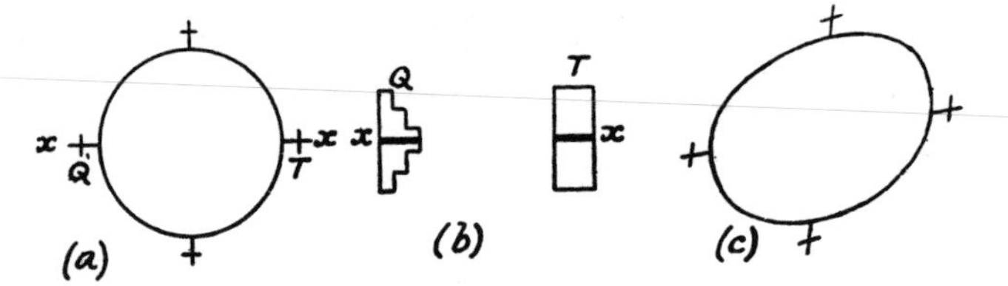

Fig. 9.3—Keratometer Mires. Case (c) as observed in astigmatic cornea with principal meridians oblique to mire.

them until they coincided with q and the corresponding image t on the other side of the axis. He then removed the subject and put in the place of his eye a graduated scale, and so obtained the image size h' and hence, by calculation, the radius r. We shall see in the next paragraph how the measurement is made, in modern instruments, by using a doubling device.

Since the determination of r depends upon the measurement of the size h', we are concerned with the extremities Q and Q′, and with corresponding extremities T and T′ on the other side of the axis. The object, or "mire" as it is called in the actual instrument, is frequently of circular form described around the axial point B as centre, with projecting hooks or crosses (Fig. 9.3 (a)) at Q and T on which the settings are made; or it may take the form of two separate mires, one at Q and the other at T, as indicated in Fig. 9.3 (b). It will be observed from Fig. 9.2 that the portion of the cornea concerned in the image formation of these extremities consists of two isolated areas, displaced a distance from the axis approximately equal to the size of the image B′Q′. We wish to make our measurement of curvature within the optical zone and so keep the total image size, Q′T′, from exceeding about 3 mm. This in turn limits the size of the object or mire to be used, for it should subtend at the centre of curvature C an angle not exceeding $\tan^{-1}$ B′Q′/CB′ i.e. $\tan^{-1} \frac{3}{8}$* or, say, 22° or so, on each side of the axis.

In a spherical cornea the image of the mire of Fig. 9.3 (a) will be circular and similar to the mire itself on a reduced scale. In an astigmatic cornea the image will be distorted into an elliptical shape, Fig. 9.3 (c), the directions and lengths of the long and short axes of the ellipse depending upon the radii of curvature of the corneal anterior surface in these meridians.

It is to be noted that the keratometer gives us information as to the radius of curvature, and hence the focal power, *only* of the anterior surface of the cornea. It tells us nothing of the other refracting surfaces of the eye, or of the axial length, and so we obtain no information (except what we may be pleased to infer, or in special cases) from it concerning the refractive error of the eye. By making measurements in the two principal meridians of an astigmatic cornea, we know the amount of astigmatism contributed by the anterior surface of this membrane, by assuming some value for its refractive index. The earlier investigators considered that ocular astigmatism lay wholly, or at least predominantly, in the cornea; and so the instrument came to be used clinically for objective determination of this astigmatism. Keratometers are therefore scaled to read in dioptres of power, the refractive index for the calibration being so chosen that the effect of the weak posterior surface of the cornea is allowed for. The value 1·3375 for this index used for the earlier instruments has been continued in all keratometers.† A small discrepancy

---

* Using the round figure 8 mm. for the radius of curvature.

† Listing, and Helmholtz in his first schematic eye, gave the value $\frac{103}{77}$ (=1.3375) for the combined index of cornea and aqueous. Accepting the carefully prepared and generally accepted constants determined later by Gullstrand (Chapter X), it would appear preferable to use the figure $\frac{4}{3}$ for the combined refractive index in scaling the keratometer. The fact that with the index 1.3375 a radius of 7.5 mm. corresponds exactly to 45 D seems also to have had some bearing on the choice of this index for the instruments.

between this value and what may in fact be a more accurate value for the index matters scarcely at all since it is the *difference* between the two powers in the principal meridians that is of any clinical value. On a cornea with radius of the average value 7·8 mm. the keratometer will thus give a reading of 43·27 D (= 337.5/7.8) for the dioptric power.*

With regard to the slight error arising from the substitution of the distance d for the more correct distance x in the keratometer formula (9·2), simple calculation of a numerical example will show that the error is extremely small. For a spherical cornea of radius 8 mm., it is about 0·1 D when the object distance AB is 72 mm. as in the BAUSCH & LOMB keratometer ;† and about 0·02 D when this object distance is 150 mm. This is brought out by deriving the correct expression for r in terms of d, which may be of interest to some students. We have

$$r = -\frac{2x}{h}\,h' = -2mx$$

Putting the object distance AB $= l$ and the conjugate image distance AB$' = l'$, we have

$$BB' = -d = -l + l' \qquad FB = x = -\frac{r}{2} + l$$

$$\frac{h'}{h} = \frac{l'}{-l} \text{ or } \frac{h'+h}{h} = \frac{-l+l'}{-l} = \frac{d}{l}$$

$$\text{hence } r = -\frac{2h'}{h}\,x = \frac{-2h'}{h}\left(-\frac{r}{2} + \frac{hd}{h+h'}\right)$$

$$\text{or } r = \frac{-2dhh'}{(h^2 - h'^2)} = \frac{-2d}{m - \dfrac{1}{m}} \qquad (9\cdot3)$$

In practice the object is twenty to fifty times larger than the image, depending upon the particular make of instrument, so that h'^2 is an extremely small quantity in relation to h^2. This expression reduces to the approximate one (9·2) when h'^2 is neglected.

9.3. The Doubling of the Image.

The above instrumental application of the keratometer formula (9.2) would provide the accuracy needed and be quite satisfactory if the mirror being measured were a fixed body, such as a glass or steel ball. A scale could be inserted in the focal plane of the eyepiece at b, so graduated as to read off the radius of curvature and power directly. The eye of a living subject cannot remain sufficiently steady, however, for accurate measurements to be made in this manner. Hence HELMHOLTZ introduced the doubling principle, which was already used in the heliometer.

* Compare §2.2.

† §9.5.

Whatever optical mechanism is employed for producing this doubling, and there are many such mechanisms, it is inserted in the path of the light returning to the examiner after reflection at the cornea ; that is, somewhere between A and b in Fig. 9.2. Its effect is to divide the pencil from each point of the corneal image into two pencils, so that the examiner looking through the instrument sees in the plane qbt, two images of the corneal reflex, separated from one another laterally by a certain interval. The setting then consists in placing the inner extremities of these two laterally displaced images into coincidence as represented in Fig. 9.6 (b). When this coincidence has been achieved, movements of the original corneal image, due to involuntary

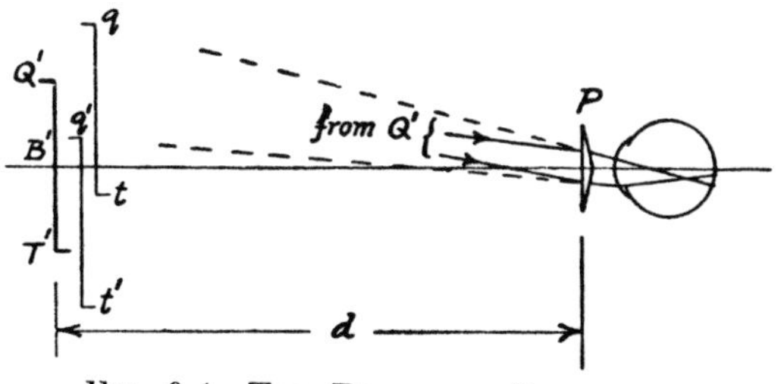

FIG. 9.4—THE DOUBLING PRINCIPLE.

oscillations of the subject's eye, will not affect the measurement ; for both images will move together without disturbing the coincidence of their extremities.

The student can perform for himself a useful experiment illustrating the doubling principle. Draw a line Q′T′ say 8 cm. long on a piece of paper and hang this on the wall with the line horizontal. Observe it through a double prism, such as the one frequently supplied as an accessory in the trial case, the prism being held close to the eye with its base-apex line horizontal and the vertical joining line of the two component prisms bisecting the pupil (Fig. 9.4). The line Q′T′ will be seen doubled as two images qt and q′t′, which may overlap (as shown) or be entirely separated according to the distance B′P of the prism from the object line Q′T′. Move backwards or forwards, the two images thereby separating from or approaching one another, until the end q′ of the one exactly coincides with the end t of the other. Assuming the component prisms to be each 4△, the distance B′P for this to occur will be one metre, since at this distance one prism displaces each point of the object 4 cm. to the left and the other prism 4 cm. to the right, making a total separation, or " doubling " of 8 cm. Thus when contact of the inner extremities of the images is secured, *the doubling is equal to the size of the object.* Clearly an object of unknown size, or the reflection of an object in a mirror such as the cornea, could be measured in this way. If, for example, contact of the images is secured, with the above prism, at a distance of 75 cm., we conclude that the object is 6 cm. long.

If d = the separating distance in metres, h' the size of the object in cm. (i.e. the size of the catoptric image Q′T′ in the case of the keratometer) and P the total deviation in prism dioptres produced by the prism or other doubling device, then

$$h' = \mathrm{P} \times d$$

To conclude the experiment observe that if another person causes the paper to oscillate on the wall, this does not interfere with the measurement.

The doubling can be effected in many other ways, a few of which will be mentioned presently. In the last paragraph we saw that to determine the radius r of the corneal surface, two alternative methods (A) and (B) were open to us. In accordance with method (A), an object mire of fixed dimensions, such as the one illustrated at (a) and (c) in Fig. 9.3, is used and the doubling device is one in which the amount of doubling can be varied so as to secure contact of the two images for corneal surfaces of different curvatures. Keratometers using this arrangement are described as VARIABLE DOUBLING instruments. HELMHOLTZ'S ophthalmometer, the keratometer made by BAUSCH & LOMB (§9.5) and the SUTCLIFFE keratometer are of this type. On the other hand, in instruments adopting method (B) the doubling mechanism is fixed and invariable, the contact of the two images being accomplished by an arrangement which alters the size of the object by displacing the separate mires Q and T (Fig. 9·3 (b)) symmetrically towards or away from the axis. Instruments of this class are FIXED DOUBLING keratometers. The Javal-Schiötz instrument is of this type.

FIXED DOUBLING.

The Javal-Schiötz keratometer is represented diagrammatically in Fig. 9.5. The fixed amount of doubling required is produced by means of a Wollaston prism inserted between the two halves of the compound objective of the microscope. The mires Q and T are on opal glass illuminated by electric lamps; and by a rack and pinion mechanism are made to move equally in opposite directions along a circular arc, the centre of curvature of which coincides with the subject's eye. When the instrument is moved up towards the subject until the corneal image is in focus, the double image formed in the focal plane of the eyepiece may present the appearance represented in Fig. 9.6 (a). Evidently the images qt and q′t′ and hence the corneal

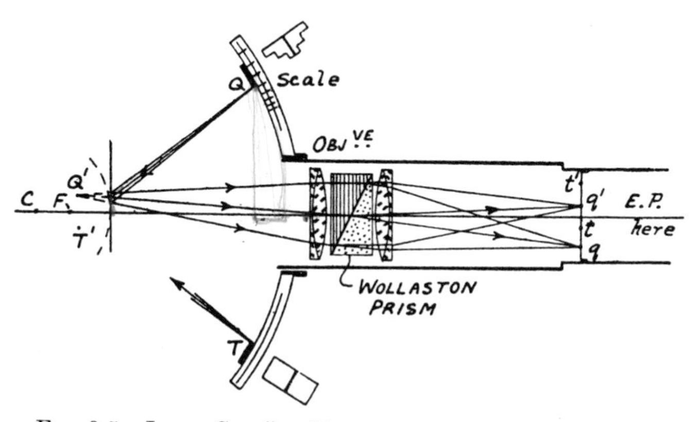

FIG. 9.5—JAVAL-SCHIÖTZ KERATOMETER (DIAGRAMMATIC).
Corneal image Q′T′, and hence microscope image *qt* or *q′t′*, are too small for contact.

image Q′T′ from which they are derived, are too large for contact. The separate object mires Q and T are therefore racked in towards the axis of the instrument (thus decreasing the value of h) until contact is obtained as shown at (b) Fig. 9.6. If, on first looking through the instrument, the images overlap as in (c), the corneal image is too small and the mires must be moved outwards over the arc. Thus the larger the corneal radius being measured, the smaller must the object size (h) be made; in other words, the corneal radius varies inversely as the object size (h) when the size (h') of the corneal image is kept constant by a fixed doubling device. This follows from equation (9·2). Two scales are engraved on the arc, one giving the corneal radius (r) in mm. and the other the corresponding power (F)

in dioptres ; the former scale is a reciprocal one in this instrument, and the latter uniform.*

In using the instrument the examiner need pay attention only to the two middle images q′ and t.

The direction in which doubling takes place and the circular arc over which the mires travel, both lie in the same plane (the plane of the paper in Fig. 9.5). The instrument is so mounted as to be capable of rotation around its own axis, carrying this plane with it. If the cornea under examination be astigmatic with its principal meridians

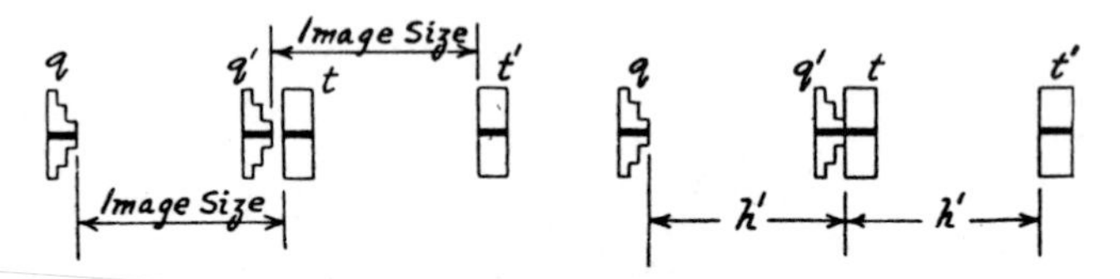

(a) Image too large—less powerful meridian of cornea. (b) Contact. Doubling = Image Size.

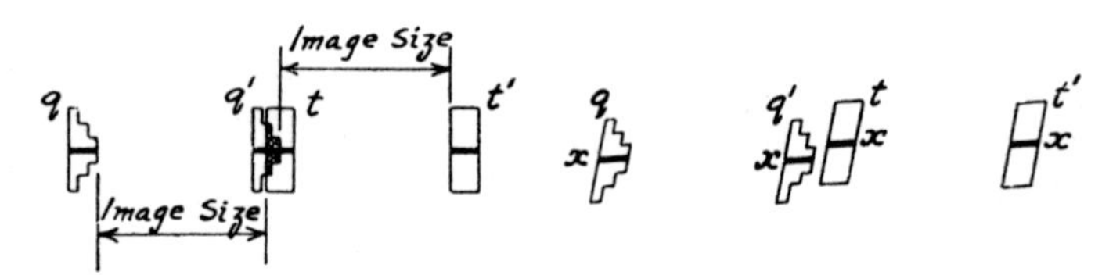

(c) Image too small—more powerfull meridian of cornea. (d) Astigmatic cornea—mires out of step.

FIG. 9.6—APPEARANCES OF IMAGES OF MIRES.

at, say, 30° and 120° ; and if it be observed with the abovementioned plane of doubling and collimation lying in the horizontal, the corneal image of the mires will be somewhat distorted. And since the doubling takes place in a meridian (the horizontal) not coinciding with either principal meridian of the cornea, the doubled image will appear somewhat as indicated in Fig. 9.6 (d), the central lines of the mires (xx) being out of step. Such an appearance indicates the presence of corneal astigmatism in a direction oblique to the plane of doubling. The keratometer is therefore rotated around its axis until the central lines xx are in alignment,

* Or practically so ; the fact that the scale is on a circular arc may modify this slightly.

which occurs when this plane contains a principal meridian. The orientation of it is read off on a scale of degrees. Contact is obtained in this meridian and the dioptral reading taken from the scale on the arc. Let us suppose the meridian is 30° and the scale reading 44·50 D. The instrument is rotated through 90° into the 120° meridian. If the cornea is more steeply curved in this meridian, the corneal image will be smaller and the images seen in the instrument will overlap as in Fig. 9.6 (c), except that they will all lie in the 120° meridian. Contact is again obtained by moving the mires Q and T (Fig. 9.5) along the arc and the scale reading again taken. Let it be 46·25 D. These readings indicate that corneal astigmatism is present to the extent of 1·75 D, *reckoned at the cornea*, the 120° meridian being the more myopic. If there were no additional astigmatism, due to the posterior surface of the cornea or to the crystalline lens, we could say that the ocular astigmatism is 1·75 D. The power of the correcting lens would depend upon how much myopia or hypermetropia there may be, due to axial error, and upon the fact that the lens is worn 12 mm. or so in front of the cornea.*

The Wollaston prism is liable to produce chromatism and to deteriorate the definition and brilliance of the images.

We see that in astigmatic cases it is necessary to take two readings. In a keratometer such as the Javal-Schiötz, with a doubling device which produces doubling in one meridian only, it is necessary to rotate the instrument around its axis through 90° in order to take the second reading. Such instruments are called TWO-POSITION instruments. There is a possibility that the subject may be unconsciously disturbed by the bright moving mires and so change his position slightly while the settings are being made, or in the interval between the two settings ; a disadvantage not associated, except perhaps in a minor degree, with one-position instruments to be described below.

9.4. Variable Doubling Devices.

Numerous optical arrangements for producing a variable amount of doubling have been tried. HELMHOLTZ used two small glass plates with plane parallel faces, placed side by side in front of the microscope objective, each plate covering half of the objective. The principle is illustrated

* §§ 4.4 and 9.9.

in Fig. 9.7. If the plates A and B are rotated by equal amounts and in opposite directions about a vertical axis, then the corneal image Q′T′ ($= h'$) as seen through the plates will be divided into two images displaced in opposite directions with respect to the axis of the system. The double images qt and q′t′ will be seen in the focal plane of the eyepiece as before. The lateral displacement of Q′T′ by each plate depends upon the orientation θ of the plate and upon its thickness t and refractive index n.

For a certain value of θ this displacement will be equal to $\frac{1}{2}h'$, in which case contact of the extremities q′ and t will occur.

It will be observed that the images qt and q′t′ are formed by separate halves of the objective; the mean direction

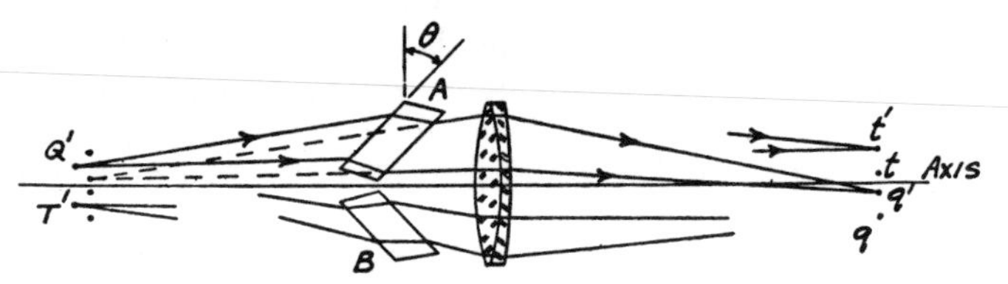

FIG. 9.7—ILLUSTRATING THE DOUBLING SYSTEM IN THE HELMHOLTZ OPHTHALMOMETER.

of the beam of light forming each of them is consequently inclined to the axis. In arrangements of this kind where the aperture of the observing instrument is split into separate portions—adaptations of the Scheiner principle (§2.13)—it is necessary to secure accurate focusing of the images or appreciable errors will arise in the measurement.

It will be understood from §9.3 that variable doubling may be obtained by inserting a double prism in the instrument between the objective O and the focal plane of the eyepiece (Fig. 9.2); the common base-apex line of the prism being parallel to the contact points Q and T of the mire, each component prism intercepting the light from one half of the objective, and the whole prism being capable of longitudinal motion along the axis of the instrument. Or the prism could be a single prism inserted on one side of the axis. These methods and many others, too numerous to mention, have been applied by different manufacturers. The fixed mire in these variable doubling instruments usually takes a form similar to that illustrated in Fig. 9.3 (a).

If the mechanism adopted produces doubling in one plane only, then it is necessary to rotate the instrument through 90° to take the second reading on an astigmatic cornea, as already explained. A device which doubles the corneal image in two mutually perpendicular directions,

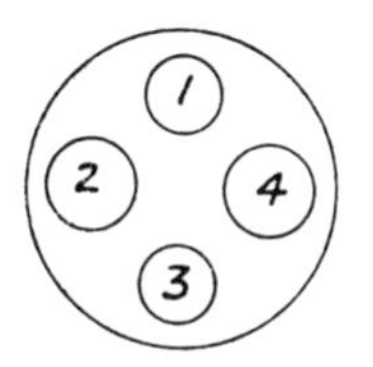

FIG. 9.8—SPLITTING OF APERTURE OF OBSERVING MICROSCOPE IN ONE-POSITION KERATOMETERS; SEE TEXT.

in which case three images are produced in the focal plane of the eyepiece (Fig. 9.9) renders it unnecessary to rotate the instrument between the readings taken in the first and second principal meridians of the cornea. The so-called ONE-POSITION keratometers are provided with such a dual doubling device. The first instrument of this kind was introduced by J. H. SUTCLIFFE in 1907.

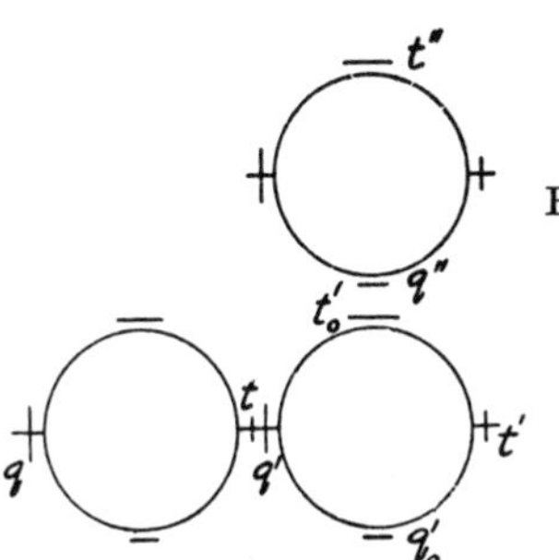

FIG. 9.9—TRIPLED IMAGE OF MIRE AS SEEN IN EYEPIECE OF ONE-POSITION KERATOMETER.

9.5. A Modern One-position Keratometer.

Figs. 9.10 and 9.11 illustrate a variable doubling one-position keratometer made by BAUSCH and LOMB. The objective aperture is divided into four parts (Fig. 9.8). In the converging beam admitted by aperture 2 is placed an achromatic prism V (Fig. 9.11) with base-apex line

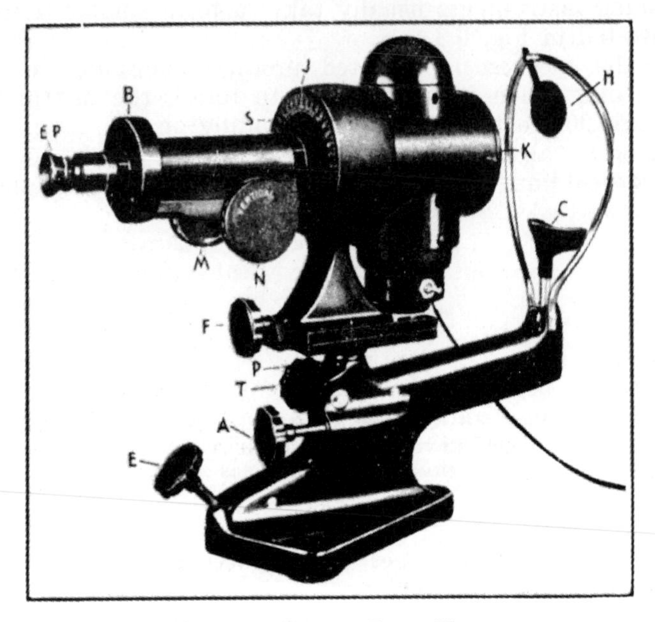

FIG. 9.10—THE BAUSCH AND LOMB KERATOMETER.

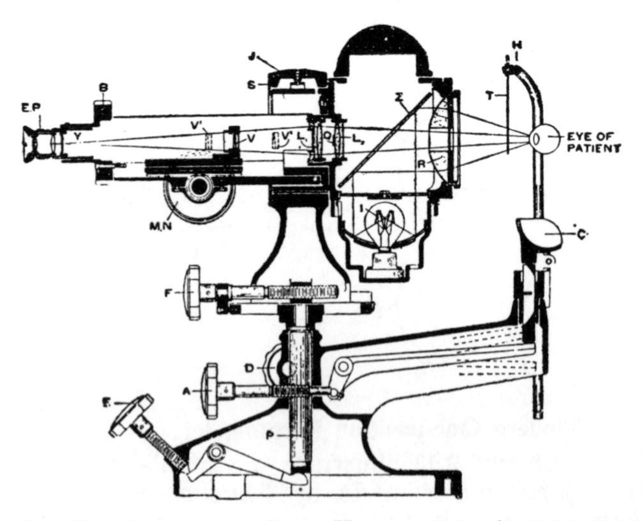

FIG. 9.11—THE BAUSCH AND LOMB KERATOMETER (SECTIONAL VIEW).

horizontal; a similar prism with base-apex line vertical intercepts the light from aperture 4; both prisms are made to move longitudinally, parallel to the axis of the instrument, by rotating the scaled drums M and N. In this way the images qt and q″t″, are given horizontal and vertical displacements respectively. The setting consists in putting the two vertical strokes, t and q′ for one meridian and the strokes t'_0 and q″ for the other meridian, into superposition. The prisms take up different positions in their travel in order to produce this contact for corneal surfaces of different radii. The travel of the prism is directly proportional to the size (h') of the corneal image and hence to the corneal radius (r); and therefore inversely proportional to the dioptric power (F) of the cornea. The scale of dioptres on each operating drum, M and N, is consequently a reciprocal scale. The value 1·3375 is used for the refractive index in the calibration.

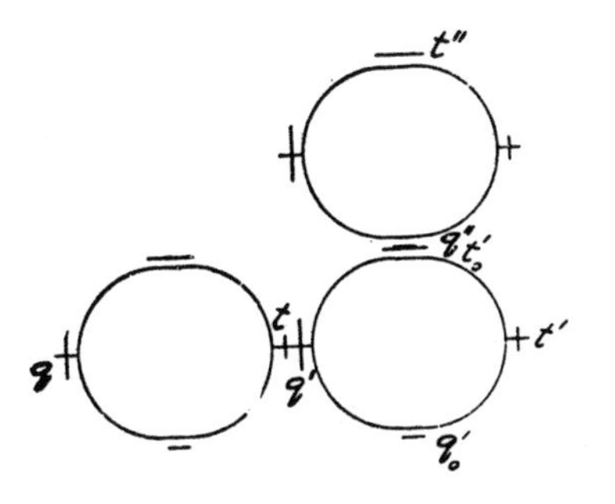

FIG. 9.12—KERATOMETER ROTATED UNTIL IMAGES OF MIRE ARE IN STEP WHEN EXAMINING A CORNEA THE PRINCIPAL MERIDIANS OF WHICH LIE ALONG qt′ AND q'_0t''.

When the instrument is directed towards the subject's eye, if the corneal image is not in focus the image q′t′ will appear doubled since it is formed by light which has passed through the *two* apertures 1 and 3, Fig. 9.8—the Scheiner principle again. On obtaining sharp focus by racking in the instrument, the images may be out of step in a manner analogous to Fig. 9.6 (d), in which case the whole instrument is rotated around its own axis until the mire images are in step, Fig. 9.12 which occurs when the two planes of doubling lie along the principal meridians of the eye under examination. Having obtained this position, no further rotation of the instrument is required. Contact of t and q′, and then of q″ and t'_0, is secured and the two dioptric readings taken from the drums.

The construction of the instrument, including the method of illuminating the mire by means of the lamp I and the mirror Z, is well illustrated in Fig. 9.11. Q is a small mirror within which the subject sees an image of his own eye which serves as a fixation object. It is scarcely necessary to add that before readings are taken the subject's head must be arranged comfortably in the headrest with the outer canthi of the two eyes lying on a horizontal line. A sighting device is provided on the instrument for this purpose.

One-position keratometers have the advantage that both readings on an astigmatic cornea can be taken with the instrument in the one position. This is satisfactory in cases of regular astigmatism ; but these instruments are probably less convenient than the two-position keratometers in cases of irregular astigmatism, where two well defined meridians at right angles cannot be found.

A keratometer has been designed by H. HARTINGER of Messrs. ZEISS, in which the doubling is produced in a novel manner, the instrument being free from moving parts.*

9.6. Artificial Cornea and Calibration.

The scale of a keratometer can be checked by taking readings on a series of spheres made of glass or steel (such as ball bearings) and ranging in radius from about 6·5 mm. to 9·0 mm. If the refractive index 1·3375 has been used in calibrating the instrument, the relationship between dioptric power and radius of curvature in mm. is given by

$$F = \frac{(n-1)}{r} 1000 = \frac{337 \cdot 5}{r} \text{ dioptres}$$

Some values are given in the Table.

Power in D ..	52	50	48·21	48	46	45	44	43·27	42·19	42	40	38	36
Radius in mm. ..	6·49	6·75	7·0	7·03	7·335	7·5	7·67	7·80	8·0	8·035	8·435	8·88	9·375

While the radius changes by 1 mm. from 7 to 8 mm. the power changes by practically 6 dioptres. Round about the mean value of the radius, 7·8 mm., the change of power per mm. of radius is 5·55 D. Conversely, to produce a

* Described in the first edition.

change in power of one dioptre the radius is required to change by 0·18 mm.

A positive cylinder has the effect of decreasing or weakening the reflecting power of the cornea in the meridian perpendicular to its axis. A negative cylinder increases the corneal reflecting power. That is, a spherical cornea to which is added a positive plano-cyl. axis horizontal becomes in effect an astigmatic cornea with the lesser power along the vertical. The change of power in the affected meridian is not equal to the power of the cylinder applied, but to *approximately* one third of that power.

Let the power of the cylinder be F_1. If R is the curvature in dioptres of the spherical cornea of radius r, its focal power as a mirror is $-2R$. The cylinder, in its power meridian, changes the vergence of the light incident on the cornea and again changes it after reflection. The total change in the vergence of the light, or the reflecting power of the equivalent cornea is

$$F_R = 2F_1 - 2R$$

The curvature $(= -\frac{1}{2}F_R)$ of the equivalent cornea is therefore given by

$$R' = R - F_1 \tag{9·4}$$

The reading given by the keratometer scale depends, of course, on the reflected light. It will register the power

$$\left.\begin{array}{l} F' = \dfrac{337\cdot 5}{r'} = 0\cdot 3375R' = 0\cdot 3375R - 0\cdot 3375F_1 \\ \text{or } F' = (\text{refracting power of cornea alone}) - 0\cdot 3375F_1 \end{array}\right\} \tag{9·5}$$

Hence the cylinder of power F_1 introduces an astigmatic effect equal to about one third of its own power. The cylinder used for the purpose should be thin and its curved surface should be placed in contact with the artificial cornea, or slight error due to " effectivity " may arise.

9.7. Corneal Astigmatism and Total Astigmatism.

The TOTAL ASTIGMATISM of the eye, as determined for example by retinoscopy or subjectivity, is quite likely to differ from the astigmatism of the corneal anterior surface, which determines the reading given by the keratometer. The corneal and total astigmatisms may differ not only in degree, but also in axis direction. Thomas YOUNG'S astigmatism was not due to the anterior surface of the cornea and would consequently not have been detected by the keratometer. The accompanying table gives the subjective, retinoscopy, and keratometer findings on the eyes of a number of students examined at the Northampton Polytechnic, London, in 1927. Similar results have been published from other sources, notably by Dr. E. JACKSON.

Empirical relations between the keratometer astigmatism and the total astigmatism have been published from time to time, with the intention of enabling the astigmatism of the correcting lens to be written down from the keratometer finding. JAVAL put forward a rule for this purpose. With certain reservations such relationships can show the *general tendency* of the relationship that exists between the two quantities, which may be useful for statistical purposes, but they are of no value in deciding upon the correction to be prescribed for a given eye.

In making comparisons between the subjective or retinoscopy astigmatism and the keratometer astigmatism, it is to be remembered that the latter is measured at the cornea whereas the former is the astigmatism at the spectacle

		Subjective			Retinoscopy			Keratometer	
Age	Sex	Sph.	Cyl.	Axis	Sph.	Cyl.	Axis	Cyl.	Axis
27	M	+0·50	−0·50	170	+0·75	−0·50	160	−1·12	180
		+0·25	−0·75	15	+0·50	−0·75	10	−1·25	5
18	F	+0·75	−0·12	50	0·00	−0·25	90	−0·87	180
		+0·75	−0·25	80	0·00	−0·50	90	−0·37	170
27	F	+1·25	−0·50	110	+0·25	−0·37	90	−0·62	120
		+1·00	—	—	0·00	—	—	−0·75	180
18	M	+0·75	−0·25	150	+0·50	−0·25	150	−1·25	90
		+0·75	−0·62	5	+0·50	−0·62	5	−1·50	90
22	M	*	−0·25	180	*	−0·37	180	−2·00	175
			−1·00	15		−1·00	15	−2·50	180

* Only the cylinder portion of the correction given in this case.

point. An effectivity correction is to be applied to the keratometer readings, therefore, which will increase somewhat the minus cylinder; but this correction cannot be made, except in the case of weak astigmatism and approximately, unless the spherical portion of the correction is known also.*

Although the readings obtained with the keratometer are not subject to uncertainty on account of possible variations of the subject's accommodation or pupil diameter, yet certain errors can arise. It has already been pointed out that the keratometer result appertains only to isolated portions of the cornea; one on each side of, and about 1·25 mm. from, the visual axis; so that the effect of the important central portion, of over 2 mm. diameter, is not recorded. Moreover, accuracy depends upon a reasonably steady position of the subject's head and upon accurate focusing. It is true that in one-position instruments a want of focus is revealed by the doubling of one, or two, of the three images seen in the eyepiece; but since this is brought about by the splitting of the aperture of the instrument into separate portions, error may arise in setting the marks (t, q′, etc.) into coincidence or superposition, due to lateral parallactic movement of the examiner's eye. Hence the possible error in the keratometer determination of the corneal curves is equal to, if not sometimes greater than, the possible error in determining refractive error by retinoscopy or by subjective methods.

9.8. Use of Keratometer in Special Cases.

It appears that the keratometer is not required in the clinical testing of refractive error in ordinary cases. It may, however, supply useful information in certain special circumstances.

Irregularities in the cornea, indicative of keratitis or other pathological condition, or which may account for irregular refraction and poor vision, are shown up well by the keratometer. When vision is poor, due to such causes or to amblyopia, or in the case of a squinting astigmatic eye, in which cases little or nothing can be done by subjective methods or, perhaps, by retinoscopy, some useful information concerning the eye is provided by the keratometer that will enable a correction to be prescribed. Similarly in cases of high astigmatism; the poor vision may prevent a satisfactory subjective test, and if retinoscopy is difficult because of a small pupil, we can fall back on the keratometer to determine the corneal astigmatism and with the indicated

---

* §9.9.

cylindrical lens in the trial frame, proceed to improve it subjectively.

Surgeons find the instrument useful in deciding upon the direction along which to make the incision in the cornea when performing a keratotomy, since the corneal curve is found to decrease in the meridian perpendicular to the incision.*

In the aphakic condition of the eye after a cataract operation, when any modifying influence on the corneal astigmatism due to the lens has been removed, the keratometer may be useful in measuring the astigmatism, especially in determining its axis direction.

When fitting some contact glasses† it is necessary to measure the corneal radius when deciding upon the curves of the glass to be prescribed. The keratometer is definitely necessary in such cases.

If we know the refractive condition of an eye as well as its corneal power, the information gives some indication as to whether the condition is axial or refractive. Thus a corneal power of, say, 39 dioptres and a refractive error of 4 or 5 dioptres of hypermetropia indicates refractive, and not axial, hypermetropia. Information of this kind may be useful in anisometropia cases, in which the possibilities of comfortable binocular vision depend upon the relative sizes of the two retinal images, which in turn vary according to whether the ametropia is axial or refractive.

The use of the keratometer, or ophthalmometer, as a laboratory instrument when determining the optical constants of the eye has already been referred to.

9.9. Correcting Cylinder and Keratometer Reading.

In those special cases, just referred to, where the correction for astigmatism may be, or may have to be, prescribed from the reading given by the keratometer of the corneal astigmatism, it is necessary to apply an effectivity correction to the keratometer reading in order to obtain the cylinder power of the correcting lens. If we knew the refractive error, at the cornea, in each principal meridian we could calculate the cylindrical component, C, of the correcting lens. The reading given by a keratometer on an astigmatic eye is merely the astigmatism of the cornea; it is not even the difference between the meridian refractive errors, that is the astigmatism, of the eye.

---

* §3.14.

† § *Ophthalmic Lenses*: Ch. XVII.

Values of the (minus) correcting lens corresponding to keratometer readings, for various values of positive and negative spherical powers are given in the following table.

KERATOMETER READING AND CORRECTING CYLINDER.

Distance separating spectacle point and cornea = 12⅓ mm.

Spherical Component of Correcting Lens. S Dioptres.	When Keratometer reading (A_K) of corneal astigmatism in dioptres is							
	−1	−2	−3	−4	−5	−6	−7	−8
	corresponding cylinder (C_K) in dioptres to be prescribed is							
+10	−0·78	−1·57	−2·38	−3·21	−4·06	−4·93	−5·82	−6·73
8	−0·82	1·66	2·52	3·40	4·30	5·22	6·17	−7·12
6	−0·87	1·75	2·66	3·59	4·55	5·52	6·52	−7·55
5	−0·89	1·80	2·73	3·69	4·67	5·67	6·71	−7·76
4	−0·91	1·85	2·81	3·79	4·80	5·83	6·89	−7·98
3	−0·94	1·90	2·88	3·90	4·93	5·99	7·07	−8·19
2	−0·96	1·95	2·96	4·00	5·06	6·15	7·27	−8·42
+ 1	−0·99	2·00	3·04	4·10	5·19	6·31	7·47	−8·65
0	−1·01	−2·05	−3·11	−4·21	−5·33	−6·48	−7·66	−8·88
− 1	−1·04	2·10	3·19	4·32	5·47	6·65	7·86	9·12
2	−1·06	2·15	3·27	4·42	5·60	6·82	8·07	9·35
3	−1·09	2·21	3·35	4·53	5·74	6·99	8·27	9·58
4	−1·12	2·26	3·43	4·64	5·88	7·16	8·47	9·83
5	−1·14	2·32	3·52	4·76	6·03	7·34	8·69	10·08
6	−1·17	2·37	3·60	4·87	6·18	7·52	8·90	10·32
8	−1·22	2·48	3·78	5·11	6·48	7·89	9·34	10·84
10	−1·28	2·59	3·95	5·34	6·77	8·26	9·78	11·36
12	−1·34	2·71	4·13	5·59	7·09	8·64	10·24	11·89
15	−1·43	2·89	4·41	5·97	7·58	9·24	10·96	12·73
−20	−1·58	−3·20	−4·89	−6·63	−8·42	−10·28	−12·22	−14·18

9.10. The Placido Disc and Photo-Keratometry.

The Placido disc was introduced many years ago for the detection and rough measurement of corneal astigmatism. It consists of a disc with a series of concentric white and black circular rings and a magnifying lens of about 4 D mounted in its central aperture. It is held up in front of the subject's eye and illuminated by a light placed behind the subject. The examiner looks through the lens and approaches until the reflected image of the disc, formed in the subject's cornea, is in focus. If the image rings are elliptical there is corneal astigmatism, the principal meridians being indicated by the long and short axes of the ellipse. Irregular rings point to irregularities in the corneal front surface, or to conical cornea.

GULLSTRAND used a disc of this kind, with rings of specially calculated diameters, in order to obtain the corneal radius at different portions of its surface and not just at two isolated small areas as in the keratometer. He photographed the corneal image of the rings and measured the

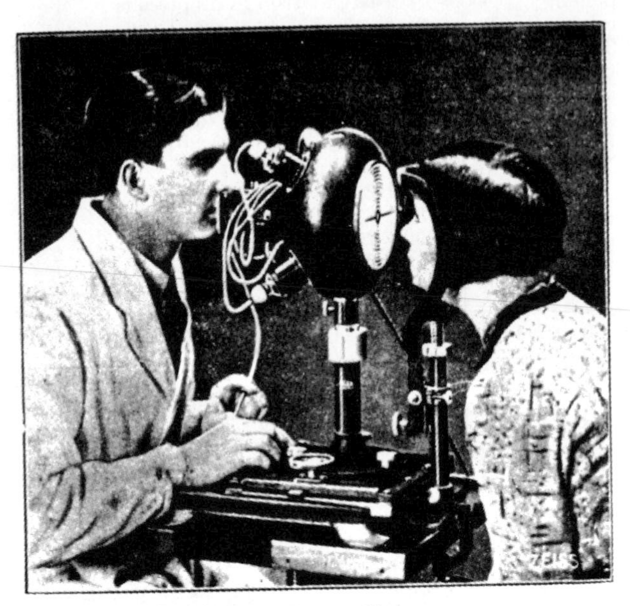

FIG. 9.13—THE PHOTO-KERATOSCOPE.

photograph with a measuring microscope. At the suggestion of M. AMSLER of Lausanne, Messrs. ZEISS have produced an instrument, the PHOTO-KERATOSCOPE, to enable such photographs to be obtained with precision and rapidity. Its general construction is illustrated in Fig. 9.13. The opal disc of concentric rings is illuminated by four lamps within the body of the instrument. The objective at the centre of the disc forms an image of the corneal reflection on the plate of a reflex camera. The examiner obtains sharp focus by viewing the image through an auxiliary eyepiece. By measuring the sizes of the rings on the resulting photograph, the radii of curvature of the anterior surface of the cornea at different parts of its surface can be calculated.

The manufacturers supply tables, calculated from the known constructional constants of the instrument, to enable the required information to be obtained quickly from the

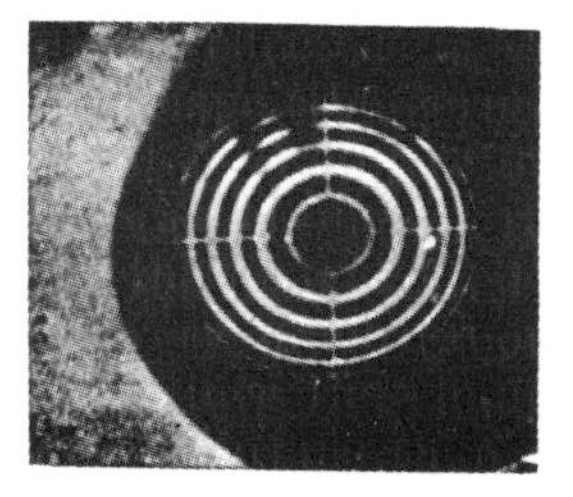

(*a*) Regular Astigmatism of 5·5 D, with the rule.

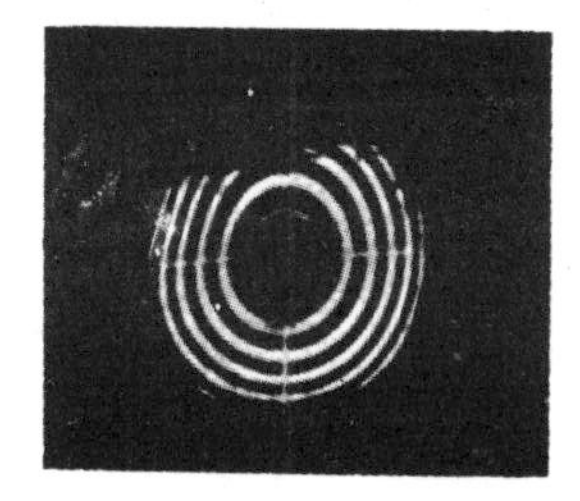

(*b*) Regular Astigmatism, against the rule, after operation for cataract (needling).

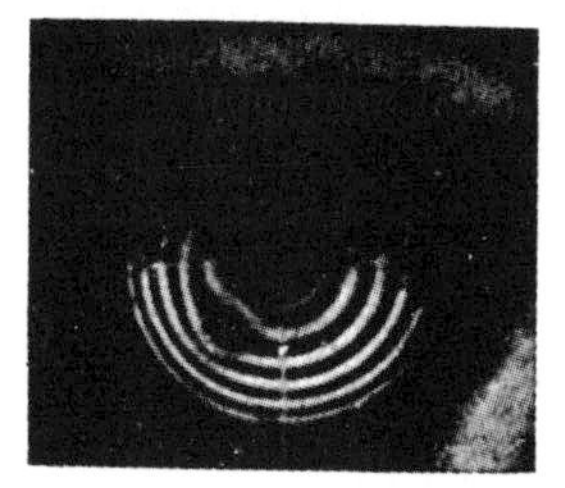

(*c and d*) Irregular Astigmatism. Eczematous Keratitis—course of affection within period of fourteen days.

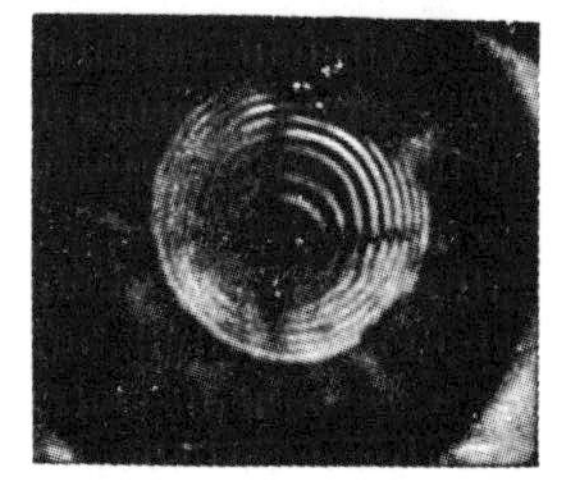

(*e*) Conical Cornea—base of cone.

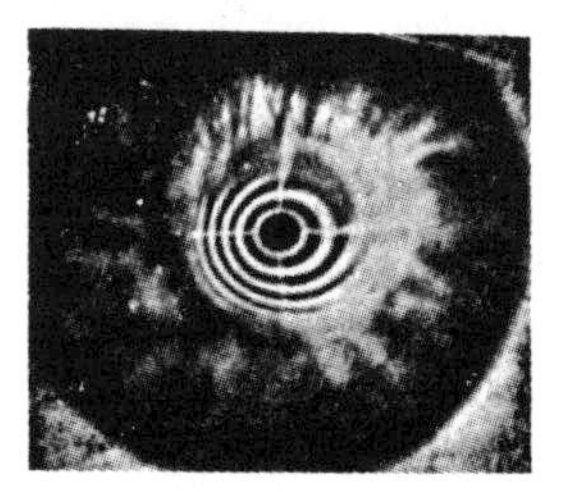

(*f*) Conical Cornea—apex of cornea.

FIG. 9.14—APPEARANCES OF PHOTO-KERATOSCOPE IMAGES.

measurements of the photograph. Fig. 9.14 illustrates the appearances of the images in various conditions of the cornea.

EXERCISES. CHAPTER IX.

1. Find by graphical construction the position and size of the image, formed by a convex mirror of 10 cm. radius of an object 3 cm. long placed 10 cm. from the mirror and perpendicular to its axis.

Check your result by calculation.

Repeat the calculation for the following case: radius of mirror 10 mm.; object 30 cm. long and 40 cm. from the mirror. What is the reflecting power of this mirror ?

2. In the ophthalmometer or keratometer the curvature of the corneal anterior surface is determined by measuring the size h' of the image of an object h, formed by reflection. Show that the radius of curvature r of the cornea is given approximately by the expression:

$$r = \frac{-2dh'}{h}$$

where d is the distance from image to object.

Hence calculate the image size when the object is 12 cm. long, the cornea radius 7·5 mm. and the distance d is 10 cm.

3. Describe the purpose and mode of action of the keratometer. Derive the formula on which it is based.

Explain why a doubling device is necessary in the instrument and what is meant by a fixed doubling and by a variable doubling instrument.

4. Describe with the aid of the appropriate formulæ the optical construction of the keratometer. (B.O.A. Hons.)

5. In determining corneal radius by means of a keratometer, three quantities are involved, viz.: the object (or mire) size, the corneal image size, and the separation of these two.

Explain how, in the instrumental arrangement, one of these quantities is rendered constant and how two main methods of making the measurement depend upon the manipulation of the two remaining quantities.

6. Explain, with a diagram, the principle and optical construction of the keratometer. Explain the reason for the doubling device and describe two methods of doubling.

In a given case the distance from the mire to its corneal image was 40 cm., the separation of the two mire objects being 30 cm. and of the corneal images of these, 3 mm. Find the corneal radius.

7. In a certain keratometer the mire consists of a single circle with projections. Show on a careful diagram the appearance observed by the examiner when using the instrument on an astigmatic cornea with principal meridians at 30° and 120°, the 120° meridian being the more steeply curved. The plane of doubling of the instrument is supposed horizontal.

If the readings obtained are 44·25 D in the 30° meridian and 47 D in the 120° meridian, what are the radii of curvature of the cornea ?

8. An object in the form of a horizontal straight line 8 cm. long is observed through a double prism with B.A. line horizontal. Each prism has an apical angle of 4° 34′ and they are made of glass of refractive index 1·50. How far from the object will the prism have to be placed in order that the two images will just touch, end to end ?

If the prism be placed (*a*) 60 cm. and (*b*) 160 cm. from the object, what will be the relative positions of the images ?

Give a diagram showing the ray paths in all three cases.

9. In an ophthalmometer the distance between the two mires is 35 cm. and these are situated in a plane 50 cm. from the cornea of the eye being tested. Find the size of the reflected image in the horizontal and vertical meridians, the radius of curvature of the cornea being 8 mm. in the horizontal and 8·5 mm. in the vertical.

Given the refractive index of calibration as 1·336, find the amount and type of astigmatism due to the cornea.

10. Explain with diagrams two methods of "doubling" employed in the objective measurement of curvature of the cornea. (B.O.A.)

11. Describe with the aid of carefully drawn diagrams the principal optical and mechanical details of any instrument in the ophthalmometer class with which you are familiar ; and discuss briefly any special advantage of principle or of construction. (S.M.C.)

12. With elementary apparatus how would you measure the radius of curvature of the cornea ? Give the theory of your method and indicate possible difficulties of measurement. (S.M.C.)

13. Describe with the aid of careful diagrams some accurate method of measuring the curvature of the cornea objectively. Obtain formulæ for the numerical calculation of the curvature. (B.O.A. Hons.)

14. Provided with two small (ophthalmoscope) lamps, a +12 D spherical lens and a double prism, each half of the latter having a deviation of 2△, explain with a diagram how you would proceed to measure the radius of curvature of a subject's cornea.

Using assumed values for the quantities concerned, show how you would calculate the radius from the observations made.

15. The following particulars apply to an ophthalmometer of the variable doubling type :

power of objective (assumed thin)	6·5 D
size of object (mire)	8 cm.
distance of objective from corneal image when in focus ..	25 cm.
distance of object from corneal image when in focus ..	12·5 cm.

The doubling device is a double image prism each half of which produces a deviation of one prism dioptre. Find the two positions of this prism along the axis of the instrument when coincidence of the images has been obtained on an astigmatic cornea of radii 7·0 and 7·8 mm.

What is the astigmatism of this cornea ?

Give a sketch of the optical arrangement of the instrument.

16. If, in a keratometer, the object or mire is 72 mm. from the observed cornea, the radius of which is 8 mm., find the error made in the determination of the refracting power of the cornea by basing the measurement on the approximate expression $r = -2dh'/h$ instead of the correct expression $r = -2xh'/h$. The quantities h and h' refer to the object (mire) and corneal image sizes ; x is the distance from the focal point of the cornea, as a reflector, to the object ; d is the distance from the corneal image to the object.

Find the error also when the object distance from cornea is 150 mm.

17. In the keratometer, if $h=$ size of object or mire, $h'=$ size of corneal image, $d=$ distance from image to object when the instrument is in focus, prove that the radius of curvature of the cornea is given by :

$$r=\frac{-2dhh'}{(h^2-h'^2)}$$

which reduces to the usual approximate expression $r=-2dh'/h$ when the small quantity h'^2 is neglected.

18. Explain clearly the meaning of the terms : fixed doubling ; variable doubling ; one-position instrument ; two-position instrument —as applied to the keratometer.

Give a diagram of the optical construction of a fixed doubling instrument, showing clearly the shape and orientation of the mires. Give diagrams also indicating the appearance to the examiner when using the instrument on a cornea that is too steep for contact of the images ; also when the images are in contact.

19. Describe the principle of a one-position and a two-position keratometer. Compare the two types with respect to their general efficiency and mode of use. Give a careful diagram of the optical construction of a typical two-position instrument.

20. Describe a doubling device for a one-position keratometer in which longitudinally moving prisms are used. Show how the dioptric scale of such an instrument is related to the travel of the prisms.

21. Discuss in detail the possible seats of astigmatism in the eye and the ability of the keratometer to reveal and measure the errors produced.

A spherical polished steel ball has a diameter of 16 mm. A thin concave plano-cylindrical lens is placed in contact with it and by measurement with the keratometer the resultant artificial astigmatism is found to be 2 D with the rule. Calculate the power and axis position of the cylindrical required. (S.M.C. Hons.)

22. A $-8\cdot00$ D cylindrical lens, axis vertical, is placed in contact with a polished steel ball of $7\cdot85$ mm. radius and readings are taken in both principal meridians with an ophthalmometer calibrated for a refractive index of $1\cdot3375$. Calculate the amount and type of astigmatism which should be recorded by the instrument.

23. Write short notes on the relations between astigmatism measured by the ophthalmometer and astigmatism measured by subjective methods. (S.M.C.)

24. It is sometimes stated that the measurement made with the keratometer is the most accurate of any measurement obtained concerning the eye's optical performance. Discuss this statement and point out sources of error arising in the result given by the keratometer.

25. Explain carefully just what is measured by the keratometer and discuss briefly the relationship between this quantity and the total astigmatism of the eye.

In what circumstances and for what purposes might it be desirable to use a keratometer ? Give reasons.

26. Describe tests by which you could establish the existence of an irregular corneal surface. Explain how the subject's vision may be improved by optical treatment.

27. In cases where, for some reason, the cylindrical portion of the correcting lens is to be determined from the keratometer reading, explain carefully how the value of the correcting cylinder is obtained from the keratometer reading and the spherical portion of the correction, supposed to have been measured in some other way, subjectively or objectively.

If the spherical portion of the correction has been found to be − 8 D in the more hyperopic meridian and the corneal astigmatism revealed by the keratometer is 5 D axis H., find the prescription of the correcting lens to be worn 12 mm. from the cornea.

28. Assume a thin cornea and the following meridian radii :

Anterior surface : vertical, 7·8 mm. ; horizontal, 8·0 mm.

Posterior ,, ,, 6·8 mm. ; ,, 7·0 mm.

Refractive index of cornea 1·376, refractive index of aqueous 1·336. Calculate the anterior surface astigmatism and the total corneal astigmatism. Comment on the ophthalmometric interest of the results. (S.M.C.)

29. In a keratometer with a fixed doubling device, this and the mire are situated $\frac{1}{3}$ metre from the subject's cornea, the radius of which is 7·5 mm. The angle of doubling of the doubling device is one prism dioptre. What is the size of the mire for correct setting with this cornea ? What will be the size of mire when the setting is correct on a cornea of radius 7·337 mm ? Hence, what is the mire movement in mm. per dioptre of corneal refracting power ?

30. Explain with the aid of good diagrams the optical and mechanical construction of a moving-mire type of ophthalmometer, paying special attention to the "doubling action."

What would be the angle of doubling, in prism dioptres, if the ophthalmometer mire movement is 5 mm. per dioptre, the front objective, doubling apparatus and mires being placed in correct adjustment at 25 cm. from the cornea ; basic refractive index 1·3375 ? (S.M.C.)

31. Describe with the aid of diagrams the optical portion of a keratometer which obtains the correction in both meridians simultaneously (B.O.A.)

VISUAL OPTICS

CHAPTER X

THE SCHEMATIC EYE—UNAIDED AND AIDED

10.1. The Optical System of the Eye.

WITHIN the narrow zone of about 4 mm. diameter exposed by the circular pupil under ordinary conditions—the OPTICAL ZONE—the anterior and posterior surfaces of the cornea and lens are practically spherical, although there is a definite tendency for the meridian of the corneal anterior surface lying in or near the vertical to be more steeply curved than the perpendicular meridian; more especially in young people. This gives rise to the physiological astigmatism already mentioned.* This corneal surface was at one time considered to be ellipsoidal, but modern measurements have caused this view to be abandoned in favour of the spherical or slightly toric, form.

In more peripheral regions outside the optical zone the surfaces flatten out considerably, affecting the form of the wider refracted pencil of light admitted to the eye when the pupil is dilated, as in darkness.†

The surfaces are not exactly centred upon a common axis, but we shall see presently that they are approximately so.

The aqueous and vitreous humours have, for all practical purposes, a common refractive index of 1·336. This is the mean of the results obtained by many investigators, using the Abbe or the Pulfrich refractometer. In myopia the anterior chamber, from cornea to front surface of crystalline lens, may be somewhat deeper than the average value of 3 mm. Apart from the thin film of lacrimal fluid on the anterior surface and the corneal epithelium, both of which are thin concentric laminæ and may therefore be neglected, the cornea has a practically uniform refractive index of 1·376. The crystalline lens, on the other hand, is not homogeneous but consists of a series of laminæ, the refractive indices of which increase gradually from the value 1·386 at the anterior surface inwards until at a point

* §4.11. † §§ 4.5 and 11.3.

about 1·6 mm. from the anterior surface the index reaches a maximum value of 1·406. Over the 2 mm. distance from this point to the posterior surface the index decreases to its original value of 1·386. This variation of index has received much attention, the investigations of MATTHIESSEN (1883) and FREYTAG (1907) using an Abbe refractometer, being probably the most comprehensive. As the lens develops, the central nuclear portion or core becomes more sharply separated as to index from the surrounding cortical portions, the anterior and posterior surfaces of optical discontinuity between the two portions being sufficiently definite to form images by reflection when light from a small bright source enters the eye.

10.2. The Catoptric Images of the Eye.

When light is incident upon the surface separating two optical media, part is reflected and the remainder enters the second medium. The ratio between these two portions of the total light depends upon the difference between the refractive indices of the two media and upon the angle of incidence; the percentage of light entering the second medium* increases as the incidence becomes more nearly normal, and as the difference between the indices of the two media becomes less pronounced. Of the reflected light, some is reflected regularly, in a definite direction according to the law of reflection; the remainder is diffusely reflected and renders the surface visible from any direction. The quantity of light reflected diffusely is small if the surface is optically smooth.

An image of the source will be formed by the regularly reflected light, its position, size and attitude (i.e. whether erect or inverted) depending upon the curvature of the surface.

The light that enters the second medium is partly absorbed and partly transmitted, the latter portion increasing with the transparency of the second medium.* In transparent media such as clear water, optical glass, etc., most of this transmitted light follows a definite path according to the laws of refraction, forming an image at a position depending upon the curvature of the surface and the refractive indices of the media. A small proportion of the transmitted light will be scattered irregularly in various directions. Since no

---

* See §**19.10.**

medium is ideally transparent, the path of the beam through the medium is rendered visible by this diffused light.

If a small source of light be held in front of a lens or optical system, the regularly reflected or *catoptric* images formed by the surfaces may be observed from a position on the same side as the source. If the surfaces, or lenses, are tilted or laterally displaced relatively to one another, the images will appear separated laterally. When the centres of curvature of the various surfaces are made to lie on one common axis, that is when the system is "centred", the images will be superimposed on one another, when the source and the observation station coincide on this axis.

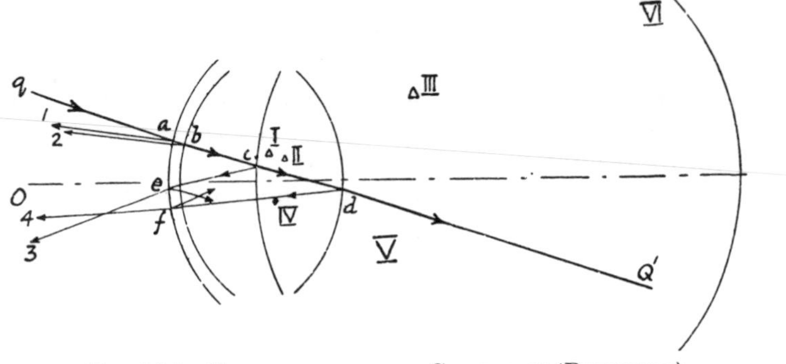

FIG. 10.1—FORMATION OF THE CATOPTRIC (PURKINJE) IMAGES IN THE EYE.

Lenses for optical instruments are centred in their mounts in a manner depending on these considerations.

When light from a luminous object is incident at any ordinary angle upon the eye, the bulk of it enters the eye and traverses the optical media, being refracted at every surface of optical discontinuity; and it finally forms an image somewhere in the region of the retina. This is the *dioptric* image, formed by refracted light and is, of course, the one of paramount importance. A small proportion of the incident light is, however, reflected at each surface, most of this being reflected regularly and giving rise, therefore, to a catoptric image at each surface where there is a sufficiently marked change of refractive index. Each of these pencils of regularly reflected light travels back in the opposite direction, traversing the media anterior to the surface in question, and so the images are visible to an observer situated in front of the eye. In Fig. 10.1 the incident narrow pencil qa is mainly refracted along the path abcd, forming an image Q′ on or near to the retina, depending upon the distance of the object and the refractive condition of the eye. But some light is reflected at the corneal anterior surface along a1 and an image (the corneal reflex) is seen in this direction at the point I. Light is also reflected at b and c and d, the pencils emerging in the directions 2, 3, and 4 and giving rise to the images II, III and IV. The anterior corneal reflex is very much (about 100 times) brighter than the other three, since the change of refractive index is much greater at this surface than at

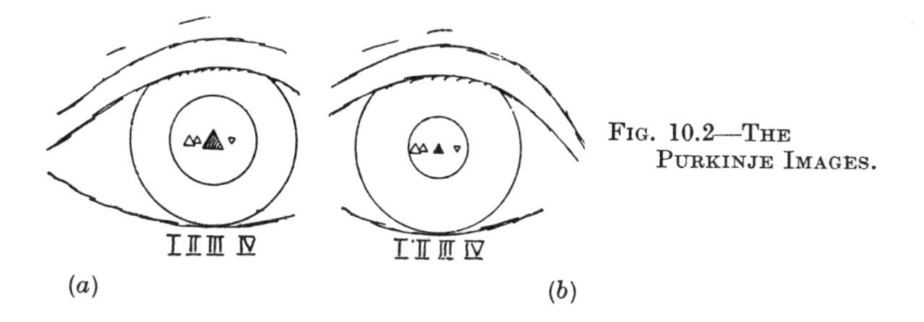

FIG. 10.2—THE PURKINJE IMAGES.

any of the others. The image formed by the reflection at the posterior lens surface is inverted, this surface being concave to the incident light.

These catoptric images of the eye were first described by PURKINJE (1823) and SANSON (1837) and are usually called the Purkinje-Sanson, or simply the Purkinje, images. They are of service in determining the positions and curvatures of the ocular surfaces, as we shall see.

Some of the light in the reflected pencils (except the first) is reflected a second time. Thus some light of pencils 3 and 4 is reflected by the corneal anterior surface at e and f, giving rise to faint real images in the positions indicated roughly by V and VI. Whereas the four Purkinje images represent light lost to the eye, these latter (sometimes called images of the second order) are harmful, since they may be seen by the subject.

To an observer in front observing from about the position marked O in Fig. 10.1 the images appear somewhat as indicated in Fig. 10.2 (a). In agreement with the previous diagram, the images I, II, III and IV are formed respectively by the front and back surfaces of the cornea and the front and back surfaces of the crystalline, in that order. The first three are situated towards the same side as the source of light; the fourth on the opposite side. Under favourable conditions, two more images may be observed, formed by reflection at the two surfaces of the lens nucleus. These are faint and diffuse showing that the change of refractive index between the cortical layers and the nucleus does not take place suddenly. These two images we will neglect. We will also usually ignore image No. II, due to the corneal posterior surface; it is the faintest of the four Purkinje images, the media it separates differing in refractive index by only 0·04 (1·376—1·336). Even the third image, from the lens anterior surface, is badly defined as it is really the result of the overlapping of images from the capsule and other surfaces of discontinuity in the lens immediately behind the capsule.

Fig. 10.2A shows the three images I, III and IV as photographed by E. F. FINCHAM in the living eye. By using an arc lamp and three concave mirrors, three sources of illumination were obtained, disposed in the shape of a triangle with apex down. The anterior corneal image, on the left, is seen to be much brighter than the others. The diminution in size of the anterior lens image, in the middle, when the eye accommodates is shown in the illustration and has already been mentioned.* The small image on the right (No. IV) is inverted.

10.3. The Centring of the Optical System of the Eye.

THE OPTICAL AXIS.

If, with the subject steadily fixing some stationary fixation object, the source of light is moved about laterally before the eye and observation of the catoptric images is made from a point immediately below the light, so that the directions of illumination and observation coincide, a position will be found in which the images are most nearly superimposed. This direction is then the nearest approach we can obtain to an optical axis, and as such we will define it. We shall assume, which is very nearly the case, that the centre of curvature of the optical zone of the corneal anterior surface and the optical axis of the crystalline lens, both fall on this line.

* §2.14.

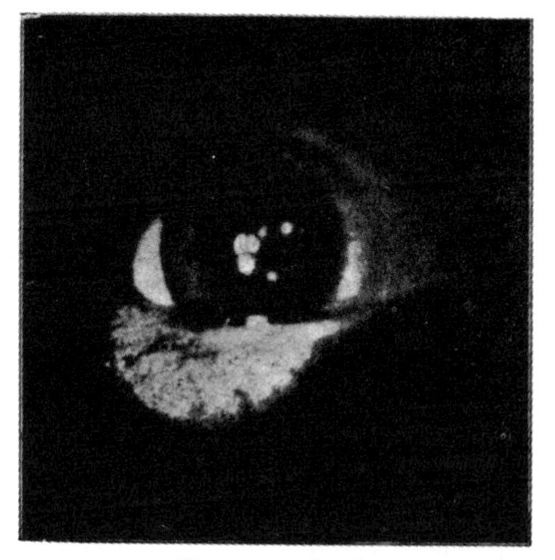

Unaccommodated.

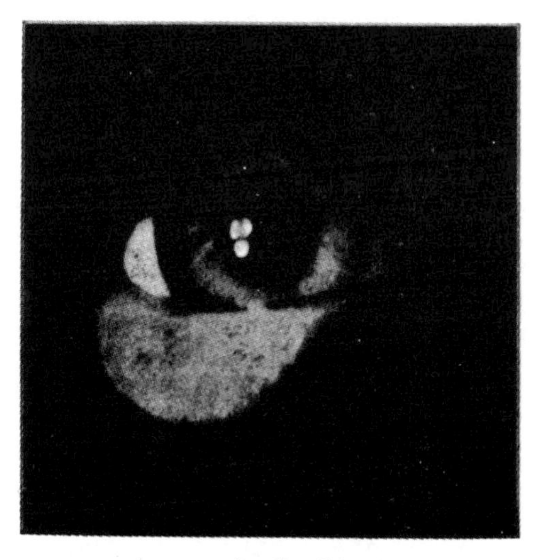

Accommodated 8 Dioptres.

Fig. 10.2A.—Photographs of Purkinje Images. (Fincham.)

THE ANGLE ALPHA.

In the above experiment it will be found in most eyes that the common point of illumination and observation lies to the temporal side of the fixation point; that is, outside the eye the optical axis lies temporalwards from the *visual axis*.* Actually the visual axis is a double line consisting of two very close and parallel portions, one from the fixation point to the anterior nodal point of the eye and the other from the posterior nodal point to the fovea.† As we shall see, we can replace the two nodal points by one point (the nodal point N of the reduced eye) and consider the visual axis, as we have done heretofore, as one line. The optical and visual axes intersect in this nodal point and the angle between them is the ANGLE ALPHA.

The experimental method just described for measuring this angle is facilitated by observing the reflected images through a telescope mounted on a circular arc placed with its centre at the eye's nodal point. Such an arrangement, called by TSCHERNING an OPHTHALMOPHAKOMETER, is used also for determining other constants of the eye, and will be referred to again.

The pupil is approximately centred on the optical axis, although it may be decentred slightly in the nasal or the temporal direction, more frequently the former. When the optical axis passes through the centre of the pupil the visual axis penetrates it somewhat on the nasal side for positive values of the angle alpha, a circumstance to which is attributed the stereoscopic effect of differently coloured objects lying in the same plane.‡

We gather from the above that, except when investigating special attributes of the eye or examining particular portions of its interior, we are justified in considering the optical system of the eye as a centred system of spherical surfaces with its circular aperture (pupil) centred upon the optical axis. The visual axis is usually inclined to the optical axis, however, by about 5° so that the image-forming pencils from the object fixed pass obliquely through the system.

HELMHOLTZ and LANDOLT defined the angle alpha as that between the visual axis and the major axis of the corneal ellipse, the cornea being considered ellipsoidal. DONDERS described the angle in the same way, but since he considers the axis of the corneal ellipse to coincide with the optical axis, his definition agrees with the one we

---

* §2.4. † Fig. 10.3 (b). ‡ §12.21.

have adopted above. It was considered easier in practice to measure the angle between the visual axis and the so-called central pupillary line, which angle was given the name " kappa " by LANDOLT. The definition of this pupillary line and the method usually described for measuring the angle kappa are, however, open to question. Modern views concur in defining the angle alpha in the manner we have adopted.

10.4. The Schematic Eye.

Accepting the eye as a centred system of spherical surfaces it is convenient to be able to represent it in a simple form when making calculations concerning it or when considering the performance of lenses and instruments used in conjunction with it. Being in fact a living organ, the eye differs in its structure and dimensions from one individual to another; there are appreciable variations even among emmetropic eyes, but analysis of repeated measurements on hundreds of eyes has enabled average figures for the " constants " of the eye, that is for the curvatures and separations of the surfaces and the refractive indices of the media, to be obtained. An eye drawn up on paper to represent the optical performance of this eye of average dimensions is a diagrammatic or SCHEMATIC EYE. Since LISTING'S first attempt in 1851, many investigators have essayed to construct such a schematic eye. Their results differ from one another according to the extent and accuracy of the measurements available at the time.

In drawing up the schematic eye a difficulty arises on account of the heterogeneous character of the crystalline lens. It is possible to represent such a complex lens fairly closely by assuming it to consist of two portions; a central biconvex nucleus or core to which a certain calculated index is assigned, contained in a larger biconvex lens with a lower refractive index (Fig. 6.4). This was done in the schematic eye (No. 1) constructed by the Swedish ophthalmologist, A. GULLSTRAND. The data for this eye are given in the accompanying table, both in the unaccommodated state (third column of figures) and also (in the fourth column) when accommodated on a point distant 102·3 mm. from the anterior surface of the cornea, an amount of accommodation corresponding to the maximum amplitude of a youth of 15 years or so. The powers of the whole eye and of its parts and the positions of its cardinal points, as calculated from the given constants, are also included.*

* The calculation is as for any optical system; see FINCHAM'S *Optics* and p. 347.

All dimensions are stated in millimetres, positions being referred to the anterior surface of the cornea as reference origin.

It will be observed that the refractive condition of this Gullstrand No. 1 eye, when relaxed, is one dioptre of hypermetropia. According to GULLSTRAND, when this is the state

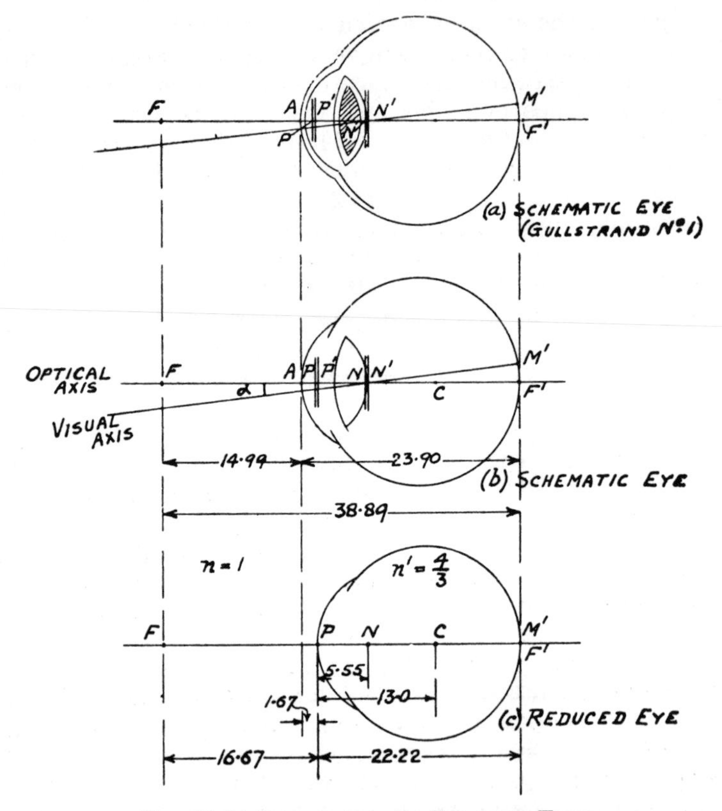

FIG. 10.3—SCHEMATIC AND REDUCED EYES.
(See Table §10.4 for constants.)

of affairs along the axis, the eye, with a normal pupil, will be emmetropic, having regard to the effects of the eye's aberrations on the form of the refracted pencils.*

This eye, which GULLSTRAND refers to as the "exact" schematic eye is illustrated, to scale, in Fig. 10.3 (a).

* §11.3.

The eye's optical system is represented less rigorously, but still with sufficient accuracy for most purposes, by considering the crystalline lens as homogeneous, assigning to it an appropriate refractive index, which has to be higher than that of the core, for reasons already mentioned;* and by omitting the posterior surface of the cornea which has but little power (− 5·9 D), increasing the anterior corneal radius slightly to allow of this. The eye is then simplified to one of three surfaces only. Such simplified schematic eyes have been proposed by various writers, LISTING, HELMHOLTZ, TSCHERNING and GULLSTRAND being the most prominent.

The data for such an eye, at rest, is given in the first column of figures of the Table; and the eye is depicted, to scale, in Fig. 10.3 (b). The data is that supplied by GULLSTRAND for his so-called No. 2 or simplified schematic eye, except that his figures of 1·336 for the humours and 1·413 for the lens have been altered by the author to 4/3 and 1·416 respectively.† The effect of these alterations is that the "reduced eye" to be derived later from this schematic eye will have a dioptric power of almost exactly 60 dioptres.

It is seen from the table that the eye is emmetropic; it has a dioptric power of 60·48 D; the anterior focal point is very nearly 15 mm. in front of the cornea; and the principal points are very close together and not far removed from the anterior corneal surface. As in all optical systems, the separation of the nodal points is the same as that of the principal points and the nodal points are displaced towards the surrounding medium with the higher index. In future, when we have occasion to refer to the unaccommodated schematic eye, it will be to this simplified form of it, as set out in the first column.

THE SCHEMATIC EYE ACCOMMODATED.

When the eye accommodates, the extra power it assumes is derived mainly from the steepening of the anterior surface of the lens. Measurements show that there are wide variations between individuals as to the change of curvature

---

* §6.3.

† Many measurements made at the Northampton Polytechnic, London, are in good agreement with Gullstrand's figures; we have found, however, that the radius of the anterior lens surface seems to be nearer 11 than 10 mm.

TABLE. SCHEMATIC EYE DATA

		Gullstrand No.2 (Simplified) Eye—modified (see text)			Gullstrand No. 1 (Exact) Eye.	
		Relaxed.		Accom.	Relaxed	Accom.
Refractive Indices	Cornea ..	—	—	—	1·376	1·376
	Aqueous & Vitreous ..	n_2 n_4	4/3	4/3	1·336	1·336
	Lens :—Cortex	—	—	—	1·386	1·386
	,, Core	n_3	1·416	1·416	1·406	1·406
Positions	Cornea :— anterior ..	—	0	0	0	0
	posterior ..	—	—	—	0·5	0·5
	Lens :— anterior ..	d_2	3·6	3·2	3·6	3·2
	posterior ..	$(d_2 + d_3)$	7·2	7·2	7·2	7·2
	core, anterior	—	—	—	4·146	3·872
	core, posterior	—	—	—	6·565	6·527
Radii of Curvature	Cornea :— anterior ..	r_1	7·8	7·8	7·7	7·7
	posterior ..	—	—	—	6·8	6·8
	Lens :— anterior ..	r_2	10·0	5·0	10·0	5·33
	posterior ..	r_3	− 6·0	− 5·0	− 6·0	− 5·33
	core, anterior	—	—	—	7·911	2·655
	core, posterior	—	—	—	− 5·76	− 2·655
Powers	Cornea ..	F_1	42·735	42·735	43·05	43·05
	Lens ..	F_2	21·76	32·30	19·11	33·06
	Complete Eye	F_o	60·48	69·72	58·64	70·57
Focal lengths of complete eye.	First ..	f_o	− 16·54	− 14·35	− 17·05	− 14·17
	Second ..	f_o'	+22·05	+19·13	+22·78	+18·93
Positions	Principal, first ..	$A_1 P = e$	1·55	1·78	1·348	1·772
	second ..	$A_1 P'$	1·85	2·13	1·602	2·086
	Nodal, first ..	$A_1 N$	7·06	6·56	7·08	6·53
	,, second	$A_1 N'$	7·36	6·91	7·33	6·85
	Focal, first ..	$A_1 F$	− 14·99	− 12·57	− 15·70	− 12·40
	,, second	$A_1 F'$	23·90	21·26	24·38	21·02
	Fovea ..	k'	23·90	23·90	24·0	24·0
Refractive Condition ..		K	0	− 8·48	+ 1	− 9·6
Position of Near Point ..		$(b - e)$	—	− 116·2	—	− 102·3

and position of this surface, for a given amount of accommodation.* There is some doubt as to the extent to which the posterior lens surface changes its curvature and position, although it is known that this surface alters by only a small amount. It is not easy to determine the alterations in the living eye.†

The figures given in the second column of the table, for our schematic eye of column 1 when it accommodates by about 8·5 dioptres, agree tolerably well with the experimentally ascertained values. The refractive index of the lens and the position of its posterior surface, 7·2 mm. from the cornea, are assumed to remain unchanged. The only changes are in the curvature of the anterior lens surface which steepens from 10 mm. to 5 mm.; the position of this surface, which advances 0·4 mm., increasing the axial thickness of the lens by this amount; and the curvature of the posterior lens surface, which steepens slightly, from – 6 mm. to – 5 mm. As a result of these changes the dioptric power of the lens increases by 10·54 D and of the whole eye by 9·24 D, the refractive condition assuming the value – 8·476 D, measured from the first principal point. The point on which the eye is focused in this accommodated condition is 116·22 mm. from the anterior surface of the cornea. The mean position of the principal points has been shifted backwards by 0·25 mm., a very small displacement.

It may be of service to give the calculations for the relaxed simplified schematic eye of column 1.

Cornea. power $F_1 = \dfrac{n' - n}{r} = \dfrac{(4/3 - 1)\,1000}{7\cdot 8} = 42\cdot 73\ \text{D}$

Crystalline Lens

Ant. Surface $F_{2A} = \dfrac{(1\cdot 416 - 1\cdot 333)\,1000}{10} = 8\cdot 27\ \text{D}$

Post. ,, $F_{2P} = \dfrac{(1\cdot 333 - 1\cdot 416)\,1000}{-6} = 13\cdot 78\ \text{D}$

Total power $F_2 = F_{2A} + F_{2P} - \dfrac{d}{n_3} F_{2A}.\ F_{2P}$

$$= 8\cdot 27 + 13\cdot 78 - \frac{3\cdot 6 \times 8\cdot 27 \times 13\cdot 78}{1\cdot 416 \times 1000} = 21\cdot 76\ \text{D}$$

Principal points: in any system of two components, $e =$ distance from first component to first principal point and e' from second component to second principal point.

* See E. F. Fincham, "Changes in the Form of the Crystalline Lens in Accommodation," *Trans. Opt. Soc.*, XXVI, 5, 1924-25.

† See §10.5.

$$\text{first}: \quad e = n_2 \frac{d}{n_3} \frac{F_{2P}}{F_2} = \frac{4}{3} \times \frac{3 \cdot 6 \times 13 \cdot 78}{1 \cdot 416 \times 21 \cdot 76} = 2 \cdot 146 \text{ mm.}$$

$$\text{second}: \quad e' = -n_2 \frac{d}{n_3} \frac{F_{2A}}{F_2} = -\frac{4}{3} \times \frac{3 \cdot 6 \times 8 \cdot 27}{1 \cdot 416 \times 21 \cdot 76} = -1 \cdot 288 \text{ mm.}$$

Complete Eye

Separation of cornea and first principal point of crystalline

$$d = 3 \cdot 6 + 2 \cdot 146 = 5 \cdot 746 \text{ mm.}$$

$$\text{Total power } F_o = F_1 + F_2 - \frac{d}{n_2} F_1 F_2$$

$$= 42 \cdot 73 + 21 \cdot 76 - \frac{5 \cdot 746 \times 42 \cdot 73 \times 21 \cdot 76}{1 \cdot 333 \times 1000} = 60 \cdot 48 \text{ D}$$

Principal points :

$$\text{first}: \quad e = \frac{d}{n_2} \frac{F_2}{F_o} = \frac{5 \cdot 746 \times 21 \cdot 76}{1 \cdot 333 \times 60 \cdot 48} = 1 \cdot 55 \text{ mm.}$$

$$\text{second}: \quad e' = -n_4 \frac{d}{n_2} \frac{F_1}{F_o} = -\frac{4}{3} \times \frac{5 \cdot 746 \times 42 \cdot 73}{1 \cdot 333 \times 60 \cdot 48} = -4 \cdot 06 \text{ mm.}$$

thus second principal point of complete eye is $-4 \cdot 06$ mm. from second principal point of crystalline ; that is

$7 \cdot 2 - 1 \cdot 29 - 4 \cdot 06 = 1 \cdot 85$ mm. from anterior corneal surface.

Focal lengths :

$$\text{first}: \quad f_o = -\frac{1}{F_o} = -\frac{1000}{60 \cdot 48} = -16 \cdot 54 \text{ mm.}$$

$$\text{second}: \quad f'_o = \frac{n'}{F_o} = \frac{4}{3} \times \frac{1000}{60 \cdot 48} = +22 \cdot 04 \text{ mm.}$$

Focal points :

first : distance from cornea $= 1 \cdot 55 - 16 \cdot 53 = -14 \cdot 98$ mm.
second : ,, ,, ,, $= 1 \cdot 85 + 22 \cdot 04 = +23 \cdot 89$ mm.

Nodal points :

first : distance from cornea $= -14 \cdot 98 + 22 \cdot 04 = +7 \cdot 06$ mm.
second : ,, ,, ,, $= 23 \cdot 89 - 16 \cdot 53 = +7 \cdot 36$ mm.

10.5. Ophthalmometry. Measurement of Curvatures and Positions of Ocular Surfaces.

HELMHOLTZ set out systematically to measure the optical constants of the eye with his ophthalmometer ; we have seen how the curvature of the corneal anterior surface is measured with this instrument.*

In seeking to measure the curvature or position of any internal surface of the eye's optical system, observation has to be made through the optical parts of the eye lying anteriorly to the surface in question. Thus we see the *image* of the surface formed by this intervening portion of the optical system. The anterior surface of the lens, for example, is viewed through the

* Chapter IX.

corneal system. If its vertex appears to be at a distance l' from the cornea, that is if l' is the *apparent depth* of the anterior chamber, its true depth l is to be obtained from the conjugate foci expression.

$$\frac{n_2}{l} = \frac{1}{l'} + F_1 \qquad (10\cdot1)$$

in which n_2 is the refractive index of the aqueous humour and F_1 the power of the cornea. (If the light is considered as travelling from left to right and the measured value of l' entered positive in the equation, the true position is the image of the apparent position.)

Example. In a certain eye the measured apparent depth of anterior chamber is 3·15 mm. Calculate the true depth.

Answer. We must assume values for n_2 and F_1. It will be permissible to use the simplified schematic values of 4/3 and 42·73 D;

$$\text{then } \frac{4 \times 1000}{3 \times l} = \frac{1000}{3\cdot15} + 42\cdot73 = 360\cdot23 \text{ D}$$

$$\text{and } l = \frac{4000}{3 \times 360\cdot23} = 3\cdot70 \text{ mm.}$$

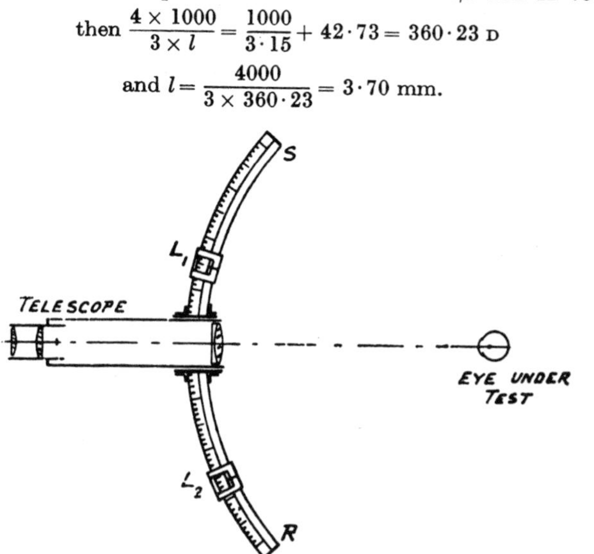

FIG. 10.4—THE OPHTHALMOPHAKOMETER (DIAGRAMMATIC).

Several experimental methods have been adopted to measure the internal ocular surfaces. We will first describe TSCHERNING'S procedure, which is interesting. He used his OPHTHALMOPHAKOMETER, which is diagrammatically represented in Fig. 10.4. The telescope is fixed on a stand and the arc SR is rotatable around the axis of the telescope in the same way as a perimeter arc. Cursors such as L_1,

L_2, etc., slide along the arc which is graduated in degrees, the zero coinciding with the telescope axis. The cursors carry electric lamps or a fixation device, as required. The eye under examination is placed at the centre of curvature of the arc, the subject's head being held in a suitable head-rest. Each lamp is mounted in a short tube at the front end of which is fixed a strong plano convex lens acting as a condenser to concentrate the light on the eye. In TSCHERNING'S model the radius of the arc was 86 cm. We have already referred to the use of this instrument in measuring the angle alpha.

MEASUREMENT OF THE CRYSTALLINE LENS; ANTERIOR SURFACE.

The same general procedure is to be adopted in measuring any internal surface; we will illustrate by considering the anterior surface of the lens. To obtain the position of its vertex A_2 (Fig. 10.5) and its radius of curvature $A_2C_2 = r_2$

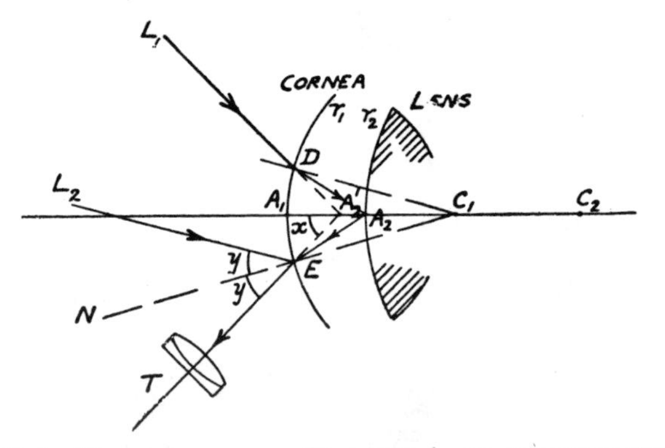

FIG. 10.5—MEASUREMENT OF POSITION A_2 OF ANTERIOR SURFACE OF CRYSTALLINE LENS (TSCHERNING).

we must in some way determine A_2 and the position of its centre C_2. We will neglect the posterior corneal surface and represent the cornea as a single surface at A_1, of radius $r_1 = A_1C_1$.

Position of A_2

With the arc of the instrument horizontal one lamp, a bright one, is moved to a position L_1 and the telescope T moved round until the Purkinje image III formed by the surface A_2 is on the crosswire. The light has followed the path L_1DA_2ET, the apparent position of A_2 being at A'_2; the image is seen in the direction TEA'_2. The cursor carrying the fixation mark is moved round to such a position that the eye's *optical* axis $A_1C_1C_2$ bisects the angle between L_1 and T. The angle alpha for the subject must have been measured previously; the fixation mark will be somewhere between L_1 and the optical axis (for a left eye and positive value of α). A second and feeble lamp L_2 is then moved round until the image of it formed by the corneal surface is in line with the above-mentioned crystalline image of L_1. The second lamp is feeble so that its corneal image will not prevent the fainter crystalline image from being seen.

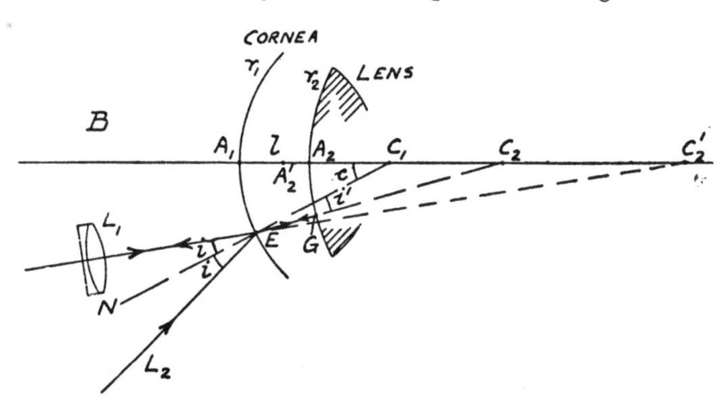

FIG. 10.6—MEASUREMENT OF RADIUS OF CURVATURE r_2 OF ANTERIOR SURFACE OF CRYSTALLINE LENS (TSCHERNING).

We now have sufficient data to calculate the apparent distance $A_1A'_2$. From the triangle A'_2C_1E

$$A'_2C_1 = r_1 \frac{\sin A'_2 \, EC_1}{\sin A_1 \, A'_2 \, E} = r_1 \frac{\sin y}{\sin x}$$

The angle y is half the angle between the telescope (the zero position) and second lamp and x half the angle between the telescope and first lamp; $2x$ and $2y$ are read off on the circular scale.

$$l' = A_1A'_2 = \text{apparent depth of anterior chamber}$$

$$= r_1\left(1 - \frac{\sin y}{\sin x}\right) \qquad (10 \cdot 2)$$

The real depth $l = A_1A_2$ is obtained from l' as explained above. The schematic value 42·73 D may be assumed for the power of the cornea, or preferably the corneal radius r_1 could have been measured with the ophthalmometer for the particular subject. In any case a schematic value would have to be assumed for the refractive index of the aqueous which we take to be 4/3.

Position of C_2.

For this measurement the apparatus is arranged as in Fig. 10.6. The bright lamp L′ is placed immediately above the telescope, the fixation mark being moved to one side until the optical axis occupies a position $A_1C_1C_2$. When the reflected image of L_1, formed by the crystalline lens surface, is seen in the telescope and set on the crosswire, the ray EG must be normal to the lens surface. The light from L_1 traverses the path L_1EGEL_1, emerging along EL_1 as if from C'_2, the apparent position of the centre of curvature C_2. The second lamp L_2 is positioned until its corneal image is in line with the lens image of L_1; from the diagram

$$C_1C_2 = (r_2 + l)\frac{\sin i'}{\sin c} = (r_2 + l)\frac{\sin i}{n_2 \sin c}$$

$$\text{also } C_1C_2 = A_1C_2 - A_1C_1 = l + r_2 - r_1$$

$$\text{hence } (r_2 + l) = r_1 \frac{n \sin c}{n \sin c - \sin i} \qquad (10 \cdot 3)$$

The angle i is half the angle between the telescope (zero) and the second lamp: angle c is equal to i added to the angle between the telescope and optical axis. Here again the subject's angle alpha (α) must be known. $2i$ and $(c - i + \alpha)$ are read off on the scale. For a left eye the fixation mark will be in the region marked B for positive value of α.

Having determined l ($= A_1A_2$) in the first experiment, we now know r_2.

Example. Using TSCHERNING's method on a certain eye to determine the depth of the anterior chamber, the anterior corneal radius was found to be 7·95 mm.; the angle between the telescope and bright lamp L_1 was 27·2° and between the telescope and second lamp L_2, 17°. Calculate the chamber depth from these readings.

Answer. We have $r_1 = 7 \cdot 95$; $x = 13 \cdot 6°$; $y = 8 \cdot 5°$; we will assume $n_2 = 4/3$. Let apparent depth of chamber be l' and the true depth, l. Then

$$l' = 7 \cdot 95\left(1 - \frac{\sin 8 \cdot 5}{\sin 13 \cdot 6}\right) = 7 \cdot 95 \times \cdot 3714 = 2 \cdot 953 \text{ mm.}$$

$$\text{Power of cornea} = F_1 = \frac{\frac{4}{3} - 1}{7 \cdot 95} \times 1000 = 41 \cdot 93 \text{ D.}$$

$$\text{From (10·1)} \qquad \frac{4 \times 1000}{3l} = \frac{1000}{2 \cdot 953} + 41 \cdot 93 = 380 \cdot 63 \text{ D.}$$

$$l = \frac{4000}{3 \times 380 \cdot 63} = 3 \cdot 50 \text{ mm.}$$

Example. In determining the position of the centre of curvature of the anterior lens surface in the above eye, the angle between the telescope and fixation mark is 9·3° and between the telescope and second lamp L_2, 13°. The angle α for this eye is 4·8°. Calculate the radius of the anterior lens surface.

Answer. We have $i = 6\cdot 5°$; $(c - i + \alpha) = 9\cdot 3°$ or $c = 11°$

$$\text{Hence } (r_2 + l) = 7\cdot 95 \frac{\frac{4}{3}\sin 11}{\frac{4}{3}\sin 11 - \sin 6\cdot 5}$$

$$= 7\cdot 95 \frac{\cdot 2544}{\cdot 2544 - \cdot 1132} = 14\cdot 33 \text{ mm.}$$

and $r_2 = 14\cdot 33 - 3\cdot 50 = 10\cdot 83$ mm.

10.6. Measurement of Lens Anterior Surface : Other Methods.

If we know the radius of the corneal anterior surface we can measure the anterior lens radius directly by employing

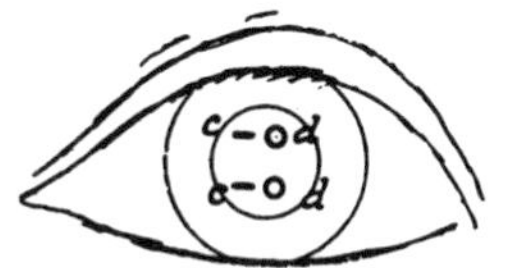

Fig. 10.7—Measurement of Radius of Curvature of anterior surface of Lens by comparing Purkinje Images I and III

the ophthalmometer principle and comparing the sizes of the images that the two surfaces form by reflection. We have to remember that whereas the one image is formed by the actual corneal surface, the other is formed by the apparent lens surface of apparent radius $A'_2\, C'_2$ (Figs. 10.5 and 10.6). The surfaces, or the reflected images they produce, are not quite at the same distance from the telescope, but the difference may be neglected, if the observing distance is not too small. In the experiment two objects are used, each consisting of two lamps placed in a vertical line. The separation of each pair of lamps is adjusted until the image of one pair, cc in Fig. 10.7, formed by the cornea is equal to the image dd of the other pair, formed by the apparent lens surface. When the adjustment has been made, we have

$$\frac{\text{Apparent radius of lens } (A'_2\, C'_2)}{\text{Radius of cornea}} = \frac{\text{size of object for cornea}}{\text{size of object for lens}}$$

Adding to the value of $A'_2C'_2$ so obtained the apparent depth of anterior chamber, $A_1A'_2 = l'$, we obtain the apparent position C'_2 of the centre of the lens surface. Its true position A_1C_2 may then be calculated from the conjugate foci expression; finally, subtracting the true anterior chamber depth, we obtain the true radius $r_2 = A_2C_2$.

In the above proportion, the assumption that the images produced by the corneal and apparent lens surfaces are at the same time distance from the observation station leads to the result for the apparent radius being too small by something less than 5 per cent for an observing distance of about 30 cm.

Position of Lens Surface using the Slit Lamp.

The FINCHAM combined slit lamp and corneal microscope may also be used for this purpose. It is arranged, as indicated in Fig. 10.8, that the direction of illumination I coincides with the subject's optical axis. The angle alpha has therefore to be determined previously; the subject looks along the direction NB which is his visual axis. The subject's head is held as steadily as possible in a rigidly constructed headrest. The examiner observes, through the microscope, along the direction indicated by O_1 and obtains an oblique view of the cornea and such portion of the anterior chamber depth A_1A_2 as is included within the field of the microscope. The instrument is constructed so that the microscope is directed constantly towards the focus of the illuminating system.

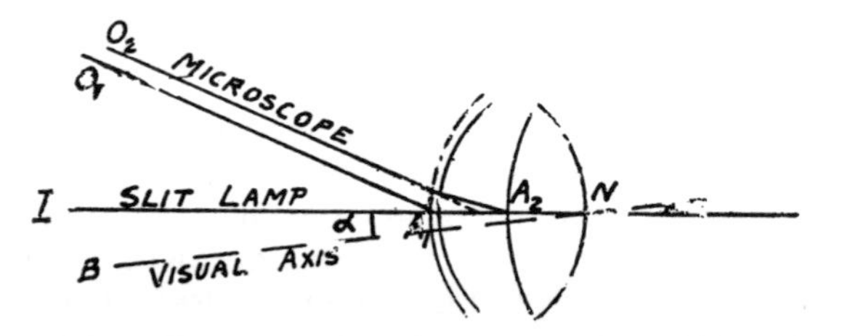

FIG. 10.8—MEASUREMENT OF APPARENT DEPTH OF THE ANTERIOR CHAMBER WITH SLIT LAMP AND CORNEAL MICROSCOPE.

The instrument (microscope and slit lamp together) is moved up towards the eye until the image of the corneal anterior surface appears coincident with the crosswire in the microscope eyepiece. A reading is taken on the focusing scale of the slit lamp; or this may have been set to zero at the start. The instrument is then racked forward along the direction IN until the image of the crystalline lens anterior surface is on the crosswire; and a second reading of the focusing scale is taken. The axis of the observation system (microscope) now lies along the direction O_2 parallel to its original direction. The difference between the two readings is equal to the apparent depth ($A_1A'_2$) of the anterior chamber.

In the above discussion and in the derivation of the expressions it has been assumed that the surfaces are spherical. If an observation of an internal surface is made through a portion of the cornea lying outside the optical zone where the curvature begins to decrease, the curvature at that portion should be determined beforehand.

The other internal surfaces, the corneal and lens posterior surfaces, may be investigated in the same way. In the

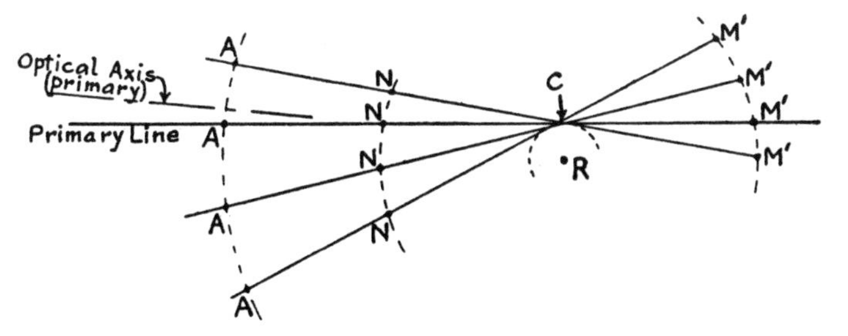

FIG. 10.9—ROTATION OF THE EYE. R = CENTRE OF ROTATION; C = CENTRE OF PROJECTION.

former case observations are made through the corneal anterior surface and in the second case through the system consisting of the complete cornea and anterior lens surface.

10.7. The Centres of Rotation and Projection.

Many attempts have been made to locate the point around which the eye executes its rotations. It is not to be expected that there is such a precise point, but such investigations as have been conducted seem to indicate that, for rotations not too pronounced, this centre (R) may be taken as approximately a fixed point situated about 15 mm. back from the anterior surface of the cornea and displaced about $1\frac{2}{3}$ mm. nasalwards from the primary line. In successive practical positions of the eye the visual axis occupies such positions as ANM′ in Fig. 10.9 and these positions intersect the primary line in points that cluster closely around a point C which we may take as lying $14\frac{2}{3}$ mm. back from the corneal anterior surface. It would appear appropriate to consider this point C as the centre through which the foveal image M′ is projected into space and we will consequently refer to it as the CENTRE OF PROJECTION of the eye. In Fig. 10·9 the dotted circles indicate the excursions of the points A (anterior surface of cornea), N and M′ as the eye rotates around R. In all positions the visual axis ANM′ is tangential to the small circle.

The principle of a student's laboratory method for finding the position of the centre of projection approximately is illustrated in Fig. 10.10. The subject with his head steady in a head-rest, looks along a line CAB drawn on a sheet of paper pinned to a drawing board which is supported horizontally in front of the eye being tested. C is

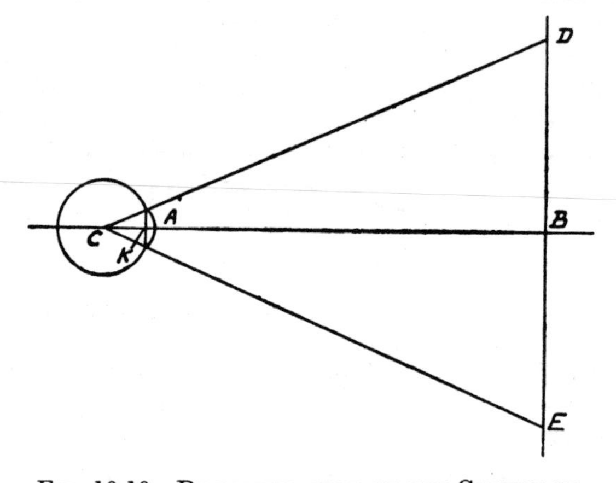

FIG. 10.10—DETERMINATION OF THE CENTRE OF PROJECTION—LABORATORY EXPERIMENT.

the centre of projection and A the vertex of the cornea. A line DBE is drawn on the paper perpendicular to CAB and some distance from the eye. A metre rule is placed (on edge) along the line DBE. The subject turns his eye until the edge of his cornea is seen to lie in line with two pins that are stuck into the paper along the line AB. The division D on the metre rule fixed by the eye is recorded. The subject then turns his eye until the opposite edge of the cornea comes into line with the two pins; the scale division E fixed by the eye in this second position is also recorded.

The difference between the two records gives the distance DE = a, say. The diameter, $2y$, of the cornea is measured with the aid of a small transparent scale. The distance AB = d, is measured by placing the zero of a metre rule against the closed eye lid. Let h be the sag AK of the cornea and x the distance CK. Then from the diagram we have

$$x = \frac{2y\,(d + h)}{(a - 2y)}$$

and the distance of the centre of projection back from the cornea is

$$AC = x + h$$

If we assume an average value of 8 mm. for the corneal radius r, h can be calculated from the relation

$$h = r - \sqrt{r^2 - y^2}$$

10.8. Entrance and Exit Pupils. Depth of Focus.

The actual aperture stop of the eye is the circular opening in the iris which we call the pupil of the eye, which appears black for reasons already given* and which varies in size reflexly due to various causes.† An examiner looking into a subject's eyes sees the image of this pupil formed by the cornea; this image is the ENTRANCE PUPIL of the eye and limits the diameter of pencils of light entering the eye from points of an object. Its position l' relative to the cornea is obtained from (10.1) and its radius p in terms of the actual pupil radius from the usual magnification formula (remembering that for light from left to right the entrance pupil is the object and the actual pupil the image)

$$\frac{p}{\text{pupil radius}} = \frac{L'}{L} = \frac{n_2 l'}{nl} \qquad (10\cdot4)$$

The actual pupil is practically coincident with the anterior surface of the crystalline lens. Taking our schematic values of 3·6 mm. for the pupil position, $n_2 = 4/3$, and 42·73 D for the power of the cornea, the position of the entrance pupil is given by l' in

$$\frac{1}{l'} = \frac{n_2}{l} - F_1 = \frac{4 \times 1000}{3 \times 3\cdot6} - 42\cdot73 \text{ D or } l' = 3\cdot05 \text{ mm.}$$

$$p = (\text{pupil radius}) \times \frac{4}{3} \times \frac{3\cdot05}{3\cdot60} = 1\cdot13 \text{ (pupil radius)}$$

Thus to an external observer the pupil appears nearer and about 13 per cent larger than it actually is.

The EXIT PUPIL is the image of the actual pupil formed by that part of the eye's optical system, namely the crystalline lens, that follows it. Calculation, using our schematic eye values, will show that the exit pupil lies 3·61 mm. from the cornea and is 3·6 per cent larger than the actual pupil. The width of pencils proceeding through the vitreous on their way to the final image are limited by the diameter of the exit pupil.

The entrance and exit pupils vary not only in size, but also slightly in position, when the eye accommodates but

* §7.1. † §2.2.

they are in any case so close to the actual pupil and so little different from it in size, that we shall make little error in assuming them to coincide with the actual pupil. Moreover, the pupil is near to the eye's principal points, especially in the accommodated state when the pupil has moved forward with the anterior surface of the lens and the principal points have moved backward (Table §10.4); so that we may still further simplify matters, at any rate for approximate calculations, by assuming the pupils all to coincide at the mean principal point position.

DEPTH OF FOCUS OF THE EYE.

When the eye is focused upon some point M distant c metres (Fig. 10.11), the image B′ of a nearer object B is

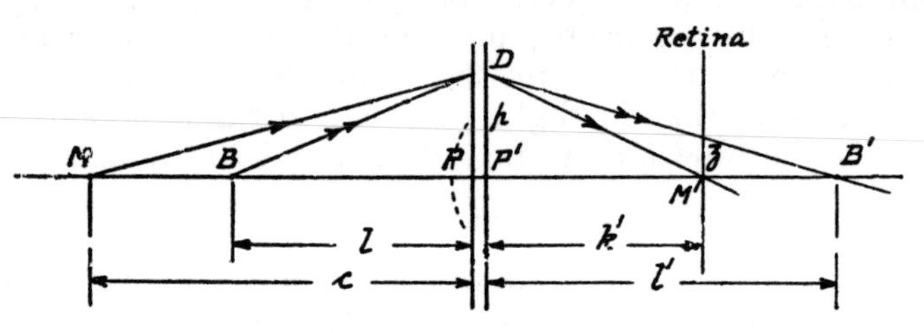

FIG. 10.11—DEPTH OF FOCUS IN THE EYE.

behind the retina and corresponding to B a blur circle of radius z is formed on the retina. If this blur circle is sufficiently small, it will be interpreted by the brain as a point and an object lying in the plane through B will be seen as sharply as one occupying the plane through M. Thus objects will be seen clearly over a region extending from B to a point approximately equidistant from M but on the other side of it. This region is called the DEPTH OF FOCUS of the eye in the object space, or the DEPTH OF FIELD.

With the assumptions we have just made concerning the coincidence of the pupils with the mean principal points position, a simple expression for this depth of focus region is easily obtained. We have first to decide, however, on the value of z. We have seen* that under the best conditions the central bright disc of the image of a point overlaps several cones when the image is in sharp focus on the

* §2.7.

retina, although the central cone is stimulated very much more intensely than its neighbours. Taking into account the aberrations of the eye the conditions are worse.* Thus the individual "sees" a point when several cones are stimulated. The intensity will probably fall, from the centre outwards, less rapidly in an out of focus blur circle, however, and so we will limit the size of the blur circle to one cone; that is the radius $z = 0 \cdot 0015$ mm.

From Fig. 10.11 we have

$$z = \frac{(l' - k')\,p}{l'} = p\left(1 - \frac{L'}{K'}\right) = p\left(1 - \frac{L + F_e}{C + F_e}\right) = p\,\frac{(C - L)}{K'}$$

In an emmetropic eye the vergence K' within the eye is equal to the power of the eye F_e. The quantity $(C - L)$ is the difference between the dioptral distances of the points M and B; and one half of the total depth of focus is given by

$$(C - L) = \frac{z}{p} F_e \text{ dioptres.} \qquad (10 \cdot 5)$$

$$= \frac{0 \cdot 0015}{p} F_e = \frac{0 \cdot 09}{p} \text{ dioptres} \qquad (10 \cdot 5a)$$

in the standard eye, p being expressed in millimetres.

Taking the pupil diameter as 3 mm., when the eye is accommodated for the average reading distance of one third metre,

$$\text{Depth of focus} = \frac{2 \times 0 \cdot 09}{1 \cdot 5} = 0 \cdot 12 \text{ D}.$$

Thus the eye sees clearly within the region extending between two points distant respectively $3 \cdot 06$ D and $2 \cdot 94$ D, or $32 \cdot 68$ cm. and $34 \cdot 01$ cm., from the eye; that is, the depth of focus is $1 \cdot 33$ cm. at the reading distance.

When the point M on which the eye fixes is at infinity, we have $C = 0$. Assuming the pupil diameter is 4 mm. in this case

$$L = \frac{0 \cdot 09}{2} = 0 \cdot 045 \text{ D}$$

or the eye sees distinctly from infinity up to a point distant about 22 metres.

It is to be noted that these figures have been obtained from geometrical considerations and can be regarded only as approximations.

10.9. The Illumination of the Retinal Image.

The illumination of the retinal image is of considerable importance. The distinctness with which the object is

* §2.7.

seen, or indeed whether it is seen at all, depends upon this illumination and upon the state of adaptation of the eye. In §18.8 it is shown that the illumination of the retinal image is given by

$$E' = n'^2 B \omega' \text{ lumens per unit area} \qquad (18\cdot 8)$$

B is the brightness of the object in the direction of observation, which is its brightness in any direction if it be a perfectly diffusing surface as we suppose it to be in §18.8 ; ω' is the solid angle subtended at the retina by the aperture of the eye's optical system ; and n' is the refractive index of the eye's interior.

It follows from the above expression that the retinal illumination, and hence the apparent brightness of the object, is independent of the object distance ; and, from §§18.6 to 18.8, that it is independent of the inclination of the object to the direction of observation when the object is a perfect diffuser.

Equation (18.8) can be extended, if desired. If p is the radius of the pupil of the eye, its area $a = \pi p^2$

then

$$E' = n'^2 B \omega'$$

$$= n'^2 B \frac{\pi p^2}{k'^2}$$

$$= \pi p^2 BK'^2 \qquad (10\cdot 6)$$

or

$$E' = \pi p^2 BF_e^2 \text{ in emmetropia} \qquad (10\cdot 6a)$$

E' in lumens per unit area when B is expressed in candles per unit area. It is to be remembered that these expressions neglect any losses of light that occur, by reflection and absorption, when traversing the eye media.

10.10. The Reduced Eye.

Examination of Table §10.4 or Fig. 10.3 (b) will show that the pair of principal points, and the pair of nodal points, in our schematic eye are very close together ; they are separated by only 0·30 mm. It is therefore but a short step to simplify the eye still further by considering each pair to coalesce into a single intermediate point ; in which case the eye reduces to a single spherical surface, separating air from water, with its vertex at the imtermediate principal point P and its centre of curvature at the intermediate nodal point N, Fig. 10.3 (c). In calculations concerning the eye we have then only one surface to consider. Such an eye is referred to as the REDUCED EYE and was first proposed by LISTING.

It is desirable that the anterior and posterior focal points of the reduced eye shall coincide with those of the schematic eye. This fixes the power, and hence radius of curvature, and position of the single surface at once. For, if f_e and f'_e are the focal lengths of the reduced eye, we have

$$-f_e + f'_e = FF' = 38\cdot 89 \text{ mm. in the schematic eye}$$

$$\text{also } \frac{f'_e}{f_e} = -\frac{4}{3}$$

$$\text{hence } f_e = -\frac{3}{7} \times 38\cdot 89 = -16\cdot 67 \text{ mm. and } F_e = \frac{1000}{16\cdot 67} = 60\cdot 0 \text{ D}$$

$$f'_e = \frac{4}{3} \times 16\cdot 67 = +22\cdot 22 \text{ mm.}$$

$$\text{radius of curvature} = PN = r = f'_e + f_e = 22\cdot 22 - 16\cdot 67 = 5\cdot 55 \text{ mm.}$$

The position of the reduced surface P in relation to the anterior surface A of the cornea of the schematic eye is equal to $16\cdot 67 - 14\cdot 99 = +1\cdot 68$ mm. (say $1\frac{2}{3}$ mm.).

The basic features of the reduced eye then are : *the single surface has dioptric power* 60 D ; *it separates air from water of refractive index* 4/3 ; *and it is situated* $1\frac{2}{3}$ *mm.* (100/60) *back from the schematic eye cornea.*

This is the eye we have been using for calculation purposes throughout the preceding chapters. We have already seen that the principal points are moved only very slightly during accommodation and that the pupils are very close to these points. We are therefore justified in assuming, for ordinary purposes, that the pupil coincides with the reduced surface at P and that this point remains fixed during accommodation. The surface becomes steeper, of course, and so there is a small shift forwards of the nodal point N, amounting to 0.7 mm. for $8\cdot 5$ dioptres of accommodation.

The APHAKIC EYE has already been considered (§3.13).

SIZE OF RETINAL IMAGE. UNAIDED EYE.

10.11. In Emmetropic and Ametropic Eyes.

We shall see that the sizes of the retinal images in the two eyes may be a matter of importance in binocular vision, the attainment of which may be impeded, or even prohibited, by too great a disparity between the two images. And in §§ 2.2, 2.3, 3.11 and 3.12, which the student should revise, we have seen how to calculate the size of the retinal image in the unaided and aided eye. This subject we will here pursue a little further though still limiting ourselves to paraxial image formation and using the conception of the reduced eye.

All symbols have the significance that has been explained heretofore. F_e represents the power of the eye generally and F_o ($= 60$ D) the power in the standard emmetropic eye and axially ametropic eyes. F_e is less than F_o in refractive hyperopia and greater in refractive myopia.

To see clearly an object at the dioptral distance L an eye with ametropia K has to accommodate by an amount given by

$$A' = K - L \qquad \text{(see §3.6)}$$

The myope can do this only if his far point lies beyond the object. If the object happens to coincide with his far point, then

$$K = L \text{ and } A' = 0$$

In all cases, without exception, the size h' of the sharp or blurred retinal image of an object, distant or near, subtending an angle w is given by

$$h' = -\frac{w}{n'} \times \text{(length of eye, PM')} \qquad (2\cdot 6)$$

$$= -\frac{w}{n'}\, k' = -\frac{w}{K'} \qquad (10\cdot 7)$$

In general, $K' = K + F_e$; in emmetropia and axial ametropia F_e assumes the special value F_o; in emmetropia $K = 0$; in refractive ametropia $K' = F_o$ since these eyes have the same axial length as the standard Em. eye,

$$\text{hence} \quad h' = -\frac{w}{F_o} \text{ in Em. and refractive Am.} \qquad (10\cdot 8)$$

$$h' = -\frac{w}{K + F_o} \text{ in axial Am.} \qquad (10\cdot 8\text{a})$$

If the object is distant the myope cannot sharpen the image; the hyperope can do so by accommodating an amount K to increase the power F_e to the value K', which makes the eye virtually emmetropic.

Example. Find the sizes of the retinal images of an object 6 feet high at a distance of 300 yards in the following eyes: (*a*) emmetropic; (*b*) hyperopic 5 D; (*c*) myopic 5 D.

Answer. The object subtends an angle

$$w = -\frac{h}{l} = -\frac{6}{-900} = \frac{1}{150} \text{ radian.}$$

In all cases $h' = -\dfrac{w}{K'}$ (10.7)

(*a*) In Emmetropia $K' = F_o = 60$ D and

$$h' = -\frac{1}{150} \cdot \frac{1000}{60} \text{ mm.} = -\frac{1}{9} \text{ mm.} = -0 \cdot 111 \text{ mm.}$$

the minus sign signifying that the image is inverted.

This is also the size of the image in both the ametropic eyes if the ametropia be refractive. The image would be blurred in the myopic eye and sharp in the hyperopic eye if the accommodation is sufficient.

(*b*) In axial hyperopia of 5 D, $K' = K + F_o = 5 + 60 = 65$ D and

$$h' = -\frac{w}{K + F_o} = -\frac{1}{150} \cdot \frac{1000}{65} = -0 \cdot 1025 \text{ mm.}$$

(*c*) In axial myopia of 5 D, $K' = K + F_o = -5 + 60 = 55$ D, and

$$h' = -\frac{w}{K + F_o} = -\frac{1}{150} \cdot \frac{1000}{55} = -0 \cdot 121 \text{ mm.}$$

SIZE OF RETINAL IMAGE. AIDED EYE (Thin Lenses).

10.12. In Corrected Ametropia.

The distance correcting lens images a distant object at the far point of the relaxed ametropic eye; the image will then be seen distinctly. As explained in §3.12, the spectacle lens has the effect also of changing the angle at which the principal ray enters the eye at P from the value w_o subtended by the object to the value w; and so the size of the retinal image is changed since it depends upon these angles; see Fig. 3.9.

The SPECTACLE MAGNIFICATION is given by

$$\text{S.M.} = \frac{w}{w_o} = \frac{\text{SM}_R}{\text{PM}_R} = \frac{K}{F_1} \qquad (3 \cdot 4)$$

$$\text{since } F_1 = \frac{K}{1 + dK} \text{ or } K = \frac{F_1}{1 - dF_1} \qquad (3 \cdot 2)$$

$$\text{we have S.M.} = \frac{K}{F_1} = 1 + dK = \frac{1}{1 - dF_1} \qquad (10 \cdot 9)$$

giving the ratio between the sharp retinal image of a distant object in the corrected ametropic eye and the retinal image (blurred or sharp according to the accommodative state of the eye) of the same object in the same eye when uncorrected. The spectacle magnification depends only on the magnitude of the refractive error and the position of the correcting lens; whether the ametropia is axial or refractive does not affect it.

In myopia (K negative) the spectacle magnification is less than unity; in hyperopia (K positive) it is greater than unity ; in emmetropia ($K = 0$) it is unity—no correcting lens is required in this case. Spectacle magnification is unity also, even in an ametropic eye, when $d = 0$, that is when the correcting lens coincides with the reduced surface (or principal point) P. This condition is approximately realised in CONTACT GLASSES, which are fitted on to the sclera, nearly in contact with the cornea. In ordinary practice d is a small quantity and spectacle magnification varies very little from unity in ordinary refractive conditions ; but it is to be remembered that the image obtained in the uncorrected eye will have been blurred in myopia and the sharpening of the image produced by the correcting lens will in itself result in an apparent minification. To a newly corrected myope familiar small objects appear smaller than before, shillings being mistaken for sixpences, etc., largely on this account.

Expressions for the RELATIVE SPECTACLE MAGNIFICATION (R.S.M.) may be derived with the help of Fig. 3.9 B or C. Here we have to find the ratio which the size (h'_c) of the retinal image of a distant object formed in a corrected ametropic eye bears to that (h') formed in the standard emmetropic eye. Let h'_1, be the size of the image $M_RQ'_1$, formed in the eye's far point plane by the correcting lens of power F_1 and focal length f'_1, placed at S ; then

$$h'_1 = -w_o \cdot f'_1 = -\frac{w_o}{F_1}$$

This image subtends at the eye the angle

$$w = M_R\widehat{P}Q'_1 = -\frac{h'_1}{k} = \frac{w_o K}{F_1} = \frac{w_o}{1-dF_1}$$

$$h'_c = -\frac{w}{K'} \qquad \text{from (10·7)}$$

$$= -\frac{w_o}{1-dF_1} \cdot \frac{1}{K+F_e}$$

The size (h') of the retinal image in the standard emmetropic eye is given by

$$h' = -\frac{w_o}{F_o} \qquad \text{from (10·8)}$$

In *axial* ametropia $F_e = F_o$ and substituting $F_1/(1-d\,F_1)$ for K we obtain $h'_c = -\dfrac{w_o}{F_1 + F_o - d\,F_1 F_o}$

and relative spect. magnification

$$= \frac{h'_c}{h'} = \frac{F_o}{F_1 + F_o - d\,F_1 F_o} = \frac{1}{1-(f_o + d)\,F_1}$$

$$= \frac{1}{1 + a\,F_1} \qquad (10·10)$$

The quantity $a = -(f_o + d)$ is the distance of the spectacle lens from the anterior focal point of the eye. When $d = -f_o$ the spectacle lens is *at* this anterior focus and the relative magnification is unity. The denominator $(F_1 + F_o - dF_1F_o)$ of equation (10.10), which will be recognised as the equivalent power of the system of the lens and eye, then becomes equal to F_o, a result well known in geometrical optics. The lens is never more than a few millimetres removed from the eye's focal point, so that the relative magnification departs appreciably from unity only in very high refractive errors; e.g. in high myopia or in aphakia.*

In *refractive* ametropia, $K' = K + F_e = F_o$

so that $h'_c = -\dfrac{w_o}{(1 - dF_1)F_o}$

and relative spect. magnification $= \dfrac{1}{1 - dF_1}$ (10·10a)

which is equal to the spectacle magnification (10.9) as would be expected since the retinal image in the uncorrected eye is the same size as the emmetropic image (equation 10.8).

The student is reminded again that in the above discussion the spectacle lens has been assumed thin, its vertices and principal points all coinciding at the spectacle point and its back vertex power F'_v being the same quantity as its equivalent power, which we have designated by F_1.

It will be observed, too, that the spectacle magnification concerns the change that occurs in the size of the retinal image *of a given eye*, when it is corrected for distance; whereas the *relative* spectacle magnification has to do with the *comparison* between the image formed in the corrected ametropic eye and the emmetropic eye. The relative spectacle magnification is consequently the important quantity when we have to compare the retinal images in the two eyes of a subject, as in considering the binocular vision of an anisometrope. For the ratio between the relative spectacle magnifications of the two eyes is the ratio between their retinal images.

The above discussion is summarised in Fig. 10.12, which shows graphically the manner in which the retinal image varies in size for different positions of the correcting lens, both in axial and in refractive ametropia. Pz represents the size of the retinal image in emmetropia. The diagram

---

* §3.13.

shows clearly that, whether the ametropia be axial or refractive

as correcting lens is fitted farther from eye } retinal image < increases in H. / decreases in M.

In *axial* ametropia

Retinal image starts < smaller than Em. size in H / larger than Em. size in M > { becomes Em. size with lens at F_e

In *refractive* ametropia

Retinal image starts at Em. size and becomes < larger in H. / smaller in M.

In an eye the hyperopia of which gives a retinal image of size Pa, or of this size if the hyperopia were corrected

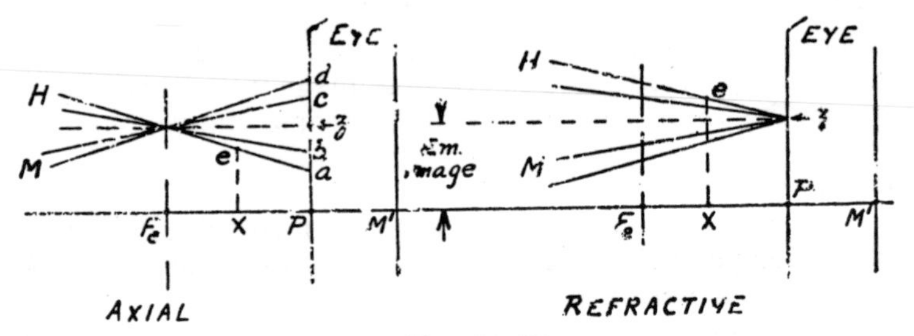

FIG. 10·12

by a lens placed at P (e.g. contact glass), the retinal image when the correction is fitted at X is given by the ordinate Xe. Hence

	Axial	*Refractive*
Spectacle magnification	Xe/Pa	Xe/Pz
Relative spectacle magnification	Xe/Pz	Xe/Pz

Example. An anisometrope has axial myopia in one eye and axial hyperopia in the other, the error being corrected by a − 2 D Sph. and a + 3 D Sph. respectively, worn 14 mm. from the eye's principal point. Compare the retinal images of a distant object formed in the two corrected eyes.

Answer. We may find the relative spect. magnification from (10·10) for each eye, and compare the results.

For the myopic eye:

$$\text{rel. spect. mag.} = \frac{60}{-2 + 60 + \dfrac{14 \times 2 \times 60}{1000}} = \frac{60 \times 1000}{59680} = 1{\cdot}006$$

For the hyperopic eye : $=\dfrac{60}{3+60-\dfrac{14\times 3\times 60}{1000}}=\dfrac{60\times 1000}{60480}=0\cdot 9922$

Comparison between the two eyes $=\dfrac{1\cdot 006}{0\cdot 9922}=1\cdot 0137$

or one image exceeds the other by 1·37 per cent. (Compare with table in next paragraph).

We will work out the myopic case without interpolating in the derived formula, to illustrate again the principle involved—compare also §3·11.

Image in Em. eye $=-\dfrac{w}{F_o}=-16\tfrac{2}{3}.\ w$ mm.

Myopic eye : since corr. lens is 14 mm. from P, the ocular refraction is $-\dfrac{1000}{514}=-1\cdot 946$ D

hence $K'=-1\cdot 946+60=58\cdot 054$ D and $k'=\dfrac{n'}{K'}=22\cdot 97$ mm.

Image formed by correcting lens $=500\,w$ mm.

This subtends at P the angle $w\times\dfrac{500}{514}$

$\therefore$ image in eye $=\tfrac{3}{4}\times w\times\dfrac{500}{514}\times 22\cdot 97=-16\cdot 76\,w$ mm.

and relative spect. magni. $=\dfrac{16\cdot 76}{16\tfrac{2}{3}}=1\cdot 006$, as above.

10.13. Retinal Disparity in Corrected Anisometropia (*Thin Lenses*).

The disturbing effect of the different sizes of the two retinal images in corrected anisometropia is discussed in Chapter XVI.

We will use suffixes L and R for the left and right eyes respectively.

When the ametropia is axial :

After distance correction, the relative spectacle magnifications in the two eyes are respectively :

$$\frac{1}{1+a_L F_L} \text{ and } \frac{1}{1+a_R F_R} \qquad \text{from } (10\cdot 10)$$

where $a=-(f_o+d)=$ distance *from* eye's anterior focus *to* correcting lens.

The ratio between the two images is therefore given by

$$\frac{\text{Right}}{\text{Left}}=\frac{1+a_L F_L}{1+a_R F_R}$$

$$=(1+a_L F_L)(1-a_R F_R)=1+a_L F_L-a_R F_R$$

very approximately, since a is a small quantity.

The disparity $(a_L F_L - a_R F_R)$ could be reduced to some extent by making a for the stronger lens smaller than a

for the weaker lens ; that is, by fitting the stronger lens at a position closer to the eye's anterior focus than the weaker lens ; or when the thickness is taken into account, by arranging for the second principal point of the stronger lens to lie nearer to the eye's anterior focus. Both lenses, or the second principal points of both lenses, must be on the same side of the eye's anterior focus (Fig. 10.12).

Assuming, as will ordinarily be the case, that the lenses are fitted at equal distances from the eyes ($a_L = a_R = a$), the ratio is

$$\frac{\text{Right}}{\text{Left}} = 1 + a\,(F_L - F_R)$$
$$= 1 + \frac{8\,(F_L - F_R)}{3000}$$

when the lenses are placed 14 mm. from the reduced surface of the standard 60 D eye, of focal length $16\frac{2}{3}$ mm. The percentage differences between the sizes of the retinal images in a few selected degrees of anisometropia, are given in the table opposite.

When the ametropia is refractive :

On the assumption that the reduced surface, or principal point, of the refractively ametropic eye occupies the same position as the reduced surface of the emmetropic eye, so that the eyes have the same equivalent globe length (PM′),* then after the distance correction the relative spectacle magnifications in the two eyes are respectively

$$\frac{1}{1 - d_L F_L} \quad \text{and} \quad \frac{1}{1 - d_R F_R} \qquad \text{from } (10\cdot 10a)$$

The ratio between the two images is therefore given by

$$\frac{\text{Right}}{\text{Left}} = \frac{1 - d\;F_L}{1 - d_R\,F_R}$$

which ratio approaches unity as the products $d_L F_L$ and $d_R F_R$ approach equality. Thus the disparity is reduced by fitting the weaker lens (or its second principal point) farther away from the eye than the stronger lens (or its second principal point).

If the lenses are fitted at equal distances, d, from the eyes, then the ratio becomes

$$\frac{\text{Right}}{\text{Left}} = \frac{1 - d\,F}{1 - d\,F}$$

---

* Which is not the case in an aphakic eye previously emmetropic ; its length, which is measured from the *cornea*, exceeds the emmetropic length.

Except for large values of F_L and F_R this fraction cannot be expanded as in the axial case, the quantity d being hardly small enough. The Table contains a few approximate values for the percentage difference of image size, when the two lenses are fitted equidistant from the eyes.

Retinal Disparity in Corrected Anisometropia.
Distant Object.

Anisometropic Difference Dioptres.	Percentage difference in sizes of retinal images, for $d = 14$ mm., when the ametropia is		
	Axial	Refractive	
		+ corrections	− corrections
2	0·55%	3·0%	2·6%
5	1·4	7·5	6·2
10	2·75	15·5	13
20	5·5	35	27

10.14. The Magnifying Glass or Loupe. Monocular.

Optical instruments may be divided into image-forming and non-image forming instruments; examples of the latter are photometers, colorimeters, refractometers, etc. The image-forming instruments may be sub-divided into visual and non-visual instruments; examples of the latter are projection systems such as the cinematograph and photographic lenses. VISUAL INSTRUMENTS are used directly to aid the eye; the eye is an integral part of the complete system and the final image is formed on its retina; visual instruments include spectacle lenses, magnifiers of various kinds, the microscope, telescope and periscope; and in many cases they may be binocular.

The main function of most of these visual instruments (but not spectacle lenses) is to magnify objects so that their details, which cannot be resolved by the unaided eye, may be seen distinctly. They produce an image which subtends at the eye an angle w which is larger than the angle w_o subtended by the object itself; and, in consequence, the final retinal image is enlarged.

We shall confine ourselves to magnifiers, that is to single lens systems like the simple magnifying glass or loupe. Even these may comprise two or three components, but these are cemented together or are in close contact and not separated like the objective and eyepiece of a compound microscope or telescope. In order that they shall produce good images, sufficiently free from such aberrations as chromatism, curvative and distortion, they have to be carefully computed (except in the cheaper varieties). Here we are not concerned with the quality of the image, however, but only with its size and position, which we shall investigate by simple paraxial methods and assuming the lens to be thin.

Fig. 10.13 depicts an eye, which may be ametropic, viewing an object of size h at BQ through a lens of power F placed at L. The object is at a distance l from the lens and the latter is distant d (always positive) from the reduced

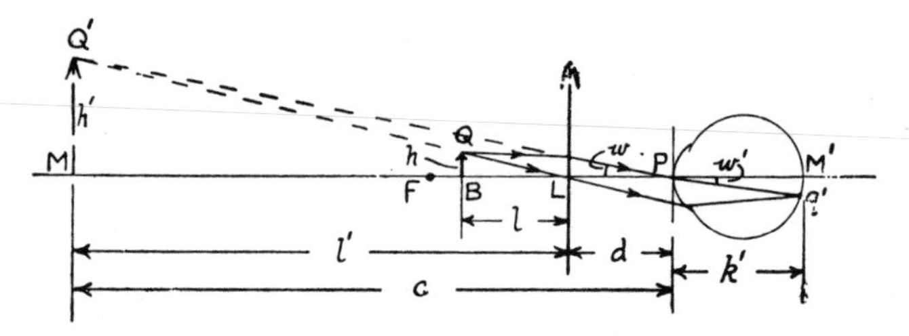

FIG. 10.13. MAGNIFYING GLASS OR LOUPE.

eye surface at P. In contrast with telescopes which are used to observe distant objects, magnifiers are used for near objects; in some industrial applications of magnifiers the position of the object or of the lens in relation to the object and the distance of the eye from the lens are not completely under the control of the observer; in many cases, however, they are under his control, at least within limits. The degree of magnification that will be obtained depends upon the inter-relationship of these distances and the power of the lens.

The object, lens and eye are to be so positioned that the image MQ′ $= h'$ formed by the lens is seen clearly and comfortably by the eye; that is, the image is to be formed at the point M upon which the eye is accommodating. Let this point, which we may call the accommodation point, be c metres from P. Were the eye completely relaxed, which is very seldom the case when observing an object known to be near, the point M would coincide with the eye's far point M_B. As it is, the static refraction of the eye, K dioptres, has been changed by the accommodation brought into play, which we will call A', into the dynamic refraction $C = \frac{1}{c}$ existing at the moment. The dioptric power of the eye has increased from its static value F_e to the accommodated value $(F_e + A')$ and the point M is conjugate to the fovea M′. Thus the static condition

$$K' = K + F_e$$

has become $$K' = C + (F_e + A')$$

and $$A' = K - C \qquad \text{(see §10·11)}$$

From the well-known conjugate foci relationship we have

$$\frac{h'}{h} = \frac{l'}{l} = \frac{L}{L'} = \frac{L' - F}{L'} = 1 - (d + c)\,F.$$

The angle subtended at P by the image h' is

$$w = -\frac{h'}{c} = -\frac{h\left\{1 - (d + c)\,F\right\}}{c}$$

$$= -h\left\{C - F\,(1 + dC)\right\} \qquad (10·11)$$

For the magnifier to fulfil its function of enlarging the retinal image this angle must exceed the angle subtended by the object when observed by the unaided eye. The magnification (apparent or angular magnification or magnifying power) provided by a visual instrument is defined as

$$M = \frac{\text{Angular subtense of image produced by instrument}}{\text{Angular subtense of object seen with unaided eye}}$$

For telescopes, the object being distant and not under control, this definition is quite adequate as it stands. For magnifiers and microscopes the denominator depends upon where the object is supposed to be placed when observed unaided; it cannot be approached nearer than the near point, which is much closer for young people and myopes than for older people and hyperopes. For defining angular magnification a standard distance $q = -25$ cm. or -10 inches is adopted and called " the (conventional) least distance of distinct vision ".

Placed at this distance the object subtends at P the angle

$$w_o = -h/q$$

and $\therefore$ $$M = \frac{w}{w_o} = \frac{-h\left\{C - F\,(1 + d\,C)\right\}}{-(h/q)}$$

$$= q\left\{C - F\,(1 + d\,C)\right\} \qquad (10·12)$$

The distance c on which the eye accommodates when using the magnifier will scarcely ever be infinity as is commonly supposed but, at least in young people and older people provided with presbyopic assistance, will be at about the normal reading distance. It may even be closer to the eye than this, especially in females.

The "working distance" l of the object from the lens is, of course, dependent upon the other distances and may be calculated from

$$l = \frac{q}{M}(1 + d\,C) \qquad (10 \cdot 13)$$

Values of angular magnification and working distance for various values of F, c and d are given in the table on p. 373.

The general expression (10.12) assumes simpler forms for special cases. Thus: when $c = q$ we obtain $M = 1 - (d + q)\,F$; and when an emmetrope or corrected ametrope is relaxed, $c = \infty$ and $M = -qF = \frac{1}{4}F$; this is the expression usually stated for loupe magnification.

It is of interest to note that when a magnifying glass is held at a distance from the eye equal to its focal length (f'), the magnification remains at a constant value for all eyes and all conditions of accommodation; for we have under these conditions

$$\begin{aligned} M &= q\left\{C - F\left(1 + \frac{C}{F}\right)\right\} \\ &= -q\,F \\ &= \tfrac{1}{4}\,F \end{aligned}$$

The above discussion gives the magnification obtained from purely geometrical considerations. The mental appreciation of the amount of magnification obtained depends, however, upon the distance to which the retinal image is mentally projected.* For example: in the case of an unaccommodated emmetrope using a magnifying glass, the object will be placed at the anterior focal point of the glass, to be seen distinctly. After refraction by the lens the pencil from Q is a parallel one entering the eye at a certain inclination, w, to the axis. Wherever the eye is placed behind the lens, the retinal image remains unchanged in size. If, however, an object is observed through the lens with the eye at first close to the lens, and the eye is then withdrawn, the observed image appears to increase in size. This occurs because the brain, supposing the observed image to be at a fixed distance behind the lens, expects it

---

* §2.5.

LOUPE MAGNIFICATION.

Based on the conventional least distance of distinct vision of 25 cm.

	$c = -25$ cm. $C = -4$ D					$c = -50$ cm. $C = -2$ D					$c = -100$ cm. $C = -1$ D					$c = \infty$	
$d =$	0	5	10	20	30	0	5	10	20	30	0	5	10	20	30		
F 10 D	3·5	3·0	2·5	1·5		3·0	2·75	2·5	2·0	1·5	2·75	2·62	2·5	2·25	2·0	2·5	M
	−7·14	−6·7	−6·0	−3·3		−8·3	−8·2	−8·0	−7·5	−6·7	−9·1	−9·0	−9·0	−8·9	−8·75	−10·0	l
15 D	4·75	4·0	3·25	1·75		4·25	3·87	3·5	2·75	2·0	4·0	3·81	3·62	3·25	2·87	3·75	M
	−5·26	−5·0	−4·6	−2·9		5·9	−5·8	−5·7	−5·5	−5·0	−6·25	−6·2	−6·2	−6·1	−6·1	−6·67	l
20 D	6·0	5·0	4·0	2·0		5·5	5·0	4·5	3·5	2·5	5·25	5·0	4·75	4·25	3·75	5·0	M
	−4·16	−4·0	−3·75	−2·5		−4·55	−4·5	−4·4	−4·3	−4·0	−4·8	−4·75	−4·7	−4·7	−4·7	−5·0	l
40 D	11·0	9·0	7·0	3·0		10·5	9·5	8·5	6·5	4·5	10·25	9·75	9·25	8·25	7·25	10·0	M
	−2·27	−2·22	−2·1	−1·6		−2·4	−2·4	−2·3	−2·3	−2·2	−2·44	−2·4	−2·4	−2·4	−2·4	−2·5	l

c = Distance on which the eye accommodates when using the magnifier.
d = Distance between back surface of magnifier and the eye.
F = Focal power of magnifier.
l = Working distance.
M = Magnification (Loupe).

to decrease in size in the same proportion as does the lens itself, due to the increased distance from the receding eye. The fact that the retinal image of the object remains unchanged produces the illusion that the observed image becomes larger. This was noted by Robert SMITH in his *Compleat System of Optics*, London, 1738.

Example. A hyperope of 2 D observes an object through a magnifying glass of 20 D, held 10 cm. from his eye. Find the magnification obtained and the distance of the object from the lens when (*a*) he accommodates 6 D; (*b*) he remains relaxed.

What would a myope of 10 D do with this glass?

Answer. $q = -25$ cm. $= -\frac{1}{4}$ m.; $d = 10$ cm.; $F = 20$ D

(*a*) $C = K - A' = -4$ D

$$M = q\left\{C - F - d\,CF\right\}$$

$$= -\frac{1}{4}\left(-4 - 20 + \frac{10 \times 4 \times 20}{100}\right) = 4 \qquad \text{(compare table)}$$

$$l = \frac{q}{M}(1 + d\,C)$$

$$= -\frac{25}{4}\left(1 - \frac{10 \times 4}{100}\right)$$

$$= -\,3{\cdot}75 \text{ cm.}$$

(*b*) $C = K = +2$ D

$$M = -\frac{1}{4}\left\{2 - 20 - \frac{10 \times 2 \times 20}{100}\right) = 5{\cdot}5$$

$$l = -\frac{25}{5{\cdot}5}\left(1 + \frac{10 \times 2}{100}\right) = -5\frac{5}{11} \text{ cm.}$$

In this second case the image formed by the lens is behind the eye.

It may be instructive to work out the first case from first principles: image is 25 cm. from eye, i.e. at $l' = -15$ cm. from lens.

$$L = L' - F = -\left(\tfrac{100}{15}\right) - 20 = -26\tfrac{2}{3} \text{ D}$$

$$l = \frac{1}{L} = -3{\cdot}75 \text{ cm.}$$

$$\frac{h'}{h} = \frac{L}{L'} = \frac{l'}{l}$$

$$h' = \frac{h \times 15}{3{\cdot}75} = 4\,h$$

This image is 25 cm. from eye and subtends an angle $w = \frac{4h}{25}$; the object h seen by the unaided eye at $q = -25$ cm. subtends angle $w_0 = \frac{h}{25}$; so $M = \frac{w}{w_0} = 4$.

With regard to the myope, his far point coincides with the lens, 10 cm. from the eye. To see distinctly in the relaxed condition the object must be placed at the lens; the image is in the same position and the lens provides no assistance. The object cannot be placed in any convenient position to form an image on which the myope can reasonably accommodate. The lens must be brought nearer to the eye. If approached to a position 2 cm. from the eye the magnification proves to be 6·5 if the eye is relaxed and 7·1 if the eye accommodate 4 dioptres.

10.15. The Magnifying Glass or Loupe. Binocular.

In many cases—industrial operations, medical and ophthalmic examinations, scientific investigations—where magnification is needed, it is desirable if not essential that both eyes be used. If the object under observation possesses depth which is to prevail in the magnified view, binocular vision is essential; and even with flat objects it is often less tiring and more satisfactory to observe them binocularly.

In unaided binocular vision there is "balance" in a normal person between the amounts of accommodation

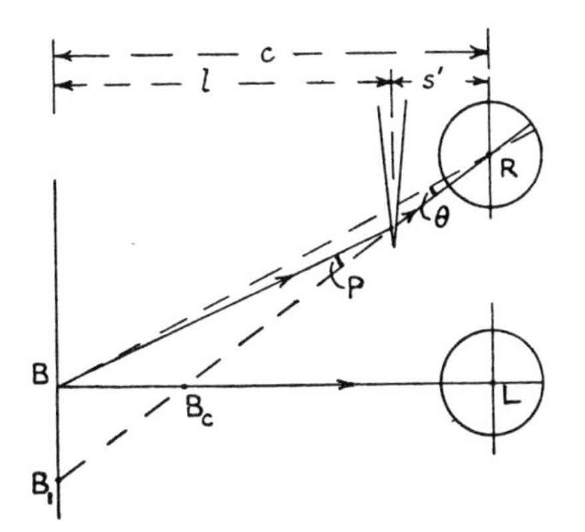

FIG. 10.14—IMBALANCE θ INTRODUCED BY RELATIVE PRISM.

and convergence that have to be exerted in order to see a given object clearly and singly. An imbalance, i.e. a disparity between accommodation and convergence, causing difficulty in maintaining single as well as clear vision, arises in heterophoria and may also occur in normal people when they are older because of the undue accommodative effort they have to exert, which induces overconvergence.

Any condition which introduces relative prism effect before the eyes will upset the normal balance. When observing an object B (Fig. 10.14) in unaided vision the visual axes of a normal person whose eyes are at R and L take up the positions RB and LB and the eyes accommodate for the distance c, without undue effort. If optical elements are introduced which place, in effect, a prism before one eye or the other (or both), accommodation is needed for the object at B but the convergence needed is for an object at B_c. It is as if the observer were looking at two objects in the object plane; B with the left eye and B_1 with the right eye.

The convergence that is needed in excess of the normal amount is angle θ. If $L = \frac{1}{l}$ is the dioptral distance of the object from the plane containing the optical element(s) and P is the deviation produced by the prism, then

$$\theta = \frac{BB_1}{-l + s'} = \frac{-l.P}{-l + s'} = \frac{P}{1 - s'L}$$

This angle is the same, within limits, wherever B may be placed in the object plane; problems are often simplified by putting the object on the primary line of one eye, as in the diagram.

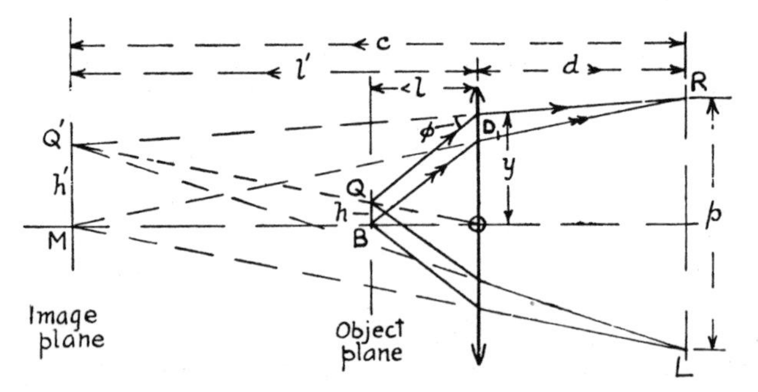

Fig. 10.15—Magnifying Glass—Binocular Vision.

If an object is to be observed binocularly under magnification, we may use a single lens of sufficient aperture centred at O, as in Fig. 10.15, in which case the object point B is imaged as a single point at M and the normal balance between accommodation and convergence is preserved. If, alternatively, we use two separate lens elements, one before each eye, they must have a common optical centre at O, i.e. they must be portions of one lens centred at O, if the condition of balance is to be maintained. Or, if their optical centres do not coincide, the relative prism effect thereby introduced must not exceed the allowable tolerances. These tolerances vary considerably between individuals*; for continuous observation of near objects, or images, they may be taken roughly as

relative convergence: young pecple 6△; over 45 years, 8△ both eyes.

relative divergence: 4△, both eyes.

Points and distances have the same symbols in Fig. 10.15 as in Fig. 10.13 and the eyes, with projection centres at R and L, are accommodated as before for the distance c. The inter-ocular distance $RL = p$. The chief ray of the pencil of light entering the right eye from a point Q follows the path QD_1R; Q is imaged at Q′; the lens must have a semi-aperture not less than $OD_1 = y$ if the field of view is to include Q. The angular magnification M is derived as in the previous section; y, easily obtained from the geometry of the diagram, is given by

$$y = \tfrac{1}{2}p\left(1 + \frac{d}{c}\right) - hM\frac{d}{q} \qquad (10\cdot 14)$$

when $c = \infty$ this becomes

$$y = \tfrac{1}{2}p - hM\frac{d}{q} \qquad (10\cdot 14a)$$

The deviation of the chief ray at D_1 is equal to

$$\phi = \angle D_1QO - \angle D_1Q'O = y(L - L') = yF \qquad (10\cdot 15)$$

F being the power of the magnifying glass.

In order to provide sharp and comfortable binocular vision, not only must the above conditions be fulfilled, but the lens surfaces must be computed so that distortion is reduced and the right and left image fields occupy such positions and have such curvatures that the accom-conv. relationship between the eyes shall not be unduly disturbed. To provide really good results one surface must be aspherical or a corrector plate of the Schmidt type must be incorporated.†

The following table gives values of F in dioptres, c, d, l and y in cm. and ϕ in centrads for stated values of M defined on the basis of $q = -25$ cm. It is assumed that $p = 6$ cm. and the semi-object size $BQ = 1$ cm.

---

* §5.4.

† C. E. Coulman and G. R. Petrie, *Nature*, 164, 586 (1949). R. E. Hopkins, *Journ. Opt. Soc. Am.* 36 (10), Oct. 1946; "Aspheric Corrector Plates for Magnifiers."

LOUPE MAGNIFICATION. BINOCULAR.

Based on the conventional least distance of distinct vision of 25 cm.

M		$c = -25$ cm. $C = -4$ D					$c = -50$. $C = -2$ D					$c = -100$. $C = -1$ D					$c = \infty$ $C = 0$				
	$d =$	0	5	10	20	30	0	5	10	20	30	0	5	10	20	30	0	5	10	20	30
1·5	F	2	2·5	3·3	10		4	4·4	5	6·7	10	5	5·3	5·5	6·2	7·1	6				
	l	−16·7	−13·3	−10	−3·3		−16·7	−15	−13·3	−10	−6·7	−16·7	−15·8	−15	−13·3	−11·7	−16·7				
	y	3	2·7	2·4	1·8		3	3	3	3	3	3	3·1	3·3	3·6	3·9	3	3·3	3·6	4·2	4·8
	ϕ	6	6·75	8	18		12	13·3	15	20	30	15	16·6	18	22·5	28	18	20	21·6	25	29
2	F	4	5	6·7	20		6	6·7	7·5	10	15	7	7·4	7·8	8·7	10	8				
	l	−12·5	−10	−7·5	−2·5		−12·5	−11·2	−10	−7·5	−5	−12·5	−11·9	−11·2	−10	−8·75	−12·5				
	y	3	2·8	2·6	2·2		3	3·1	3·2	3·4	3·6	3	3·25	3·5	4	4·5	3	3·4	3·8	4·6	5·4
	ϕ	12	14	17·3	44		18	21	24	34		21	24	27	35	45	24	27	30	37	43
2·5	F	6	7·5	10	30		8	8·9	10	13·3	20	9	9·5	10	11·2	12·9	10				
	l	−10	−8	−6	−2		−10	−9	−8	−6	−4	−10	−9·5	−9	−8	−7	−10				
	y	3	2·9	2·8	2·6		3	3·2	3·4	3·8	4·2	3	3·3	3·7	4·4	5·1	3	3·5	4	5	6
	ϕ	18	22	28			24	28	34			27	32	37			30	35	40		
3	F	8	10	13·3	40		10	11·1	12·5	16·7	25	11	11·6	12·2	13·7	15·7	12				
	l	−8·3	−6·7	−5	−1·67		−8·3	−7·5	−6·7	−5	−3·3	−8·3	−7·9	−7·5	−6·7	−5·8	−8·3				
	y	3	3	3	3		3	3·3	3·6	4·2	4·8	3	3·5	3·9	4·8	5·7	3	3·6	4·2	5·4	
	ϕ	24	30	40			30	37	45			33	40	48			36	43			
6	F	20	25	33·3			22	25·5	27·5	36·7	55	23	24·2	25·5	28·7	32·9	24				
	l	−4·2	−3·3	−2·5			−4·2	−3·75	−3·3	−2·5	−1·67	−4·2	−4	−3·75	−3·3	−2·9	−4·2				
	y	3	3·6	4·2			3	3·9	4·8			3	4				3	4·2			
	ϕ																				

VISION THROUGH ASTIGMATIC LENSES.

10.16. Distortion and Scissors Movement.

When an object situated laterally with respect to the eye's primary direction is observed through a spherical lens, the apparent position of the object and the amount of rotation required of the eye in order to maintain foveal vision of it depend upon the power of the lens and upon its

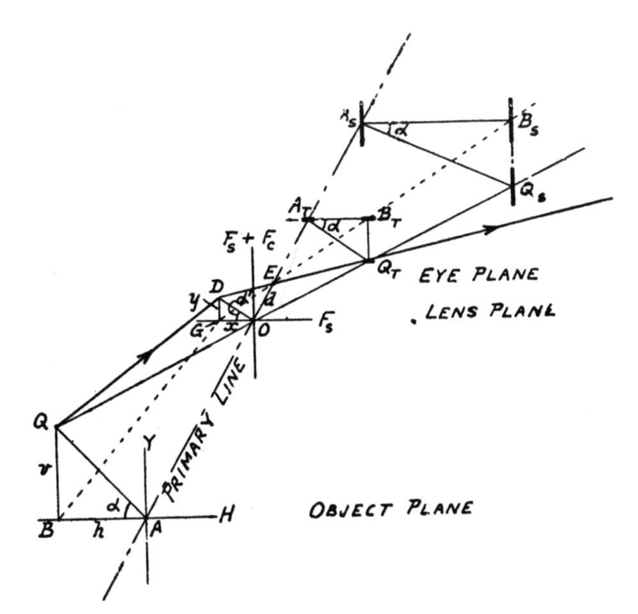

FIG. 10·16—VISION BY AN EYE AT E THROUGH AN ASTIGMATIC LENS AT O.

position in relation to the eye.* It is of interest to enquire into this effect in the case when the spherical lens is replaced by an astigmatic lens and particularly when the object viewed is a line lying along some meridian in the object plane perpendicular to the eye's primary direction, which is considered as the axis of the system. This problem has several important applications; e.g. (*a*) the scissors movement of the crosslines when neutralising a sphero-cyl. or toric lens; (*b*) the appearances of the reflex in retinoscopy of an astigmatic eye, etc.

* §§ 12.23 and 16.5.

Referring to Fig. 10.16 consider the observation of an object point Q by an eye at E* through a centred astigmatic lens at O. We will first assume the principal meridians of the lens to be horizontal and vertical and both the spherical power F_S and the cylindrical power F_C to be positive; the cylinder axis will be taken horizontal. The co-ordinates of Q in the object plane QBA are h and v. To be in agreement with the convention that inward vergence—convergence—of the eyes is positive, h will be considered positive inwards; v is positive upwards. In the figure, h is positive if we imagine E to be a left eye. After refraction by the lens, light from Q travels as an astigmatic pencil along the general direction QOQ_TQ_S. Neglecting aberrations, a horizontal focal line will be formed at Q_T in the plane $A_TB_TQ_T$ and a vertical focal line at Q_S in the plane $A_SB_SQ_S$. The distances OA_T and OA_S along the axis depend upon the powers F_S and F_C and the object distance OA $= l$ metres, measured from O.

Of all the rays from Q refracted by the lens and passing through the two focal lines, one (QDE) proceeds so as to cut the axis at the point E where the eye (more particularly its principal point, P) is situated; this ray having passed through the lens at the visual point D where it was deviated both horizontally and vertically. The co-ordinates x, y of the point D evidently depend upon the position of the eye, as well as upon the position of Q and the powers of the lens. Let the eye be d metres behind the lens plane, d being always positive.

Consider the deviation in the horizontal, by projecting the ray QDE on to the horizontal plane; this projection is BGE. The angles between BG and the primary line and between GE and the primary line are respectively

$$\frac{h - x}{-l} \text{ and } \frac{x}{d} \text{ which may be written}$$

$$-L(h - x) \text{ and } Dx \qquad L \text{ and } D \text{ in dioptres.}$$

The horizontal prismatic effect of the lens at D $= F_S$.x.

$$\text{Hence } Dx + L(h - x) = F_s x$$

$$\text{or } x = \frac{-hL}{D - L - F}$$

The eye would have to rotate, in the horizontal plane, through an angle

$$H_E = xD$$

to receive the ray on the fovea.

* We will consider the centre of rotation and the principal point of the eye to coincide at E.

Similarly, by projecting on to the vertical plane and considering the deviation in the vertical, we obtain

$$y = \frac{-v.L}{D - L - (F_s + F_c)} \text{ and } V_E = y\,D$$

V_E being the extent of the rotation required of the eye in the vertical plane so as to receive the ray on the fovea.

For object points lying along the line AQ the visual points on the lens will lie along the line OD. To the eye at E the line AQ at inclination α will thus appear to lie along the direction OD at inclination α'. We obtain

$$\tan \alpha' = \frac{y}{x} = \frac{v}{h} \cdot \frac{D - L - F_s}{D - L - (F_s + F_c)} = \frac{p}{p - F_c} \tan \alpha = q \tan \alpha$$

where $p = D - L - F_s$, and q is put $= \dfrac{p}{p - F_c}$ (10·16)

For real objects the quantity $(D - L)$ is always positive and may vary from infinity, when either the distance d or l is zero, to a minimum value when $d = -l$, i.e., when the lens is midway between the object and the eye. The quotient q may have a wide range of positive and negative values according to the values of L, D, F_S and F_C; and so the fixed object line AQ may apparently rotate around the point A from the positive quadrant in which it exists into the negative quadrant HAY as astigmatic lenses with certain principal powers are moved along the primary line AE. As a corollary; as a strong +/+ sphero-cyl. combination is withdrawn from the crossline chart towards the eye, the individual lines of the cross as seen through the lens will approach one another until they are parallel, cross over and again become parallel, and finally return to their true mutually perpendicular directions when the lens is close to the eye.

When the lens is held close to the object plane, the astigmatic image planes $A_T B_T Q_T$ and $A_S B_S Q_S$ are virtual and beyond the object plane. As the lens is approached towards the eye these planes, in the case of a positive lens combination, move to infinity and then approach the eye from behind. If the two positive powers of the lens are sufficiently strong, the image planes then cross over the eye plane and give rise to the interesting appearances just mentioned.

Such marked effects do not arise with negative sphero-cyls. since the virtual image planes are always on the object side of the lens, remote from the eye. This will be gathered also from equation 10.16, for if F_S and $(F_S + F^C)$

are negative, the quotient q is always positive; consequently α' has the same sign as α and the apparent direction OD of the object line AQ does not leave the quadrant in which AQ exists.

The expression 10.16 may be derived in an alternative manner; by finding the sizes of the retinal images of the horizontal and vertical sides of a rectangular object as seen through an astigmatic lens with principal meridians horizontal and vertical the horizontal and vertical sides of the rectangle being h and v respectively. The image of, say, the vertical side formed by the vertical meridian power of the lens ($F_V = F_s + F_C$) is $v\ L/(F_V + L)$; this subtends at the eye an angle $v\ L/\{1 - d\ (F_V + L)\} = v\ LD/(D - L - F_s - F_c)$. Obtaining the corresponding expression for the horizontal side, equation 10.16 is obtained by division.

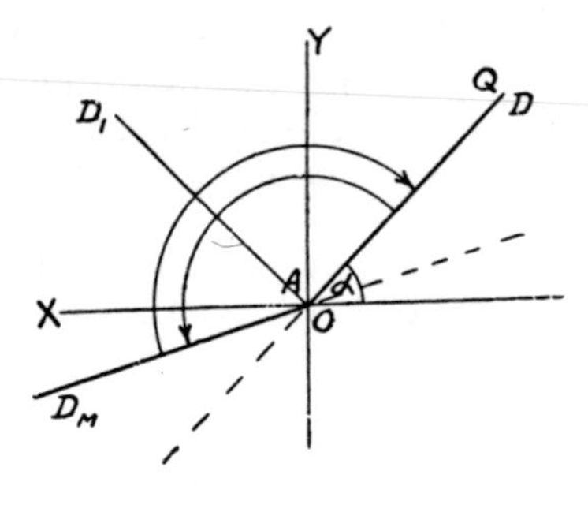

FIG. 10·17—APPEARANCES OF AN OBJECT LINE INCLINED AT 45° AS SEEN THROUGH LENS + 10·00 S./+ 5·00 C. AX. H.

Before considering certain special cases and practical applications, we will work through a few simple examples.

Example. A line inclined at 45° is observed through the lens + 10·00 S/+ 5·00 C. ax. H., the distance separating the object line and eye being fixed at 50 cm. Calculate the apparent slopes of the object line as the lens is approached from the object towards the eye. Find also the horizontal and vertical rotations required of the eye, when the lens is in the mid-position, in order to obtain foveal vision of a point of the line distant $\sqrt{2}$ cm. from the axial point.

Answer. We have $F_s = +\ 10$ D; $F_c = +\ 5$ D; $\alpha = 45°$; $-l + d = 50$ cm.

(i) $l = 0$; $L = \infty$; $\dfrac{p}{p - F_c} = 1$; $\alpha' = \alpha = 45°$

When the lens is in contact with the object, the line appears at OD (Fig. 10·17) coincident with its true position AQ.

(ii) $l = -5$ cm.; $L = -20$ D; $d = 45$ cm.; $D = 2{\cdot}22$ D; $D - L = 22{\cdot}22$ D

$$\frac{p}{p - F_c} = \frac{12{\cdot}22}{7{\cdot}22} = 1{\cdot}692 = \tan\alpha';\quad \alpha' = 59°\ 25'$$

(iii) $l = -7\cdot5$ cm. ; $L = -13\cdot33$ D ; $d = 42\cdot5$ cm. ; $D = 2\cdot353$ D ; $D - L = 15\cdot687$ D

$$\frac{p}{p - F_c} = \frac{5\cdot687}{0\cdot687} = 8\cdot282 = \tan\alpha' ; \quad \alpha' = 83^\circ\ 11'$$

the apparent line OD is approaching the 90° position OY.

(iv) $l = -10$ cm. ; $L = -10$ D ; $d = 40$ cm. ; $D = 2\cdot5$ D ; $D - L = 12\cdot5$ D

$$\frac{p}{p - F_c} = \frac{2\cdot5}{-2\cdot5} = -1 = \tan\alpha' ; \quad \alpha' = 135^\circ\ (-45^\circ)$$

the line now appears along OD_1 perpendicular to its true position

(v) $l = -12\cdot5$ cm. ; $L = -8$ D ; $d = 37\cdot5$ cm. ; $D = 2\cdot667$ D ; $D - L = 10\cdot667$ D

$$\frac{p}{p - F_c} = \frac{0\cdot667}{-4\cdot333} = -0\cdot1539 = \tan\alpha' ; \quad \alpha' = 171^\circ\ 15'\ (-8^\circ\ 45')$$

the line has approached closely to the horizontal position OX, having rotated through nearly 135°.

(vi) $l = -25$ cm. ; $L = -4$ D ; $d = 25$ cm. ; $D = 4$ D ; $D - L = 8$D.

$$\frac{p}{p - F_c} = \frac{-2}{-7} = 0\cdot2857 = \tan\alpha' ; \alpha' = 15^\circ\ 57'$$

This is the mid-position of the lens. To find the approximate eye rotations to view a point the co-ordinates of which are h = 1 cm. and v = 1 cm., we have

$$x = \frac{-hL}{D - L - F_s} = \frac{4}{-2} = -2 \text{ cm.} ; \quad H_E = xD = -2 \times 4 = -8\Delta$$

Similarly

$$y = \frac{-vL}{D - L - (F_s + F_c)} = \frac{4}{-7} \text{ cm.} ; \quad V_E = yD = -\tfrac{4}{7} \times 4 = -1\tfrac{1}{7}\Delta$$

The eye has to rotate outwards by 8△ and downwards by $1\frac{1}{7}$△.

Seen through the lens, the line has now passed through the horizontal position and occupies its position of maximum rotation OD_M ; its prolongation OD′ lies in the original quadrant. The total apparent rotation has been 150° 57′. If the withdrawal of the lens continues from this mid-position, the previous positions will be repeated in the reverse order, the line rotating back until, when the lens is in contact with the eye, it appears again in its true position though very indistinct ; thus :

(vii) $l = -50$ cm. ; $L = -2$ D ; $d = 0$; $D = \infty$;

$$\frac{p}{p - F_c} = 1 ; \qquad \alpha' = \alpha = 45^\circ$$

The lens has passed through certain special positions.

(*a*) When either l or d is zero and $(D - L)$ consequently infinite, we obtain $\alpha' = \alpha$, or the object line appears in its true direction. Thus when examining a crossline through an astigmatic lens there is no scissors movement on rotating the lens when it is held either in contact with the crossline or *in contact* with the eye. It follows that objects do not appear distorted to an astigmatic eye; except possibly to a slight extent in extremely high degrees of astigmatism, in consequence of the fact that the seat of the astigmatism, probably the cornea mainly, is removed a few millimetres from the pupil.*

(*b*) When $p = 0$, we have from equation (10.16) $\alpha' = 0$, or the object line appears horizontal; i.e. along the direction of the cylinder axis, whatever may be the actual inclination of the object line.

The condition $p = 0$ gives $D - L = F_s$, which is true when the object plane and eye are conjugate with respect to the spherical power of the lens; that is, when the lens is in such a position between A and E (Fig. 10.16) that the astigmatic image plane $A_S B_S Q_S$ coincides with the eye plane. In the above example, we have

$$p = D - L - F_s \text{ or } D - L = +10\text{ D}$$

Since $-\frac{1}{L} + \frac{1}{D} = \frac{1}{2}$ metre, calculation gives $l = -13 \cdot 82$ cm. as this special position.

(*c*) When $p = F_C$, we find $\tan \alpha' = \infty$ or $\alpha' = 90°$, the object line appearing vertical, i.e. perpendicular to the direction of the cylinder axis, whatever may be the actual inclination of the object line.

This condition gives $D - L = F_S + F_C$, which is true when the object plane and eye are conjugate with respect to the power $(F_S + F_C)$ in the other principal meridian of the lens; that is, when the lens occupies such a position between A and E that the plane $A_T B_T Q_T$ coincides with the eye plane. In the above example:

$p = D - L - F_S = F_C$ or $D - L = F_S + F_C = +15$ D, from which we obtain in the same way as before, $l = -7 \cdot 925$ cm.

(*d*) When $q = -1$, we obtain $\alpha' = -\alpha$, the object line appearing perpendicular to its true direction.

In this condition we have

$$p = \tfrac{1}{2} F_C \text{ or } D - L = F_S + \tfrac{1}{2} F_C = +12 \cdot 5\text{ D}$$

which is case (IV) of the above example.

(*e*) When $F_C = 0$. $\alpha' = \alpha$, as would be expected from the fact that the lens is now merely a spherical lens.

---

* See §13.21.

(*f*) When $F_s = o$, equation (10.16) becomes

$$\tan \alpha' = \frac{D - L}{D - L - F_c} \tan \alpha$$

and the apparent movements of the object line depend upon the relationship between $(D - L)$ and F_C.

The student should confirm the above appearances by means of the + 10 S and + 5 Cyl. from the trial case, placed in contact, observing first a single line and then two lines at right angles.

10.17. Application to Retinoscopy.

Suppose the lens at O (Fig. 10.16) to be the optical system of the astigmatic subject's eye and the object plane the subject's retina. If the light from a circular source is reflected by the examiner at E into the subject's eye along the axis EOA, a small elliptical blur will be formed on the retina at A. Suppose the mirror is tilted so as to drive the light along a direction inclined at angle α to the horizontal. We may look upon this direction of travel of the virtual source formed by the mirror as a line of light at inclination α. From the special case (*a*) in the preceding paragraph, there being just the one optical system *at* the subject's eye, the image of this on the subject's retina will be a line AQ also inclined at angle α to the horizontal. The line consists of blurred elliptical patches.

With regard to the light returning along the direction AE to the examiner, he is in effect observing an object line AQ through an astigmatic lens (the optical system of the subject's eye) situated at a distance d from his own eye. The reflex will appear to move along the direction OD as the retinal patch is driven along AQ. In general OD will not be parallel to AQ nor will it coincide with either of the principal meridians of the subject's eye,* since $\tan \alpha'$ is not generally equal to $\tan \alpha$, nor equal to 0 or ∞.

But when reversal has been obtained in one meridian, the retina (object plane) is conjugate to the working point E with respect to that meridian ($p = 0$ or F_C), in which circumstances the reflex will move along that meridian whatever may be the direction (AQ) along which the light is driven. The speed of the movement will, however, be infinite. If then the examiner were to shift his position until he is conjugate to the retina with respect to the other

---

* §8.7 *et seq.*

principal meridian of the subject's eye (p= F_C or 0), the reflex will move along this second meridian although the light is still being driven as originally. Thus the direction of reflex movement swings through 90° as the examiner moves from the reversal point for one meridian to the reversal point for the other.

Example. The (ocular) refraction of an eye with compound myopic astigmatism is 2 D of myopia in the horizontal meridian and 5 D in the vertical. In carrying out a retinoscopy on this eye the light is driven along the 60° meridian. Along which meridian will the reflex travel ? The working distance is one metre.

Answer. Assuming an eye of standard axial length—the ametropia being refractive—we have $L= -60$ D, $D= 1$ D, $F_s= 62$ D, $F_C= 3$ D.

$$\tan \alpha' = \frac{D-L-F_s}{D-L-(F_s+F_C)} \cdot \tan 60$$

$$= \frac{61-62}{61-65}\sqrt{3} = 0 \cdot 433 \text{ or } \alpha' = 23° \, 24'$$

The *edge* of the reflex will appear to move along a direction more nearly approaching the horizontal or vertical, however (§8·8).

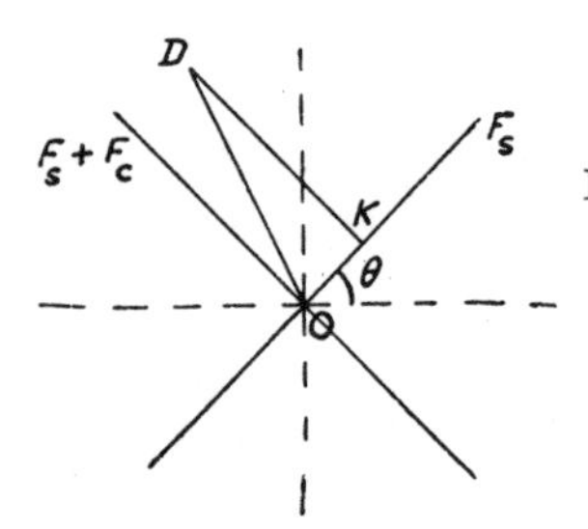

FIG. 10·18—VISION OF A LINE THROUGH AN ASTIGMATIC LENS WITH PRINCIPAL MERIDIANS AT AN ARBITRARY ORIENTATION, θ.

10.18. More General Expression.

In the discussion of §10·16 the principal meridians of the lens were respectively horizontal and vertical. It may be of interest to some readers to obtain a more general expression in which the principal meridians of the lens occupy any arbitrary position.

Let the cylinder axis of the lens be inclined at an angle θ to the horizontal, as indicated in Fig. 10·18. The lens is still centred on the primary line. With respect to the eye of an individual (subject) at E (Fig. 10·16), the direction of the cylinder axis is now θ degrees in standard notation (as shown in Fig. 10·18), and the co-ordinates (x.y.) of the visual point D are positive for a left eye. Through this lens the eye at E observes a line AQ inclined at angle α to the horizontal as before. The ray from Q passing through E after refraction is deviated both horizontally and vertically at the point D. As in the previous case, we equate the horizontal prismatic effect of the lens at D to the difference between the horizontal projections of the rays QD and DE.

Let H and V be the horizontal and vertical prismatic effects at the point D.

DK = perpendicular on cyl. axis OK

$= y \cos \theta + x \sin \theta$

$H = F_s x + F_c (y \cos \theta + x \sin \theta) \sin \theta$ base right

Angles made by the horizontal projections of the ray with the primary line are

$$\frac{h - x}{-l} \quad \text{and} \quad \frac{x}{d} \quad \text{as before}$$

hence $Dx + L(h - x) = F_s x + F_c \sin \theta (y \cos \theta + x \sin \theta)$

Similarly for the vertical:

$V = F_s y + F_c \cos\theta (y \cos\theta + x \sin\theta)$ base down

and the projections of the ray on the vertical plane make with the primary line the angles:

$$\frac{v - y}{-l} \quad \text{and} \quad \frac{y}{d}$$

hence $Dy + L(v - y) = F_s y + F_c \cos\theta (y \cos\theta + x \sin \theta)$

Rearranging the terms:

$$\left.\begin{aligned} x(D - L - F_s - F_c \sin^2\theta) &= y F_c \sin\theta \cos\theta - hL \\ y(D - L - F_s - F_c \cos^2\theta) &= x F_c \sin\theta \cos\theta - vL \end{aligned}\right\} \quad (10\cdot17)$$

Putting $p = D - L - F_s$

$$\tan \alpha = \frac{v}{h} = \frac{x F_c \sin \theta \cos \theta - y (p - F_c \cos^2 \theta)}{y F_c \sin \theta \cos \theta - x (p - F_c \sin^2 \theta)}$$

$$= \frac{F_c \sin \theta \cos \theta - \tan \alpha' (p - F_c \cos^2 \theta)}{\tan \alpha' F_c \sin \theta \cos \theta - (p - F_c \sin^2\theta)}$$

$$\text{and } \tan \alpha' = \frac{F_c \sin \theta \cos \theta + (p - F_c \sin^2 \theta) \tan \alpha}{(p - F_c \cos^2\theta) + F_c \sin \theta \cos \theta \tan \alpha} \quad (10\cdot18)$$

By evaluating x in the equations, we obtain for the horizontal rotation of the eye to maintain foveal vision of the point Q (h.v.)

$$H_E = x D = \frac{DL}{p(p - F_c)} \left\{ F_c (h \cos^2 \theta - v \sin \theta \cos \theta) - hp \right\} \quad (10\cdot19)$$

and similarly

$$V_E = y D = \frac{DL}{p(p - F_c)} \left\{ F_c (v \sin^2 \theta - h \sin \theta \cos \theta) - vp \right\} \quad (10\cdot20)$$

Certain special cases can be deduced:

(1) When the object line is horizontal; here $\tan \alpha = 0$ and $v = 0$ Equation (10.18) becomes

$$\tan \alpha' = \frac{F_c \sin \theta \cos \theta}{p - F_c \cos^2 \theta} = \frac{\sin \theta \cos \theta}{\frac{p}{F_c} - \cos^2 \theta} \quad (10\cdot18a)$$

from (10·19) $$H_E = \frac{h D L}{p(p - F_c)} (F_c \cos^2 \theta - p) \quad (10\cdot19a)$$

from (10·20) $$V_E = \frac{h D L}{p(p - F_c)} \cdot F_c \sin \theta \cos \theta \quad (10\cdot20a)$$

(2) Object line at angle α, but $\theta = 0$, the meridians of the lens being horizontal and vertical; this is the special case of §10·16
Equation (10·18) becomes

$$\tan \alpha' = \frac{p}{p - F_c} \tan \alpha \qquad \text{as before} \qquad (10\cdot16)$$

$$H_E = -\frac{h D L}{p} \qquad \text{and } V_E = -\frac{v D L}{(p - F_c)}$$

(3) If $F_c = 0$, the lens reduces to a sphere of power F,
$\tan \alpha' = \tan \alpha$

$$H = -\frac{h D L}{p} \qquad V_E = -\frac{v D L}{p}$$

the value of H_E agreeing with the corresponding angle θ of equation (12·5) when D is replaced by the dioptral distance S at which the distance correcting lens is worn and $c = 0$ since the lens is not decentred.

The expression (10·18a) might have been obtained in an alternative manner. If the lens and object plane of §10·16 are rotated through an angle α to bring the object line AQ into the horizontal and the cylinder axis to inclination α (standard notation), then the inclination of the line OD to the horizontal, i.e. the apparent slope of the horizontal line AQ, is given by $(\alpha' - \alpha)$; and we obtain from equation (10·16)

$$\tan(\alpha' - \alpha) = \frac{\tan \alpha' - \tan \alpha}{1 + \tan \alpha \tan \alpha'}$$

$$= \frac{\left(\frac{p}{p - F_c} - 1\right) \tan \alpha}{1 + \frac{p}{p - F_c} \cdot \tan^2 \alpha}$$

$$= \frac{F_c \tan \alpha}{p - F_c + p \tan^2 \alpha}$$

$$= \frac{F_c \sin \alpha \cos \alpha}{p - F_c \cos^2 \alpha} \qquad (10\cdot18a)$$

which is the expression (10·18a), α here being the angle θ in that expression.

RETINAL IMAGE. AIDED EYE (Thick Lenses)

10.19. Size of Retinal Image with Thick Lenses—*Distant Object.*

When dealing with the effect of the distance correcting lens on the size of the retinal image in §§ 3.12, 10.12, 10.13, the spectacle lens was assumed to be thin and, for a given eye, the retinal image depended only on the position of the lens with respect to the eye. Actually, however, it depends also on the form and thickness of the lens, since these quantities determine the positions of the principal points of the lens and hence its *equivalent* power and focal length, which govern the image size.

If, for example, a person with spectacle refraction + 10 D changes his correcting lens from the equiconvex form to the ordinary meniscus form with back surface power − 6 D, both lenses having the same back vertex power + 10 D, the same thickness of 5 mm. and being placed with their back surfaces in the same position, then the retinal image of a distant object is increased in size by 3·6 per cent by the meniscus lens (see below). Or if the equiconvex form of the lens is retained, but its axial thickness is increased from, say, 5 to 8 mm., the retinal image is increased by about 1·5 per cent. In both cases the effect has been to move the principal points farther from the eye and increase the equivalent focal length, although the back vertex power has been maintained constant, as it must be in order to correct the refractive error.

Thus to increase the size of the retinal image in hyperopia, or to decrease it in myopia, the correcting lens is to be bent to such a form, or made of such thickness, or both, that its second principal point moves away from the eye. In *axial* ametropia the image progressively approaches the standard emmetropic size as the second principal point of the lens approaches the eye's anterior focal point. In *refractive* ametropia the image is of the standard emmetropic size with the second principal point of the lens *at* the eye (i.e. at P_e) and progressively increases in hyperopia, or decreases in myopia, as this point moves away from the eye. In all these changes of form and thickness the effective power of the lens at the eye must remain constant and equal to K.

ANISOMETROPIA. The effect of the form and thickness of the correcting lenses on retinal image size has particular reference to cases of anisometropia.

Refractive Ametropia. From §10.13 we see that the second principal point of the stronger of the two lenses is to be nearer to the eye. Hence in hyperopia the weaker lens is to be more bent or thicker than the stronger lens; in myopia the stronger lens is to be more bent or thicker than the weaker lens, since the principal points are displaced towards the eye, in a negative lens, the more the lens is bent and the thicker it is.

Axial Ametropia. This is of greater practical importance. The second principal point of the stronger lens is to be nearer to F_e of the eye than that of the weaker lens, both being on the same side of F_e. Hence in myopia the weaker lens is to be more bent or thicker than the stronger lens; this is opposed to the condition for reducing the relative prismatic effect (§16.4). In hyperopia the question is a little complicated by the fact that with the back surface of the lens in the region of 14 mm. from the eye's reduced surface, the second principal point is in close proximity to F_e with bent positive lenses, and is displaced to a position *beyond* F_e when the power of the lens passes a certain limit. Thus when the stronger of the two lenses has appreciable positive power (the limiting power depending upon the form and thickness of the lens), the weaker lens should be more bent or thicker than the stronger; the second principal points of both lenses lie outside F_e. This agrees generally with the condition for reducing relative prismatic effects (§16.4). But when the powers of both lenses are sufficiently small that their second principal points both lie within F_e, the stronger lens is to be more bent or thicker than the weaker.

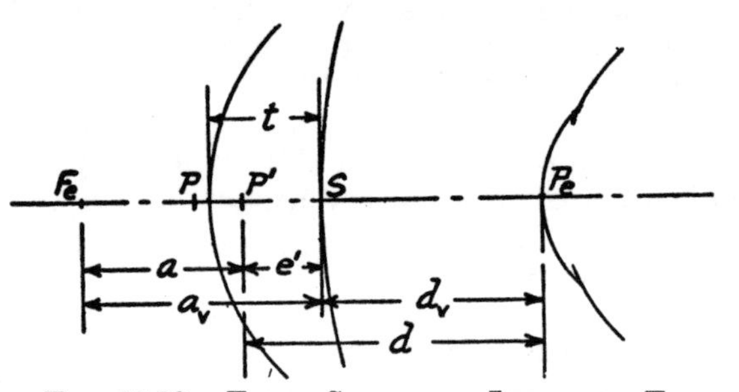

FIG. 10.19. THICK SPECTACLE LENS AND EYE.

Consider a person requiring for the right eye a lens of B.V.P. + 10 D with its back surface 14 mm. from the eye (of power 60 D). If the lens is of meniscus form, back surface power − 6 D and thickness 5 mm., its second principal point is distant $-5\cdot25$ mm. from its back surface or $2\cdot59$ mm. outside the eye's anterior focus. If the correcting lens for the left eye is + 5 D (strictly, if its *equivalent* power is half that of the right lens), then to equalise the retinal images its second principal point has to be $2\times 2\cdot59 = 5\cdot18$ mm. beyond F_e, or $7\cdot84$ mm. beyond the spectacle point. Assuming that the back surface of this lens is 14 mm. from the eye, the above can be accomplished either by making the left lens of very deep meniscus form, namely

F_2 about -15 D, assuming a normal thickness of 3 mm.; or by increasing its thickness to about 5·4 mm., if it be given the same back surface power, -6 D, as the right lens.

CALCULATION OF RETINAL IMAGE. THICK LENSES.

It may be a convenience to express the size of the retinal image in terms of the form and back vertex power of the distance correction. The positions of F_e and P_e (of the eye) with respect to the second principal point P′ of the lens will be denoted by a and d; that is, $a = F_eP'$ and $d = P'P_e$. The corresponding distances reckoned from the back surface of the lens at S will be designated a_v and d_v—see Fig. 10.19.

If F'_v represent the back vertex power (B.V.P.) of the lens, F its equivalent power, F_1 and F_2 its surface powers t its thickness and n its refractive index, we have (§2.1):

$$F'_v = \frac{F_1}{1 - \frac{t}{n} F_1} + F_2 = \frac{F}{1 - \frac{t}{n} F_1} = F \left\{ 1 + \frac{t}{n} (F'_v - F_2) \right\}$$

$$e' = -\frac{t}{n} \frac{F_1}{F} = -\frac{t}{n} \frac{F_1}{F'_v (1 - \frac{t}{n} F_1)} = -\frac{t}{n} \frac{F'_v - F_2}{F'_v}$$

$$a = F_eP' = a_v + e' \text{ and } d = d_v - e'$$

The retinal image of a distant object subtending an angle w_o, formed in an ametropic eye corrected with a lens of power, F is given (§10.12) by

$$h'_c = -\frac{w_o}{(1 - dF)\, K'}$$

Replacing the thin lens by the thick lens, the second principal point of the latter occupying the thin lens position, we have in AXIAL ametropia, $K' = K + F_o$

$$\text{and } h'_c = -w_o \cdot \frac{1}{(1 - dF)\left(\frac{F}{1 - dF} + F_o\right)}$$

$$= -\frac{w_o}{F_o} \cdot \frac{1}{1 + aF}$$

which, on substituting for a_v and F'_v, becomes on simplifying

$$\left.\begin{aligned} h'_c &= -\frac{w_o}{F_o} \cdot \frac{1}{\left(1 - \frac{t}{n} F_1\right)(1 + a_v F'_v)} && \text{in terms of } F_1 \\ &= -\frac{w_o}{F_o} \cdot \frac{1 + \frac{t}{n}(F'_v - F_2)}{(1 + a_v F'_v)} && \text{in terms of } F_2 \end{aligned}\right\} \quad (10{\cdot}21)$$

In REFRACTIVE ametropia, $K' = F_o$

and $h'^c = -\frac{w_o}{F_o} \cdot \frac{1}{(1 - d\,F)}$

$$\left.\begin{aligned} &= -\frac{w_o}{F_o} \cdot \frac{1}{\left(1 - \frac{t}{n} F_1\right)(1 - d_v F'_v)} && \text{in terms of } F_1 \\ &= -\frac{w_o}{F_o} \cdot \frac{1 + \frac{t}{n}(F'_v - F_2)}{(1 - d_v F'_v)} && \text{in terms of } F_2 \end{aligned}\right\} \quad (10 \cdot 22)$$

These expressions show the dependence of the retinal image of a distant object, for a lens of given B.V.P. and with its back surface in a given position, on the form (F_1 or F_2) and thickness (t) of the distance correcting lens. It will be remembered that the quantity $-\frac{w_o}{F_o}$ is the size of the retinal image formed in the standard emmetropic eye, so that the factor by which this quantity is multiplied in the above expressions is the relative spectacle magnification.

In the case of *symmetrical* lenses, where $F_1 = F_2$, substitution of F_1 or F_2 in terms of F'_v, which is known, gives a rather awkward quadratic; it will be sufficiently accurate to put $F_1 = F_2 = \frac{1}{2} F'_v$ in lenses of practical powers, so that

in *axial* ametropia, $h'_c = -\frac{w}{F_o} \cdot \frac{1 + \frac{t}{2n} F'_v}{(1 + a_v F'_v)}$ very nearly (10.21a)

in *refractive* ametropia, $h'_c = -\frac{w}{F_o} \cdot \frac{1 + \frac{t}{2n} F'_v}{(1 - d_v F'_v)}$,, (10.22a)

We can alter the size of the retinal image in an emmetropic eye. In this special case we have $F'_v = 0$ and equations (10.21) and (10.22) reduce to

$$h'_c = -\frac{w}{F_o}\left(1 - \frac{t}{n} F_2\right) = -\frac{w}{F_o}\left(\frac{1}{1 - \frac{t}{n} F_1}\right) \quad (10.23)$$

That is, a bent glass of thickness t, a back surface of power F_2 and a front surface of such curvature that the B.V.P. is zero, will magnify the retinal image by the amount $\left(1 - \frac{t}{n} F_2\right)$, a change in the image of $100 \frac{t}{n} F_2$ per cent.

Since this glass has no power, it is equivalent to a telescope, the front surface being the objective, the back surface the eyepiece and the intervening medium, glass. If the back surface is concave to the eye, the telescope is of

Galilean form. Such a glass does not alter the parallelism of pencils of light from distant object points, but changes the directions of pencils from extra-axial points of the object and so alters its apparent size. Lenses, the form or thickness of which are modified for the express purpose of increasing or decreasing the size of the retinal image without disturbing the refractive correction are called *size* lenses or *iseikonic* lenses ; they will be referred to in Chapter XV.

NEAR OBJECTS.

If the retinal image of a distant object has been increased or decreased by a certain percentage amount by appropriately modifying the form or thickness of the correcting lens, the retinal image of a near object will not be increased or decreased to the same extent. Or, if the retinal images of a distant object formed in the right and left eyes have been equalised by suitable choice of form for the two lenses, then the retinal images of a near object will not be equal.

We will use the above expressions to obtain some idea of the extent of the effect produced on the retinal image by changing the form of the correcting lens. The student, should, however, check the results by calculating from first principles, as indicated in §§ 2.1 and 3.12.

Examle. A hyperope (axial) is corrected for distance by an equiconvex lens the B.V.P. of which is +10·0 D. A meniscus lens is prescribed and worn with its back surface, of power −6 D, at the same distance from the eye as the first lens. In both lenses the refractive index and thickness are 1·523 and 5 mm. Compare the sizes of the retinal images of the same distant object obtained with the two lenses.

Answer. Suppose the distant object subtends an angle w. With the first (symmetrical) lens,

$$h'_c = -\frac{w}{F_o} \cdot \frac{1 + \frac{t}{2n} F'_v}{1 + a_v F'_v} = -\frac{w}{F_o (1 + a_v F'_v)} \times \left(1 + \frac{5 \times 10}{2 \times 1523}\right)$$

With the second (meniscus) lens,

$$h'_c = -\frac{w}{F_o} \frac{1 + \frac{t}{n}(F'_v - F_2)}{1 + a_v F'_v} = -\frac{w}{F_o (1 + a_v F'_v)} \times \left(1 + \frac{5 \times 16}{1523}\right)$$

$$\therefore \frac{\text{Retinal image with meniscus}}{\text{Retinal image with symmetrical}} = \frac{1603}{1548} = 1 \cdot 036$$

With the meniscus lens the retinal image is 3·6 per cent larger.

Example. The same eye is corrected first by the above-specified meniscus lens and then by a meniscus with the same B.V.P. and back surface power, but the thickness of which is increased to 8 mm. Compare the two retinal images.

Answer. In the first lens $t_1 = 5$ mm. and in the second $t_2 = 8$ mm.

$$\therefore \text{ Ratio of images } = \frac{1 + \frac{t_2}{n}(F'_v - F_2)}{1 + \frac{t_1}{n}(F'_v - F_2)}$$

$$= \frac{1 + \frac{8 \times 16}{1523}}{1 + \frac{5 \times 16}{1523}} = \frac{1651}{1603} = 1 \cdot 030$$

The thicker lens increases the image by 3 per cent.

Example. In an anisometrope the right and left spectacle refractions, at 14 mm. from the eye, are respectively + 10 D and + 5 D, the ametropia being axial. The lenses are of refractive index 1·523, their axial thicknesses are 5 mm. and 3 mm. respectively and the back surface power of the right lens is − 2·0 D. What must be the power of the back surface of the left lens in order that the two retinal images shall be equal ?

Answer. In each eye, $a_v = 16\frac{2}{3} - 14 = 2\frac{2}{3}$ mm.

For right eye,

$$h'_c = -\frac{w}{F_o} \cdot \frac{1 + \frac{5 \times 12}{1523}}{\left(1 + \frac{8 \times 10}{3000}\right)} = -\frac{w}{F_o} \cdot \frac{\frac{1583}{1523}}{\frac{3080}{3000}}$$

For left eye

$$h'_c = -\frac{w}{F_o} \cdot \frac{1 + \frac{3(5 - F_2)}{1523}}{1 + \frac{8 \times 5}{3000}} = -\frac{w}{F_o} \cdot \frac{1 + \frac{3(5 - F_2)}{1523}}{\frac{3040}{3000}}$$

$$\text{hence } 1 + \frac{3(5 - F_2)}{1523} = \frac{1583}{1523} \times \frac{3040}{3080} = 1 \cdot 026$$

$$F_2 = 5 - \left(\cdot 026 \times \frac{1523}{3}\right) = -8 \cdot 2 \text{ D.}$$

The left (weaker) lens is of deeper meniscus form than the right (stronger) lens.

EXERCISES. CHAPTER X.

(*Note.*—In working out exercises involving numerical calculation the student is strongly advised not merely to interpolate in the appropriate formula given in the text. In order to become clear as to the principles involved and to fit himself to tackle unusual problems that may arise, the student should work through each problem from first principles ; he should wherever possible draw a careful ray diagram and deduce his method from it.)

1. Describe the optical system of the human eye and give a brief general account of the methods and appliances used in obtaining the measurements of its constants.

2. Give a careful diagram indicating the positions and the manner of formation of the catoptric images of the eye. How can these images

be of service in studying the optical properties of the eye; and how may they, or any one of them, be disadvantageous ?

3. Give a careful diagram to show the formation of the Purkinje images of the eye. Describe the changes in the crystalline lens in accommodation that can be shown by a study of these images.

4. Explain with the aid of diagrams how the corneal and crystalline lens reflexes can be observed. What information do they afford as to the mechanism of accommodation ? (B.O.A.)

5. Describe an experiment to show that the surface of the normal cornea is not spherical. What is meant by the "optical zone" ? How does the radius of curvature vary for different parts of the surface of the cornea along a horizontal meridian ?

6. Give a short account of the centring of the optical system of the eye. Explain what meaning can be attached to the term "optical axis" as applied to the eye. Explain also the angle alpha.

7. Describe a method of measuring the angle alpha. How may it be shown that in most cases the axes of the cornea and lens are not coincident ? Discuss briefly the centring of the pupil of the eye.

8. Describe the ophthalmophakometer. Explain two measurements, concerned with the optical system of the eye, that can be obtained by its use. Give appropriate diagrams.

9. What is meant by, and what is the purpose of, the schematic eye ? What investigators have been concerned in obtaining data for drawing up schematic eyes ? Give a careful diagram of a schematic eye, marking clearly the positions of the salient points and explain briefly what happens to these points when the eye accommodates.

10. Describe the schematic and reduced eyes and explain clearly, with carefully drawn diagrams, their dependence one on the other.

A reduced eye of power 60 dioptres and refractive index 4/3, has an axial length of 25 mm. What lens, placed 14 mm. in front of the reduced eye surface, is required to enable light from a distant object to be focused on the retina ?

11. If the eye be regarded as equivalent to two lenses in air, viz.: a cornea lens of power + 43 D and a crystalline lens in air of power + 20·5 D separated by 4 mm., calculate the effect of a small displacement of the crystalline lens forward or backward and discuss the matter with reference to accommodation effect. (S.M.C.)

12. Distinguish between schematic, reduced and aphakic eyes.

Calculate the refractive error of an aphakic eye which, prior to removal of the lens, was emmetropic. Assume: effective corneal radius = 8 mm.; reduced eye front focal length = 15 mm.; refractive index of media = 4/3.

Discuss the possible reasons for actual findings in practice not agreeing with your theory. (S.M.C.)

13. Using the following constants, calculate the power of the unaccommodated schematic eye and the positions, relative to the cornea, of the focal, principal and nodal points. Then find the power, radius of curvature and position of the reduced eye surface which will be

equivalent to the schematic eye in that its focal points will occupy the same positions.

$r_1 = 7 \cdot 8$ mm.		$n_1 = 1 \cdot 000$
$r_2 = 10 \cdot 0$,,	$d_1 = 3 \cdot 6$ mm.	$n_2 = n_4 = 4/3$
$r_2 = -6 \cdot 0$,,	$d_2 = 3 \cdot 6$,,	$n_3 = 1 \cdot 416$

Use four figure logs.

14. Give a careful large scale diagram of the optical system of the schematic eye showing the approximate positions of its cardinal points.

From this construct the diagram of the reduced eye and show the formation of the retinal image of a distant object subtending an angle of 5°. Give the size of the image.

15. At a certain stage in its development the constants of the crystalline lens of a certain eye are those given in the Table, §10.4 for the Gullstrand No. 1 (Exact) eye. Later in life the constants are: $r_1 =$ 11 mm. $r_2 =$ 8 mm., $r_3 = -6$ mm., $r_4 = -6 \cdot 5$ mm.; the positions of the surfaces, reckoned from the cornea, are 3·55 mm., 4·10 mm., 6·53 mm. and 7·20 mm.; the index of the cortical portions has increased from 1·386 to 1·396, the index of the nucleus remaining unchanged.

Calculate the new power of the crystalline lens. What will be the nature of the resulting change in the refractive condition of the whole eye?

16. Calculate the position and magnification of the pupil of the accommodated eye, as seen by an observer in front of the eye, the actual pupil being 3·2 mm. behind the anterior corneal surface. Assume the cornea to be a single surface of radius 7·7 mm. and the refractive index of the interior of the eye as 4/3.

17. (*a*) In a certain eye the pupil is centred on the optical axis and the angle alpha is 5°, positive. The eye fixes a bright point of light distant one metre from the cornea. An observer, whose eye coincides with this source, views the eye in question. Where will the corneal reflex appear to lie in relation to the centre of the apparent pupil?

(*b*) Along what direction, relative to the visual axis, must the observer view the eye so that the corneal reflex shall appear central in the apparent pupil?

Assume the standard schematic eye values given in the Table §10·4, column 1.

18. Explain, with a careful diagram of the arrangement, Tscherning's method of determing the position of the anterior surface of the crystalline lens in the living eye, using his ophthalmophakometer. Explain what readings are to be taken and how the result, the depth of the anterior chamber, is calculated from these readings.

19. With a careful diagram of the arrangement, describe the measurement of the radius of curvature of the anterior surface of the crystalline lens with Tscherning's ophthalmophakometer.

Assuming that the corneal radius and depth of anterior chamber have already been found to be 7·9 mm. and 3·4 mm. respectively, and that the angle alpha for the eye is 4·5 degrees, positive, calculate the radius of the crystalline lens anterior surface from the following readings; angle between telescope and fixation mark, 9°; angle between telescope and second lamp 12° 30′.

20. The radius of curvature of the front surface of the crystalline lens is determined by the method of adjusting the sizes of two bright objects, placed at a common distance from the eye, until the image of one formed by reflection at the cornea is equal in size to the image of the other formed by reflection at the lens surface. In a case in which the radius of curvature of the cornea is 7·9 mm. and the apparent depth of anterior chamber 2·9 mm., the sizes of the objects are found to be 285 mm. for the cornea and 125 mm. for the lens. Give a diagram showing clearly the quantities involved and calculate the radius of curvature of the front surface of the crystalline lens.

21. Describe a method of measuring the curvature of the front surface of the crystalline lens in the living eye. Show clearly, with a careful diagram, how the curvature is obtained from the readings taken in the experiment.

22. Show, with the aid of a diagram, how the slit lamp and corneal microscope apparatus should be arranged to make measurements of the depth of the anterior chamber and the position of opacities in the media.

If the apparent anterior chamber depth as measured is found to be 2·8 mm. and the radius of curvature of the cornea 7·8 mm., calculate the actual chamber depth. Assume the cornea as a single surface and refractive index inside the eye as 4/3.

A small object on the anterior lens surface has an apparent diameter of 0·5 mm.; find its actual diameter.

23. The radius of curvature of the anterior surface of the crystalline lens is determined by placing two bright objects at a common distance in front of the eye and varying the sizes of the objects until the image of one formed by reflection at the cornea is equal to the image of the other formed by reflection at the lens surface. In a measurement on the eye of Exercise 22, the sizes of the objects were found to be 205 mm. for the cornea and 115 mm. for the lens. Calculate the radius of curvature of the lens surface.

Comment on any assumption made in your calculation.

24. Describe a laboratory method of measuring the change in curvature of the front surface of the crystalline lens during accommodation. Show the readings to be taken and the calculation required to obtain the true radius of curvature of the surface.

25. Explain how to obtain the apparent depth of the anterior chamber of the living eye; e.g. by making the corneal image of an illuminated cursor coincide with the image of a second illuminated cursor formed by the anterior surface of the crystalline lens. Obtain the formula for obtaining the apparent depth from your readings. How can the real depth be found when the apparent depth is known? (B.O.A. Hons.)

26 Explain how the approximate position of the centre of rotation of the eye has been obtained. (S.M.C.)

27. Write a short note on the information that has been obtained by recent measurements concerning the position of the centre of rotation of the eye.

Describe, with the aid of a diagram, a laboratory method for determining its approximate position.

28. Calculate the positions of the entrance and exit pupils in the accommodated schematic eye the constants of which are given in the second column of the Table §10.4. Find also the magnification of each pupil and hence the magnification of the one (the exit pupil) with respect to the other.

What is the distance of the mean position of the entrance and exit pupils from the mean position of the principal points (*a*) in the relaxed schematic eye; (*b*) in the accommodated schematic eye?

29. Explain, with the aid of a diagram, what is meant by the depth of focus of the eye in the object space, or the depth of field.

Find, from paraxial considerations, the depth of focus of the reduced emmetropic eye with a pupil diameter of 4 mm. when it is focused on an object at one metre, assuming that a blur circle of diameter as high as 0·003 mm. is interpreted as sharply as the focused image of a point.

30. Show that a surface "looks" equally bright from whatever direction it may be viewed, its apparent brightness to a given eye depending only upon the brightness of the object and the size of the pupil.

Find the illumination of the retinal image when a test chart is observed by an eye of pupil diameter 5 mm., the illumination on the chart being 10 foot-candles and its reflection co-efficient 60 per cent.

31. Explain why, if the effects of atmospheric absorption are neglected, the apparent brightness or luminosity of an extended surface is independent of its distance from the observer whereas this is not the case when the object is very small.

32. Explain clearly, with the aid of diagrams related to one another, how the reduced eye is derived from the schematic eye.

Suppose the contents of the standard emmetropic reduced eye were changed so that their refractive index becomes 1·375 instead of 4/3, other conditions remaining the same. Find the refractive condition of this eye. If an object 1 cm. high were placed at its far point what would be the size of the retinal image?

33. Draw, five times full size, a (reduced) eye that is axially myopic 10 dioptres; mark carefully its focal points and nodal point. Repeat for an eye that is refractively myopic 10 D. In each case find graphically, by drawing the appropriate rays, the size of the retinal image of an object 1 cm. high standing on the axis of the eye at its far point.

Check the graphical results by calculation.

34. A hyperope, assumed to possess sufficient accommodation, observes an object at 50 cm. from the eye first without his correction and secondly with his distance correction, which is + 4·0 D.S. placed 15 mm. in front of the reduced eye surface or principal point. Find the magnification obtained in viewing this object with the correction and the amount of accommodation exerted by the eye.

35. A young myope, with ample accommodative amplitude, observes an object placed at his far point first unaided by any lens and secondly when wearing his distance correction of – 7·50 D placed 15 mm. from the reduced eye surface. Compare the sizes of the retinal images obtained in the two cases. What is the ocular refraction of this eye

and how much accommodation is needed to fix the object stated when the distance correction is worn ?

36. Define the terms spectacle magnification and relative spectacle magnification. Derive expressions for these quantities for eyes that are (*a*) axially ametropic ; (*b*) refractively ametropic.

Show from your work that spectacle magnification is very nearly unity in the case of contact spectacles ; and that relative spectacle magnification is unity when the correcting lens is worn at the eye's anterior focal point.

37. Compare the sizes of the retinal images of a distant object in the following four cases of a hyperope, each corrected with + 5 D sphere placed 15 mm. in front of the eye-plane :*

(*a*) uncorrected axial defect ; (*c*) corrected axial defect ;
(*b*) uncorrected curvature defect ; (*d*) corrected curvature defect.

(Assume static power for axial defect is + 60·0 D). (S.M.C.)

*i.e. in front of the principal point or reduced eye surface.

38. Draw careful diagrams to show the effect on the size of the retinal image of placing a + 1·00 D sphere (*a*) in the anterior focal plane of the eye, (*b*) nearer to, and (*c*) further from the eye than this plane. (B.O.A. Hons.)

39. Explain what is meant by spectacle magnification and by relative spectacle magnification.

An aphakic eye is corrected for distance with a + 8 D sphere placed 12 mm. from the cornea. What is the size of the retinal image of the 60 metre Snellen letter seen at a distance of 6 metres ? Assume corneal radius 7·8 mm. and refractive index in eye = 4/3.

40. In what circumstances does a forward displacement of a convex lens placed before an eye fail to produce an apparent increase of positive effective power ? Give reasons for your answer. (S.M.C.)

41. Compare the sizes of retinal images formed in : (*a*) an axial myope, principal refraction − 10·0 D, (*b*) an axial hyperope, principal refraction + 10 D, with that formed in an emmetrope of static power + 60 D. The object viewed is 10 cm. in front of the eyes and accommodation is ample in all cases. (S.M.C.)

42. Explain, with the aid of a careful diagram, why a correcting lens placed at the anterior focus of the eye will not alter the size of the image so long as the eye does not accommodate. (B.O.A. Hons.)

43. State concisely, with the necessary reasons, the differences you would expect to find in the graphs of an optic disc plotted on a scotometer when the eye is, and is not, wearing its correcting lens. Exemplify your answer from the following data, giving a careful diagram and full numerical details :

Correcting lens + 6 D placed 20 mm. in front of the nodal point ; distance of node to retina 15 mm. ; distance between fovea and centre of optic disc 4 mm. ; diameter of disc 2 mm. ; distance of scotometer to eye one third of a metre. (S.M.C. Hons.)

44. An eye is corrected by a convex meniscus lens whose posterior surface is 15 mm. from the cornea, the reflecting power of the latter being 250 D. If the surface powers of the lens are + 12·00 D and

$-6 \cdot 00$ D, thickness 5 mm. and index $1 \cdot 523$, calculate the radius of the equivalent afocal contact glass. Assume corneal and fluid index to be 4/3. (S.M.C. Hons.)

45. A myope whose spectacle correction is $-10 \cdot 0$ D sphere placed 15 mm. in front of the eye has his apparent near point with this lens at a distance of 10 cm. in front of the lens. Compare the size of the retinal image when the uncorrected eye views a small object at 10 cm. in front of the spectacle plane with the largest retinal image that can be formed of the same object viewed through a magnifying glass of $+10 \cdot 00$ D sphere which is also placed 15 mm. in front of the eye. (S.M.C.)

46. Show that a converging or positive spectacle lens produces an apparent "magnifying" effect when used to correct the vision of a hypermetropic eye, inasmuch as the sharp image appears larger than the diffuse image seen without optical aid.

If the eye can only focus light converging to a point $0 \cdot 5$ metre behind its front principal point, and a spectacle lens of power $+4$ D is used with a separation of 12 mm. between the adjacent principal points of lens and eye, find the apparent magnification produced if the test object is fixed at such a distance that a sharp image is obtained with the aid of the lens. (S.M.C. Hons.)

47. Using the matter of §10.13, check the figures given in the Table in that paragraph for the percentage difference in size of the right and left retinal images in anisometropia, both when the ametropia in each eye is axial and when it is refractive.

48. An antimetropic person, whose ametropia is axial in both eyes, is corrected for distance by the lenses R. $+5 \cdot 00$ D sphere worn 18 mm. from the eye plane and L. $-5 \cdot 00$ D sphere worn $15\frac{1}{3}$ mm. from the eye plane. Compare the sizes of the retinal images of a distant object in the two eyes.

How much accommodation is required of each eye to see clearly an object at 25 cm. from the eye plane, the above distance correction being worn as stated ?

Enumerate the disadvantages ordinarily attendant on the wearing of the correction by an anisometrope.

49. An axially myopic eye, after being rendered aphakic by the removal of the crystalline lens, is exactly emmetropic. Compare the size of the retinal image of a distant object formed in this eye with the image previously formed in it when wearing its distance correction $12\frac{1}{3}$ mm. in front of the cornea. Assume the standard eye of power 60 D, internal refractive index 4/3, and single surface cornea of radius $7 \cdot 8$ mm.

50. Define the magnifying power of a simple magnifying glass or loupe. Discuss the definition in relation to a high hyperope with little accommodation and to a high myope.

Find the magnification obtained by a hyperope of 2 D who is accommodating 4 D when using a $+16$ D lens held 4 cm. from his eye. Find also the position of the object when it is seen clearly. Give a diagram.

51. (a) A relaxed myope of $-10 \cdot 0$ D uses a convex lens of focal length 5 cm. as a magnifying glass. Find the magnifying power when

the lens is held (i) 4 cm. from the eye; (ii) in contact with the eye. In each case find also the position of the object.

(*b*) What magnification would be obtained by an unaccommodated emmetrope under the same conditions?

52. Prove that the power of a convex lens in dioptres is four times the magnifying power it produces when used, in contact with the eye, by an unaccommodated emmetrope. Give a diagram.

An emmetrope uses a 20 D magnifying glass. (*a*) Find the magnifying power obtained when the glass is held 8 cm. from the eye, the latter being (i) unaccommodated, (ii) accommodated 6 dioptres. Repeat for the case when the glass is (*b*) 5 cm. from the eye; and (*c*) in contact with the eye.

Hence discuss briefly the conditions for maximum magnifying power.

53. Find an expression for the magnifying power of a small thin lens to be used as a simple microscope, and use it to calculate the magnifying power of a + 12 D lens so employed.

Describe (giving a diagram) some means by which a magnifier and a transparent scale may be employed to measure the distance between the cornea and the posterior convex surface of a spectacle lens as held in the spectacle frame. State briefly why such a measurement may be of importance. (S.M.C. Hons.)

54. Explain, with the aid of a diagram, why the apparent inclination of an oblique line, observed through a sphero-cylindrical lens, does not in general coincide with its actual inclination. What are the factors on which the apparent inclination depends?

As a corollary, explain why objects do not appear distorted to an astigmatic eye.

55. When a line inclined at, say, 60° is observed through an astigmatic lens such as + 8·0 D.S./+ 5·00 D.C. axis H., under certain conditions the line appears in its true direction; under other conditions it appears horizontal or vertical or perpendicular to its true direction. With the aid of a diagram, derive an expression for the apparent inclination, and hence show that the above statements are true.

In particular, find the apparent inclination when the object line and eye are separated by one metre and the lens is held 25 cm. from the eye.

56. An ametropic eye wearing the lens + 10·0 D.S./+ 6·00 D cyl. axis 30° placed 25 mm. in front of the eye observes a horizontal line lying in a plane 40 cm. from the eye. Along what direction will the line appear to lie? What will happen to the apparent inclination of the line as the lens is brought closer to the eye? Give reasons.

57. An emmetropic eye views the sets of parallel lines used in the clinical testing of astigmatism (the block) through a + 3·00 D. cyl ax. H, the lines lying respectively along 30° and 120°. What will be apparently the inclination of the blocks of parallel lines to one another when the lens is mounted (*a*) 15 mm. from the eye (*b*) 50 mm. from the eye. The chart containing the lines is 6 metres from the eye.

58. The spectacle point, far point, reduced eye surface and anterior focal point of the eye being designated, as usual, by S, M_R, P and F_E, show that the spectacle magnification is given by the ratio between

the two distances SM_R and PM_R; and that in axial ametropia the relative spectacle magnification is given by the ratio between the two distances SM_R and F_EM_R; and in refractive ametropia by the ratio of SM_R and PM_R. Give diagrams.

59. Explain, with the aid of a diagram, how the size of the retinal image is affected by the form and thickness of the correcting lens, the back vertex power and position of back surface of which are maintained constant.

Illustrate by comparing the sizes of the retinal images obtained by an eye which is first corrected by an equiconvex lens and then by a meniscus lens with back surface power − 6 D. Both lenses have B.V.P. of + 8 D, both are 4 mm. thick, and the back surfaces of both are at the same distance from the eye.

60. The refractive condition of an anisometrope is corrected by lenses of B.V. powers − 5 D and − 10 D for the right and left eyes respectively, the back surfaces being 14 mm. from the eyes. The ametropia is axial. Both lenses are to have front surfaces of power + 6 D; the thickness of the stronger lens is 0·5 mm. Find the thickness of the weaker lens, for the right eye, in order that the retinal images shall be equalised. Assume power of eye is 60 D.

61. Prove the formula: $y = \frac{4x}{3p^2}$

where p is the dioptric power of a reduced eye (refractive index $1\frac{1}{3}$) x that of the correcting lens placed in the anterior focal plane, and y the axial error in terms of a metre.

If the power of such an eye is 60 D, and the axial error is 2 mm., what correction would be needed in the anterior focal plane? (S.M.C. Hons.)

62. Derive the expression 10.16, by finding the sizes of the retinal images of the sides h and v of a rectangle as observed through an astigmatic lens with vertical and horizontal principal meridians.

63. Discuss the conditions that govern the equality of the sizes of the images in the two eyes. Consider in particular the effect of the removal of the lens of one eye for cataract and the substitution of the correcting lens. (Consider the effect on the Gauss points of the removal of the lens.) (B.O.A. Hons.)

64. Describe a method of measuring the radius of curvature of the anterior surface of the crystalline lens in the living eye. Indicate how the radius is determined from the measured quantities. (S.M.C. Hons.)

65. Give an account of the design and use of so-called size or iseikonic lenses, intended to reduce the disparity in the sizes of the images of the right and left eyes. Determine by calculation a form of lens, having a concave back surface of 6 D power, to magnify the retinal image of a distant object in an emmetropic eye by 5 per cent. Assume refractive index of lens = 1·52. (S.M.C. Hons.)

66. A single lens magnifier for binocular use is to provide angular magnification of 2·5 and a field of view of 2 cm. For an observer who is accommodating for a distance of 50 cm., whose eyes (centres of projection) are 10 cm. behind the lens and whose inter-ocular distance is 60 mm., find the power and aperture of the lens required.

67. Define and explain the relation between : the nodal points of the eye ; the centre of rotation ; the point of fixation ; the fovea centralis ; the angle alpha (B.O.A.)

68. A hypermetropic eye needs a correction of + 4 D sph. when the correcting lens is placed in the front focal plane of the eye. Calculate the effect on the size of the retinal image of a distant object as the lens is moved farther away from the eye, assuming (*a*) that as the lens is moved its power is adjusted so that the second focal point of the lens remains coincident with the far point of the eye ; and alternatively (*b*) that the power of the lens remains unchanged. (B.O.A.)

ABERRATIONS OF THE EYE. ENTOPTIC PHENOMENA.

CHAPTER XI

ABERRATIONS OF THE EYE.

11.1. Classification.

EXCEPT here and there in special connections, any aberrations that exist in the optical system of the eye have been neglected in the preceding chapters. We have assumed the eye to be a centred system of spherical surfaces; its aperture has been taken as very small so that simple paraxial (Gaussian) relations apply to its image forming properties. Thus the theory of refractive errors and their correction in Chapter III depends upon the elementary conjugate foci relations connecting the far point and the fovea; and in Chapter IV the simple form of astigmatic pencil with two focal lines at right angles to one another would actually be obtained only if the pupil of the eye were of infinitely small dimensions. Such simplifications are quite sound and guide us to correct underlying principles and methods, just as they serve to provide the framework for the broad design of optical instruments.

The eye is in fact, however, an optical system of comparatively wide aperture—large aperture-ratio—and possesses on that account certain aberrations inherent in wide aperture systems. Moreover, it is not accurately centred on a common axis and, being a living organ, may be subject to anatomical imperfections and variations producing irregularities in the refracted pencils within it, and, consequently, irregularities in the retinal image. Judged by the standards adopted for artificial optical instruments these imperfections of the eye's optical system would not be acceptable in such instruments. But due to the wonderful processes of selection and integration in and behind the retina, they do not normally produce any effective impairment of vision. Except when the aberrations are abnormally pronounced or more especially when the irregular imperfections are appreciable, the visual acuity of the eye approaches the theoretical maximum allowed by the wave nature of light itself; and its performance in the domain of light and colour discrimination, its attributes of adjustment, adaptation and flexibility, place it in a unique position unapproached by the finest artificial instrument. Whereas artificially made instruments perform only one special function, the eye is called upon to do many things. Moreover, the eye carries out its own running repairs and the retina clears away the impression of one object or scene in preparation for the next with marvellous rapidity.

Nevertheless the aberrations are present and are operating continuously in every visual act. They occasionally produce what may appear to be anomalous results and intrude in some of the clinical tests to which the eyes are subjected. When present in more than the normal amount and more especially when irregular in character, they will prevent clear vision and will render the usual methods of testing the eyes difficult and unsatisfactory.*

We may subdivide the imperfections of the eye's optical system under the following heads:

(A) Aberrations of the kind met with generally in optical systems of centred spherical surfaces; principally spherical and chromatic aberration.

(B) Aberrations due to lack of centring.

(C) Irregularities in the surface curvatures of the cornea and crystalline lens.

(D) The star-shaped spreading of light by the characteristic radial structure of the crystalline lens.

(E) Local interferences with the passage of the refracted pencils caused by opacities, nebulæ and scars within the media of the eye.

(F) Diffuse scattering of light by the media which, consisting as they do of cellular tissue, are not perfectly transparent and homogeneous.

As a result of these defects, the refracted pencils within the eye are not homocentric and the retinal image of each point of the object is spread over a larger area than obtains in the ideally perfect eye, the distribution of light within this area being irregular. All but the first of the above groups are aberrations that depends particularly upon anatomical structure and which will therefore vary considerably in form and extent from one eye to another.

* e.g. §4.12.

There will be more uniformity in the first group, but even here there are appreciable individual variations.

11.2. A.1. Spherical Aberration.

As in the case of optical systems generally, we may subdivide the first group into (1) monochromatic aberrations, due to the form and position of the surfaces ; i.e. spherical aberrations ; and (2) chromatic aberrations.

We will deal first with the former. It is the quality of the image formed at the fovea, of the object fixed, that is of major importance. The images of laterally situated objects are formed on extra-foveal regions of the retina which are incapable of, and not needed for, critical discriminations.* Thus we are concerned with pencils travelling along the visual axis. Since this axis is usually inclined (the angle

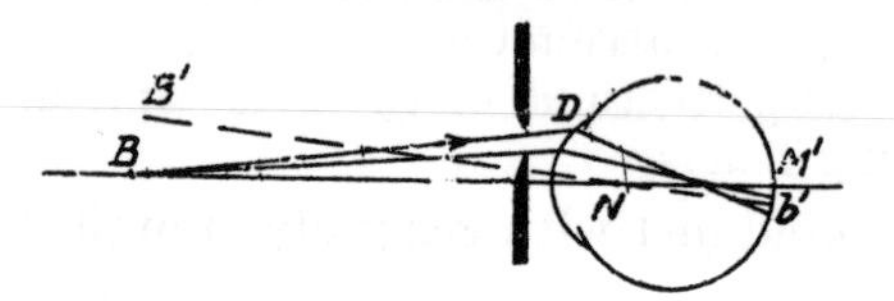

FIG. 11.1—SPHERICAL ABERRATION OF THE EYE.

FIG. 11.2—DISC USED BY VOLKMANN IN INVESTIGATING THE SPHERICAL ABERRATION OF THE EYE.

alpha) to the mean optical axis of the eye, we should expect the foveal image to suffer from coma and oblique astigmatism. To what extent the asymmetry of the refracted pencils due to the obliquity of the visual axis is offset by the physiological astigmatism of the cornea and the frequent tilt of the crystalline lens relative to the optical axis, is uncertain ; but the fact that the visual acuity of the normal eye is so good seems to indicate that any asymmetry there may be is not pronounced. In any case, it has become customary to refer to the monochromatic aberration of the foveal image as spherical aberration ; and, subject to the above qualification, we will use the term.

Over the optical zone most eyes possess under-corrected spherical aberration as does a simple positive lens. That this is so can be easily demonstrated by observing an object such as a horizontal window bar and moving a small aperture

---

* Although peripheral vision is of great importance, the peripheral images need not be sharp.

—a pinhole in a small card—vertically before the eye. The object will be seen to execute an apparent movement in the same direction. This can be explained with reference to Fig. 11.1. When the aperture has been raised to D, the rays of the laterally displaced pencil intersect the axis BM′ on the near side of the fovea M′, producing a somewhat blurred image of the object point B at b′. This is projected outwards through the nodal point N, the object appearing to be situated along the direction NB′. When the aperture is central, B appears in its true position.

It was known to DESCARTES (1677) that the eye possesses spherical aberration of this kind. It was investigated and measured by YOUNG with his optometer* and by VOLKMANN with the aid of a Scheiner disc containing four small apertures arranged as in Fig. 11.2. TSCHERNING and, later, GULLSTRAND employed the method of "stigmatoscopy", in

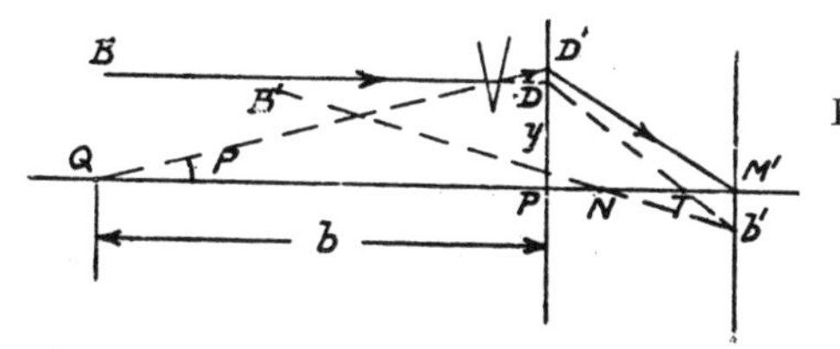

FIG. 11.3—MEASUREMENT OF THE SPHERICAL ABERRATION OF THE EYE.

which a luminous point is observed by the eye under test† and different cross-sections of the refracted pencil are placed in succession on the retina by putting lenses of different powers before the eye. In this way the variations in the cross section of the refracted pencil can be analysed.

A careful series of experiments was carried out in America by AMES and PROCTOR (1922). With the eye under test maintained as far as possible in a state of relaxed accommodation, they admitted a narrow pencil of light through a small aperture which was displaced to successive positions 0·5, 1·0, 1·5, 2·0, etc., millimetres from the fixation axis. The resulting displacement M′b′ of the image on the retina (Figs. 11.1 and 11.3) was then reduced to zero by altering the vergence of the light coming from the test object and so altering the inclination to the axis of the elementary pencil, which inclination was measured. The general principle may be illustrated by Fig. 11.3. BD is the chief

* §3.10. † §4.10.

ray of a pencil coming from a distant axial object and incident on the eye at a distance y from the axis. It is refracted along Db′ cutting the axis in T and the retina in b′. The test object appears to lie along b′NB′. Suppose now a prism is inserted in the aperture as indicated; the ray enters the eye along the direction QD′ and is refracted to M′ if the prism is of correct strength.

Let PQ $= b$; P $=$ deviation produced by the prism; then $y = \text{P}.b$.

$\frac{\text{P}}{y} = \frac{1}{b} = \delta F =$ excess of power of eye's optical system at D′ over the axial power.

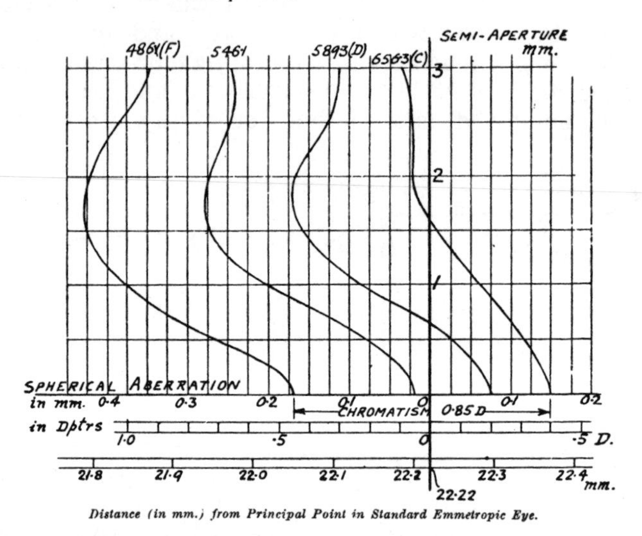

FIG. 11.4—GENERAL TREND OF SPHERICAL ABERRATION CURVES FOR THE EYE, FOR LIGHT OF FOUR WAVE LENGTHS.

The results obtained by AMES and PROCTOR varied from one individual to another; also, for the same eye, when the aperture is displaced horizontally the aberration on the nasal side differs from that on the temporal side;* and the same unsymmetrical results are obtained vertically. Other investgators find the same variation of power and hence refractive condition, over the pupil area. Such variations may be due, however, not to spherical aberration proper, but to the irregularities to be discussed below under

* The asymmetry of the pencil travelling along the visual axis, discussed above, may have a bearing on this.

headings (C), (D), and (E), the effects of which are superimposed on the spherical aberration. The general trend and average magnitude of the results obtained by AMES and PROCTOR* are indicated for light of four different wave lengths in Fig. 11.4, in which the spherical aberration is plotted in the usual manner against semi-aperture. The aberration is seen to be undercorrected and to reach a maximum at a distance of 1·5 to 2·0 mm. from the axis. Further out from the axis the aberration tends to decrease, probably because of the flattening of the cornea and lens surfaces in the peripheral parts outside the optical zone. The average amount of aberration for the four colours, at 1·5 to 2 mm. from the axis, is rather more than one half dioptre. That it does not reach higher maximum values than this is probably due to the lens core being more highly refractive than the peripheral portions.

Thus when, as in ordinary vision, the whole pupil is exposed (i.e. no artificial pupil), the patch of light on the retina is larger than the theoretical Airy disc.† The distribution of light over the patch is such, however, that it is still very much brighter at the central portion than elsewhere and so the definition of the retinal image of a point is not seriously spoiled by spherical aberration alone. Chromatic aberration and especially irregularities, at the edges of the pupil and in the lens and media, are more disturbing factors.

11.3. A.2. Chromatic Aberration.

The optical system of the eye is afflicted with chromatic aberration of the same kind as that found in a positive lens, light of shorter wavelength (blue-violet) being brought to focus before light of longer wavelength (red). This effect, which is due to dispersion and is inherent in the nature of light and refracting media, takes place whatever the aperture may be. Its presence in the normal eye can be demonstrated by the simple experiment already mentioned. When the pinhole aperture is moved upwards before the eye, the upper edge of the window bar becomes tinged an orange colour and the lower edge blue-violet. If the object be a horizontal strip of white paper on a dark background, the lower edge becomes orange and the upper edge

---

* Similar results have been obtained by BENTALL and DIPROSE at the Northampton Polytechnic, London (1932).

† §2.7.

blue-violet. The reason for this will be evident from Fig. 11.5; the light from any bright point of the strip is dispersed, a blue-violet image being formed on the retina at V and a red or orange-red image at R. Thus each bright point of an object appears as a short spectrum with violet above and red below. The overlapping of such spectra for all points of the strip leaves the edges coloured as described.

These simple tests to demonstrate the existence of spherical and chromatic aberration can be performed almost equally well without a pinhole, by merely using the edge of the card so that a gradually decreasing area of the pupil is exposed as the card is moved across.

The use of a piece of cobalt glass to accentuate the chromatic effects by absorbing the intermediate wave lengths of the spectrum and the apparatus called the Duochrome test for subjectively measuring ametropia have already been described.*

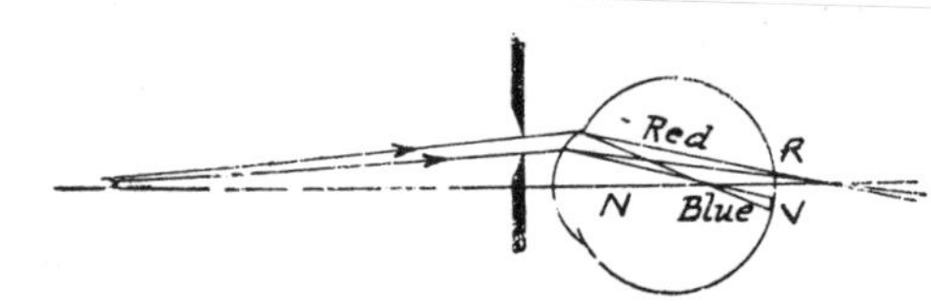

FIG. 11.5—CHROMATIC ABERRATION OF THE EYE.

NEWTON was aware of the chromatism of the eye. WOLLASTON records that if the light from a luminous point is passed through a prism before entering the eye, the spectrum observed is not a coloured line as it would be if all the colours were equally well focused, but is broadened out at the blue end when the luminous point is distant. If the point is approached towards the eye until the blue light is in focus on the retina, then the red end of the spectrum broadens out. The different colours are not in focus at the same time. YOUNG stated the chromatic aberration of the eye to be 1·3 D; FRAUNHOFER 1·5 to 3·0 D; HELMHOLTZ gives the average value 1·8 D. The value will evidently depend upon the extent of spectrum included between the extreme wavelengths used in the measurement.

Values were obtained by AMES and PROCTOR in the experiments already mentioned and an exhaustive investigation was made by the American scientist P. G. NUTTING (*ca.* 1916). The values obtained by these and other workers

* §§ 3.10 and 4.10.

are in fair agreement. They show that the chromatic aberration is about 0·85 D between red light of $\lambda = 656 \cdot 3$ mμ (Fraunhofer's C line) and blue light of $\lambda = 486 \cdot 1$ mμ (the F line) the aberration increasing rapidly towards the violet end of the spectrum. Between the wider limits $\lambda = 400$ mμ to 700 mμ, the aberration is about 3·0 dioptres. Calculation shows that these figures are very nearly the same as those obtained for a single spherical refracting surface of radius 5·55 mm. separating air from water.

The spherical aberration curves of Fig. 11.4 are for four wavelengths between the C and F lines of the spectrum. The paraxial focus for F (blue) light is shown as 0·45 D on the myopic side; for green light ($\lambda = 546 \cdot 1$) 0·05 D myopia; for sodium yellow light (the D line, $\lambda = 589 \cdot 3$) 0·2 D hyperopia and for C (red) light 0·4 D of hyperopia. The chromatic aberration is thus indicated in this diagram as 0·85 D between the wavelength limits mentioned.

Moreover, the normal eye is most sensitive to radiation of $\lambda = 555$ mμ, which is in the green-yellow part of the spectrum; in the diagram the paraxial focus for this wavelength has been placed on the retina, at the zero of the horizontal dioptric scale.

Fig. 11.6 is intended to show the actual paths of the rays of the above four colours in the region of the retina. They have been drawn to correspond to the amounts of spherical aberration given in Fig. 11.4. The paraxial focus for $\lambda = 555$ mμ is put on the retina, distant 22·22 mm. from the principal point in the standard emmetropic eye, as indicated. The nearest approach to a focus is a conical "waist" across which both the intensity and wavelength of the light vary. The narrowest portion of the waist is seen to be in the neighbourhood of 22·0 mm. or 0·6 D; the maximum concentration of light of the most effective wavelengths, round about $\lambda = 555$ mμ, seems to fall in the region 22·1 mm. or about 0·4 D within the retina. It is a matter upon which opinions differ as to which portion of this bundle of light is intersected by the retina when the eye focuses naturally upon an object point; that is, as to whether it is that portion where there is the greatest concentration of light on the axis (GULLSTRAND) or that portion where the total cross section is smallest. According to Fig. 11.6 these two portions do not appear to be far apart and we may say that the eye probably focuses until the retina occupies a position in the beam suggested by the line YY. In the standard emmetropic eye this appears to be about 0·2 mm. or 0·5 dioptre within the paraxial focus for light of wavelength 555 mμ; and about 0·7 D within the sodium yellow (589·3) paraxial focus. Expressed in another way, it would appear from this diagram that the eye is actually about 0·5 D hyperopic compared with the theoretical eye based upon paraxial considerations and assuming $\lambda = 555$ mμ to be the mean wavelength.*

Due to spherical and chromatic aberration there is, even in the most favourable position of the retina, a spread of

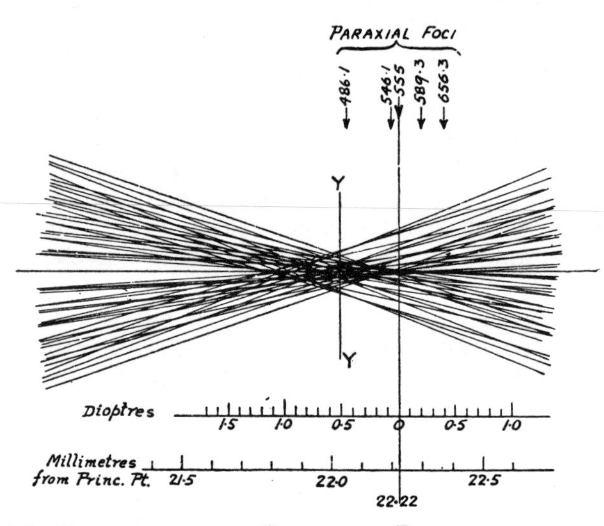

FIG. 11.6—THE FORM OF THE REFRACTED PENCIL IN THE REGION OF THE RETINA. COMPARE FIG. 11.4.

light over it much larger than the theoretical Airy disc. In Fig. 11.6 the diameter at the narrowest portion of the waist is about 0·05 mm.; which is about twenty times the diameter of a foveal cone. But most of the light intensity, especially with the usual moderate sized pupil, is concentrated in a very small central area. The outer portions of the blurred patch at YY consist mainly of light belonging to the extremities of the spectrum, to which the retina is relatively insensitive. Thus there is a concentration of *stimulus* over a small central area and subjectively the effect of these aberrations is but slight in ordinary

* See §10.4.

circumstances, especially having regard to the effect of spatial inductioı *

Due to the existence of this narrow cylindrical waist of subjectively effective light there is appreciable depth of focus in the eye, probably more than the amount given by the geometrical considerations of §10.8.

The manner, just described, in which the rays of light refracted by different zones of the optical system come together to form the refracted bundle in the region of the retina, will be modified during accommodation. It has been fairly conclusively established that during accommodation the anterior surface of the crystalline lens bulges over the optical zone and flattens, relatively, outside this zone. This has the effect of increasing the refracting power of the axial portion more than the peripheral portion and so the spherical aberration of the optical system is reduced in the accommodated eye.

11.4. B. Centring of the Optical System.

The inclination of the visual axis, which determines the direction of the progress of the image-forming pencils to the fovea, to the optical axis, upon which the refracting surfaces are approximately centred, was discussed in §11.2. The oblique aberrations of coma and astigmatism thereby introduced are to some extent compensated for by the physiological astigmatism of the cornea; for whereas the cornea tends to be more powerful around the vertical meridian, the effect of the inclination α is to increase the power of the optical system in the horizontal meridian. There does appear to be some slight asymmetry in the pencils along the visual axis, however. We have seen that the so-called spherical aberration of the eye is often greater on one side of the axis than the other; and it may be that the obliquity of the visual axis is the cause of the effect, described by HELMHOLTZ, whereby horizontal lines are not seen sharply in focus at the same time as vertical lines.

If a person look intently at a fan of lines all radiating from a common centre, only one line at a time can be made to appear sharp and black, the others appearing more or less blurred. Usually rather more accommodation is required for the vertical line than the horizontal. Similarly,

* §§ 1.11 and 20.5.

a diagram consisting of a large number of concentric circles drawn very close together and equidistant, appears sharp along certain radiating sectors and blurred along the intervening sectors. As the accommodation varies slightly during the observation, the clearly defined sectors change places with the blurred ones, giving the impression that the clear sectors are rotating.

11.5. C, D and E. Irregular Aberrations.

As already mentioned, the spherical and chromatic aberrations have usually less effect on the retinal image than the anatomical irregularities now to be considered. If a small source of light, such as a tiny circular hole in a metal plate illuminated from behind, is observed monocularly and slightly out of focus, the appearance is not that of a circular blurred patch, but a star-shaped pattern is seen. Fig. 11.7 illustrates the appearance of such a small source, or of a star, as seen by the author's left eye,* the pupil diameter being about 7 mm. The homocentric pencil incident on the eye is evidently considerably broken up as it travels as a refracted pencil through the eye. This is caused by the approximately radial or star-shaped structure of the crystalline lens, by possible irregularities, such as excavations and bucklings, in the curvature of the corneal and lens surfaces, by local opacities in the media of the eye and perhaps by serrations around the edge of the pupil. The surface irregularities may be congenital or may in some cases be the effects or after-effects of disease or operation. The radiating streaks and patches of the projection disappear one after another as a straight edge is passed across the pupil. If the object point is further away than the point for which the observer is accommodating, then the lower parts of the projection will disappear first if the straight edge is moved from below upwards. This is so since the refracted light has crossed over the visual axis and the upper portion of the retinal image has been eclipsed by the straight edge.

This kind of appearance is familiar to most people when viewing a star in the night sky. It results also in multiple images (monocular polyopia) of the tips of the crescent moon. The student should carefully examine the appearance of a star or small source, first with one eye and then

* The eye is myopic about 1 dioptre and has a small amount of astigmatism.

the other, with and without distance correction, or with and without spheres of ± 1 D and ± 2 D. Move a card slowly across the pupil in various directions and note the successive disappearance of different portions of the star figure. Observe also through a stenopaic slit and through a pinhole moved about so as to expose different parts of the pupil.

These effects, in moderate degree, pass unnoticed in ordinary vision when there are many other objects in the field and an appreciable amount of general illumination around them.

The size of the composite image of the small source increases and its intensity diminishes, as the blurring is

Fig. 11.7—Appearance of Star to Author's Left Eye; pupil diameter 7 mm.

increased. The appearance also changes according to the intensity of the source. When the illumination is low, only the brightest parts of the pattern are visible, and the small source appears as a small cluster of spots, one brighter than the remainder. When the illumination is intense, the separate parts of the pattern of Fig. 11.7 merge together and are surrounded by brilliantly coloured radiating fine lines—the so-called "ciliary corona". This appearance results, for example, when a motor headlight is looked at in dark surroundings.

When the eye accommodates for the luminous point, it is seen as a small round spot without irregularities in moderate illumination, but the irregularities manifest themselves again when the illumination is increased. They may even be present to some extent in moderate illumination in eyes with marked opacities or other local blemishes.

Every point of a bright object is imaged in the manner described above.

The out-of-focus image of a bright vertical stroke does not consist of a vertical patch in which the intensity decreases gradually to zero ; after falling to zero the intensity rises again, forming a faint " ghost " image on each side of the central streak ; there may even be more than one such ghost image on each side.

A black line on a bright background gives the same kind of effect as the bright line, the central black image being flanked on either side by a dark ghost image.

From the preceding paragraphs we see that the theoretical distribution of light in the retinal image is affected by spherical and chromatic aberration, by errors of centring of the eye's optical system, but mainly by the irregular aberrations. Owing to the adaptability of the central nervous mechanism in interpreting the resulting nervous impulses transmitted to it, however, the presence of these imperfections in the retinal image does not, in most cases, seriously impair the acuity of the eye in carrying out its normal tasks ; the imperfections generally are physiological.

Nevertheless it is important to realise that the aberrations are present and that they are of the same order of magnitude as the errors of refraction we seek to determine and correct ; at least this is so in a large proportion, say 60 per cent or more, of subjects. They must, therefore, influence matters during the progress of a test, whether subjective or objective, the more so as they are irregular in character. It is almost certainly the case that they are responsible, in some measure, for the discrepancies that arise between the refraction as determined subjectively, by retinoscopy, or by objective optometers. And when the irregularities are marked, the ordinary methods of testing are rendered difficult or impossible. Further progress in the development of routine methods of examination and of instruments depends upon an appreciation of the effects of these aberrations.

ENTOPTIC PHENOMENA.

11.6. Muscae Volitantes.

Such opacities, changes of density and surface irregularities as have been mentioned above, and other opaque or semi-opaque bodies that are to be found in the various media of all eyes, are not noticed in ordinary vision except in so far as they spoil the homocentric character of the refracted pencil within the eye and so reduce the visual acuity, if they are sufficiently prominent. But under suitable conditions these small bodies and filaments within the eye are made evident subjectively. Most people have noticed shadowy objects, mostly dark, apparently floating about in front of the eye when looking towards some broad and more or less uniformly illuminated background such as the sky. Some of them are circular with bright centres; others appear like long wavy filaments or strings of pearls. If the gaze is lowered and then quickly raised, these floating projections also fall and rise again in the field of view, rising higher than the point of fixation and then gradually settling down again. Usually, if the observer attempts to fix one of these objects with the intention of examining it more closely, the object floats away and cannot be overtaken. On this account these particular entoptic appearances were called MUSCAE VOLITANTES (flying gnats) by early investigators. They are due to small opacities in the vitreous gel and have varying degrees of freedom of movement within that body. They are visible because of the shadows they cast on the retina and are observed the more easily the closer they lie to the retina.

There are many other entoptic appearances but these require special conditions of illumination, especially a small source of light, to render them apparent.

We may divide entoptic phenomena into two broad classes: (A) those caused by objects in the ocular media and (B) those associated with the retinal circulation or with the structures within the retina itself.

11.7. Conditions for Visibility of Entoptic Phenomena.

In order that the shadow cast on a screen by an opaque body shall be well defined and sharp at the edges, the source of light must be small and the object not too far removed from the screen. (We will neglect here the effects on the shadow edge of diffraction of the light passing the edge of the obstacle.) When the source of light is large, no perceptible shadow of a small object is produced on the screen unless the object is very close to it. In ordinary vision light enters the pupil, which is large in comparison with the bodies we are considering, in all directions. The

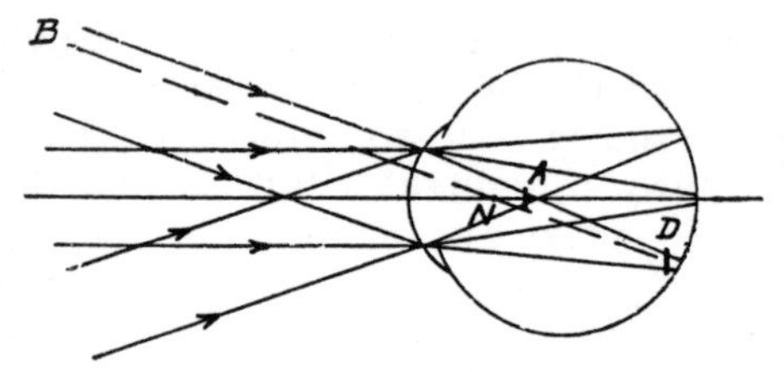

FIG. 11.8—SHADOW ON RETINA OF OPACITY AT D.

effect of an opacity, unless it is very near to the retina, is merely to reduce slightly the general illumination of a considerable area of the fundus. Thus an opacity at A (Fig. 11.8) will obstruct some of the light in a large number of pencils coming from points of the source, for example the sky, in various directions. An opacity at D, however, close to the retina, will obstruct most of the light in but a few pencils entering the eye in the general direction BND, and so will produce a relatively easily perceptible shadow on the retina just behind D. This explains why the so-called muscae volitantes, caused by bodies in the vitreous lying near to the retina, are made visible by merely gazing at the sky ; whereas small bodies lying farther from the retina, including those within the crystalline lens, aqueous and cornea, require the source to be very small.

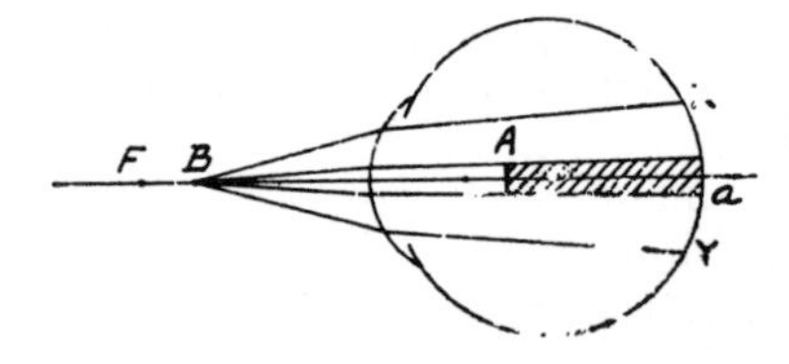

FIG. 11.9—SHARPER SHADOW OF OPACITY AT A WHEN SOURCE B IS SMALL.

If the light from, say, an electric lamp is condensed by means of a lens of fairly wide aperture and short focus on to a small hole B in an opaque screen held close to the eye (Fig. 11·9) the pencil within the eye will be slightly divergent, parallel, or slightly convergent according as the hole B is within, at, or without the anterior focus of the eye. In Fig. 11.9 the hole is within the eye's anterior focus and the pencil inside the eye divergent. The circular area XY of the retina that is illuminated is the blur circle of the luminous point B and within this the shadow a of an opacity A is moderately sharp. The shadow must be blurred to a small extent since the source at B is not strictly a point.

If the luminous source B be moved laterally across the line of sight, or if the eye be moved correspondingly, the shadows of opacities will move across the retina and their projections across the field of view bounded by the pupil. The extent and the apparent direction of the apparent movement depend upon the distance of the opacity from the retina. In Fig. 11.10 (a) the opacities situated at A, D and E produce their shadows in the same place, in the centre of the illuminated area of the retina. When the source is displaced laterally as in (b), the shadow

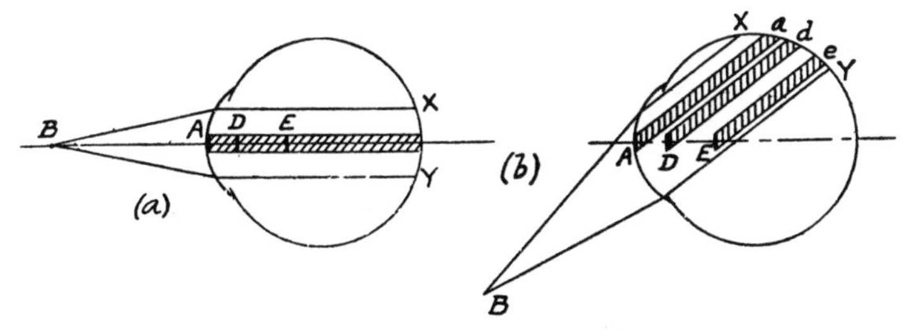

FIG. 11.10—RELATIVE ENTOPTIC PARALLAX.

d of the opacity D lying in the pupillary plane still remains in the centre of the illuminated area; the opacity A near the cornea will appear to have moved in the same direction as the source; and the opacity E in the opposite direction. LISTING who continued the earlier work of PURKINJE on these entoptic appearances, first pointed out (1845) how the situation of opacities could be roughly estimated by this method of *relative entoptic parallax.*

11.8. A. Entoptic Appearances due to Objects in the Media.

In addition to the muscae volitantes already described, there are other entoptic appearances caused by small bodies of optical density different from the media in which they lie. They are made evident by using a small source of light as explained in the last paragraph and include:

Drops of tears, mucus and irregularities on the corneal surface:

Small bodies in the lens substance; the star-figure of the lens; dark lines radiating inwards from the periphery of the luminous field due to incipient cataract.

DIFFRACTION HALOS.

Not only do individual bodies in the media produce shadows or specks of light on the retina, as above, but any small structures that are congregated together in large

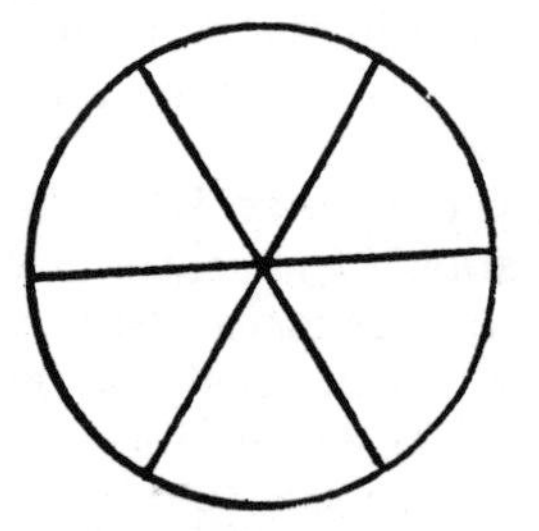

FIG. 11.11—PHYSIOLOGICAL HALO AND CORRESPONDING POSITION OF LENS STAR.

numbers will act as a diffracting screen and so produce light patterns on the retina characteristic of their formation. If a small bright light such as a lighted match is observed immediately on waking on a dark morning, the light will usually appear surrounded by a circular ring of colours with blue inside and red outside—a diffraction halo similar to the one obtained on looking through a lycopodium plate. In the case of the author the angular diameter of the red ring is about 14 degrees. This halo is caused by globules of mucus on the cornea and disappears when these are wiped away at the first blink or so of the eyelids.

Although the bright halo due to mucus on the cornea disappears upon blinking, there are still certain phenomena, though less prominent, to be noticed when a small bright source is observed in dark surroundings. In the first place there are circular black diffraction rings immediately surrounding the source and caused presumably by diffraction at the border of the pupil of the eye. Secondly, the source is surrounded by an immense number of narrow streaks of the spectrum colours radiating outwards from the source as centre—the ciliary corona;* this becomes fainter as the intensity of the source is decreased. Thirdly, the source is seen to be surrounded by a somewhat irregular coloured ring (or, on occasion, rings) showing a gradation of colours from violet nearest the source to red outside, the more prominent colours being the green and red.

The angular diameter of this halo varies somewhat between individuals; the mean diameters obtained on several subjects by EMSLEY and FINCHAM† (1922) were

Violet 4° 30′
Blue 5°
Green 5° 26′
Yellow 6°

The ring as seen by the observer and the corresponding position of his lens star are indicated in Fig. 11.11. It cannot be seen when the pupil is less than 2 to 3 mm. in diameter and increases in intensity as the pupil diameter is increased. It is not of equal brilliancy at all portions. Six equidistant portions, each of angular extent roughly 20°, stand out more clearly than the remainder. It is fairly conclusively established that this halo is caused by the approximate radial structure of the crystalline lens, which extends to within a millimetre or two of its centre. If a stenopaic slit is passed across the pupil as indicated in

---

* §11.5.

† "Diffraction Halos in Normal and Glaucomatous Eyes": *Trans. Opt. Soc.*, XXIII, 4, 1921-22.

Fig. 11.12, the halo assumes the successive appearances shown in the lower part of the diagram. In A the horizontal fibres at one side of the lens are exposed and the diffraction pattern aa′ is observed. As the slit is moved across, exposing fibres lying in various directions, the observed diffraction spectrum takes up different orientations in succession. It appears to rotate with a wheel-like motion.

The above halo is seen by all normal eyes when the circumstances as to brightness of source, surrounding darkness, large pupil, etc., are favourable. It is referred to as the normal or *physiological halo.* A much brighter halo is observed around a bright source by persons suffering from glaucoma. The size of this *glaucomatous halo* varies at

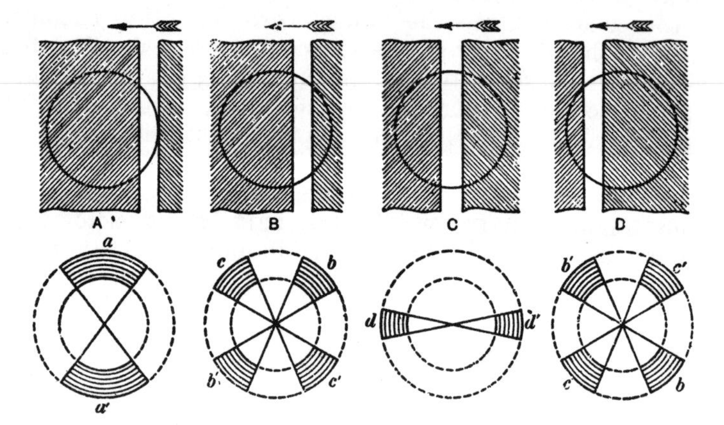

FIG. 11.12—BEHAVIOUR OF PHYSIOLOGICAL HALO ON PASSING A STENOPAIC SLIT ACROSS THE PUPIL.

different stages of the attack, presumably because the œdematous globules formed in the corneal tissues, or the tiny hillocks raised in the corneal epithelium,* by the increased intraocular pressure that accompanies the disease, vary in size as the attack progresses. When a stenopaic slit is traversed across the pupil, the ring decreases in intensity because of the reduction in the area of pupil exposed, but otherwise there is no effect. This establishes the fact that this halo is not due to radial structure but to a large number

* E. E. MADDOX considered that glaucomatous halos are due to tiny hillocks raised in the epithelium.

of equal small particles, as in the case of diffraction by a plate dusted over with lycopodium grains.

The stenopaic slit test thus forms a useful means of differentiating between the physiological halo caused by the crystalline lens and the pathological halo accompanying such a condition as glaucoma.

11.9. B. Entoptic Appearances due to Retinal Circulation and Structure.

To be perceived entoptically any object in the eye must lie in front of the percipient layers of the retina. The retinal blood vessels are thus situated and, although not observed in the ordinary way, they can be made evident subjectively by causing light to enter the eye at an unusual angle. The shadow of a given portion of a vessel is then cast upon a percipient area that does not receive that shadow in ordinary vision. Thus the retina receives a shadow pattern of the

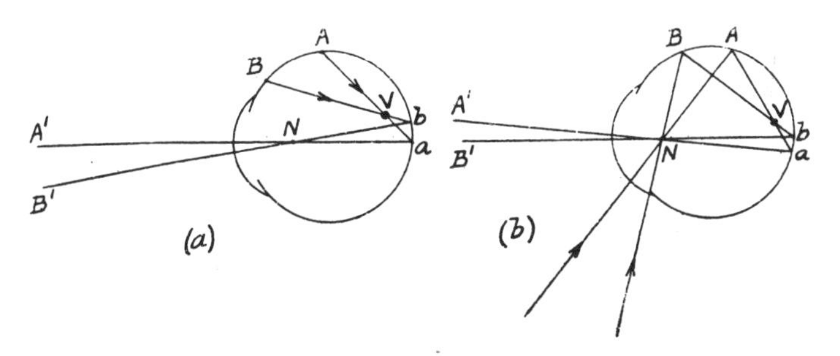

Fig. 11.13—Entoptic View of the Retinal Blood Vessels under Oblique Illumination.

retinal vessels to which it is unaccustomed and the vascular system, with the optic disc and the vessels ramifying in all directions, is then seen subjectively against a reddish yellow background. This was noted by Purkinje (1825) and explained by H. Müller (1855).

Suppose the light is made to enter the eye at a point A on the sclera (Fig. 11.13 (a)); the light from an intense source may be concentrated on A by a short focus positive lens. The sclera being translucent, this point then becomes a small source sending light into the eye in all directions. A blood vessel at V casts a shadow on the retina at a; this shadow is projected outwards through the nodal point

N and is seen in the direction A′ in the field of view. If the source is shifted to B, the shadow moves from a to b and the projection from A′ to B′. Thus the projection of the system of vessels in the field of view moves in the same direction as the source.

This phenomenon probably derives its chief importance from the fact that it affords a means of estimating the position of the percipient elements of the retina. H. MÜLLER measured the movement A′ B′ of the shadow projection when the source was shifted a known amount AB. Using the known average dimensions of the eye we obtain the distance ab of the actual shadow movement on the retina and so, from the geometry of the triangles abV and ABV, the distance of V from the percipient layer of the retina. In this way H. MÜLLER found that this layer lies 0·17 to 0·36 mm. behind the blood vessels and anatomical measurements showed that the layer of rods and cones lies in this region. This somewhat indirect evidence provides the only proof we have that the rods and cones are the percipient elements in the retina.

The above experiment may be varied by causing the light to enter obliquely through the cornea as indicated in Fig. 11.13 (b).

There are still further appearances to be observed entoptically. The capillaries in the macular region can be seen by looking at the sky through a pinhole or slit. They surround an area, of angular diameter 1° 30′ or so, free from vessels. The small bright spots seen shooting along circuitous paths, when a bright surface such as the sky is regarded through a blue glass, are considered to be the blood corpuscles moving along the capillaries just mentioned. The yellow spot may be observed in intermittent diffuse illumination, as by placing blue and yellow glasses before the eye alternately ; it appears as a circle surrounded by a blue halo.

When the eyes are completely covered so that no light can enter them, the field does not become black but presents a slightly luminous background upon which there is a scintillation of spots, figures and clouds of light moving about in various ways. The after-images of objects previously seen should be allowed to fade before looking for these appearances. They have been called the *intrinsic light of the retina, luminous dust*, etc., and their origin is controversial.

EXERCISES. CHAPTER XI.

1. Write out a classification of the imperfections or aberrations of the optical system of the eye. Give some account of the relative importance of these imperfections from the point of view of the subject's acuteness of vision. Why is it that, in the presence of these imperfections, the eye is able to discriminate such fine detail ?

2. Make a list of the optical defects of an emmetropic eye considered as an optical instrument. Explain briefly what each defect means and how it can be demonstrated. Why is it usually not noticed ? (B.O.A. Hons.)

3. With the aid of a diagram describe Young's optometer. Explain how the instrument may be used to obtain a measure of the spherical aberration of the eye. Give some figures as to the spherical aberration of the average eye.

4. Describe simple experiments that show that the eye has spherical and chromatic aberration. Give explanatory diagrams. Describe a piece of apparatus for subjectively measuring the refractive condition of eyes, the apparatus being based upon the existence of chromatic aberration in the eye.

5. A standard emmetropic eye (power 60 D) views a small object, situated on its primary direction, through a pinhole displaced laterally by 3 mm. from the fixation line. The object appears to be displaced through an angle of 0·25△. Find the axial spherical aberration of the eye for this zone, in mm. and in dioptres. Give an explanatory diagram.

6. If a red light and a green light are viewed simultaneously through a pinhole which is moved vertically upwards in front of the eye, the lights appear to move. Describe the movements seen by an emmetropic eye and account for the effect with the aid of diagrams.

7. A person with a large pupil and provided with a positive lens to bring the far point to within a convenient distance, observes a small object such as a pin through a diaphragm pierced with four small holes arranged as in Fig. 11.2. Give diagrams showing the successive appearances to the observer as the pin is approached close to the eye from a position beyond the artificial far point. Explain the appearances with the aid of a ray diagram.

8. Using the following figures for the refractive indices of water for the standard wavelengths, calculate the chromatic aberration of the reduced eye of radius 5·555 mm. separating air from water, between $\lambda = 486 \cdot 1$ mμ and $\lambda = 656 \cdot 3$ mμ.

λ	486·1	589·3	656·3
index	1·3378	1·3336	1·3317

Write a brief note comparing this result with the values that have been obtained by different investigators for the chromatic aberration of the actual eye.

9. Write a brief account of the chromatic aberration in the eye, including a description of the conditions under which it can be rendered manifest. Why is it not so noticeable during ordinary acts of vision ? (S.M.C.)

10. Describe, giving an explanatory diagram, the general principle of a method for measuring the spherical aberration of the eye with some accuracy. Show how the aberration is derived from the measurements made.

Draw graphs, approximately to scale, indicating the general trend of the eye's spherical aberration, for light of different colours, from the visual axis outwards ; and comment briefly on them.

11. Describe, with a diagram, the form of the refracted pencil in the neighbourhood of the retina, in the presence of both spherical and chromatic aberration. Comment upon the distribution of light across the section of the pencil and upon the sharpness of vision of the eye.

What kind of changes take place in this pencil when the eye accommodates ?

12. Comment upon the effects of the oblique astigmatism that might be expected to arise because of the relative inclination of the visual and optical axes of the eye.

A diagram consisting of many equally spaced concentric circles appears more sharply defined along certain radiating sectors than others and these clear sectors appear to rotate. Give a possible explanation of this.

13. Discuss the "irregular" aberrations of the eye ; and explain the characteristic appearance of a star in a clear sky and the monocular polyopia of an object such as the crescent moon.

Write a short note on the relation between the aberrations of the eye and the detection and measurement of small amounts of ametropia.

14. Give a diagram of, and explain the typical appearance of, a star and of a bright vertical stroke on a dark background, when slightly out of focus. What would happen to the appearance if a pinhole disc were held before the eye and moved about to expose different areas of the pupil ? In what circumstances is this procedure of service in clinical practice ?

15. Explain, with a diagram, the conditions to be satisfied in order that entoptic phenomena shall be visible. What is meant by "relative entoptic parallax" and what information concerning opacities within the eye can be gathered from its application ?

16. Describe briefly any two entoptic phenomena and the method of observing them. (B.O.A.)

17. Describe the physiological halo that is seen when, under suitable conditions, a small bright source is observed in dark surroundings. Describe the conditions ; and explain how the halo is formed.

Explain carefully, with diagrams, what happens to the halo if a card with a vertical straight edge is passed slowly across the pupil.

18. Explain the cause of the so-called physiological halo seen when a small bright source is viewed in dark surroundings ; and the halo seen by an eye suffering from an attack of glaucoma. Describe a simple test for differentiating between the two halos and explain why the behaviour is different in the two cases.

19. One of the subjective symptoms of glaucoma is the appearance of coloured halos surrounding sources of light. How would you

establish whether the halos seen by a given subject were due to glaucoma or whether they were normal physiological halos ? Give a careful explanation, with appropriate diagrams, of the basis of your test.

20. Give a description of some entoptic phenomena that are caused by the anatomic structure of the normal eye. Describe briefly the methods necessary to demonstrate these effects.

21. Give the theory of an optical method designed to prove that the rod and cone layer of the retina is the sensitive layer. (S.M.C.)

22. Explain how it is possible to see the shadows of the blood vessels in your own eye. What significance has this phenomenon on the theory of vision ? (B.O.A.)

23. Describe the conditions under which entoptic phenomena can best be observed. Indicate how an incipient cataract would appear by this method of observation. How can the method be used to confirm that the light-sensitive layer of the retina corresponds to the rod-cone layer ? (B.O.A.)

24. What are entoptic phenomena ? Describe two such phenomena, saying how they can be observed. (B.O.A.)

25. Describe two experiments to show that the eye is not perfectly achromatic. (B.O.A.)

26. Assuming that the optical system of the eye can be represented by a single spherical refracting surface of radius $5 \cdot 73$ mm. enclosing a medium of refractive index $1 \cdot 336$, calculate the longitudinal chromatic aberration of the eye when $N_F - N_C = 0 \cdot 0065$. How can the existence of this chromatic aberration be demonstrated ? (B.O.A.)

APPENDIX

Short biographical notes of scientists, most of whom are mentioned in the text, who have contributed to the advancement of physiological optics.

ABNEY, Sir William de W. (1844–1920). British. Researches in photography, spectrum analysis and colour vision. Author of *Colour Vision* (London, 1895; last edition 1913).

AGUILLON, Francois (1567–1617). Author of *Opticorum* (Antwerp, 1613). First used the term *horopter* and laid the foundations of "*horoptology*".

AIRY, Sir George B. (1801–92). Lucasian professor of Mathematics and Plumian professor of Astronomy at Cambridge. His activities included research in physical and instrumental optics; first to use sphero-cylindrical lenses for correcting ocular astigmatism (1827).

AUBERT, Hermann (1826-92). Professor of physiology in Rostock. Researches in visual sensations; first to define light sense.

BABBAGE, Charles (1792–1871). Lucasian professor at Cambridge. Inventor of calculating machines. Made the first ophthalmoscope.

BADAL, Jules (1840–1929). Professor of ophthalmology at Bordeaux. Inventor of several clinical instruments, including his optometer and ophthalmometer.

BALMER, Johann Jakob (1825–98). Teacher and lecturer at Basle University. Paper "Notig über die Spektrallinien des Wasserstoffs", *Ann. der Phys. und Chemie*, 1885.

BERRY, Sir George A. Ophthalmologist; surgeon-oculist to His Majesty in Scotland. Author of works on eye diseases. E. E. MADDOX was at one time his assistant at Edinburgh.

BOEHM, Ludwig (1811–69). Researches in squint and therapy with coloured lights (1862).

BOLL, Fr. (1849–78).

BOLTZMANN, Ludwig von (1844–1906). Professor of Physics at Vienna from 1895 until his death. Contributions to kinetic theory and second law of thermodynamics.

BOWMAN, Sir William (1816–92). Ophthalmic surgeon. Professor of physiology, King's College, London; friend of DONDERS. Recorded reflex movements (1859) that led later to retinoscopy. The cornea contains a layer known as Bowman's membrane.

BREWSTER, Sir David (1781–1868). Scottish physicist. Researches in physical optics (inc. polarisation) and stereoscopy. Invented the kaleidoscope. Principal of Edinburgh University from 1859.

BRÜCKE, Ernst W. R. von (1819–92). Professor of physiology at Vienna. Researches in ocular anatomy (ciliary muscle), and physiology, stereoscopic vision, colour vision.

BUFFON, George L. L. Comte de (1707–88). French scientist. Author of *Histoire Naturelle* (1749–67).

CHARPENTIER, A. (1852–1916).

COUPER, John (1836–1918). Surgeon and ophthalmic physician at Moorfields Hospital. A pioneer in ophthalmoscopy and retinoscopy.

CRAMER, Antoine (1822–55). Researches on accommodation of eye and binocular vision.

CUIGNET, Ferdinand (? –1889). French army surgeon. First introduced retinoscopy (keratoscopie) into practice (1874).

CUMMING, William (1822–55). British (Glasgow and London) ophthalmic surgeon. Apparently the first to illuminate the eye for the purpose of examining its interior (1846).

CZERMAK, J. (1828–73). Work on ocular dioptrics.

DALTON, John (1766–1844). English chemist, celebrated for the atomic theory. The first to describe colour blindness scientifically (Daltonism).

DESCARTES, René (1596–1650). French philosopher, especially celebrated in mathematics. Author of *Discours de la Méthode* (1637).

DOLLOND, John (1706–61) F.R.S. Born in London. Instrument maker. Famed for his introduction of achromatic lenses (1758), although such lenses had been made earlier by Chester MOORE HALL.

DONDERS, Franciscus Cornelius (1818–89). Professor of physiology and ophthalmology at Utrecht. One of the great figures of ophthalmology. Elucidated the anomalies of refraction and accommodation and laid the foundations for modern methods of refraction. His work *Accommodation and Refraction of the Eye* (1864) is a classic.

DOVE, Heinrich W. (1803–79). Professor of natural philosophy at Berlin. Applied stereoscopy to the detection of forged banknotes. Author of *Optical Studies* (1859).

DUANE, Alexander (1858–1926). American ophthalmologist. Known best for his work on ocular muscles and as the translator of FUCH's *Textbook of Ophthalmology*.

FECHNER, Gustav Theodor (1801–87). Professor of physics at Leipzig. Author of *Elemente der Psychophysik* (1860). Worked also on colour vision.

FRAUNHOFER, Joseph von (1787–1826). German. From humble beginnings earned a world-wide reputation in the field of optics. Best known to opticians in association with the dark lines of the solar spectrum and diffraction phenomena.

FUCHS, Ernst (1850–1930). Professor of ophthalmology at Vienna, in succession to JAEGER. Author of *Textbook of Ophthalmology*, translated by DUANE.

GALILEI, GALILEO (1564–1642). An Italian, born at Pisa; belonged to a noble family whose original family name of BONAJUTI was changed to GALILEI in 1343. Mathematician and astronomer; designer of the Galilean type of telescope; discoverer of the laws of motion. He was persecuted by the Inquisition for his teachings on the Copernician system of the Universe.

(Note: Many famous men of mediæval and renaissance times were known by their Christian names; others by their surnames. Galileo was one of the former.)

GAUSS, Johann K. F. (1777–1855). Professor of mathematics at Göttingen. Simplified the mathematical expressions dealing with the passage of light through optical systems. Author of *Dioptrische Untersuchungen* (1840).

GOETHE, Johann Wolfgang (1749–1832). Famous chiefly as a German writer and critic, but interested also in science. He attacked YOUNG's views on colour vision.

GRAEFE, Albrecht von (1828–70). Famous Berlin ophthalmic surgeon. Active in all branches of ophthalmology, particularly concerning binocular vision anomalies and squint. Adapted the Galilean telescope to optometry. Contemporary with von Graefe was Alfred GRAEFE, who was also prominent in researches on binocular vision.

GULLSTRAND, Allvar (1862–1930). Swedish ophthalmologist. Professor of ophthalmology at Upsala and at Stockholm. Researches in dioptrics of the eye (e.g. schematic eye) and instrumental devices for ocular examination (e.g. slit lamp, reflex-free ophthalmoscopy).

HECHT, Selig (1893–1948). Professor of Biophysics at Columbia University, U.S.A. Work on colour vision, adaptation, quantum aspects of vision.

HELMHOLTZ, Hermann von (1821–94). Descended on mother's side from WM. PENN. Professor of physiology successively at Königsberg, Bonn and Heidelberg; professor of physics at Berlin from 1871. Equally distinguished in physiology, mathematics and physics. The physicist HERTZ was one of his pupils. His physiological works are connected mainly with the eye, ear and nervous system. His great classic on *Physiological Optics* appeared first in 1856–66; its third edition (1909–11) was translated into English by the Optical Society of America to commemorate the hundredth anniversary of HELMHOLTZ's birth. YOUNG and HELMHOLTZ are the two great pioneers in physiological optics.

HERING, Ewald (1834–1918). Professor of physiology at Prague. Opposed the Young-Helmholtz three components theory of colour vision and put forward his more psychological opponent-colours theory (1876).

HERSCHEL, Sir John (1792–1871). Great astronomer; supported the wave theory of light in his article in the "Encyclopædia Metropolitana" (1827). Son of Sir William HERSCHEL (1738–1822), also a famous astronomer.

HIRSCHBERG, Julius (1844–1925). German ophthalmologist; studied in von GRAEFE's clinic in Berlin. Founded the *Zentralblatt für Augenheilkunde* in 1877. Historian of ophthalmology.

HOLMGREN, Alarik F. (1831–97). Swedish ophthalmologist. Professor of Physiology at Upsala. Introduced the wool colour vision test. Worked also on poisons, retinal currents.

HOOKE, Robert (1635–1703). Famous British instrument maker and inventor. He designed and built the Monument to mark the origin of the great fire of London. Author of *Micrographia* (1665) containing the first suggestion of the transverse character of light undulations. A contemporary and opponent of NEWTON.

ISHIHARA, Shinobu. Professor of ophthalmology of Tokyo. Designer of the colour vision card test bearing his name.

JACKSON, Edward (1856–1942). American ophthalmologist. Professor of ophthalmology in the University of Colorado until 1921. Has written extensively on all branches of ophthalmology.

JAEGER, E. von (1818–84). Professor of ophthalmology at Vienna. His reading types are still used.

JAVAL, L. Emil (1839–1907). French engineer and mathematician who became the first director of the Laboratory of physiological optics, Sorbonne, Paris. Translated HELMHOLTZ's Physiological Optics (1st Edition) into French (1867). Researches in binocular vision and keratometry. His *Manuel du Strabisme* appeared in 1896. JAVAL contracted glaucoma and became blind; he was succeeded by TSCHERNING.

KEPLER, Johann (1571–1630). German (Würtemberg) astronomer and mathematician. He and SCHEINER were probably the earliest to formulate clear ideas of the eye and vision. In his *Dioptrics* (1611) he referred to a "visual substance" in the retina and made acute observations on ametropia, accommodation and binocular vision.

KOHLRAUSCH, Rudolph Hermann Arndt (1809–58). Measurement of corneal curvature.

KÖNIG, Arthur (1856–1901). Researches on colour vision.

KRIES, Johannes von (1853–1928). Professor of physiology at Freiburg im Breisgau. Researches in colour vision, supporting the trichromatic theories. Joint editor of 3rd edition of HELMHOLTZ's *Physiological Optics*.

KÜHNE, Willy (1837–1900). Succeeded HELMHOLTZ to chair of Physiology at Heidelberg. Work on chemistry of retina and on enzymes.

LADD-FRANKLIN, Christine (1848–1930). Lecturer in psychology and logic at Columbia University. Opposed the trichromatic theory of colour vision and proposed the more psychological theory bearing her name (1892).

LAMBERT, Johann Heinrich (1728–77). German (Alsace) philosopher and mathematician. Author of *Photometria* (1760) dealing with photometry. Lambert's law.

LANDOLT, Edmond (1846–1926). After studying under HELMHOLTZ and DONDERS became oculist to the Institution Nationale des Jeunes Aveugles, Paris. Author of numerous works on ophthalmology. Researches in ocular muscles and their anomalies.

LE CONTE, Joseph. Professor of geology and natural history in the University of California. Author of *Sight* (1880) containing useful experimental observations on binocular vision.

LEONARDO da VINCI (1452–1519). Italian painter, sculptor, architect and engineer. He incorporated acute observations of natural phenomena into his works of art.

LISTING, Johann Benedict (1808–82). Professorship at Göttingen. Researches in ocular dioptrics; introduced the nodal points (due to L. MOSER) into the optical system of the schematic eye.

MADDOX, Ernest Edmond (1860–1933). Ophthalmic surgeon. Researches in anomalies of binocular vision. Author of *Tests and Studies of the Ocular Muscles* (1895).

MARIOTTE, Edmé (1620–84). Prior of a monastery near Dijon. Investigator in physics and physical geography.

MATTHIESSEN, L. (1830–1906). Researches in ocular dioptrics, refractive index of crystalline lens.

MAXWELL, James Clerk (1831–79). Professor of experimental physics at Cambridge. His great work, *Electricity and Magnetism*, was published in 1873; predicted the identity of electric waves and light—the electro-magnetic theory of light—which led to HERZ's experiments (1886) and modern "wireless". The first to make colour measurements.

MEISSNER, G. (1829–1905). Researches in binocular vision.

MOSER, L. (1805–80). Applied the theoretical work of GAUSS to the optical system of the eye and first suggested the idea of nodal points (1844).

MÜLLER, Heinrich (1820–64), of Würzburg. Investigations into rod and cone layer as percipient layer.

MÜLLER, Johannes (1801–58). Professor of physiology at Bonn and Berlin. Founder of modern physiology. His *Handbuch der Physiologie des Menschen* (1833–40) was translated into English (1840–49) by Dr. Baly.

NAGEL, W. Albrecht (1833–95). German ophthalmologist. Suggested the metre-angle as a unit for measurement of ocular convergence. His son, W. A. NAGEL (1870–1911) of Rostock, was one of the editors of the third edition of HELMHOLTZ's *Physiological Optics* and designer of the anomaloscope.

NEWTON, Sir Isaac (1642–1727). Lucasian professor at Cambridge (at age 26). One of the greatest scientists of all time. His theory on the laws of gravitation and motion published in his famous *Principia* (1687). Discovered the methods of differential calculus, elaborated by LEIBNITZ. His work on dispersion, colour and optics was published in *Opticks* (1706); *Lectiones Opticæ* (1669, 1728).

PANUM, P. L. (1820–85). Professor of physiology at Kiel. Researches in binocular vision.

PARENT, H. Parisian and London ophthalmologist. A pioneer of retinoscopy (ca. 1880).

PERCIVAL, Archibald Stanley (1862–1935). Ophthalmic surgeon. Author of works and papers on optics including *The Prescribing of Spectacles* (1910). Designer of "best form" spectacle lenses.

PLANCK, Max K. E. L. (1858–1947). Professor of Physics, Berlin; originator of the conception of quantum of action (h) and quantum theory of radiation.

PLATEAU, J. (1801–83) of Ghent. Author of *Bibliographie Analytique des Principaux Phénomenes Subjectifs de la Vision*, embracing the literature to 1882.

PORTER, T. C. (1822–1901). Researches on flicker phenomena.

PORTERFIELD, W. (*d.* 1768, age about 70). Scottish ophthalmic surgeon and professor at Edinburgh (1724–26). Author of *A Treatise on the Eye* (Edinburgh, 1759). The first to adapt the Scheiner principle in the construction of an optometer, which was later improved by YOUNG.

PRENTICE, Charles F. (born 1854). Engineer ; writer on ophthalmic lenses.

PULFRICH, Carl (1858–1927). German scientist. Researches in many branches of applied optics, including binocular vision ; author of article on *Stereoscopy* in Encylopædia Britannica (11th Edition). Designer of the Pulfrich refractometer.

PURKINJE or PURKYNĚ, Johannes Evangeliste (1787–1869). Born in Bohemia. Professor of physiology at Breslau and Prague. A brilliant observer of ocular phenomena, described in his *Commentatio de Examine physiologico Organi Visus et Systematic cutanie* (1823).

RAMSDEN, Jesse (1735–1800). Mathematical instrument designer. F.R.S. Designed spectacle lenses. Ramsden eyepiece and Ramsden circle (exit pupil).

RAYLEIGH, John William Strutt, Lord (1842–1919). Professor of experimental physics at Cambridge ; succeeded TYNDAL as professor of natural philosophy at the Royal Institution. Author of *Theory of Sound* (1878). Joint discoverer with RAMSAY of argon. Researches on flight and explosives, optical polish, diffraction.

ROBERTSON, Douglas Argyll (1837–1909). Ophthalmic surgeon at Edinburgh Infirmary. Paper on effect of spinal diseases on pupil light reflex (1870). Lectured in practical physiology in Edinburgh University.

ROHR, Louis Otto Moritz von (1868–1940). German scientist associated with the firm ZEISS of Jena from 1895 ; Professor at the University, Jena. Author of numerous works and papers on applied optics, including *Die Binokularen Instrumente* (1907) and *Das Brillenglas als optisches Instrument* (1934).

First trigonometrically computed "best form" spectacle lenses, anisometropia spectacles.

RUETE, T. (1810–67).

SANSON, L. J. (1790–1841). Author of *Leçons sur les maladies des yeux* (Paris, 1837).

SCHEINER, Christopher (1573–1650). Professor in one of the colleges of the Society of Jesus in Germany. Made and used telescopes for astronomical observations. His *Oculus sive fundamentum opticum* (Innsbruck, 1619) was probably the first formal treatise on physiological optics and contains many acute observations on ocular anatomy and refraction.

SCHIÖTZ, Hjalmar August (1850–1927). Professor of opthalmology at Oslo (Christania). Associated with JAVAL in designing the clinical ophthalmometer.

SCHMIDT-RIMPLER, H. (1838–1915).

SCHULTZE, Max (1825–74).

SEEBECK, L. F. W. A. (1805–49).

SMITH, Priestley (1845-1933). Ophthalmic surgeon. Professor of ophthalmology at Birmingham. Founder of the *Ophthalmic Review*. Researches in glaucoma.

SMITH, Robert (1689–1768). Plumian professor of astronomy at Cambridge from 1716. Author of *A Compleat System of Optics* (1738) and *Harmonics* (1748).

SNELLEN, Herman (1834–1908). Professor of ophthalmology at Utrecht, succeeding DONDERS, whose pupil he had been. He was succeeded at Utrecht in 1899 by H. SNELLEN, Junr., who died in 1929.

STEFAN, Josef (1835–93). Professor of Physics, Vienna, and Director of Physical Institute. Researches in sound, light and electricity. Laws embodying first successful connection between radiation and absolute temperature; *Sitzungber der Akad. der Wissenschaften*, Vienna, 1879.

STEVENS, George T. American ophthalmologist. Author of *Motor Apparatus of the Eyes* (1906).

STILLING, J. (1842–1915). Introduced the Stilling colour vision test cards.

STOKES, Sir George Gabriel (1819–1903). Lucasian professor at Cambridge. Discovered fluorescence; researches in solar and stellar chemistry. A pioneer in the detection of ocular astigmatism. Delivered the Burnett lectures on Light (1887).

TALBOT, William Henry Fox (1800–77). Pioneer in photography. Author of *Pencil of Nature* (on photography, 1846) and an early decipherer of the Ninevite cuneiform inscriptions. Talbot-Plateau law.

THORNER, Walther. Investigations in ophthalmoscopy.

TSCHERMAK, A. (1870–). Professor of physiology, Prague Researches on visual processes, binocular vision.

TSCHERNING, Marius H. E. (1854–1939). Former Director of Laboratory of physiological optics, Sorbonné, Paris. Researches in ocular aberrations, mechanism of accommodation. Author of *Physiologic Optics* (English edition, 1900).

VOLKMANN, Alfred W. (1800–77). Professor of physiology at Leipzig and Halle. Author of *Physiologische Untersuchungen im Gebiete der Optik* (1864).

WEBER, Ernst Heinrich (1795–1878). Professor of anatomy and physiology at Leipzig. Researches on the senses.

WHEATSTONE, Sir Charles (1802–75). Professor of experimental philosophy at King's College. Associated with FARADAY. Pioneer of electrical signalling. Explained the principle of the stereoscope in a paper to the Royal Society (1838). *Scientific Papers* published by the Physical Society (1879).

WHEWELL, William (1794–1866). Master of Trinity College. Philosopher and historian of science. Collaborated with AIRY (1826–28) in experiments on the earth's density; researches on binocular vision.

WIEN, Wilhelm (1864–1928). German physicist; awarded Nobel prize in 1911 for his work on optics and radiation. Discoveries about cathode rays and canal rays. Professor of Physics at Würzburg, 1900, and at Munich, 1920.

WOLLASTON, William Hyde (1766–1828). Physician, chemist and natural philosopher. Invented the reflecting goniometer and camera lucida; discovered the dark lines in the solar spectrum; initiated critical angle refractometry; designed the first periscopic spectacle lenses (1801).

WORTH, Claud (d. 1936). Ophthalmic surgeon. Surgeon at Moorfields Eye Hospital (1905–21). Author of *Squint* (1903).

YOUNG, Thomas (1773–1829). A self-educated genius who became professor of natural physiology at the Royal Institution. Was familiar with a dozen languages and fluent in several at age of fourteen. Researches in accommodation of the eye, colour vision (three components theory), interference, etc. were all brilliant. Transcribed the Egyptian hieroglyphics on the Rosetta stone. His doctrines were expounded in his *Bakerian Lecture*, Royal Society (1801); Phil. Trans. (1802); *Lectures* (1807). A great pioneer of physiological optics. Discovered astigmatism in his own eye, 1793.

ZINN, Johann Gottfried (1727–59). Researches in ocular anatomy.

SOME UNITS AND USEFUL RELATIONS

$\pi = 3\cdot1416$. Log $\pi = 0\cdot4971$.

1 metre = 39·371 inches ; 1 inch = 25·40 mm.

1 square metre = 10·76 square feet.

1μ = 1 micron = 10^{-3} mm. = $3\cdot937 \times 10^{-5}$ inch.

1 mμ = 1 millimicron = 10^{-6} mm. = $3\cdot937 \times 10^{-8}$ inch.

$$1 \text{ radian} = \frac{180}{\pi} \text{ deg.} = 57\cdot3° = 3438' = 206{,}300''.$$

$$1\ \nabla = 1 \text{ centrad} = \frac{1}{100} \text{ radian.}$$

$$1\ \triangle = 1 \text{ prism-dioptre} = \tan^{-1} \frac{1}{100} = 1\ \nabla \text{ very nearly.}$$

Force : 1 lb. = 444974 dynes.

Work or Energy : 1 erg = work done by 1 dyne acting through distance of 1 cm.

1 joule = 10^7 ergs ; 1 foot-lb. = 1·35626 joules.

Power : rate of doing work—

1 watt = 1 joule per sec. ; 1 horse-power = 746 watts.

1 B. of Trade unit $\doteqdot$ 1 kilowatt-hour = 1·34 horsepower-hour.

$$\text{If } ax^2 + bx + c = 0, \text{ then } x = \frac{-b \pm \sqrt{b^2 - 4ac}}{2a}$$

$$\text{sine} = \frac{\text{perp}}{\text{hypot}}; \quad \text{cosine} = \frac{\text{base}}{\text{hypot}}; \quad \text{tangent} = \frac{\text{perp}}{\text{base}}$$

$$\tan A = \frac{\sin A}{\cos A}; \quad \sin^2 A + \cos^2 A = 1$$

$$\sin 2A = 2 \sin A \cos A; \quad \cos 2A = 2\cos^2 A - 1 = 1 - 2\sin^2 A$$

Triangles : a, b, c are the sides ; A, B, C the opposite angles—

$$\frac{a}{\sin A} = \frac{b}{\sin B} = \frac{c}{\sin C}$$

$$a^2 = b^2 + c^2 - 2bc \cos A; \quad \text{Area} = \tfrac{1}{2}bc \sin A.$$

ANSWERS TO EXERCISES

CHAPTER II. Page 75.

1. 1·38 mm.
2. (*a*) 26·1 mins.; 0·76 △; 0·126 mm.
   (*b*) 20·6 „ 0·6 △; 0·10 „
   (*c*) 5 „ 0·146 △; 0·0243 „
3. (*a*) 37 secs. (*b*) H. 61$\frac{2}{3}$ minutes; V. 41$\frac{1}{3}$ minutes. H. 10·8 cm. V. 7·2 cm.
5. V. 4·08 cm.; H. 2·91 cm.
6. 66$\frac{2}{3}$ D; – 15 and 20 mm.; 1·25 mm.
10. 35 seconds.
15. (*a*) 0·625 mm.; (*b*) 0·437 mm.
16. 0·50 mm.; 1·72 degrees ; 167 cones.
18. 8·75, 13·10, 52·5 and 87·5 mm.
    images: 0·0242, 0·0363, 0·145 and 0·242 mm.
19. 5/12·4 or 6/14·9.
20. 52·4 mm.
24. V. = 3/60 very nearly; V.A. = 6/28·9.
28. About 6/4 to 6/5; probably about 2 minutes.
29. 0·0122 mm.; 0·073 △; 75·4 seconds.
30. 23·09 metres.
31. 25·1, 100·5 seconds.
35. 0·028 mm.

CHAPTER III. Page 116.

2. Ocular: + 0·50, + 4·00, – 0·667 and – 3·00 dioptres.
   Spectacle: + 0·497, + 3·79, – 0·673 and – 3·13 dioptres.
3. – 4 D; – 3 D.
4. 57·1 mm.; 166·7 mm.
5. (*a*) 0·364 mm.; (*b*) 0·333 mm.
6. (*a*) 5 cm. in front; (*b*) 10 cm. behind; (*c*) infinity.
7. 62·48 D; 5·335 mm.
8. + 9·01 D; + 7·63 D; + 8·62 D.
9. Myopia, 9 D.
10. 3·0 mm.; 0·54 mm.
11. 0·35 mm.; 118 mm.
12. 8/24 = 6/18.
13. 17·81 mm. from cornea.
15. 1·43°; 2·5 △; 0·417 mm. per second.
16. When refraction referred to eye's anterior focal point; – 0·363 mm. per dioptre.
18. (*a*) 0·35, 0·14 mm.; (*b*) 0·883, 0·353 mm.

20. 2 D ; 6 D.
21. 9·09 cm. ; 20·0 cm. ; 8·33 cm. in front of eye.
23. Infinity ; – 16·67 cm., 6 D.
24. 12·31 cm. ; $K = +2$ D ; $A = 6$ D.
25. – 11·11 cm.
26. 7·31 D.
27. 3 D ; 3·50 D.
28. At infinity.
29. 127 and 77·1 mm. in front of eye ; – 4·20 D.
30. + 5·71 D.
31. None ; myopia 3 D.
32. + 2 D ; 6 D.
33. All of it.
34. Manifest 4 D, latent 3 D.
35. Man. 5·0 D ; fac. 0·50 D ; abs. 4·50 D.
36. H_T + 4·50 D ; H_M + 3·50 D ; H_L + 1·00 D ; H_A = + 1·50 D. Amp + 3 D ; age about 46.
37. (a) H_T 7·5 D ; H_L 0 ; H_A 5·0 D ; Amp. 2·50 D.
(b) H_T 7·5 D ; H_M 6·0 D ; H_L 1·5 D ; H_A 3·0 D ; Amp. 4·5 D.
(c) H_T 7·5 D ; H_M 3·0 D ; H_L 4·5 D ; H_A 0 ; Amp. 10 D.
39. (a) Patches 0·225 mm. diam., separated 1·8 mm.
(b) 0·30 mm. diam., separated 2·4 mm.
40. Upper red patch 10·14 cm. above lower white patch. Patches 3·38 cm. diameter.
42. Scale for ocular refraction :
Myopia : in, 0·89, 1·75, 2·58, 3·39, 4·19 mm.
Hyperopia : out, 0·91, 1·86, 2·83, 3·83 and 4·87 mm.
43. Scale for ocular refraction :
Myopia : in, 2·68, 5·82, 9·48, 13·89 and 19·23 mm.
Hyperopia : out, 2·34, 4·39, 6·20, 7·82 and 9·25 mm.
44. $13\frac{1}{3}$ D.
46. x (in mm.) $= -\frac{1000}{P^2} E$; $P = 14·14$ D.
49. 20·40 mm. ; 0·2225 mm. ; 0·239 mm. ; 0·988.
50. Assuming axial myopia and 4 D spectacle refraction, $h' =$ 0·1263 mm.
51. 271 mm. ; blind spot appears nearer to fixation point.
52. 4·5 mm. ; axial error in mm. $= -\frac{n'}{F_o^2} \times 1000 = 0·37$ mm. per dioptre of refractive error.
53. 25·25 mm. (reduced eye) ; 0·242 mm. ; 0·237 mm. (Em.) ; ratio = 1·022 ; 0·213 mm.
56. + 11·25 D ; + 14·35 D ; + 3·8 D.
57. + 15·02 D ; + 19·02 D.
58. – 14·84 D (ocular).
59. + 9·38 D.

60. + 11·3 D ; 49·8 mm. from cornea.
61. Aphakic image 1·297 times larger.
62. 6·07 mm. ; 5·91 mm.
64. 20·04 mm. from reduced surface ; 61·08 D.
65. + 78·88 D.
66. + 7·775 D ; 0·99.
67. 1/65 ; 1/60 ; 1/55.
68. H. 4·76 mm. ; Em. 5·13 mm.
69. – 10 mm.
70. Assuming hyperopia reckoned from eye lens, 5·55 mm. out.
72. Aphakic image 1·075 times larger than Em. image.

CHAPTER IV. Page 160.

1. 20, 33·33 and 25 cm. ; horizontal.
2. First line distant 54·55 cm. ; 21·82 mm. long ; horizontal ; Second line distant 120 cm. ; 48 mm. long ; vertical ; Confusion disc, 75 cm.
3. Oval, vertical 0·4 mm., horizontal 0·2 mm. ; – 2·00 S./ – 2·00 C. ax. H.
4. Horizontal streak 0·0813 mm. vertically and 0·4227 mm. horizontally ; S.M.A.
8. Ocular refractions are : (a) + 5·09 S./ – 2·50 C. ax. 30 ; (*b*) – 4·65 S./ – 2·09 C. ax. 100 ; (*c*) – 4·19 S./ + 6·26 C. ax 135.
9. Accom. required 3·32 D in vertical and 3·13 D in horizontal.
10. (*a*) + 2·415 S./+ 1·82 C. ax. 45 ; (*b*) + 1·95 S./ – 4·01 C. ax. 60 ; (*c*) – 5·24 S./ – 1·10 C. ax. 70.
13. F_V 59 D ; F_H 57 D. Far points: V. + 33⅓ cm. ; H. + 20 cm. Amp. 10 D.
14. (*a*) About 9/15 to 9/18 ; (*b*) about 9/12 to 9/15 ; (*c*) about 9/48 or worse.
15. Amp. 6 D ; + 5·0 S./ – 2·0 C. ax. H. ; C.H.A. with the rule.
16. – 1·00 S./ – 3·00 C. ax. H. ; Amp 2 D ; vertical.
17. + 6·0 S./ + 0·41 C. ax. V. ; 0·50 D ; Amp. 2·6 D.
21. 25 cm., 140° line ; 13⅓ cm., 50° line.
22. R.E., 33⅓ cm., 90° ; 40 cm., 180° ; 90° line.
    L.E. 22·2 cm., 50° ; 20 cm., 140° ; 140° line.
23. 0·19 mm.
24. Vertical oval streak 0·44 mm. × 0·25 mm.
34. Broadly :
    (*a*) 1·0 to 1·25 D of myopia ; 2·0 to 2·5 D of Mx. A. or S.H.A. or C.H.A. ; 1·5 D or so of S.M.A.
    (*b*) Astigmatism with the rule of about 2 D of mixed or combined with some H. ; less if combined with some M.
39. Correction should be : – 2 25 S./ – 1·00 C. ax H.
47. Approx. 2·9 D against the rule.
48. + 1·39 S./ – 3·28 C. ax. 31 ; 121° line ; + 1·36 S./ – 3·31 C. ax. 31.

49. (*a*) 64·52 mm.; 4·17 mm.; (*b*) confusion disc in same place; 8.36 mm., (*c*) astigmatism is annulled; point focus at 64·52 mm.

CHAPTER V. Page 190.

2. Prism not overcome; two apparent objects seen in uncrossed diplopia; separation of these and angle between visual axes depend upon passive position taken up by eyes (§13.5).
4. 6 △; 5·56 △.
6. (*a*) 94′; (*b*) 103′; (*c*) 120′.
10. 14·5; 45·7; 13·61; 43·55; for each eye in every case.
16. (*a*) Prism overcome; single vision obtained.
    (*b*) Prism not overcome; uncrossed diplopia.
    (*c*) Prism overcome; single vision.
17. (*a*) Prism not overcome; uncrossed diplopia.
    (*b*) Prism overcome; single vision.
21. (*a*) Prism overcome; single vision; (*b*) prism not overcome; uncrossed diplopia; (*c*) prism overcome; single vision.
22. Two spots seen, that by R.E. vertically above that by L.E.; if eyes are normally balanced vertically, two spots separated by $2\frac{2}{3}$ cm. (neglecting effectivity).
25. Amp. = 20 △ or 6·25 M.A.; range from infinity to 16 cm.
27. Pair of 10·15 △ base out prisms.
28. Vertical diplopia; R. projection 8 △ higher than left.
30. 3·63, 7·0, 12·12 and 14·0 △, base horizontal.
32. Each prism 56° 26′ base out.
33. Total R. supravergence of 6·27 △.
35. Two spots separated 10·98 △ or 65·88 cm.; a third spot to the left or right; 30 cm. to left or right if passive position is primary position.

CHAPTER VI. Page 219.

2. 1·43 D; about 55 years.
3. Ref. error + 9·52 D at eye; Acc. 9·52 D. If correction (+ 8·55 D) worn 12 mm. from cornea, near point is 12·9 mm. from cornea.
4. To see a distant object; (*a*) 3·51 D; (*b*) 3·0 D.
6. Assuming stated near points found with distance correction in position; Amps. are 6·39 D and 4·02 D.
7. A = 2·064 D; near correction − 4·66 D or near addition 1·34 D.
10. (*a*) 1·75 D; (*b*) 0·75 D; lenses worn 14 mm. from eye.
11. R. 22·75 cm. from lens; L. 25·0 cm. from lens.
12. Far point 50 cm. behind eye; near point 125 cm. behind eye.
13. 140 D; (*a*) 120 D; (*b*) 140 D.
14. + 0·50 S./+ 1·75 C. ax. 30.
18. Range 13 cm.; Amp. 3·85 D; lenses at eye; distance − 3·85 D; reading ($\frac{1}{3}$ metre) − 3·41 D.
20. 69·6 mm.; H_M 4·0 D; H_L 2·0 D; lens (at eye) for near work 4·67 D.
21. Myopia 4 D; Amp. 3·5 D; age about 45.

22. 0·90 mm.; 6/6·2.
23. Amps. are 3·25 D and 1·87 D; near work addition 1·33 D in each case (using $F_A = -L - \frac{2}{3} A_S$).
24. (*a*) +2·0 D. (*b*) +2·062 D. (*c*) 5·836 D. (*d*) 6·0 D.
25. 7·12 D.
26. Assuming lenses at eye: myopia 5·06 D; Amp. 4·0 D; age about 44; correction: distance −5·06 D; near ($\frac{1}{3}$ metre) −4·73 D.
27. 37·45 cm.; in Em. 29·37 cm. from S.
28. Myopia 1 D to hyperopia 1 D.
29. +6·61 Cyl. ax. V.
30. Distances from optometer lens:
   R.E. Vertical: Far 28·57 cm.; Near 7·55 cm.
   Horizontal: Far 33·33 cm.; Near 7·84 cm.; V. line clear first.
   L.E. Vertical: Far 20·0 cm.; Near 6·78 cm.
   Horizontal: Far 22·22 cm.; Near 7·02 cm.; V. line clear first.
34. (*a*) −9·67 S./−5·33 C. ax. V.; (*b*) −8·17 S./−5·14 C. ax. V.; assuming eye accommodates amount proper to H. meridian.

CHAPTER VII. Page 259.

3. −14·29 D; field is smaller.
5. 12·96.
6. If radius of subject's pupil is p and w = half angular field, $\tan w = (2/100)p$ for half illumination; $\tan w = (6/100)p$ for extreme field.
7. +9·53 D.
8. −20·66 D; 1·29; (reduced surface taken 1·67 mm. from *cornea.*)
9. −43·8 D; magnification changes from 15·15 for Em. subject to 21·9 for this myopic subject.
13. Axial error; (*a*) −16·5 mm. (*b*) +19·5 mm.; refractive error: (*a*) −18·0 mm. (*b*) 18·0 mm. Image at far point in each case.
14. When eye accommodates, illuminated area is reduced.
15. 33$\frac{1}{3}$.
16. 9·06 cm. from subject's eye; say 9 cm. from cornea.
17. (*a*) 6·92 mm.; (*b*) 6·72 mm.; (*c*) 7·18 mm.
23. (*a*) −4·53 to −3·975; (*b*) −4·71 to −5·615.
25. Field of view about 53°; magnification of aerial image −5; total −2·75.
26. 10 cm. from subject's eye; about 28°.
27. Approx. 37° and 62 cm.
28. 7·67 mm.
30. Field about 68°; lens 2·93 cm. from subject's eye.
32. −50 D.
35. −3·75.
52. 48·2 mm. behind eye's reduced surface; parallax movement "against" retina.

CHAPTER VIII. Page 303.

1. $-2 \cdot 58$ D.
2. $\dfrac{-6 \cdot 00 \text{ S.}}{+6 \cdot 00 \text{ C. ax. } 70/+7 \cdot 25 \text{ C. ax. } 160}$
3. $\dfrac{-10 \cdot 00 \text{ S.}}{+4 \cdot 00 \text{ C. ax. H.}/+7 \cdot 00 \text{ C. ax. V.}}$; oval with long axis vertical.
4. 0·68 mm. ; up, 1·583 mm.
10. With ; no change (or possibly slightly against) ; from "with" to reversal.
12. R.E. along 45° ; against, +0·50 D.
    along 135° ; with, – 0·50 D.
    L.E. along 90° ; against, + 1·50 D.
    along 180° ; against, + 2·50 D.
16. – 1·50 S. /– 3·00 C. ax. V. ; vertical, – 2·5 D ; horizontal, – 5·5 D.
18. Immediate source formed in subject's pupil ; reflex disappears instantaneously irrespective of refractive condition.
19. If source lies in pupillary plane, angular speed of reflex is equal and opposite to angular speed of mirror.
24. $-\frac{1}{3}\,\theta$.
25. Myopia of 2 D ; when source moved to 2 metres, reflex speed is increased by one third.
26. (*a*) 1/5 rad. per sec. ; (*b*) 2/15 rad. per sec. ; (*c*) 2/25 rad. per sec.
31. (*a*) 4·27 mm. ; (*b*) 7 mm. ; (*c*) 10 mm. ; (*d*) – 4·78 mm.
37. 0·254 mm. ; (*a*) patch remains same size ; becomes brighter ; (*b*) reflex disappears rapidly, similar to reversal.
39. If acc. = 3 D error is – 1·50 C. ax. H. ; if acc. = 0, error is – 1·50 C. ax. V./ – 3·00 C. ax. H.

CHAPTER IX. Page 332.

1. $3\frac{1}{3}$ cm. behind mirror ; size 1 cm. ; 4·938 mm. behind mirror ; size 3·704 mm. ; – 200 D.
2. 4·5 mm.
6. 8 mm.
7. See Fig. 9.3. 7·625 mm. ; 7·18 mm. ; assuming $n = 1 \cdot 3375$.
8. 1 metre. (*a*) ends overlap by 3·2 cm. ; (*b*) ends separated by 4·8 cm.
9. Horiz. 2·78 mm. ; Vert. 2·95 mm. ; 2·47 D against the rule.
15. 220·8 mm. and 200·3 mm. from objective ; astigmatism 4·95 D ; assuming index of 1·3375.
16. 0·12 D ; 0·02 D.
21. 5·927 D or approx. 6 D ax. H.
22. 2·7 D against the rule.
27. – 8·00 S./ – 6·45 C. ax. H.
28. Anterior, 1·205 D with the rule ; Total, 1·037 D with the rule.
29. 30·29 cm. ; 30·95 cm. ; 6·6 cm.
30. 1·35 △.

CHAPTER X. Page 394.

10. – 7·35 D.

11. Equivalent power = 60 D, very nearly. Back vertex power = 72·43 D and length of eye, if Em., is 13·81 mm. If lens is in contact with cornea, this provides 7·35 D of accom. If lens move forward 2 mm., this provides only 3·61 D of accom. Moving lens backwards provides no accom.

12. Assuming reduced surface 1·5 mm. back from cornea, ocular refraction = + 20·36 D ; spectacle refraction at 12 mm. from cornea = + 16·36 D.

13. See §§ 10.4 and 10.10.

14. 1·46 mm.

15. First power, 19·11 D ; new power 17·42 D. Hyperopia acquired.

16. 2·677 mm. from cornea ; 1·116, or 11·6 per cent increase.

17. (*a*) Reflex 0·41 mm. to right of centre of apparent pupil ; (*b*) 27° to visual axis.

19. 10·65 mm.

20. 11·36 mm.

22. 3·335 mm. ; 0·446 mm.

23. 9·665 mm.

28. Entrance 2·674 mm. ; exit 3·248 mm. ; magnifications : Ent. 1·114 ; Exit 1·049 ; Exit ; Ent. = 0·9416. (*a*) 1·685 mm. ; (*b*) 1·006 mm.

29. 9·0 cm. ; 95·7 cm. to 104·7 cm.

30. 4·564 metre-candles or 0·424 foot-candles.

32. Myopia 5·625 D ; 0·909 mm.

33. Retinal image : axial 2·00 mm. ; refractive $1\frac{2}{3}$ mm.

34. 1·062 ; accom. 2·26 D.

35. 0·908 ; accom. 5·51 D.

37. a : b : c : d = 1/65·405 : 1/60 : 1/60·5 : 1/55·5.

39. 0·282 mm.

41. a : b : c = 1/50 : 1/70 : 1/60.

43. Details of optic disc will appear larger without lens in the ratio 1·094. This assumes that in both cases the eye accommodates the amount appropriate to the scotometer distance.

44. 6·82 mm., neglecting thickness of fluid lens.

45. Magnification is 2·65 with glass—under the conditions. (N.B. $q = -115$ mm.)

46. 1·049.

48. Retinal images are equal. Accom. : R. 4·796 D ; L. 3·466 D.

49. Image in aphakic eye 1·334 times larger.

50. On conventional definition, M = 4·18 ; object 5·50 cm. from lens. But if magnification is based on size of image obtained by unaided eye when object is placed at 50 cm., the eye's near point, then M = 8·36.

51. (*a*) (i) M = 5·5 ; object 2·73 cm. from lens ; (ii) M = 7·5 ; object 3·33 cm. from lens.
   (*b*) M = 5 in both cases ; object 5 cm. from lens.

52. (*a*) (i) 5 ; (ii) 4·1 ; (*b*) (i) 5 ; (ii) 5 ; (*c*) (i) 5 ; (ii) 6·5.
   Magnifying power increases as lens approached to eye and accommodation used.

53. Optical axis of magnifier is perpendicular to subject's line of sight. Scale is placed as close to eye and spectacle lens as possible ; a small aperture on the other side of magnifier at its second focal point. System is then telecentric on object side, no parallax between object (cornea and posterior surface of spectacle lens) and scale ; hence distance between cornea and spectacle lens can be read off on scale. Instrument is sometimes (unfortunately) called a keratometer.

55. 31° 4′.

56. 5° 16′. Line will approach its true direction.

57. (*a*) 87° 43′ ; (*b*) 82° 2′.

59. Image with meniscus lens 2·6 per cent larger.

60. 3·93 mm.

61. Use $x\,x' = f_e f'_e$; 5·4 D.

65. Front surface +5·715 D ; thickness 12·7 mm.

66. 10 D ; 6·8 cm.

CHAPTER XI. Page 425.

5. 0·305 mm. ; 0·81 D approx.

8. 1·1 D.

26. 1·134 D.

AUTHOR'S ACKNOWLEDGMENTS

I have to thank the following firms for the loan of illustration blocks :

ALLIED INSTRUMENT MANUFACTURERS LTD., Figs. 7.11, 13.14A, 13.16, 14.8.

BAUSCH AND LOMB OPTICAL CO. LTD., Figs. 9.10 and 9.11.

CLIFFORD BROWN LTD., Fig. 4.9.

ELLIOTT OPTICAL CO. LTD., Fig. 13.14.

J. & R. FLEMING LTD., Figs. 4.6, 7.17, 13.13.

GOWLLANDS LTD., Fig. 7.10.

CARL ZEISS (London) LTD., Figs. 7.14, 9.13, 9.14.

INDEX